Teacher's Edition

Earth Science

by
Robert H. Marshall
Allen B. Rosskopf

AGS Publishing
Circle Pines, Minnesota 55014-1796
800-328-2560
www.agsnet.com

About the Authors

Robert H. Marshall, M.Ed., teaches high-school physics and algebra at the Baltimore School for the Arts. He is a coauthor of several AGS textbooks, including *Physical Science, General Science,* and *Matter, Motion, and Machines.*

Allen B. Rosskopf, M.L.A., has taught English, journalism production, and desktop publishing for 30 years in the Baltimore City Public Schools. He is a coauthor of the AGS textbook *General Science.*

Photo credits for this textbook begin on page 395.

The publisher wishes to thank the following consultants and educators for their helpful comments during the review process for *Earth Science.* Their assistance has been invaluable.

Susan B. Board, Exceptional Student Education Department Chair, Terry Parker High School, Jacksonville, FL; **Bonnie Buratti,** Research Astronomer, Jet Propulsion Laboratory, California Institute of Technology, Pasadena, CA; **Sean Madden,** Special Education Teacher, Summit School, St. Laurent, Quebec; **Suzanne McKinley,** Special Education Teacher, El Capitan High School, Lakeside, CA; **Esterina Mignacca,** Special Education Teacher, Summit School, St. Laurent, Quebec; **Harrison H. Schmitt,** Geologist and former *Apollo 17* Astronaut; **Lorraine S. Taylor,** Ph.D., Professor of Special Education, State University of New York at New Paltz, New Paltz, NY; **Wayne Wendland,** State Climatologist, Illinois State Water Survey, Professor of Geography, University of Illinois at Champaign-Urbana, Urbana, IL

Publisher's Project Staff

Vice President, Product Development: Kathleen T. Williams, Ph.D., NCSP; Associate Director, Product Development: Teri Mathews; Senior Editor: Julie Maas; Assistant Editor: Jan Jessup; Development Assistant: Bev Johnson; Senior Designer/Illustrator: Tony Perleberg; Creative Services Manager: Nancy Condon; Purchasing Agent: Mary Kaye Kuzma; Senior Marketing Manager/Secondary Curriculum: Brian Holl

Editorial services provided by Creative Services Associates, Inc.

Printed in the United States of America
ISBN 0-7854-3636-7
Product Number 93942
A 0 9 8 7 6 5 4 3 2

Contents

Overview

Earth Science Overview.. T4
Skill Track Software... T5
Earth Science Student Text Highlights................................ T6
Earth Science Teacher's Edition Highlights........................... T8
Earth Science Teacher's Resource Library Highlights.................. T10
Other AGS Science Textbooks... T11
Correlation of Earth Science to the National Science Education Standards T12
Skills Chart.. T14
Learning Styles... T16

Lesson Plans

How to Use This Book: A Study Guide xii
The Nature of Science xviii
Chapter 1   Studying the Earth.................................... 1
Chapter 2   Describing the Earth.................................. 24
Chapter 3   The Earth and Moon System............................ 54
Chapter 4   The Solar System..................................... 76
Chapter 5   Stars and Galaxies................................... 106
Chapter 6   Earth Chemistry 130
Chapter 7   Minerals 152
Chapter 8   Rocks.. 176
Chapter 9   The Earth's Atmosphere 202
Chapter 10   Weather and Climate.................................. 228
Chapter 11   The Earth's Water.................................... 254
Chapter 12   Weathering and Erosion 278
Chapter 13   Forces in the Earth.................................. 306
Chapter 14   A Record of the Earth's History 332
Appendix A: Metric and Customary Measurement 356
Appendix B: Alternative Energy Sources 358
Appendix C: The Solar System 364
Appendix D: Space Exploration 366
Appendix E: Constellations... 368
Appendix F: The Periodic Table of Elements 372
Appendix G: World Map.. 374
Appendix H: North America Map 376
Glossary 377
Index.. 385
Photo Credits 395

Teacher's Resources

Midterm and Final Mastery Tests.................................... 397
Teacher's Resource Library Answer Key.............................. 400
    Workbook Activities 400
    Alternative Activities... 403
    Lab Manual 406
    Community Connection 411
    Self-Study Guide 411
    Tests 411
Materials List for Earth Science Lab Manual 415
Some Suppliers of Science Education Materials...................... 416

Earth Science is designed to help students and young adults learn about the earth and its movement in space, planets and stars, elements, minerals, rocks, oceans, weather, erosion, plate tectonics, and more. Written to meet national standards, it offers students who read below grade level the opportunity to practice working with data and sharpen their abilities to infer, classify, and theorize. Throughout the text, comprehension is enhanced through the use of simple sentence structure and low-level vocabulary.

The textbook's short, concise lessons hold student's interest. Clearly stated objectives given at the beginning of each lesson outline what students will learn in the lesson. Diagrams, maps, and illustrations aid in students' understanding of the content presented. Lesson Reviews and Chapter Reviews offer some open-ended questions to encourage students to use critical thinking skills. Hands-on Investigations and Science in Your Life activities lead students to apply the skills they are learning to everyday life. Full-color photographs and illustrations add interest and appeal as students learn key earth science concepts.

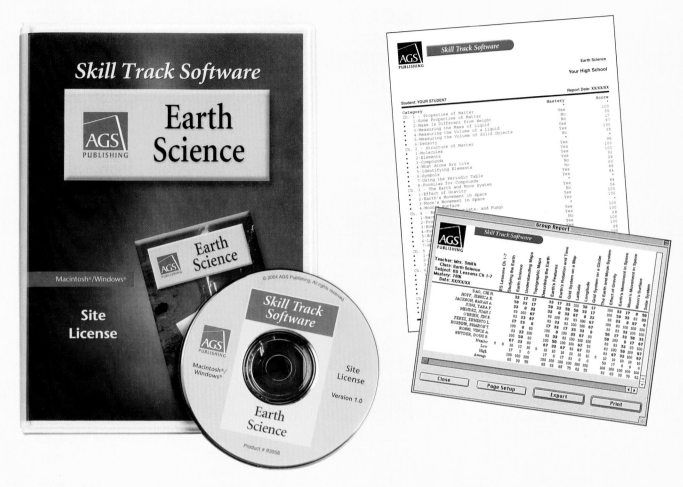

Skill Track Software The Skill Track Software program allows students using AGS Publishing textbooks to be assessed for mastery of each chapter and lesson of the textbook. Students access the software on an individual basis and are assessed with multiple-choice items.

Students can enter the program through two paths:

Lesson
Six items assess mastery of each lesson.

Chapter
Two parallel forms of chapter assessments are provided to determine chapter mastery. The two forms are equal in length and cover the same concepts with different items. The number of items in each chapter assessment varies by chapter, as the items are drawn from content of each lesson in the textbook.

The program includes high-interest graphics to accompany the items. Students are allowed to retake the chapter or lesson assessments over again at the instructor's discretion. The instructor has the ability to run and print out a variety of reports to track students' progress.

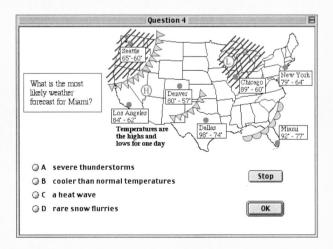

Student Text Highlights

◆ Each lesson is clearly labeled to help students focus on the skill or concept to be learned.

◆ Vocabulary terms are bold-faced and then defined in the margin and in the Glossary.

◆ Notes in the margin reinforce lesson content.

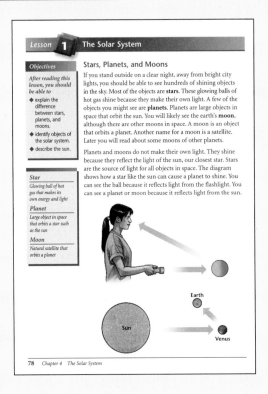

◆ Goals for Learning at the beginning of each chapter identify learner outcomes.

Goals for Learning

◆ To explain what the solar system is

◆ To identify the four inner planets

◆ To identify the five outer planets

◆ To tell something about each planet

◆ To describe the motions and positions of the planets

◆ To compare comets and asteroids

One of the most well-known comets is Hale-Bopp. It was discovered in 1995 by two astronomers named Alan Hale and Thomas Bopp. The comet's closest approach to Earth was on March 22, 1997.

◆ Chapter Reviews allow students and teachers to check for skill mastery. Multiple-choice items are provided for practice in taking standardized tests.

◆ Test-Taking Tips at the end of each Chapter Review help reduce test anxiety and improve test scores.

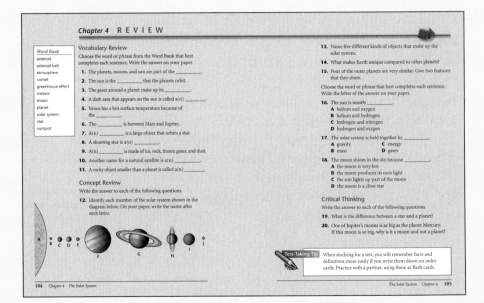

Technology Note

Nuclear energy is produced by a process called fission. During fission, uranium or plutonium atoms are split. When this occurs, energy is released in the form of heat. The heat is used to change water from liquid to steam. The steam spins a generator that produces electricity.

Did You Know?

Matter can exist in a fourth state called plasma. This is a very hot gas made of electrically charged particles. Plasma is rare on the earth. It occurs in lightning and in stars.

Achievements in Science

The Struggle to Accept the Solar System

In the early 1500s, a Polish astronomer named Nicolaus ... idea. Using careful observations and ... uded that the sun must be at the ... . In such a system, Earth and the ... round the sun. Other astronomers at ... Earth was at the center of everything. ...n't move. They rejected Copernicus's ... or solar, system.

... not picked up again until almost ...early 1600s, an Italian astronomer ...oncluded that not all objects in space ...Galileo was one of the first astronomers ... more he observed the moon and the ...inced he became that Copernicus's ...o published a book explaining the ... Still, this idea was very unpopular.

... Newton, an English scientist, took ...'s idea. He was able to prove that ... were right. P... ...lves around th... ...ed by the que...

◆ Achievements in Science offers information about historic science-related events, achievements, or discoveries.

Science Myth

Many people think of deserts as hot, sandy places.

Fact: Deserts are harsh environments with little rainfall and extreme temperatures. Parts of frozen Antarctica are considered deserts.

◆ Many features reinforce and extend student learning beyond the lesson content.

Science at Work

Cartographer

Cartographers create maps that describe features of the earth ...graphs and ...tive visual ways to present data. Tools used by ...atellite images, and computers.

To make a... research a... area to be ... systems st... Such syste... data into ... example, ... geograph... changes o... three-dim... are laid on ... combined ... three-dimensional images are helpful to city planners and meteorologists.

Most cartographers have a bachelor's degree in engineering, forestry, geography, or physical science. They need to be detail-oriented and have strong computer and math skills. Good communication and organization skills are helpful.

Science in Your Life

A Solar House

The sun not only warms our planet, but it also provides us with energy. Solar energy is energy that comes from the sun.

Solar energy can be used in many ways. For example, a solar house is specially built to capture solar energy. Solar panels are mounted on the roof of the house. The panels collect radiant energy from the sun and change it to heat energy. This heat energy is used to run electric appliances and heat water.

The main benefit of using solar energy is that it saves our natural resources. Oil, gas, and coal are natural resources that are burned for energy. These resources are limited and will run out someday. But the sun's energy is unlimited. The sun will keep producing energy for about another 5 billion years.

Are there any solar houses or solar panels in your neighborhood? To learn about other ways to save our natural resources, read Appendix B: Alternative Energy Sources.

◆ Science in Your Life helps students relate chapter content to everyday life.

◆ Science at Work provides some examples of science careers.

10-1 INVESTIGATION

Measuring Air Pressure

Purpose
Does the air pressure change in your classroom? In this investigation, you will construct a barometer and collect weather data.

Materials
- large, round balloon
- scissors
- glass baby-food jar
- rubber band
- drinking straw
- glue
- marking pen
- index card
- centimeter ruler
- masking tape

Procedure
1. Copy the data table on your paper.

Date and Time	Barometer Reading	Weather Observations

2. Cut off the neck of a balloon. Stretch the balloon tightly over the top of a jar. Hold the balloon in place with a rubber band. Safety Alert: Use care when stretching the balloon. It can snap and cause injury.

3. Cut one end of a drinking straw so that it forms a point. Glue the other end of the straw to the center of the balloon cover, as shown in the figure.

4. With a pen, mark a scale on the unlined side of an index card, as shown. Make the lines 0.5 centimeter apart. Number them from −4 to 4.

5. Place your barometer near a wall. Tape the index card to the wall so that the straw on the barometer points to the zero line. Make sure the barometer is not in direct sunlight.

6. When the glue has dried, observe the position of the straw. In your data table, record the number indicated by the straw. Also record the date, time, and outside weather conditions.

7. Repeat step 6 at least once each day for the next four days.

Questions and Conclusions
1. What does an upward movement of the straw indicate about air pressure?

2. What does a downward movement of the straw indicate about air pressure?

3. How did air pressure change during the five days of observations?

4. Use your readings to make a prediction about upcoming weather. Explain your prediction.

Explore Further
Find out how accurate your predictions were. Use a local newspaper to compare your data with weather reports for the same days.

◆ Investigation activities give students hands-on practice with chapter concepts. Students use critical thinking skills to complete each investigation.

Teacher's Edition Highlights

The comprehensive, wraparound Teacher's Edition provides instructional strategies at point of use. Everything from preparation guidelines to teaching tips and strategies are included in an easy-to-use format. Activities are featured at point of use for teacher convenience.

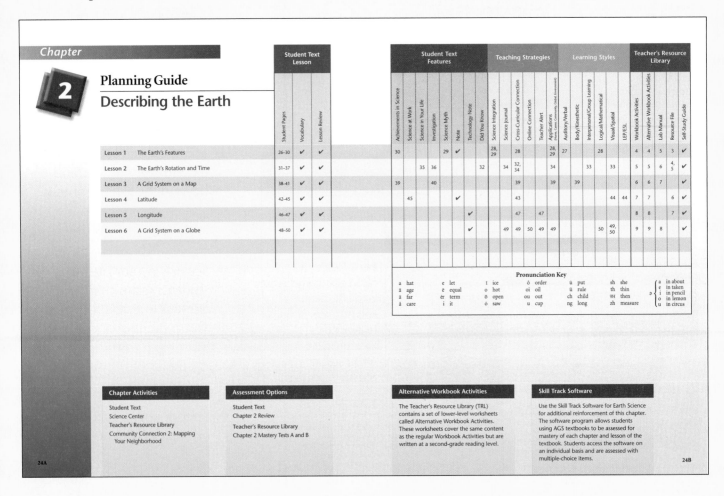

Chapter Planning Guides

◆ The Planning Guide saves valuable preparation time by organizing all materials for each chapter.

◆ A complete listing of lessons allows you to preview each chapter quickly.

◆ Assessment options are highlighted for easy reference. Options include:

  Lesson Reviews
  Chapter Reviews
  Chapter Mastery Tests, Forms A and B
  Midterm and Final Tests

◆ Page numbers of Student Text and Teacher's Edition features help customize lesson plans to your students.

◆ Many teaching strategies and learning styles are listed to support students with diverse needs.

◆ All activities in the Teacher's Resource Library are listed.

◆ A Pronunciation Key is provided to help you as you work with students to pronounce difficult words correctly.

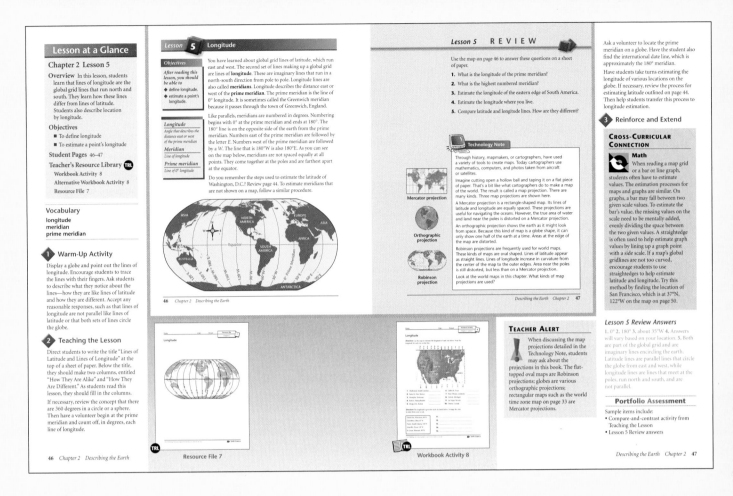

Lessons

◆ Quick overviews of chapters and lessons save planning time.

◆ Lesson objectives are listed for easy reference.

◆ Page references are provided for convenience.

◆ Easy-to-follow lesson plans in three steps save time: Warm-Up Activity, Teaching the Lesson, and Reinforce and Extend.

◆ Teacher Alerts highlight content that may need further explanation.

◆ Science Journal activities give students an opportunity to write about science.

◆ Cross-Curricular Connections tie science to a variety of curriculum areas.

◆ Applications: Five areas of application—At Home, Career Connection, Global Connection, In the Community, and In the Environment—help students relate science to the world outside the classroom. Applications motivate students and make learning relevant.

◆ The Portfolio Assessment, which appears at the end of each lesson, lists items the student has completed for that lesson.

◆ Online Connections list relevant Web sites.

◆ Learning Styles provide teaching strategies to help meet the needs of students with diverse ways of learning. Modalities include Auditory/Verbal, Visual/Spatial, Body/Kinesthetic, Logical/Mathematical, and Interpersonal/Group Learning. Additional teaching activities are provided for LEP/ESL students.

◆ Answers for all activities in the Student Text appear in the Teacher's Edition. Answers for the Teacher's Resource Library (TRL), Student Workbook, and Lab Manual appear at the back of this Teacher's Edition and on the TRL CD-ROM.

◆ Worksheet, Workbook, Lab Manual, and Test pages from the Teacher's Resource Library are shown at point of use in reduced form.

TRL All of the activities you'll need to reinforce and extend the text are conveniently located on the AGS Publishing Teacher's Resource Library (TRL) CD-ROM. All of the reproducible activities pictured in the Teacher's Edition are ready to select, view, and print. You can also preview other materials by linking directly to the AGS Publishing Web site.

Workbook Activities

Workbook Activities are available to reinforce and extend skills from each lesson of the textbook. A bound workbook format is also available.

Alternative Activities

These activities cover the same content as the Workbook Activities but are written at a second-grade reading level.

Lab Manual

These activities build critical thinking and teamwork skills. A bound format is also available.

Community Connection

Relevant activities help students extend their knowledge to the real world and reinforce concepts covered in class.

Resource File

These reference sheets on lesson content are tools for student study as well as teaching aids.

Self-Study Guide

An assignment guide provides the student with an outline for working through the text independently. The guide provides teachers with the flexibility for individualized instruction or independent study.

Mastery Tests

Chapter, Midterm, and Final Mastery Tests are convenient assessment options.

Answer Key

All answers to reproducible activities are included in the TRL and in the Teacher's Edition.

Earth Science
Teacher's Resource Library

4201 Woodland Road
Circle Pines, MN 55014-1796
800-328-2560
www.agsnet.com

© 2004 AGS Publishing

Permission is granted to print and reproduce the contents of this CD-ROM for classroom use only.

SELECT AN ITEM
- Activities and Tests
- Activities by Chapter and Lesson
- Answers for Activities and Tests
- Instructions
- AGS Web Site

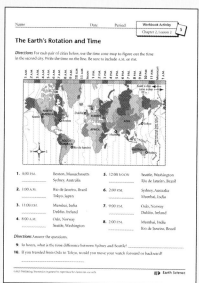

Workbook Activities

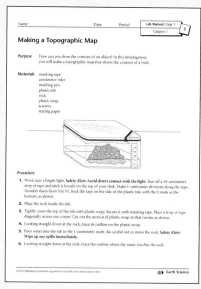

Lab Manual

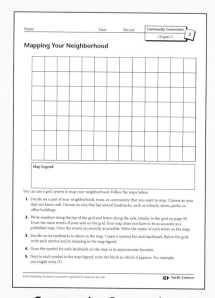

Community Connections

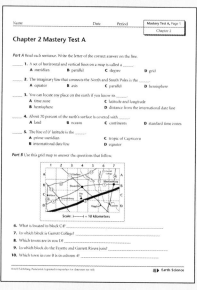

Mastery Tests

Enhance your science program with AGS Publishing textbooks—an easy, effective way to teach students the practical skills they need. Each AGS Publishing textbook meets your science curriculum needs. These exciting, full-color books use student-friendly text and real-world examples to show students the relevance of science in their daily lives. Each presents a comprehensive coverage of skills and concepts. The short, concise lessons will motivate even your most reluctant students. With readabilities of all the texts below fourth-grade reading level, your students can concentrate on learning the content. AGS Publishing is committed to making learning accessible to all students.

STANDARD A   Science as Inquiry

As a result of activities in grades 5–12, all students should develop:

Earth Science

◆ Abilities necessary to do scientific inquiry

Pages 3–5, 11, 13–14, 17–20, 36–37, 39–41, 48, 58–59, 63–64, 69, 72, 82, 84–85, 90, 97–99, 108, 111–113, 116, 119, 120, 125–126, 133, 135–136, 140, 147–148, 162–163, 168–169, 190–191, 196–197, 210, 215, 219–220, 230–237, 241–243, 246, 265–266, 273–274, 283–285, 292–293, 299, 312, 320–321, 323, 326–328, 337–339, 342–343, 345–346, 351, 356–357

◆ Understandings about scientific inquiry

Pages 5, 13–14, 17, 19–20, 36–37, 40–41, 47, 48, 58–59, 63–64, 72, 84–85, 98–99, 102, 112–113, 116, 125–126, 135–136, 143, 147–148, 161–163, 168–169, 188, 190–191, 193, 196–197, 215, 219–220, 224, 236–237, 242–243, 246, 263, 265–266, 273–274, 283–285, 292–293, 319–321, 327–328, 338–339, 345–346, 351, 356–357

STANDARD D   Earth and Space Science

As a result of activities in grades 5–12, all students should develop an understanding of:

Earth Science

◆ Structure of the earth system

Pages 25–30, 176–201, 202–227, 239–246, 254–277, 278–305, 306–331

◆ Earth's history

Pages 100–101, 286–305, 306–331, 332–355

◆ Earth in the solar system

Pages 31–37, 54–75, 76–105, 364–365

◆ Energy in the earth system

Pages 55–64, 79–85, 205, 208–210, 221–224, 247–250, 267–269, 306–331

◆ Geochemical cycles

Pages 130–151, 176–201, 203–207, 255–258, 260, 307–319, 372–373

◆ Origin and evolution of the earth system

Pages 176–201, 306–331, 332–355

◆ Origin and evolution of the universe

Pages 106–129

STANDARD E   Science and Technology

As a result of activities in grades 5–12, all students should develop:

Earth Science

◆ Abilities of technological design

The ability to address this objective is available on the following pages: 13–14, 19–20, 36–37, 40–41, 58–59, 63–64, 84–85, 98–99, 112–113, 125–126, 135–136, 147–148, 162–163, 168–169, 190–191, 196–197, 215, 219–220, 236–237, 242–243, 265–266, 273–274, 284–285, 292–293, 320–321, 327–328, 338–339, 345–346

◆ Understandings about science and technology

Pages 5, 6, 17, 30, 39, 47, 48, 57, 72, 91, 102, 116, 121, 141, 143, 156, 161, 185, 188, 193, 196, 210, 218, 224, 241, 246, 263, 272, 283, 299, 312, 319, 351

STANDARD F Science in Personal and Social Perspectives

As a result of activities in grades 5–12, all students should develop an understanding of:

Earth Science

◆ Personal and community health

Pages 160, 250, 301, 302, 316, 325, 326, 358–363

◆ Population growth

This objective falls outside the scope of AGS Earth Science.

◆ Populations, resources, and environments

Pages 124, 189, 207, 214, 302, 344

◆ Natural resources

Pages 83, 102, 134, 143, 172, 188, 224, 259–264, 271–272, 302, 344, 352, 358–363

◆ Environmental quality

Pages 124, 134, 172, 188, 189, 207, 214, 224, 235, 246, 250, 272, 302, 344, 352, 358–363

◆ Natural and human-induced hazards

Pages 124, 134, 143, 172, 207, 235, 286–303, 307–331, 344

◆ Risks and benefits

Pages 124, 189, 207, 214, 235–246, 250, 272, 302, 344, 358–363

◆ Science and technology in society

Pages 2–6, 17, 47, 48, 72, 102, 116, 143, 161, 188, 193, 224, 246, 263, 283, 299, 319, 351

◆ Science and technology in local, national, and global challenges

Pages 5, 17, 47, 48, 72, 102, 116, 143, 161, 188, 193, 224, 246, 263, 283, 319, 351, 366–367

STANDARD G History and Nature of Science

As a result of activities in grades 5–12, all students should develop an understanding of:

Earth Science

◆ Science as a human endeavor

Pages 6, 12, 30, 39, 45, 57, 62, 91, 97, 111, 121, 141, 146, 156, 167, 180, 185, 196, 210, 214, 218, 235, 241, 264, 272, 299, 302, 312, 326, 344

◆ Nature of science

Pages 13–14, 19–20, 36–37, 40–41, 58–59, 63–64, 84–85, 98–99, 112–113, 125–126, 135–136, 147–148, 162–163, 168–169, 190–191, 196–197, 215, 219–220, 236–237, 242–243, 265–266, 273–274, 284–285, 292–293, 320–321, 327–328, 338–339, 345–346

◆ Nature of scientific knowledge

Pages 13–14, 19–20, 36–37, 40–41, 58–59, 63–64, 84–85, 98–99, 112–113, 125–126, 135–136, 147–148, 162–163, 168–169, 190–191, 196–197, 215, 219–220, 236–237, 242–243, 265–266, 273–274, 284–285, 292–293, 320–321, 327–328, 338–339, 345–346

◆ History of science

Pages 6, 12, 30, 39, 45, 57, 62, 91, 97, 111, 121, 141, 146, 156, 167, 180, 185, 196, 210, 214, 218, 235, 241, 264, 272, 299, 302, 312, 326, 344

◆ Historical perspectives

Pages 5, 6, 17, 30, 39, 47, 48, 57, 72, 91, 102, 116, 121, 141, 143, 156, 161, 185, 188, 193, 196, 210, 218, 224, 241, 246, 263, 272, 283, 299, 312, 319, 351, 366–367

Skills Chart

Earth Science

CHAPTER

Science Content

	1	2	3	4	5	6	7	8	9	10	11	12	13	14
Earth's History								8				12	13	14
Earth in the Solar System			3	4										
Energy in the Earth System			3	4					9	10	11		13	
Geochemical Cycles						6		8	9		11		13	
History and Nature of Science	1	2	3	4	5	6	7	8	9	10	11	12	13	14
Inquiry and Investigation	1	2	3	4	5	6	7	8	9	10	11	12	13	14
Origin and Evolution of the Earth and Universe					5			8						14
Science and Technology	1	2	3	4	5	6	7	8	9	10	11	12	13	14
Science in Personal and Social Perspectives	1	2	3	4	5	6	7	8	9	10	11	12	13	14
Structure of the Earth System								8	9	10	11	12	13	

Process Skills

	1	2	3	4	5	6	7	8	9	10	11	12	13	14
Collecting Information	1	2	3	4	5	6	7	8	9	10	11	12	13	14
Communicating	1	2	3	4	5	6	7	8	9	10	11	12	13	14
Creating Graphs, Tables, Maps, or Diagrams	1	2	3		5	6	7	8	9	10	11	12	13	14
Describing		2	3	4	5	6	7	8	9	10	11	12	13	14
Determining Compass Directions	1	2	3	4					9	10	11			
Following Written Directions	1	2	3	4	5	6	7	8	9	10	11	12	13	14
Identifying or Controlling Variables			3		5				9	10	11	12		
Making or Using Models or Scales	1	2	3	4	5	6		8	9	10	11	12	13	14
Measuring Mass, Weight, Distance, Time, or Temperature	1		3	4	5	6	7	8	9	10	11	12	13	14
Observing	1	2	3	4	5	6	7	8	9	10	11	12	13	14
Performing Experiments	1	2	3	4	5	6	7	8	9	10	11	12	13	14
Reading Graphs, Tables, Maps, or Diagrams	1	2	3	4	5	6	7	8	9	10	11	12	13	14
Recording Data	1	2	3	4	5	6	7	8	9	10	11	12	13	14
Using Formulas or Equations	1			4	5	6	7	8					13	
Using Metric Measurements	1		3	4	5	6	7		9	10	11		13	14
Using Science Lab Equipment	1		3	4	5	6	7	8	9	10	11	12	13	
Working with Numbers	1	2	3	4	5	6	7	8	9	10	11		13	14
Writing About Science	1	2	3	4	5	6	7	8	9	10	11	12	13	14

Earth Science

by
Robert H. Marshall
Allen B. Rosskopf

AGS Publishing
Circle Pines, Minnesota 55014-1796
800-328-2560

About the Authors

Robert H. Marshall, M.Ed., teaches high-school physics and algebra at the Baltimore School for the Arts. He is a coauthor of several AGS textbooks, including *Physical Science, General Science,* and *Matter, Motion, and Machines.*

Allen B. Rosskopf, M.L.A., has taught English, journalism production, and desktop publishing for 30 years in the Baltimore City Public Schools. He is a coauthor of the AGS textbook *General Science.*

Photo credits for this textbook begin on page 395.

The publisher wishes to thank the following consultants and educators for their helpful comments during the review process for *Earth Science*. Their assistance has been invaluable.

Susan B. Board, Exceptional Student Education Department Chair, Terry Parker High School, Jacksonville, FL; **Bonnie Buratti,** Research Astronomer, Jet Propulsion Laboratory, California Institute of Technology, Pasadena, CA; **Sean Madden,** Special Education Teacher, Summit School, St. Laurent, Quebec; **Suzanne McKinley,** Special Education Teacher, El Capitan High School, Lakeside, CA; **Esterina Mignacca,** Special Education Teacher, Summit School, St. Laurent, Quebec; **Harrison H. Schmitt,** Geologist and former *Apollo 17* Astronaut; **Lorraine S. Taylor,** Ph.D., Professor of Special Education, State University of New York at New Paltz, New Paltz, NY; **Wayne Wendland,** State Climatologist, Illinois State Water Survey, Professor of Geography, University of Illinois at Champaign-Urbana, Urbana, IL

Publisher's Project Staff

Vice President, Product Development: Kathleen T. Williams, Ph.D., NCSP; Associate Director, Product Development: Teri Mathews; Senior Editor: Julie Maas; Assistant Editor: Jan Jessup; Development Assistant: Bev Johnson; Senior Designer/Illustrator: Tony Perleberg; Creative Services Manager: Nancy Condon; Purchasing Agent: Mary Kaye Kuzma; Senior Marketing Manager/Secondary Curriculum: Brian Holl

Editorial and production services provided by Navta Associates, Inc.
Additional illustrations by Stephanie Pershing/John Edwards Inc.

© 2004 AGS Publishing
4201 Woodland Road
Circle Pines, MN 55014-1796
800-328-2560 • www.agsnet.com

AGS Publishing is a trademark and trade name of American Guidance Service, Inc.

Printed in the United States of America
ISBN 0-7854-3635-9
Product Number 93940
A 0 9 8 7 6 5 4 3 2 1

Learning Styles

The learning style activities in the *Earth Science* Teacher's Edition provide activities to help students with special needs understand the lesson. These activities focus on the following learning styles: Visual/Spatial, Auditory/Verbal, Body/Kinesthetic, Logical/Mathematical, Interpersonal/Group Learning, LEP/ESL. These styles reflect Howard Gardner's theory of multiple intelligences. The writing activities suggested in this student text are appropriate for students who fit

Gardner's description of Verbal/Linguistic Intelligence. The activities are designed to help teachers capitalize on students' individual strengths and dominant learning styles. The activities reinforce the lesson by teaching or expanding upon the content in a different way.

Following are examples of activities featured in the *Earth Science* Teacher's Edition:

Auditory/Verbal

Students benefit from having someone read the text aloud or listening to the text on audiocassette. Musical activities appropriate for the lesson may help auditory learners.

LEARNING STYLES

Auditory/Verbal
To help students orient themselves to compass directions, label the north wall or corner in the room with a large *N*. Have students stand facing north and give specific oral directions to follow. For example, say "Turn east. When you are facing north, east is 90 degrees to your right." Continue with directions for turning south, southeast, west, northwest, and so on.

Body/Kinesthetic

Learners benefit from activities that include physical movement or tactile experiences.

LEARNING STYLES

Body/Kinesthetic
Set up a section of the classroom as a life-size map. Lay construction paper signs, labeled A, B, C, and D, along one side of the area. Lay signs labeled 1, 2, 3, and 4 along an adjacent side. Then tape down lengths of masking tape on the floor between the rows and columns to divide the area into grid squares. Place objects, such as books or pencils, in various squares. Then ask students to move an item from a particular grid square to another, such as from A3 to C2.

Logical/Mathematical

Students learn by using logical/mathematical thinking in relation to the lesson content.

LEARNING STYLES

Logical/Mathematical
Provide students with protractors and mathematical compasses. Have them use the information on page 27 to make a circle graph showing the percentage of the earth's land area covered by each of the seven continents.

Interpersonal/Group Learning

Learners benefit from working with at least one other person on activities that involve a process and an end product.

LEARNING STYLES

Interpersonal/Group Learning
Divide the class into groups. Each member of the group should choose a major city in a different part of the world. Tell them it is 10:00 A.M. in New York. Using the time zone map on page 33 and a large world map, students should calculate what time it would be in the places they chose. Students might use sticky notes to label a map or globe with the times. They can then hold a mock conference call, in which each student describes what he or she is doing at that time of day in their chosen city.

Visual/Spatial

Students benefit from seeing illustrations or demonstrations beyond what is in the text.

LEARNING STYLES

Visual/Spatial
Give each student a copy of the month's calendar that shows the dates of the phases of the moon. In the appropriate boxes on the calendar, have students draw pictures of what the moon would look like in the sky. Encourage them to observe the moon at night.

LEP/ESL

Students benefit from activities that promote English language acquisition and interaction with English-speaking peers.

LEARNING STYLES

LEP/ESL
Refer students to the Note on page 43. The English language is full of multiple-meaning words. For English language learners, this can be very confusing. For example, when someone says "I want to get a college degree," he or she is not referring to degrees on a map or a thermometer. Help students begin a list of multiple-meaning words for reference and vocabulary development. Include the multiple meanings of *degree*. Each entry should include the word, its various meanings, and an example sentence for each meaning.

Thinking Skills	1	2	3	4	5	6	7	8	9	10	11	12	13	14
Applying Information	1	2	3	4	5	6	7	8	9	10	11	12	13	14
Classifying and Categorizing	1	2	3	4	5	6	7	8	9	10	11	12	13	14
Comparing and Contrasting	1	2	3	4	5	6	7	8	9	10	11	12	13	14
Drawing Conclusions	1	2	3	4	5	6	7	8	9	10	11	12	13	14
Explaining Ideas and Concepts	1	2	3	4	5	6	7	8	9	10	11	12	13	14
Formulating Questions	1	2	3	4	5	6	7	8	9	10	11	12	13	14
Identifying and Solving Problems	1	2	3	4	5	6	7	8	9	10	11	12	13	14
Identifying Terms and Symbols	1	2	3	4	5	6	7	8	9	10	11	12	13	14
Interpreting Data	1	2	3	4	5	6	7	8	9	10	11	12	13	14
Interpreting Visuals	1	2	3	4	5	6	7	8	9	10	11	12	13	14
Learning Science Vocabulary	1	2	3	4	5	6	7	8	9	10	11	12	13	14
Making Decisions	1	2	3	4	5	6	7	8	9	10	11	12	13	14
Making Inferences	1	2	3	4	5	6	7	8	9	10	11	12	13	14
Organizing Information	1	2	3	4	5	6	7	8	9	10	11	12	13	14
Predicting Outcomes	1	2	3	4	5	6	7	8	9	10	11	12	13	14
Recalling Facts	1	2	3	4	5	6	7	8	9	10	11	12	13	14
Recognizing Main Ideas	1	2	3	4	5	6	7	8	9	10	11	12	13	14
Recognizing Patterns	1	2	3	4	5	6	7	8	9	10	11	12	13	14
Recognizing Relationships	1	2	3	4	5	6	7	8	9	10	11	12	13	14
Understanding Concepts	1	2	3	4	5	6	7	8	9	10	11	12	13	14

Contents

How to Use This Book: A Study Guide . . . . **xii**
The Nature of Science . . . . **xviii**

Chapter 1 **Studying the Earth** 1

Lesson 1 Earth Science 2
◆ Achievements in Science: Celebrating Earth Day 6
Lesson 2 Understanding Maps 7
◆ Science at Work: Cartographer 12
◆ Investigation 1-1: Making a Map 13
Lesson 3 Topographic Maps 15
◆ Science in Your Life: Mapping a Park 18
◆ Investigation 1-2: Reading a Topographic Map 19
◆ Chapter Summary 21
◆ Chapter Review 22
◆ Test-Taking Tip 23

Chapter 2   **Describing the Earth**. **24**

Lesson 1 The Earth's Features 26

◆ Achievements in Science: A Trip Around the World 30

Lesson 2 The Earth's Rotation and Time 31

◆ Science in Your Life: Time Zones. 35

◆ Investigation 2-1: Modeling the Earth's Rotation. 36

Lesson 3 A Grid System on a Map 38

◆ Achievements in Science: Global Positioning Systems. . . 39

◆ Investigation 2-2: Describing Location on
   a Round Surface 40

Lesson 4 Latitude 42

◆ Science at Work: Air-Traffic Controller. 45

Lesson 5 Longitude 46

Lesson 6 A Grid System on a Globe 48

◆ Chapter Summary. 51

◆ Chapter Review 52

◆ Test-Taking Tip 53

Chapter 3   **The Earth and Moon System**. **54**

Lesson 1 The Effect of Gravity 56

◆ Achievements in Science: Almanacs 57

◆ Investigation 3-1: Making a Model of an Orbit 58

Lesson 2 The Earth's Movement in Space 60

◆ Science at Work: Space Shuttle and International
   Space Station Crews 62

◆ Investigation 3-2: Exploring Light Angle 63

Lesson 3 The Moon's Movement in Space. 65

◆ Science in Your Life: Natural and Artificial Satellites. . . . 69

Lesson 4 The Moon's Surface 70

◆ Chapter Summary. 73

◆ Chapter Review 74

◆ Test-Taking Tip 75

Chapter 4   **The Solar System** **76**
Lesson 1   The Solar System 78
◆ Science in Your Life: A Solar House. 83
◆ Investigation 4-1: Observing Sunspots 84
Lesson 2   The Inner Planets 86
◆ Achievements in Science: The Struggle to Accept
    the Solar System 91
Lesson 3   The Outer Planets. 92
◆ Science at Work: Astronomer. 97
◆ Investigation 4-2: Modeling Distances in the
    Solar System. 98
Lesson 4   Other Objects in the Solar System 100
◆ Chapter Summary. 103
◆ Chapter Review 104
◆ Test-Taking Tip 105

Chapter 5   **Stars and Galaxies** **106**
Lesson 1   Stars. 108
◆ Science at Work: Telescope Technician 111
◆ Investigation 5-1: Observing Brightness. 112
Lesson 2   Distances to Stars 114
Lesson 3   The Life of a Star 117
◆ Achievements in Science: Black Holes. 120
Lesson 4   Groups of Stars. 121
◆ Science in Your Life: Light Pollution 124
◆ Investigation 5-2: Making a Constellation Model 125
◆ Chapter Summary. 127
◆ Chapter Review 128
◆ Test-Taking Tip 129

Chapter 6 **Earth Chemistry** **130**
Lesson 1 Matter 132
◆ Science in Your Life: Lasting Plastic. 134
◆ Investigation 6-1: Measuring Physical Properties
     of Objects. 135
Lesson 2 The Smallest Parts of Matter 137
◆ Achievements in Science: Creating New Elements. 140
Lesson 3 Compounds and Mixtures. 141
◆ Science at Work: Chemical Engineer. 146
◆ Investigation 6-2: Separating a Mixture 147
Chapter Summary 149
Chapter Review 150
Test-Taking Tip 151

Chapter 7 **Minerals** **152**
Lesson 1 Minerals. 154
◆ Achievements in Science: Working with Metals 156
Lesson 2 Properties Used to Identify Minerals 157
◆ Investigation 7-1: Observing Color, Streak,
     and Hardness. 162
Lesson 3 Other Physical Properties of Minerals 164
◆ Science at Work: Jeweler 167
◆ Investigation 7-2: Finding Specific Gravity. 168
Lesson 4 Common Uses of Minerals 170
◆ Science in Your Life: Recycling Aluminum 172
Chapter Summary 173
Chapter Review 174
Test-Taking Tip 175

Chapter 8	**Rocks**	**176**

Lesson 1 Rocks and Rock Types 178
◆ Science at Work: Stonemason 180
Lesson 2 Igneous Rocks. 181
◆ Achievements in Science: Field Guides for Rocks
    and Minerals 184
Lesson 3 Sedimentary Rocks. 185
◆ Science in Your Life: The Good and Bad of Coal 189
◆ Investigation 8-1: Making Calcite 190
Lesson 4 Metamorphic Rocks. 192
Lesson 5 The Rock Cycle. 194
◆ Achievements in Science: The Rock Cycle Theory 196
◆ Investigation 8-2: Identifying Rocks 197
Chapter Summary. 199
Chapter Review 200
Test-Taking Tip 201

Chapter 9	**The Earth's Atmosphere**.	**202**

Lesson 1 Gases in the Atmosphere 204
◆ Science in Your Life: Ozone: Protector and Pollutant . . . 207
Lesson 2 Layers of the Atmosphere 208
◆ Achievements in Science: Balloon Pilots. 210
Lesson 3 Clouds 211
◆ Science at Work: Environmental Science Technician. . . 214
◆ Investigation 9-1: Observing Clouds. 215
Lesson 4 Precipitation 216
◆ Achievements in Science: Cloud Seeding 218
◆ Investigation 9-2: Making a Model of Rain 219
Lesson 5 Wind Patterns. 221
Chapter Summary. 225
Chapter Review 226
Test-Taking Tip 227

Chapter 10   **Weather and Climate** **228**

Lesson 1   Weather Conditions and Measurements 230

◆ Science at Work: Atmospheric Scientist 235

◆ Investigation 10-1: Measuring Air Pressure 236

Lesson 2   Weather Patterns and Predictions 238

◆ Achievements in Science: Doppler Radar 241

◆ Investigation 10-2: Using a Weather Map 242

Lesson 3   Storms 244

Lesson 4   World Climates 247

◆ Science in Your Life: Your Climate Zone 250

Chapter Summary 251

Chapter Review 252

Test-Taking Tip 253

Chapter 11   **The Earth's Water** **254**

Lesson 1   The Water Cycle 256

◆ Science in Your Life: Your Water Budget 258

Lesson 2   Sources of Fresh Water 259

◆ Science at Work: Hydroelectric Power
   Plant Operator 264

◆ Investigation 11-1: Exploring Evaporation 265

Lesson 3   Oceans 267

◆ Achievements in Science: Protecting the
   Environment 272

◆ Investigation 11-2: Measuring the Effect of Salt
   Water on Floating 273

Chapter Summary 275

Chapter Review 276

Test-Taking Tip 277

Chapter 12 **Weathering and Erosion** **278**

Lesson 1 Weathering 280

◆ Investigation 12-1: Observing Chemical Weathering . . . 284

Lesson 2 Erosion Caused by Water 286

◆ Science in Your Life: Erosion Caused by People 291

◆ Investigation 12-2: Comparing Erosion 292

Lesson 3 Erosion Caused by Glaciers 294

◆ Achievements in Science: Artificial Glaciers 299

Lesson 4 Erosion Caused by Wind and Gravity 300

◆ Science at Work: Floodplain Manager 302

Chapter Summary 303

Chapter Review 304

Test-Taking Tip 305

Chapter 13 **Forces in the Earth** **306**

Lesson 1 Movement of the Earth's Crust 308

◆ Achievements in Science: The Theory of
   Sea-Floor Spreading 312

Lesson 2 Volcanoes 313

◆ Science in Your Life: Living on a Tectonic Plate 316

Lesson 3 Mountains 317

◆ Investigation 13-1: Making Models of Folding
   and Faults 320

Lesson 4 Earthquakes 322

◆ Science at Work: Seismologist 326

◆ Investigation 13-2: Locating an Earthquake 327

Chapter Summary 329

Chapter Review 330

Test-Taking Tip 331

Chapter 14 **A Record of the Earth's History** **332**

Lesson 1 The Rock Record 334

◆ Achievements in Science: Uncovering the
   History of Life 337

◆ Investigation 14-1: Making a Model of a Fossil 338

Lesson 2 The Ages of Rocks and Fossils 340

◆ Science at Work: Petroleum Engineer 344

◆ Investigation 14-2: Making a Half-Life Model 345

Lesson 3 Eras in the Geologic Time Scale 347

◆ Science in Your Life: Cutting Down on Fossil Fuels 352

Chapter Summary 353

Chapter Review 354

Test-Taking Tip 355

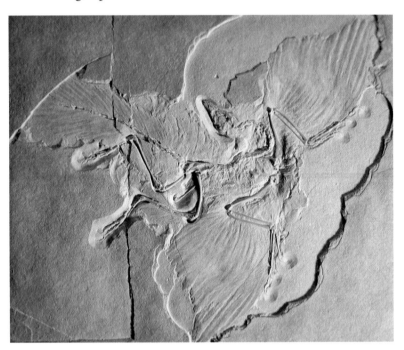

Appendix A: Metric and Customary Measurement **356**

Appendix B: Alternative Energy Sources **358**

Appendix C: The Solar System **364**

Appendix D: Space Exploration **366**

Appendix E: Constellations **368**

Appendix F: The Periodic Table of Elements **372**

Appendix G: World Map **374**

Appendix H: North America Map **376**

Glossary **377**

Index **385**

Photo Credits **395**

Earth Science   Contents   **xi**

How to Use This Book: A Study Guide

Overview This section may be used to introduce the study of earth science, to preview the book's features, and to review effective study skills.

Objectives

- To introduce the study of earth science
- To preview the student textbook
- To review study skills

Student Pages xii–xvii

Teacher's Resource Library

How to Use This Book 1–7

Introduction to the Book

Have volunteers read aloud the three paragraphs of the introduction. Discuss with students why studying science and developing scientific skills are important.

How to Study

Read aloud each bulleted statement, pausing to discuss with students why the suggestion is a part of good study habits. Distribute copies of the How to Use This Book 1, "Study Habits Survey," to students. Read the directions together and then have students complete the survey. After they have scored their surveys, ask them to make a list of the study habits they plan to improve. After three or four weeks, have students complete the survey again to see if they have improved their study habits. Encourage them to keep and review the survey every month or so to see whether they are maintaining and improving their study habits.

To help students organize their time and work in an easy-to-read format, have them fill out How to Use This Book 2, "Weekly Schedule." Encourage them to keep the schedule in a notebook or folder where they can refer to it easily. Suggest that they review the schedule periodically and update it as necessary.

Give students an opportunity to become familiar with the textbook features and the chapter and lesson organization and structure of *Earth Science*. List the

How to Use This Book: A Study Guide

Welcome to *Earth Science*. Science touches our lives every day, no matter where we are—at home, at school, or at work. This book covers the area of earth science. It also focuses on science skills that scientists use. These skills include asking questions, making predictions, designing experiments or procedures, collecting and organizing information, calculating data, making decisions, drawing conclusions, and exploring more options. You probably already use these skills every day. You ask questions to find answers. You gather information and organize it. You use that information to make all sorts of decisions. In this book, you will have opportunities to use and practice all of these skills.

As you read this book, notice how each lesson is organized. Information is presented in a straightforward manner. Tables, diagrams, and photos help clarify concepts. Read the information carefully. If you have trouble with a lesson, try reading it again.

It is important that you understand how to use this book before you start to read it. It is also important to know how to be successful in this course. Information in this first section of the book can help you achieve these things.

How to Study

These tips can help you study more effectively.

- Plan a regular time to study.
- Choose a quiet desk or table where you will not be distracted. Find a spot that has good lighting.
- Gather all the books, pencils, paper, and other equipment you will need to complete your assignments.
- Decide on a goal. For example: "I will finish reading and taking notes on Chapter 1, Lesson 1, by 8:00."
- Take a five- to ten-minute break every hour to stay alert.
- If you start to feel sleepy, take a break and get some fresh air.

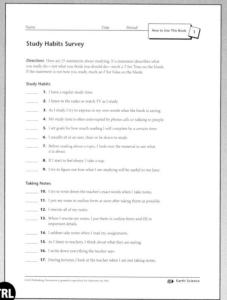

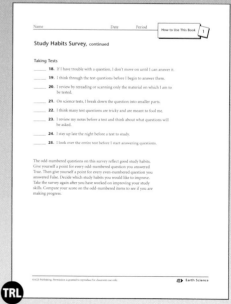

How to Use This Book 1, pages 1 and 2

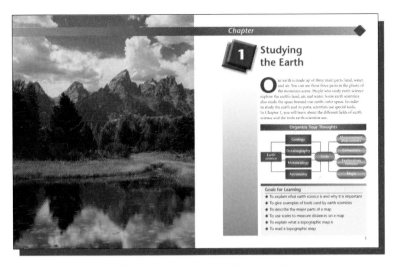

Before Beginning Each Chapter

◆ Read the chapter title and study the photo. What does the photo tell you about the chapter title?
◆ Read the opening paragraph.
◆ Study the Goals for Learning. The Chapter Review and tests will ask questions related to these goals.
◆ Look at the Chapter Review. The questions cover the most important information in the chapter.

Note These Features

Note

Points of interest or additional information that relates to the lesson

Did You Know?

Facts that add details to lesson content or present an interesting or unusual application of lesson content

Science Myth

Common science misconceptions followed by the correct information

How to Use This Book: A Study Guide   **xiii**

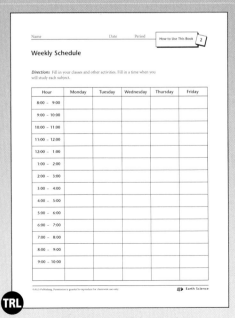

Then have volunteers take turns reading aloud the Chapter 1 Goals for Learning. Discuss with students why knowing these goals can help them when they are studying the chapter. Finally, have students skim the Chapter Summary to identify important information and vocabulary presented in the chapter. Have students turn to the Chapter Review and explain that it provides an opportunity to determine how well they have understood the chapter content.

Note These Features

Use the information on pages xiii and xiv to identify features included in each chapter. As a class locate examples of these features in Chapter 1. Read the examples and discuss their purpose.

following text features on the board: Table of Contents, Chapter Opener, Lesson, Lesson Review, Investigation, Chapter Summary, Chapter Review, Appendix A: Metric and Customary Measurement, Appendix B: Alternative Energy Sources, Appendix C: The Solar System, Appendix D: Space Exploration, Appendix E: Constellations, Appendix F: The Periodic Table of Elements, Appendix G: World Map, Appendix H: North America Map, Glossary, and Index.

Have students skim their textbooks to find these features. You may wish to remind students that they can use the Table of Contents to help identify and locate major features in the text. They can also use the Index to identify specific topics and the text pages on which they are discussed. Ask volunteers to call out a feature or topic and its page reference from the Table of Contents or Index. Have other students check to see that the specific features or topics do appear on the pages cited.

Before Beginning Each Chapter

When students begin their study of Chapter 1, you may wish to have them read aloud and follow each of the bulleted suggestions on page xiii. Actually trying the suggestions will help students understand what they are supposed to do and recognize how useful the suggestions are when previewing a chapter. At the beginning of other chapters, refer students to page xiii and encourage them to follow the suggestions. You may wish to continue to do this as a class each time or allow students to work independently.

In addition to the suggestions on page xiii, the Teacher's Edition text for each Chapter Opener offers teaching suggestions for introducing the chapter. The text also includes a list of Teacher's Resource Library materials for the chapter.

Chapter Openers organize information in easy-to-read formats. Have a volunteer find and read the Chapter 1 title on page 1. Read aloud the second bulleted statement on page xiii and have a volunteer read aloud the opening paragraphs of the chapter. Discuss the topics that students will study in the chapter. Have students examine the Organize Your Thoughts chart. It provides an overview of chapter content.

Continued at left

How to Use This Book: A Study Guide   **xiii**

Before Beginning Each Lesson

With students, read through the information in "Before Beginning Each Lesson" on page xiv. Then assign each of the three lessons in Chapter 1 to a small group of students. Have them restate the lesson title in the form of a statement or a question and make a list of features in their lesson. After their survey of the lesson, they should be prepared to report to the class on their findings.

Technology Note

Technology information that relates to the lesson or chapter

Science in Your Life

Examples of science in real life

Achievements in Science

Historical scientific discoveries, events, and achievements

Science at Work

Careers in science

Investigation

Experiments that give practice with chapter concepts

Before Beginning Each Lesson

Read the lesson title and restate it in the form of a question.

For example, write:
What are topographic maps?

Look over the entire lesson, noting the following:

◆ bold words
◆ text organization
◆ notes in the margins
◆ photos and diagrams
◆ lesson review questions

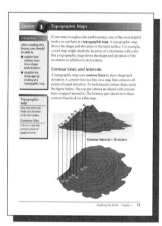

As You Read the Lesson

◆ Read the lesson title.
◆ Read the subheads and paragraphs that follow.
◆ Before moving on to the next lesson, see if you understand the concepts you read. If you do not understand the concepts, reread the lesson. If you are still unsure, ask for help.
◆ Practice what you have learned by completing the Lesson Review.

Using the Bold Words

Knowing the meaning of all the boxed vocabulary words in the left column will help you understand what you read.

These words are in **bold type** the first time they appear in the text. They are often defined in the paragraph.

> **Earth science** is the study of the earth's land, water, and air. Earth science also includes the study of outer space and the objects in it.

All of the words in the left column are also defined in the **Glossary.**

> **Earth science** (ėrth sī´əns) Study of the earth's land, water, air, and outer space (p. 2)

Bold type

Words seen for the first time will appear in bold type

Glossary

Words listed in this column are also found in the Glossary

Word-Study Tips

◆ Start a vocabulary file with index cards to use for review.
◆ Write one term on the front of each card. Write the chapter number, lesson number, and definition on the back.
◆ You can use these cards as flash cards by yourself or with a study partner to test your knowledge.

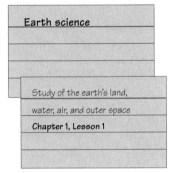

Earth science

Study of the earth's land, water, air, and outer space
Chapter 1, Lesson 1

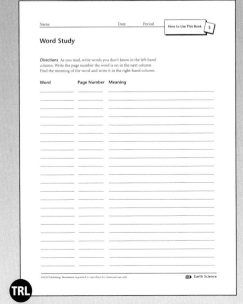

How to Use This Book 3

As You Read the Lesson

Read aloud the statements in the section "As You Read the Lesson" on page xv. Have students preview lessons in Chapter 1 and note lesson titles and subheads. Remind students as they study each lesson to follow this study approach.

Using the Bold Words

Read aloud the information on page xv. Make sure students understand what the term *bold* means. Explain to students that the words in bold are important vocabulary terms. Then ask them to look at the boxed words on page 3. Have a volunteer read the boxed term *geologist* and then find and read the sentence in the text in which that word appears in bold type. Have another volunteer read the definition of the word in the box.

Point out that boxed words may appear on any page in a lesson. Have students turn to page 4 and look at the boxed words on that page. Explain that these words appear in a box here because they are used in the text on this page. Have volunteers find and read the sentences in the text in which the vocabulary words are used. Have students turn to the Glossary at the back of the book and read the definitions of the vocabulary words on page 4.

Word-Study Tips

Have a volunteer read aloud the word-study tips on page xv. You may wish to demonstrate how to make a vocabulary card by filling out an index card for the term *earth science* and its definition (page 2).

Distribute copies of How to Use This Book 3, "Word Study," to students. Suggest that as they read, students write unfamiliar words, their page numbers, and their definitions on the sheet. Point out that having such a list will be very useful for reviewing vocabulary before taking a test. Point out that students can use words they listed on How to Use This Book 3 to make their vocabulary card file.

Using the Summaries

Have students turn to page 21 and examine the Chapter 1 Summary. Emphasize that Chapter Summaries identify the main ideas of the chapter. Suggest that students can use the summary to focus their study of the chapter content. They might write each main idea in a notebook and add a few details that reinforce it. These notes will make a useful study tool.

Using the Reviews

Have students turn to page 6 and examine the Lesson 1 Review for Chapter 1. Emphasize that Lesson Reviews provide opportunities for students to focus on important content and skills developed in the lesson. Then have students turn to pages 22 and 23. Point out that the Chapter Review is intended to help them focus on and review the key terms, content information, and skills presented in the chapter before they are tested on the material. Suggest that they complete the review after they have studied their notes, vocabulary lists, and worksheets.

Preparing for Tests

Encourage students to offer their opinions about tests and their ideas on test-taking strategies. What do they do to study for a test? List their comments on the board. Then read the set of bulleted statements on page xvi. Add these suggestions to the list on the board if they are not already there.

Discuss why each suggestion can help students when they are taking a test. Lead students to recognize that these suggestions, along with the Test-Taking Tips in their textbooks, can help them improve their test-taking skills.

Have students turn to the Chapter Review at the end of any chapter in the textbook and find the Test-Taking Tip. Ask several volunteers to read aloud the tips they find in the Chapter Reviews. Discuss how using the tips can help students study and take tests more effectively.

Using the Summaries

◆ Read each Chapter Summary to be sure you understand the chapter's main ideas.
◆ Make up a sample test of items you think may be on the test. You may want to do this with a classmate and share your questions.
◆ Read the vocabulary words in the Science Words box.
◆ Review your notes and test yourself on vocabulary words and key ideas.
◆ Practice writing about some of the main ideas from the chapter.

Using the Reviews

◆ Answer the questions in the Lesson Reviews.
◆ In the Chapter Reviews, answer the questions about vocabulary under the Vocabulary Review. Study the words and definitions. Say them aloud to help you remember them.
◆ Answer the questions under the Concept Review and Critical Thinking sections of the Chapter Reviews.
◆ Review the Test-Taking Tips.

Preparing for Tests

◆ Complete the Lesson Reviews and Chapter Reviews.
◆ Complete the Investigations.
◆ Review your answers to Lesson Reviews, Investigations, and Chapter Reviews.
◆ Test yourself on vocabulary words and key ideas.
◆ Use graphic organizers as study tools.

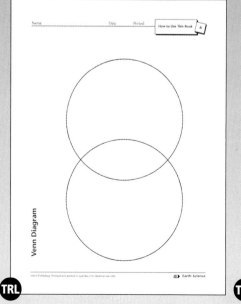

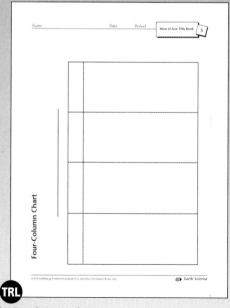

How to Use This Book 4 and 5

Using Graphic Organizers

A graphic organizer is a visual representation of information. It can help you see how ideas are related to one another. A graphic organizer can help you study for a test or organize information before you write. Here are some examples.

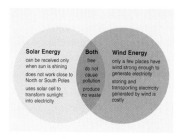

Venn Diagram

A Venn diagram can help you compare and contrast two things. For example, this diagram compares and contrasts solar energy and wind energy. The characteristics of solar energy are listed in the left circle. The characteristics of wind energy are listed in the right circle. The characteristics that both have are listed in the intersection of the circles.

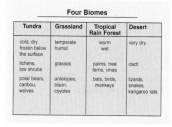

Column Chart

Column charts can help you organize information into groups, or categories. Grouping things in this format helps make the information easier to understand and remember. For example, this four-column chart groups information about each of the four biomes. A column chart can be divided into any number of columns or rows. The chart can be as simple as a two-column list of words or as complex as a multiple-column, multiple-row table of data.

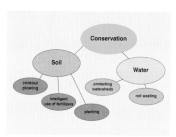

Network Tree

A network tree organizer shows how ideas are connected to one another. Network trees can help you identify main ideas or concepts linked to related ideas. For example, this network tree identifies concepts linked to the concept of conservation. You can also use network trees to rank ideas from most important to least important.

Using Graphic Organizers

Explain to students that graphic organizers provide ways of visually organizing information to make it easier to understand and remember. Emphasize that there are many different kinds of graphic organizers, including Venn diagrams, column charts, network trees, and word webs. Encourage students to look at the Organize Your Thoughts chart at the beginning of each chapter. Discuss how these graphic organizers provide a preview of the chapter content.

Tell students that they can use a variety of organizers to record information for a variety of purposes. For example, a Venn diagram is useful for comparing and contrasting information. Draw a Venn diagram on the board. Show students how to use the diagram to compare and contrast two items, such as a ball and a globe. Discuss how the diagram clearly shows the similarities and differences between the two items.

Display other organizers, such as a cause-and-effect chart, spider map, and two-column chart. Ask volunteers to suggest ways that these organizers can be used to record information. Then encourage students to record information on graphic organizers and use them as study tools.

Have students refer to the pages in this section, "How to Use This Book," as often as they wish while using this textbook.

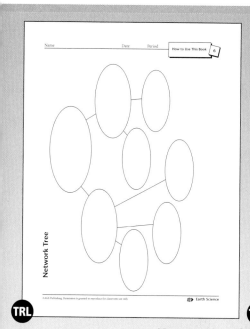

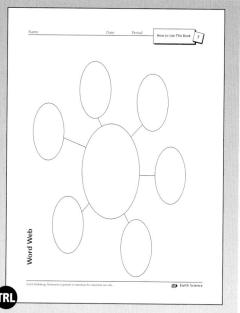

How to Use This Book 6 and 7

The Nature of Science

Write the word *science* on the board. Ask students what the word *science* brings to mind when they hear it. Record their ideas on the board. Guide the discussion to focus on the major areas of science, such as physical, earth, and life sciences; the achievements students credit to science; scientific investigations; and the kinds of information scientists need to do their work.

Following the discussion, have students read the first paragraph on page xviii. Help them conclude that science has played an important role in the development of their way of life. From the time they wake up until the time they fall asleep, they benefit from scientific knowledge and discoveries.

Read and discuss the remaining paragraphs that focus on the scientific method. Emphasize the flexibility of the method and how the steps can be reordered or eliminated depending on the circumstances of the investigation. Discuss how the method can be cyclical. Results can lead to new questions and revised hypotheses and new or refined investigations. Explain that keeping accurate records of investigation data is an extremely important step because the data are used to support conclusions and verify results.

The Nature of Science

Science is an organized body of knowledge about the natural world. It encompasses everything from atoms to rocks to human health. Scientific knowledge is important because it solves problems, improves everyday life, and uncovers new opportunities. For example, scientists develop vaccines and antibiotics to prevent and cure diseases. Scientific knowledge helps farmers grow better and more crops. Science is behind the electricity we depend on every day. And science has launched space exploration, which continues to offer new opportunities.

Scientists use a logical process to explore the world and collect information. It is called the scientific method, and it includes specific steps. Scientists follow these steps or variations of these steps to test whether a possible answer to their question is correct.

1. Ask a question.
2. State a hypothesis, or make a prediction, about the answer.
3. Design an experiment, or procedure, to test the hypothesis.
4. Perform the experiment and gather information.
5. Analyze the data and organize the results.
6. State a conclusion based on the results, existing knowledge, and logic. Determine whether the results support the hypothesis.
7. Communicate the results and the conclusion.

As a scientist researches a question, he or she may do these steps in a different order or may even skip some steps. The scientific method requires many skills: predicting, observing, organizing, classifying, modeling, measuring, inferring, analyzing, and communicating.

Communication is an important part of the scientific method. Scientists all over the world share their findings with other scientists. They publish information about their experiments in journals and discuss them at meetings. A scientist may try another scientist's experiment or change it in some way. If many scientists get the same results from an experiment, then the results are repeatable and considered reliable.

Sometimes the results of an experiment do not support its hypothesis. Unexpected observations can lead to new, more interesting questions. For example, penicillin was discovered accidentally in 1928. Alexander Fleming observed that mold had contaminated one of his bacteria cultures. He noticed that the mold had stopped the growth of the bacterium. Since the mold was from the penicillium family, he named it penicillin. A decade later, researchers found a way to isolate the active ingredient. Since then, penicillin has been used to fight bacteria and save people's lives.

Once in a while, scientists discover something that dramatically changes our world, like penicillin. But, more often, scientific knowledge grows and changes a little at a time.

What scientists learn is applied to problems and challenges that affect people's lives. This leads to the development of practical tools and techniques. Tools help scientists accurately observe and measure things in the natural world. A new tool often provides data that an older tool could not. For example, computers help scientists analyze data more quickly and accurately than ever before. Our science knowledge grows as more advanced tools and technology make new discoveries possible.

Scientists use theories to explain their observations and data. A theory is a possible explanation for a set of data. A theory is not a fact. It is an idea. Theories are tested by more experiments. Theories may be confirmed, changed, or sometimes tossed out. For example, in 1808, John Dalton published a book describing his theory of atoms. His theory stated that atoms are solid spheres without internal structures. By the early 1900s, however, new tools allowed Ernest Rutherford to show that atoms are mostly empty space. He said that an atom consists of a tightly packed nucleus with electrons whizzing around it. This theory of the atom is still accepted today.

Theories that have stood many years of testing often become scientific laws. The law of gravity is one example. Scientists assume many basic laws of nature.

In this book, you will learn about earth science. You will use scientific skills to solve problems and answer questions. You will follow some of the steps in the scientific method. And you will discover how important earth science is to your life.

Display a variety of tools that students will use in their own scientific investigations. Identify each tool and its purpose. Discuss the proper care of the tools and the need to follow safety precautions when performing investigations. You may wish to help students develop a list of safety rules to follow. They can make a poster outlining the rules for display in the classroom.

Tell students that through the investigations in *Earth Science*, they have the opportunity to perform as scientists. Remind them to use the opportunity to follow the scientific method and develop the skills that will enhance their study and understanding of science.

Planning Guide

Studying the Earth

	Student Text Lesson		
	Student Pages	Vocabulary	Lesson Review
Lesson 1 Earth Science	2–6	✔	✔
Lesson 2 Understanding Maps	7–14	✔	✔
Lesson 3 Topographic Maps	15–20	✔	✔

Chapter Activities

Student Text
Science Center
Teacher's Resource Library
Community Connection 1: Maps Are
   Everywhere

Assessment Options

Student Text
Chapter 1 Review
Teacher's Resource Library
Chapter 1 Mastery Tests A and B

	Student Text Features								Teaching Strategies						Learning Styles						Teacher's Resource Library				
	Achievements in Science	Science at Work	Science in Your Life	Investigation	Science Myth	Note	Technology Note	Did You Know	Science Integration	Science Journal	Cross-Curricular Connection	Online Connection	Teacher Alert	Applications (Home, Career, Community, Global, Environment)	Auditory/Verbal	Body/Kinesthetic	Interpersonal/Group Learning	Logical/Mathematical	Visual/Spatial	LEP/ESL	Workbook Activities	Alternative Workbook Activities	Lab Manual	Resource File	Self-Study Guide
	6					✔	✔	4, 5	5	4	3	2, 4	3	3, 5			4				1	1		1	✔
		12	13	9				9	11		9, 10, 11		7, 10	10	9	10		11		9	2	2	1, 2		✔
			18	19		✔	✔		17		17								16		3	3	3, 4	2	✔

Pronunciation Key

a	hat	e	let	ī	ice	ô	order	ù	put	sh	she		a	in about
ā	age	ē	equal	o	hot	oi	oil	ü	rule	th	thin	ə	e	in taken
ä	far	ėr	term	ō	open	ou	out	ch	child	ᵺ	then		i	in pencil
â	care	i	it	ò	saw	u	cup	ng	long	zh	measure		o	in lemon
													u	in circus

Alternative Workbook Activities

The Teacher's Resource Library (TRL) contains a set of lower-level worksheets called Alternative Workbook Activities. These worksheets cover the same content as the regular Workbook Activities but are written at a second-grade reading level.

Skill Track Software

Use the Skill Track Software for Earth Science for additional reinforcement of this chapter. The software program allows students using AGS textbooks to be assessed for mastery of each chapter and lesson of the textbook. Students access the software on an individual basis and are assessed with multiple-choice items.

Chapter 1:
Studying the Earth
pages 1–23

Lessons

1. Earth Science pages 2–6

2. Understanding Maps pages 7–14

Investigation 1-1 pages 13–14

3. Topographic Maps pages 15–20

Investigation 1-2 pages 19–20

Chapter 1 Summary page 21

Chapter 1 Review pages 22–23

Skill Track Software
for Earth Science

Teacher's Resource Library

Workbook Activities 1–3

Alternative Workbook Activities
1–3

Lab Manual 1–4

Community Connection 1

Resource File 1–2

Chapter 1 Self-Study Guide

Chapter 1 Mastery Tests A and B

(Answer Keys for the Teacher's
Resource Library begin on page 400
of the Teacher's Edition. The
Materials List for the Lab Manual
activities begins on page 415.)

Science Center

Provide an area of the classroom for
students to display maps that they find
from a variety of sources. Provide a
chalkboard or piece of tagboard for
students to write questions they have after
examining the maps. At the end of the
chapter, have students study the different
kinds of maps they have collected to
determine the kinds of information
shown in each and whether the questions
they noted have been answered.

Community Connection 1

1 Studying the Earth

O ur earth is made up of three main parts: land, water, and air. You can see these three parts in the photo of the mountain scene. People who study earth science explore the earth's land, air, and water. Some earth scientists also study the space beyond our earth: outer space. In order to study the earth and its parts, scientists use special tools. In Chapter 1, you will learn about the different fields of earth science and the tools earth scientists use.

Organize Your Thoughts

```
Earth science ── Geology
              ── Oceanography
              ── Meteorology ── Tools ── Measurement instruments
              ── Astronomy                ── Computers
                                          ── Exploration vehicles
                                          ── Maps
```

Goals for Learning

◆ To explain what earth science is and why it is important
◆ To give examples of tools used by earth scientists
◆ To describe the major parts of a map
◆ To use scales to measure distances on a map
◆ To explain what a topographic map is
◆ To read a topographic map

1

Introducing the Chapter

Have students examine the photograph on page xx. Ask them to identify parts of the earth shown. Discuss with students why this photograph is appropriate for introducing earth science. Focus the discussion on the three parts of the earth—land, water, and air—shown in the photograph.

Provide small groups of students with a variety of maps. Allow time for students to familiarize themselves with the maps and to record their observations and questions about them. Use the observations as a starting point for determining students' prior knowledge of maps.

With the class, write a list of questions that students would like answered. They can use the Organize Your Thoughts chart and the Goals for Learning to identify topics discussed in the chapter. As they read the chapter, students should record the answers to the questions.

Notes and Technology Notes

Ask volunteers to read the notes that appear in the margins throughout the chapter. Then discuss them with the class.

TEACHER'S RESOURCE

The AGS Teaching Strategies in Science Transparencies may be used with this chapter. The transparencies add an interactive dimension to expand and enhance the *Earth Science* program content.

CAREER INTEREST INVENTORY

The AGS Harrington-O'Shea Career Decision-Making System-Revised (CDM) may be used with this chapter. Students can use the CDM to explore their interests and identify careers. The CDM defines career areas that are indicated by students' responses on the inventory.

Name _____ Date _____ Period _____ *SELF-STUDY GUIDE*

Chapter 1: Studying the Earth

| Goal 1.1 | To explain what earth science is and why it is important |

Date	Assignment	Score
_____	**1.** Read pages 1, 2, and 5.	_____
Comments:

| Goal 1.2 | To give examples of tools used by earth scientists |

Date	Assignment	Score
_____	**2.** Read pages 3–4.	_____
_____	**3.** Complete the Lesson 1 Review on page 6.	_____
_____	**4.** Complete Workbook Activity 1.	_____
Comments:

| Goal 1.3 | To describe the major parts of a map |

Date	Assignment	Score
_____	**5.** Read pages 7–11.	_____
Comments:

| Goal 1.4 | To use scales to measure distances on a map |

Date	Assignment	Score
_____	**6.** Read pages 10–11.	_____
_____	**7.** Complete the Lesson 2 Review on page 12.	_____
_____	**8.** Complete Workbook Activity 2.	_____
_____	**9.** Complete Investigation 1-1 on pages 13–14.	_____
Comments:

©AGS Publishing. Permission is granted to reproduce for classroom use only.   Earth Science

---

Name _____ Date _____ Period _____ *SELF-STUDY GUIDE*

Chapter 1: Studying the Earth, continued

| Goal 1.5 | To explain what a topographic map is |

Date	Assignment	Score
_____	**10.** Read page 15.	_____
Comments:

| Goal 1.6 | To read a topographic map |

Date	Assignment	Score
_____	**11.** Read pages 15–17.	_____
_____	**12.** Complete the Lesson 3 Review on page 18.	_____
_____	**13.** Complete Workbook Activity 3.	_____
_____	**14.** Complete Investigation 1-2 on pages 19–20.	_____
_____	**15.** Read the Chapter 1 Summary on page 21.	_____
_____	**16.** Complete the Chapter 1 Review on pages 22–23.	_____
Comments:

Student's Signature _____ Date _____

Instructor's Signature _____ Date _____

©AGS Publishing. Permission is granted to reproduce for classroom use only.   Earth Science

---

TRL   TRL

Lesson at a Glance

Chapter 1 Lesson 1

Overview This lesson introduces students to the study of earth science. They learn the names of some of the fields of earth science, the focus of each field, and some of the tools used by earth scientists.

Objectives

- To state what earth science is
- To list the main fields of earth science
- To name some tools used by earth scientists
- To give examples of how earth science is important to students

Student Pages 2–6

Teacher's Resource Library

Workbook Activity 1

Alternative Workbook Activity 1

Resource File 1

Vocabulary

astronomer	meteorology
astronomy	metric system
earth science	oceanographer
geologist	oceanography
geology	submersible
meteorologist	unit

1 Warm-Up Activity

Have students look again at the photograph on page xx. Ask students how the water may be affecting the land, the land affecting the air, and the air affecting the land. For example, how might cutting trees affect the water? *(Without tree roots to hold it in place, soil will run into streams, rivers, and lakes. This can affect the food available in bodies of water for aquatic animals.)*

2 Teaching the Lesson

Before students read the lesson, write each vocabulary word on the board. Have students record what they know about each word. As students read, have them review the information they have recorded and take notes, making corrections or adding information about the words.

Objectives

After reading this lesson, you should be able to

- state what earth science is.
- list the main fields of earth science.
- name some tools used by earth scientists.
- give examples of how earth science is important to you.

Earth science
Study of the earth's land, water, air, and outer space

Geology
Study of the solid parts of the earth

Oceanography
Study of the earth's oceans

Meteorology
Study of the earth's air and weather

Astronomy
Study of outer space and objects in it

Earth science is the study of the earth's land, water, and air. Earth science also includes the study of outer space and the objects in it.

Fields of Earth Science

Earth science can be divided into many fields of science. The table describes the main fields, or subject areas, that make up earth science. Which field could answer the question, Why did it rain today? Which field would include scientists who learn about dinosaurs? Compare this table to the Table of Contents on page iii. Which chapters in this book deal with which fields of earth science?

Fields of Earth Science	
Field	**What Is Studied**
geology	the earth's land, including the surface of the earth and the inside of the earth; how the earth changes; history of the earth
oceanography	the earth's oceans, including what they contain and how they interact with the air
meteorology	the earth's air, including weather
astronomy	outer space, including planets, stars, and other objects in space

The land, water, and air of the earth are constantly changing and interacting with one another. For example, when rain washes mud off a hillside and into a river, the land and water interact with each other. When a puddle dries up, the water and air interact with each other. Because of these interactions, a change in one part of the earth affects other parts of the earth. In your local environment, how do land, water, and air affect each other? How do you affect your environment?

ONLINE CONNECTION

 The Web site www.sciencenetlinks.com provides teachers with a variety of science lessons, teaching tools, and other resources that can be applied throughout this book.

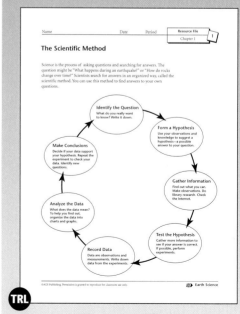

Tools Used by Earth Scientists

Geologist
Scientist who studies the solid parts of the earth and how they change

Metric system
System of measurement used by scientists

Unit
Known amount used for measuring

Scientists use many tools to help gather information about the earth. Some of these tools are simple. For example, a **geologist** can study the solid parts of the earth by using a rock hammer to break off chunks of fresh rock. A hand lens helps the geologist look more closely at the particles that make up the rock.

Some tools are complex and sensitive. They can measure small changes in the environment. For example, the geologists in the photo below are collecting data near an active volcano. They are using an instrument that measures distance with a laser beam. By collecting and comparing measurements, they learn more about the earth.

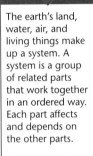

The earth's land, water, air, and living things make up a system. A system is a group of related parts that work together in an ordered way. Each part affects and depends on the other parts.

This surveying instrument sends a laser beam to a distant reflector. When the reflected beam returns, the instrument calculates the distance.

These and other scientific measurements are almost always based on the **metric system**. Scientists all over the world use tools that measure in metric **units**. For example, a scientist might measure something in meters, not feet. A meter is a metric unit of length. A foot is a customary, or ordinary, unit of length. Appendix A will help you become familiar with the metric system. As you will see, this is the measurement system used throughout this book.

Call attention to the Fields of Earth Science chart on page 2. Ask students to name the scientist who works in each field. *(geologist, oceanographer, meteorologist, astronomer)* Divide the class into groups. Have each group list four or five problems scientists might investigate as they study land, water, air, or outer space. Compile the groups' lists into a class list. Throughout the study of earth science, discuss how scientists might study and solve these problems.

Have students look at the instrument pictured on page 3. Ask them to share what they already know about tools scientists use in their investigations of land, water, air, and space. Also, help students review metric measurement units used by scientists. Have volunteers name metric units and identify what they measure.

3 Reinforce and Extend

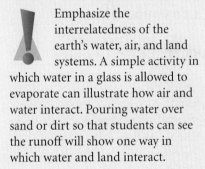

ONLINE CONNECTION

To find out more about submersibles and their uses, have students visit

oceanexplorer.noaa.gov/technology/ subs/alvin/alvin.html. There they will find information about *Alvin* and other submersibles. The site also enables students to access the Woods Holes Oceanographic Institution's site and to learn about its research operations.

LEARNING STYLES

Interpersonal/ Group Learning

A meteorologist studies the air and weather. Most people are familiar with weather forecasts prepared by meteorologists with the help of data and tools. Suggest that small groups of students identify the tools used by meteorologists and the kinds of information each tool provides. Ask the groups to cooperatively set up an exhibit of tools and/or pictures of tools and provide a written description of each tool's use and importance to the meteorologist.

SCIENCE JOURNAL

Have students write a paragraph identifying which field of earth science they find most interesting and why. At the end of the course, students can review their journal entry and determine whether their opinions have changed.

Meteorologist
Scientist who studies the air and weather

Submersible
Small underwater research vessel

Oceanographer
Scientist who studies the oceans

Astronomer
Scientist who studies outer space and objects in it

Computers are important tools in science. They store information, make rapid calculations, and let scientists communicate with one another all over the world. What helps **meteorologists**, scientists who study the weather, provide those up-to-the-minute weather reports? Computers do. Weather information is continuously put into computers. Then the computers use the information to perform calculations for developing forecasts.

Earth scientists use other tools to explore places that are hard to study directly. The vehicle shown on the left is a **submersible**. This small underwater vessel carries **oceanographers** to the ocean floor. Oceanographers are scientists who study the oceans. Remote-controlled equipment attached to the submersible can explore small, deep, or dangerous places.

Submersibles can dive to 4,000 meters.

Exploration vehicles can be used to study planets.

Did You Know?

In 1999, scientists used the submersible *Alvin* to study the Gulf of Alaska. *Alvin* helped gather data about sea life along an undersea volcanic ridge.

The vehicle on the right is an exploration robot that collects data. It is being tested and prepared to roll across the surface of Mars. **Astronomers** are scientists who study planets and other space objects. In 1997, astronomers placed a vehicle like this on Mars to take photos and soil samples. Tools like these have helped earth scientists make important discoveries.

The tools described here are only a few of the many tools earth scientists use to gather information. What others can you think of? In Lesson 2, you will learn about one important kind of tool: maps of the earth.

The Importance of Earth Science

Earth science is important in your life. In fact, you probably use earth science in some way every day. Did you ride in a car or bus today? The fuel was made from oil that geologists located underground. Have you heard a forecast for tomorrow's weather? A meteorologist made this forecast.

The meteorologist in the photo studies climate patterns. By analyzing weather and ocean conditions, he can predict warming systems called El Niños. These systems happen every three to seven years and can cause drought or extra rain.

How is the work of meteorologists important to farmers?

You can use your own knowledge of earth science to make wise decisions. For example, knowledge about soils can help you when planting a garden. Knowing about the earth's underground water table can come in handy when buying a house. Communities often face questions about how to use the land and its resources. An earth science background will help you understand such issues.

Lesson 1 Review Answers

1. Earth science is the study of the earth's land, air, water, and sometimes outer space 2. geology, astronomy, oceanography, meteorology 3. Tools help scientists gather and analyze information about the earth. 4. Computers can make measurements, store information, make calculations, and help scientists communicate with one another. 5. Earth science can help inform individuals about weather, for example. Earth science also helps communities to make wise decisions about the use of land and its resources.

Achievements in Science

Ask volunteers to read the Achievements in Science feature about Earth Day on page 6. It identifies two influential men who initiated the idea of celebrating the earth once a year. Have students form teams to investigate the Earth Day celebrations in their area. One team might research the history of local Earth Day observances. Other teams might plan an Earth Day celebration for their school or neighborhood.

Portfolio Assessment

Sample items include:
- Vocabulary development from Teaching the Lesson
- Questions based on the Fields of Earth Science chart
- Lesson 1 Review answers

Write your answers to these questions on a sheet of paper.

1. Write a definition of earth science.

2. What are the four main fields of earth science?

3. How do tools help scientists?

4. How are computers helpful to scientists?

5. Give two examples of how earth science is important to your life.

Achievements in Science

Celebrating Earth Day

Each year we celebrate our planet on a special day called Earth Day. The idea for having an Earth Day first occurred to Wisconsin Senator Gaylord Nelson in 1962. Because he was worried about the earth, Senator Nelson wrote a letter to President Kennedy. He urged the president to make the health of our planet an important issue. The president thought that was a good idea. He did his best to make people interested in taking care of our planet.

Even with President Kennedy's help, it took a while for the idea of Earth Day to catch on. Senator Nelson spoke at many college campuses. He tried to convince students that it was important to have a special day to celebrate the environment. Finally, the first Earth Day happened in 1970. Across the country, more than 20 million people, thousands of schools, and many local communities participated. Since then, Earth Day has been celebrated every year on April 22.

Name _____ Date _____ Period _____ | Workbook Activity
Chapter 1, Lesson 1 | 1

Earth Science

Directions Write the term from the Word Bank that best completes each sentence.

Word Bank				
astronomy	earth science	exploration robot	lens	oceanography
balloons	El Niño	geologist	meteorology	submersible
computer	environment	geology	metric system	weather

1. The study of the surface and inside of the earth is called _____

2. The study of the earth's water is called _____

3. The study of the earth's air and weather is called _____

4. The study of objects in space is called _____

5. Land, water, and air are everywhere on earth. These interact and affect the _____ where you live.

6. Scientists usually base their measurements on the _____

7. A very simple tool that helps a geologist study rocks is a hand-held _____

8. A(n) _____ is a complicated tool astronomers use to study rocks on Mars.

9. To study the bottom of an ocean, oceanographers may use a(n) _____

10. A(n) _____ is a tool that helps scientists store and analyze information as well as communicate with other scientists.

11. Communities depend on a knowledge of _____ to determine the best ways to use the land and its resources.

12. A(n) _____ is a scientist who might locate the oil that is used to power buses and cars.

13. Farmers rely on meteorologists to give them accurate reports on the _____

14. Scientists who study the air often depend on _____ to measure weather conditions high above the earth.

15. A strong, warm climate system that repeats itself every three to seven years is called _____

©AGS Publishing. Permission is granted to reproduce for classroom use only.   Earth Science

Workbook Activity 1

Objectives

After reading this lesson, you should be able to

◆ explain what a map is.

◆ describe the parts of a map.

◆ use a legend and scale to read a map.

Map

Drawing that shows part of the earth's surface as seen from above

When learning about the earth, you will use many models. A model shows how something looks or works. For example, a model car shows how a real car looks. Blow on a page of this book. You have just made a model that shows how wind works. A globe is a model of the earth. It shows the relative sizes and shapes of the earth's features.

Among the most useful models in earth science are **maps**. A map is a drawing that shows part of the earth's surface as seen from above. Maps are useful because they show and label information clearly. Compare the photo below with the map. They both show land, rivers, bridges, and roads. But suppose you wanted to know how to drive from Virginia to West Virginia. The map clearly shows which roads to take.

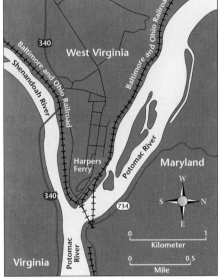

Both the photo and the map show where Maryland, Virginia, and West Virginia meet.

TEACHER ALERT

The compass rose on the map on page 7 is oriented so that north is pointing to the right. As you discuss compass directions and the Science Myth feature on page 9, explain to students that maps are not always drawn with north at the top. Emphasize the importance of locating a map's compass rose instead of assuming the direction of north.

Chapter 1 Lesson 2

Overview This lesson introduces students to the use of maps. Students learn about map legends, compass directions, and map scales.

Objectives

■ To explain what a map is

■ To describe the parts of a map

■ To use a legend and scale to read a map

Student Pages 7–14

Teacher's Resource Library

Workbook Activity 2

Alternative Workbook Activity 2

Lab Manual 1–2

....

Vocabulary

compass rose	map
legend	scale

....

Science Background

Mapmakers use lines, symbols, and colors to represent places on the earth. Mapmaking, known as cartography, is an ancient art. Long before people could read or write, they may have been sketching simple maps. The history of mapmaking began in the Stone Age. In 1966, a fragment of mammoth tusk was excavated in Ukraine. The tusk, believed to be 11,000 to 12,000 years old, shows a stream with a row of riverside dwellings. Archeologists have discovered artwork that exhibits maplike elements from later Stone Age periods. One wall painting, dating to around 6200 B.C., shows the layout of houses and streets against the backdrop of an erupting volcano.

There are large gaps in our knowledge of mapmaking, due largely to the perishable nature of the materials from which maps were typically made—wood, bark, and papyrus. However, dozens of maps from ancient Mesopotamia are still intact. The oldest known map comes from Babylonia, an ancient kingdom in what is now Iraq. The Babylonians also developed the degree system for measuring circles. This system is the basis for the latitude and longitude lines that people use to locate

Continued on page 8

Continued from page 7

places on the earth today. Mapmaking in ancient times was based largely on imagination and theory because little scientific information was available.

Mapmaking became more precise around the second century B.C. The Egyptian astronomer Ptolemy was the first to put north at the top of a map. Through his work, early scientists gained a better understanding of the actual size of the earth and the distances between landmasses. Ptolemy's maps were still being used in the 1400s. About the same time, interest in geography increased as explorers traveled to unknown parts of the world. As a result, more was learned about the actual size and shape of the world.

 1 Warm-Up Activity

Ask a volunteer to give directions to a well-known local landmark—a park, a mall, or a building. The student may give the directions in terms of turning left or right. Make sure that students realize that these directions are relative to the traveler. Ask how the directions might be made more useful and accurate. *(by using the terms* north, south, east, *and* west*)*

 2 Teaching the Lesson

Use a wall map or atlas map to reinforce the vocabulary in the lesson. Point out the legend, compass rose, and scale on the map. Help students identify the purpose of each of these map features. Have students list each vocabulary term and draw an example to illustrate the term.

Ask students to find examples of maps in books and to use the examples to identify the legends, compass roses, and scales. Encourage students to identify how color and other symbols are used on each map to convey information. Also discuss why the scales differ from map to map.

Ask students to use the lesson title and subheads as headings in an outline. Have students add information to the outline to describe the main ideas.

Legend
List of map symbols and their meanings

Map Legends

A map is useful only if you know how to read it. In order to read a map, you must understand the symbols used on it. Therefore, most maps include a **legend**, or key, that explains what the map symbols mean. Some symbols are shapes and some are colors.

What information does the map below provide? Look at the legend to find out. This map shows elevation, or how high the land is above sea level. Most of the southeastern United States is near sea level. You can tell this by matching the dark green color on the map with the legend.

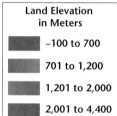

Land Elevation in Meters	
	−100 to 700
	701 to 1,200
	1,201 to 2,000
	2,001 to 4,400

Compass Directions

OK, where's north? This is the first question someone might ask when looking at a map. For a map to make sense, you have to know the map's compass directions: north, south, east, and west.

A way of showing direction is usually given on a map. Some maps show direction by using a **compass rose**, like the one shown here. This symbol shows the four major points of direction. It also shows combined points of direction: northeast, southeast, southwest, and northwest. Notice that northeast is between north and east. Between what two major direction points is southwest?

Find the compass rose on the map on page 10. In what direction would you have to travel to get from Portland to Augusta?

The compass rose on some maps gives only the four major direction points. Other maps may not have a compass rose at all. Instead, they show direction by using a single arrow with the letter *N*. The arrow shows the direction of north. From that information, you can tell where south, east, and west are located.

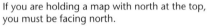

Science Myth

If you are holding a map with north at the top, you must be facing north.

Fact: The compass rose on a map does not tell you the direction you are facing as you hold the map. You could hold a map with north at the top, but be facing south. The compass rose shows only the directions within the map itself.

LEARNING STYLES

LEP/ESL

Point out to students that, in reference to maps, *key* and *legend* have the same meaning. Help students identify the specific meaning of these terms in reference to maps as well as their general-usage meaning. Then relate the two. For example, metal keys unlock doors and map keys unlock the meaning of symbols. Picture legends provide information about pictures just as map legends provide information about maps.

CROSS-CURRICULAR CONNECTION

Art

Show students ornate maps with or without compass roses. You may find such maps in bound books of historic maps. Briefly discuss how the compass rose should reflect the style of the map. Then ask students to choose a map from a newspaper or book and create a compass rose that would be compatible with the map's design or topic. For example, for a map showing forests, they might draw a tree with the branches and trunk pointing in the different directions.

Science Myth

Ask a volunteer to read the myth portion of the feature on page 9. Encourage students to suggest why this is a myth and to check their reasons against the fact portion. Explain that they need to turn the map so that north on the map faces north on the earth because the map's orientation is independent of directions on the earth.

LEARNING STYLES

Auditory/Verbal

To help students orient themselves to compass directions, label the north wall or corner in the room with a large *N*. Have students stand facing north and give specific oral directions to follow. For example, say "Turn east. When you are facing north, east is 90 degrees to your right." Continue with directions for turning south, southeast, west, northwest, and so on.

Did You Know?

Ask a volunteer to read aloud the Did You Know? feature on page 9. Use a globe or world map to locate ancient Babylon. Show students that it was located along the eastern banks of the Euphrates River in present-day Iraq. It was an important trade and religious center of the Babylonian Empire.

Body/Kinesthetic

Help students develop the concept of scale through physical activity. Have them mark a starting point with chalk, take 10 giant strides on the school grounds or in the gym, and mark the ending point. Then help students measure the distance in feet or meters and develop a scale to represent the distance on paper. Encourage students to make all three types of scales for the activity.

CROSS-CURRICULAR CONNECTION

Social Studies

Ask students to use their social studies texts, reference books, or the Internet to locate information about large-scale (small area) and small-scale (large area) maps. Ask them to provide examples of each kind of map and to use a Venn diagram to explain how they are alike and different. Have students present their information to the class and post their maps and diagrams on a bulletin board.

AT HOME

Tell students that floor plans are maps of rooms or buildings. Ask them to draw a floor plan of a room in their home that they would like to rearrange. It should be drawn to scale and show all doors, windows, and heating vents. They will need two copies of the floor plan. On one, they should show scale drawings of furnishings in their present locations. On the other, they should show scale drawings of furnishings rearranged. Provide bulletin board space where students can exhibit their before-and-after maps if they wish.

Scale

Part of a map that shows the relationship between map distance and actual distance

Map Scales

Another part of a map is the **scale**. A scale is a comparison between the distances on a map and the actual distances on the earth. Using a scale, you can find actual distances between different points on a map.

There are three common kinds of map scales. One kind is a bar scale. It is a line or a bar divided into equal parts and labeled with a unit of length, such as kilometers. One kilometer on the scale represents 1 kilometer on the earth. To find the distance between two points on the earth, use a ruler to measure the distance between those points on a map. Then hold the ruler against the bar scale and compare your measurement with the scale.

For example, you can use the map of Maine below to find out how far Portland is from Augusta. First, measure the distance between these cities with a ruler. On this map, they are a little more than 5 centimeters apart. Next, measure the bar scale that represents 80 kilometers. Compare these two measurements. You can tell that Portland and Augusta must be a little more than 80 kilometers apart (83 to be exact).

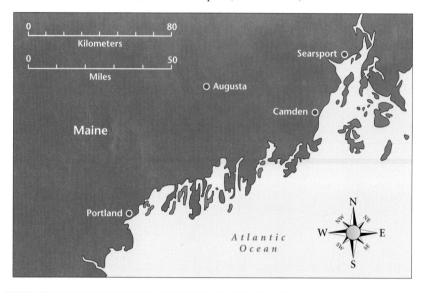

TEACHER ALERT

As you discuss scale, emphasize that the size of the area to be mapped affects the amount of detail that can be shown. Tell students that the scale of a map is the relationship between distance on the map and the corresponding distance on the earth's surface. Large-scale maps show a small area and contain much detail. Small-scale maps cover a large area, but the features and the amount of detail on the map are limited. Use the maps on pages 7 and 10 to compare map scales.

Another kind of map scale is an equivalence scale. It uses two distances and an equal sign to make a comparison. For example,

1 centimeter = 2 kilometers

This scale tells you that 1 centimeter on the map stands for an actual distance of 2 kilometers on the earth. So if two points on the map are 8 centimeters apart, they are 16 kilometers apart on the earth's surface ($8 \times 2 = 16$). How far apart would two cities be if they were 3 centimeters apart on the map?

The third kind of map scale is a ratio. A ratio may be written as follows.

1:100,000

This ratio tells you that one unit on the map equals 100,000 of the same units on the earth's surface. For example, if the measured distance on the map is 1 centimeter, then the actual distance is equal to 100,000 centimeters.

A centimeter is not a convenient unit for expressing actual distances. You will usually want to change the distances that you calculate in centimeters into meters or kilometers. Here is how you can do this.

EXAMPLE   distance in centimeters ÷ 100 = distance in meters
100,000 centimeters ÷ 100 = 1,000 meters

distance in meters ÷ 1,000 = distance in kilometers
1,000 meters ÷ 1,000 = 1 kilometer

You have learned about three main parts of a map: the legend, compass directions, and the scale. By understanding these parts, you can read almost any map.

Lesson 2 Review Answers

1. a drawing that shows part of the earth's surface as seen from above **2.** a list of map symbols and their meanings **3.** The compass rose identifies the major compass directions: north, east, south, and west. **4.** bar scales, equivalence scales, and ratios **5.** 15 kilometers

Science at Work

Ask volunteers to read aloud the Science at Work feature on page 12. Explain to students that the computer has changed the ways in which many cartographers work. They once spent many hours painstakingly drawing maps to scale by hand. The computer has helped to simplify and improve the process. If possible, invite a cartographer to the class to discuss how computers have changed the ways cartographers make maps.

Portfolio Assessment

Sample items include:
• Drawings for vocabulary terms from Teaching the Lesson
• Outline from Teaching the Lesson
• Lesson 2 Review answers

Write your answers to these questions on a sheet of paper.

1. What is a map?

2. What is a map legend?

3. Why is it helpful to have a compass rose on a map?

4. What are three kinds of map scales?

5. If a map scale reads "1 centimeter = 5 kilometers," how many kilometers does 3 centimeters represent?

▼◀▲▼◀▲▼◀▲▼◀▲▼◀▲▼◀▲▼◀▲▼◀▲▼◀▲▼◀▲▼◀▲▼◀▲▼◀▲▼◀▲▼

Science at Work

Cartographer

Cartographers create maps that describe features of the earth's surface. They also create graphs and other visual ways to present data. Tools used by cartographers include land surveys, aerial photos, satellite images, and computers.

To make a map, cartographers first research and collect data about the area to be mapped. Large computer systems store and organize the data. Such systems can also change the data into models and maps. For example, cartographers often use a geographic information system. This changes computer information into three-dimensional maps. These maps are laid on top of one another and combined into one image. These three-dimensional images are helpful to city planners and meteorologists.

Most cartographers have a bachelor's degree in engineering, forestry, geography, or physical science. They need to be detail-oriented and have strong computer and math skills. Good communication and organization skills are helpful.

Lab Manual 1, pages 1–2

Workbook Activity 2

Making a Map

Materials
◆ meterstick

Purpose

How would you make a map of the room you're in? In this investigation, you will construct a map using a map scale and legend.

Procedure

1. Copy the data table on a sheet of paper.

| Name of area to be mapped _____ |
| Actual length and width _____ |
| Map scale _____ |

Object	Symbol	Location Measurements

2. Select a familiar area to map, such as your classroom.

3. Use the meterstick to measure the length and width of the area that your map will show. Record your measurements in the data table. Remember to include units.

4. Decide on a scale for your map. Pick a scale that will allow your map to fit on a sheet of paper. Then write this scale in your data table and at the bottom of a new sheet of paper. This is the start of your map.

5. Use the scale and the measurements from step 3 to draw the outer boundaries of your map.

6. Choose several objects in the area to include on your map. The example classroom map on the next page shows some objects you might include.

Investigation 1-1

The Purpose portion of the student investigation begins with a question to draw students into the activity. Encourage students to read the investigation steps and formulate their own questions before beginning the investigation. This investigation will take approximately 30 minutes to complete. Students will use these process and thinking skills: measuring, recognizing space relationships, and making physical models.

Preparation

- Determine ahead of time the area students are to map.

- You may wish to determine a particular scale for the entire class to use for their maps.

- Students may use Lab Manual 2 to record their data and answer the questions.

- You might provide students with graph paper for this activity.

Procedure

- This activity may be done individually or in pairs.

- Allow students who are not proficient in math to use calculators.

- Some students may need help in reading the scale on the meterstick.

- Before students begin making their map, check each map to ensure that the scale students have chosen is appropriate. For a typical classroom, a scale of 1 centimeter = 1 meter will provide enough detail for the activity.

Continued on page 14

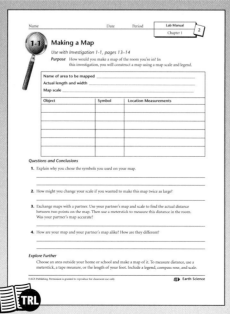

Lab Manual 2

Continued from page 13

Results

Students' maps will show variations, depending on the scale and symbols used.

Questions and Conclusions Answers

1. Answers will vary. Students might indicate that they chose symbols that were simple in design.

2. Answers will vary, but might include using a scale of 2 centimeters = 1 meter instead of 1 centimeter = 1 meter. This will result in a map of the same area being twice as large (for example, a map that measures 10 centimeters wide would become 20 centimeters wide). Some students may misread this question as asking them to change the scale so a same-size map shows twice as much area.

3. The accuracy of map scales and distances will vary.

4. Answers will vary, depending on the scale and symbols used.

Explore Further Answers

Maps should show a reasonable use of scale. Sites selected will vary. Legend symbols will differ.

Assessment

While neatness, precision, and accuracy are important map-making skills, students should be assessed mainly on their ability to make the requested two-dimensional model. You might include the following items from this investigation in student portfolios:

- Student map
- Data table
- Answers to Questions and Conclusions section
- Map from Explore Further section

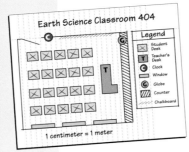

Record these objects in your data table. Design symbols for the objects and draw them in the table, too.

7. Use your meterstick to measure where these objects are in relation to nearby walls or other objects. Record these location measurements.

8. Refer to these measurements and your scale. Then draw the symbols in the correct places on your map.

9. Add a legend and compass rose to your map.

Questions and Conclusions

1. Explain why you chose the symbols you used on your map.

2. How might you change your scale if you wanted to make this map twice as large?

3. Exchange maps with a partner. Use your partner's map and scale to find the actual distance between two points on the map. Then use a meterstick to measure this distance in the room. Was your partner's map accurate?

4. How are your map and your partner's map alike? How are they different?

Explore Further

Choose an area outside your home or school and make a map of it. To measure distance, use a meterstick, a tape measure, or the length of your foot. Include a legend, compass rose, and scale.

Topographic map

Map that shows the shape and elevation of the land surface

Contour line

Line on a map that connects points of equal elevation

If you want to explore the earth's surface, one of the most helpful tools you can have is a **topographic map**. A topographic map shows the shape and elevation of the land surface. For example, a road map might mark the location of a mountain with a dot. But a topographic map shows the shape and elevation of the mountain in addition to its location.

Contour Lines and Intervals

A topographic map uses **contour lines** to show shape and elevation. A contour line is a line on a map that connects all points of equal elevation. To understand contour lines, study the figure below. The top part shows an island with contour lines wrapped around it. The bottom part shows how those contour lines look on a flat map.

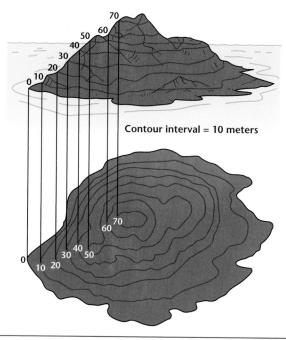

Contour interval = 10 meters

Lesson at a Glance

Chapter 1 Lesson 3

Overview In this lesson, students learn how to use the features of a topographic map.

Objectives

- To explain how contour lines show shape and elevation
- To visualize the landscape by looking at a topographic map

Student Pages 15–20

Teacher's Resource Library TRL

Workbook Activity 3

Alternative Workbook Activity 3

Lab Manual 3–4

Resource File 2

Vocabulary

contour interval   hachure
contour line   topographic map

Warm-Up Activity

Provide students with lumps of clay. Instruct students to form their clay into an irregularly shaped mountain. Then ask them to suggest ways in which they might draw a map that shows the different elevations of their mountain.

2 Teaching the Lesson

As students read the lesson, have them write down words they do not know. After reading, have students work in pairs to find definitions for the unfamiliar words. Students can then write a sentence using each word.

As students study the maps on pages 15 and 17, point out the different contour shapes. Ask students if there are local examples of land features that vary in altitude. Ask them to describe variations in height in the local area.

Ask students to list the title and subheadings of the lesson. For each, they should write one or more statements that identify its main idea.

Continued on page 16

Continued from page 15

You might provide students with copies of topographic maps that are drawn specifically for hikers. These maps can be found in hiking guidebooks or obtained from state recreational offices. Have students note the special kinds of symbols used on the maps. Locate areas on the maps where hikers would need to climb up or down. Students could plan an imaginary hike through an area shown on a map.

 3 Reinforce and Extend

Contour interval

Vertical distance between contour lines on a topographic map

Hachure

Short line that points toward the center of a depression on a topographic map

A hill and a depression can look almost the same on a topographic map. A depression is marked by hachures that point to the bottom. For a hill, the elevation increases—not decreases—as you move toward the hilltop.

Every point located on the zero contour line is at sea level. Every point located on the next contour line is 10 meters above sea level. The next contour line is 20 meters above sea level, and so on.

Notice that each contour line of the island is 10 meters higher than the one below it. This up-and-down distance between contour lines is the **contour interval**. The contour interval can be different from one map to another. The interval might be 5 meters on a map that shows mostly flat land. It might be 50 meters on a map that shows mostly mountains.

If you wanted to climb most easily to the top of the island, which side would you choose? The map tells you. One side of the island has a gentle slope and the other side has a steep slope. The topographic map shows this difference by the closeness of the contour lines. The closer the contour lines are to each other, the steeper the slope is.

What is the elevation of the highest point of this island? The highest contour line is 70 meters, so the island is at least that high. There is no 80-meter contour line, so the highest point is between 70 and 80 meters above sea level.

Using Topographic Maps

Look at the topographic map on the next page. It shows several land features. Try to find them as they are described below.

A series of closed loops shows a hill or mountain. The elevations of these contour lines increase toward the center. Find the contour lines that show Bear Mountain.

Closed loops may also show a depression, such as a watering hole or a pit. In this case, the elevations decrease toward the center. Short lines, called **hachures**, point into the depression. Find a depression in the southwest corner of the map.

Notice that some of the contour lines are bent into a V. Contour lines form a V on a map when they cross a valley. The V points up the valley. So if a river is flowing in the valley, the V points upstream. This is the direction from which the water is coming. In which direction does Beaver Creek flow?

Here are some other things to remember about contour lines.

◆ All contour lines eventually close, either on the map or beyond its borders.
◆ Contour lines never cross each other because one point cannot have more than one elevation.
◆ On most topographic maps, every fifth contour line is labeled with an elevation value.

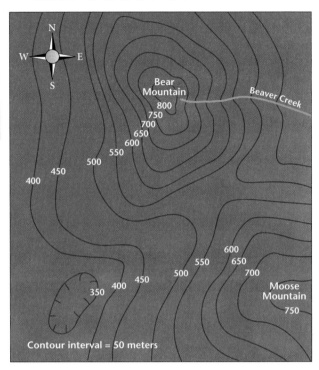

Contour interval = 50 meters

Topographic maps are useful to many people. Scientists use them to study land features and to plan expeditions. Engineers use them to plan highways and pipelines. Hikers use detailed topographic maps to locate trails, cliffs, ponds, hills, and rivers.

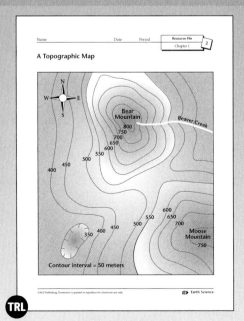

Resource File 2

Lesson 3 Review Answers

1. a map that shows the shape and elevation of a land surface **2.** a line on a map that connects points of equal elevation **3.** A steep elevation is shown by close contour lines. **4.** Contour lines form a V when they cross a valley. **5.** Bear Mountain

Science in Your Life

Ask a volunteer to read the feature on page 18. Have students work in small groups to do the initial research described in the activity. Not all students will be able to arrange a trip to the landmark. These students may prefer to research information about the park, including why this place was designated a state or national park.

Portfolio Assessment

Sample items include:
- Vocabulary sentences from Teaching the Lesson
- Main ideas from Teaching the Lesson
- Lesson 3 Review answers

Lesson 3 REVIEW

Write your answers to these questions on a sheet of paper.

1. What is a topographic map?

2. What is a contour interval?

3. How do contour lines show a steep slope?

4. On a topographic map, how can you tell where a valley is located?

5. On the map on page 17, which mountain is higher?

Science in Your Life

Mapping a Park

Which state park or national park is closest to where you live? You can find out by looking at a state map that shows all of these parks. Obtain a topographic map for a nearby park. Study the topographic map. What does the map show you about the surface features of the park? Pick out an interesting landmark or surface feature on the map. Then visit the park with a friend. Use the map to reach the landmark on foot. Take a hand compass with you to make sure you are facing the right direction as you read the map.

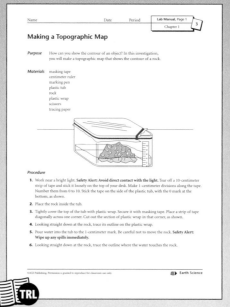

Lab Manual 3, pages 1–2

Workbook Activity 3

1-2 INVESTIGATION

Reading a Topographic Map

Purpose

How might you use a topographic map? In this investigation, you will practice reading such a map.

Procedure

Answer the following questions about the map shown below.

1. What is the contour interval of this map?

2. How far is the top of Spruce Hill from the top of Castle Rock?

3. In which direction does the Meadow River flow?

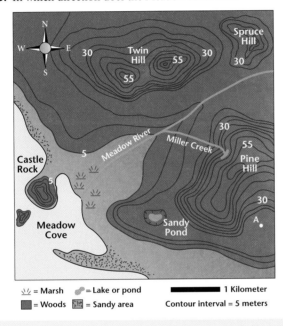

≤⌇⌇ = Marsh   ⌇ = Lake or pond   ▬▬▬▬ 1 Kilometer
▬ = Woods   ▒ = Sandy area   Contour interval = 5 meters

Investigation 1-2

The Purpose portion of the student investigation begins with a question to draw students into the activity. Encourage students to read the investigation steps and formulate their own questions before beginning the investigation. This investigation will take approximately 15 minutes to complete. Students will use these process and thinking skills: using models, recognizing space relationships, and interpreting maps.

Preparation

• Students may use Lab Manual 4 to record their answers to the questions.

Procedure

• Students may work in pairs or individually.

• Tell students to look over the map before they begin to answer the questions. Students should locate the scale, contour interval, compass rose, and symbols.

• Some students may have trouble using a map scale. Allow these students to pair with a partner who is more competent in math.

• For the Explore Further activity, you may want to direct students to the USGS topographic maps available at www.topozone.com.

Continued on page 20

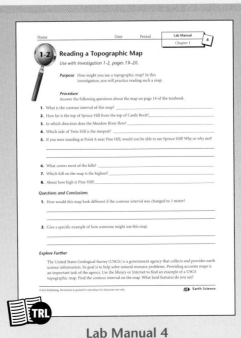

Lab Manual 4

Continued from page 19

Results

1. 5 meters
2. slightly more than 5 kilometers
3. southwest
4. the south side
5. No. Pine Hill is higher than Point A and Spruce Hill, so it blocks the view.
6. woods
7. Twin Hill
8. 60 meters

Questions and Conclusions Answers

1. The map would have many more contour lines.

2. Answers will vary, but could include choosing a hiking trail or planning a road.

Explore Further Answers

Students may work in pairs to complete this activity. Students should obtain a printout of the map they plan to use. Encourage students to share their findings with the class while displaying the USGS map they used.

Assessment

Ask students to explain their answers. You might include the following items from this investigation in student portfolios:

- Answers to Procedure questions
- Answers to Questions and Conclusions section
- Findings from Explore Further section

4. Which side of Twin Hill is the steepest?

5. If you were standing at Point A near Pine Hill, would you be able to see Spruce Hill? Why or why not?

6. What covers most of the hills?

7. Which hill on the map is the highest?

8. About how high is Pine Hill?

Questions and Conclusions

1. How would this map look different if the contour interval was changed to 1 meter?

2. Give a specific example of how someone might use this map.

Explore Further

The United States Geological Survey (USGS) is a government agency that collects and provides earth science information. Its goal is to help solve natural resource problems. Providing accurate maps is an important task of this agency.

Use the library or the Internet to find an example of a USGS topographic map. Find the contour interval on the map. What land features do you see?

- Earth science is the study of the earth's land, water, and air, and outer space.

- Earth science includes four main fields: geology, oceanography, meteorology, and astronomy.

- Scientists use many tools to study the earth. Some tools are simple; some are complex.

- Scientists around the world use the metric system for measuring.

- Studying the earth provides knowledge that improves people's lives. You can use your own knowledge of earth science to make wise decisions.

- A map is a drawing that shows part of the earth's surface as seen from above.

- A map legend explains the symbols used on the map.

- Compass directions are shown on a map in different ways.

- A map scale is a comparison between distance on the map and actual distance on the earth.

- There are three common kinds of map scales: bar scales, equivalence scales, and ratios.

- Topographic maps are especially useful in earth science because they show the shape and elevation of the land surface.

- Topographic maps have contour lines, which connect points of equal elevation.

- The vertical distance between contour lines on a map is the contour interval.

- Certain patterns of contour lines show certain land features, such as hills, depressions, and valleys.

Science Words

astronomer, 4	geologist, 3	meteorology, 2	topographic
astronomy, 2	geology, 2	metric system, 3	map, 15
compass rose, 9	hachure, 16	oceanographer, 4	unit, 3
contour interval, 16	legend, 8	oceanography, 2	
contour line, 15	map, 7	scale, 10	
earth science, 2	meteorologist, 4	submersible, 4	

Chapter 1 Summary

Have volunteers read aloud each Summary item on page 21. Ask volunteers to explain the meaning of each item. Direct students' attention to the Science Words box on the bottom of page 21. Have them read and review each word and its definition.

Chapter 1 Review

Use the Chapter Review to prepare students for tests and to reteach content from the chapter.

Chapter 1 Mastery Test

The Teacher's Resource Library includes two parallel forms of the Chapter 1 Mastery Test. The difficulty level of the two forms is equivalent. You may wish to use one form as a pretest and the other form as a posttest.

Review Answers
Vocabulary Review

1. compass rose 2. scale 3. unit 4. legend
5. topographic map 6. earth science
7. submersibles 8. contour line
9. hachures 10. contour interval

Concept Review

11. B 12. D 13. B 14. C 15. A 16. B 17. C

TEACHER ALERT

In the Chapter Review, the Vocabulary Review activity includes a sample of the chapter's vocabulary terms. The activity will help determine students' understanding of key vocabulary terms and concepts presented in the chapter. Other vocabulary terms used in the chapter are listed below:

astronomy	meteorology
geologist	metric system
geology	oceanographer
legend	oceanography
map	

Word Bank
compass rose
contour interval
contour line
earth science
hachures
legend
scale
submersibles
topographic map
unit

Vocabulary Review

Choose the word or phrase from the Word Bank that best completes each sentence. Write the answer on your paper.

1. To find directions on a map, you would look for a(n) _____.

2. An example of a(n) _____ would be 1:10,000.

3. A known amount used for measuring is a(n) _____.

4. A map's _____ shows the meaning of the map's symbols.

5. A(n) _____ shows the shape and elevation of the earth's surface.

6. The study of land, water, and air is part of _____.

7. Scientists travel to the ocean floor in _____.

8. On a topographic map, points with the same elevation are connected by a(n) _____.

9. A depression would be shown by _____ connected to contour lines on a topographic map.

10. The vertical distance between contour lines on a topographic map is the _____.

Concept Review

Choose the word or phrase that best completes each sentence. Write the letter of the answer on your paper.

11. An earth scientist who studies weather is a(n) _____.
    A geologist   **C** astronomer
    B meteorologist   **D** oceanographer

12. A scientist who studies the stars is a(n) _____.
    A geologist   **C** meteorologist
    B oceanographer   **D** astronomer

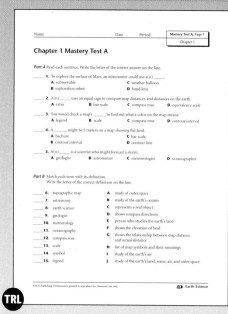

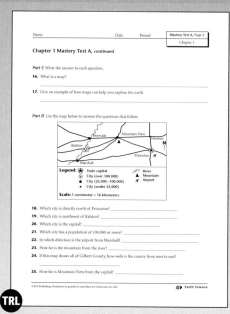

Chapter 1 Mastery Test A

13. A contour line that crosses a river makes a _____.
   A straight line   **B** V   **C** circle   **D** hachure

14. Several contour lines far apart on a map indicate a _____.
   A steep slope   **C** gentle slope
   B river   **D** flat area

15. If a map scale is 1:24,000, 1 centimeter on the map equals _____ on the earth's surface.
   A 24,000 centimeters   **C** 1 centimeter
   B 24,000 meters   **D** 24,000 feet

16. Scientists use the _____ system for measuring quantities and distances.
   A decimal   **B** metric   **C** inches   **D** customary

17. A(n) _____ is a metric unit of length.
   A inch   **B** foot   **C** centimeter   **D** mile

A

B

C

Critical Thinking

Write the answer to each of the following questions.

18. Look at the lettered illustrations. Name the land feature that each contour pattern represents.

19. You are given two maps, both of which are 10 centimeters wide by 10 centimeters long. One has a scale of 1 centimeter = 2 kilometers, and the other has a scale of 1 centimeter = 3 kilometers. Which map shows a larger part of the earth? Explain your answer.

20. Which contour interval would be better on a topographic map of a mountainous area: 5 meters or 30 meters? Why?

Test-Taking Tip If you have to choose the correct term to complete a sentence, read the sentence using each of the terms. Then choose the one that best fits the sentence.

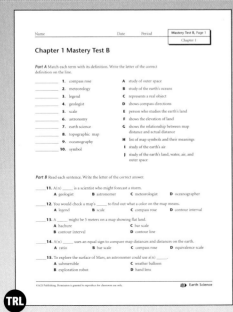

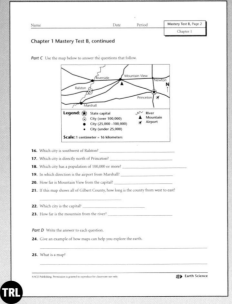

Chapter 1 Mastery Test B

Review Answers
Critical Thinking

18. A hill; **B** depression; **C** river or valley **19.** The map using 1 centimeter to represent 3 kilometers shows a larger part of the earth because it represents an area that is 30 kilometers by 30 kilometers. The other map outlines an area that is 20 kilometers by 20 kilometers. **20.** Since a mountain is very tall, the contour interval should be large in order to allow for a reasonable space between contour lines. So 30 meters makes sense.

ALTERNATIVE ASSESSMENT

Alternative Assessment items correlate to the student Goals for Learning at the beginning of this chapter.

■ Ask students to name four areas of earth science and to give an example of what a scientist in each area might study and why.

■ Show pictures of some tools that earth scientists use. Ask students to identify which earth scientists would use each tool and why.

■ Give students a map and have them label the legend, compass rose, and scale.

■ Refer students to the map on page 7. Ask students to use string or a ruler and the map scale to estimate the length of the southern branch of the Baltimore and Ohio Railroad located between Highways 340 and 734.

■ Display several different kinds of maps, including a topographic map. Ask students to identify the topographic map and explain how they knew it is the topographic map.

■ Have students examine the map on page 19 to identify the direction Miller Creek flows and from what height it flows.

Planning Guide

Describing the Earth

		Student Text Lesson	
		Student Pages	Vocabulary	Lesson Review
Lesson 1	The Earth's Features	26–30	✔	✔
Lesson 2	The Earth's Rotation and Time	31–37	✔	✔
Lesson 3	A Grid System on a Map	38–41	✔	✔
Lesson 4	Latitude	42–45	✔	✔
Lesson 5	Longitude	46–47	✔	✔
Lesson 6	A Grid System on a Globe	48–50	✔	✔

Chapter Activities

Student Text
Science Center

Teacher's Resource Library
Community Connection 2: Mapping
    Your Neighborhood

Assessment Options

Student Text
Chapter 2 Review

Teacher's Resource Library
Chapter 2 Mastery Tests A and B

Achievements in Science	Science at Work	Science in Your Life	Investigation	Science Myth	Note	Technology Note	Did You Know	Science Integration	Science Journal	Cross-Curricular Connection	Online Connection	Teacher Alert	Applications (Home, Career, Community, Global, Environment)	Auditory/Verbal	Body/Kinesthetic	Interpersonal/Group Learning	Logical/Mathematical	Visual/Spatial	LEP/ESL	Workbook Activities	Alternative Workbook Activities	Lab Manual	Resource File	Self-Study Guide
30				29	✔			28, 29		28			28, 29	27			28			4	4	5	3	✔
		35	36				32		34	32, 34			34			33		33		5	5	6	4, 5	✔
39		40						39					39		39					6	6	7		✔
	45				✔			43										44	44	7	7		6	✔
						✔		47			47									8	8		7	✔
						✔			49	49	50	49	49				50	49, 50		9	9	8		✔

Pronunciation Key

a	hat	e	let	ī	ice	ô	order	ů	put	sh	she	
ā	age	ē	equal	o	hot	oi	oil	ü	rule	th	thin	
ä	far	ėr	term	ō	open	ou	out	ch	child	ᵺ	then	
â	care	i	it	ȯ	saw	u	cup	ng	long	zh	measure	

ə { a in about / e in taken / i in pencil / o in lemon / u in circus }

Alternative Workbook Activities

The Teacher's Resource Library (TRL) contains a set of lower-level worksheets called Alternative Workbook Activities. These worksheets cover the same content as the regular Workbook Activities but are written at a second-grade reading level.

Skill Track Software

Use the Skill Track Software for Earth Science for additional reinforcement of this chapter. The software program allows students using AGS textbooks to be assessed for mastery of each chapter and lesson of the textbook. Students access the software on an individual basis and are assessed with multiple-choice items.

Chapter at a Glance

Chapter 2:
Describing the Earth
pages 24–53

Lessons

1. **The Earth's Features**
   pages 26–30

2. **The Earth's Rotation and Time**
   pages 31–37

   Investigation 2-1 pages 36–37

3. **A Grid System on a Map**
   pages 38–41

   Investigation 2-2 pages 40–41

4. **Latitude** pages 42–45

5. **Longitude** pages 46–47

6. **A Grid System on a Globe**
   pages 48–50

Chapter 2 Summary page 51

Chapter 2 Review pages 52–53

Skill Track Software
for Earth Science

Teacher's Resource Library (TRL)

Workbook Activities 4–9

Alternative Workbook Activities
4–9

Lab Manual 5–8

Community Connection 2

Resource File 3–7

Chapter 2 Self-Study Guide

Chapter 2 Mastery Tests A and B

(Answer Keys for the Teacher's
Resource Library begin on page 400
of the Teacher's Edition. The
Materials List for the Lab Manual
activities begins on page 415.)

Science Center

Post a world map that includes lines of
latitude and longitude. Have students
refer to it frequently throughout the
study of this chapter. Sticky notes can be
attached to the map to call out examples
of vocabulary terms in the chapter as
well as to explain the major science
concepts presented.

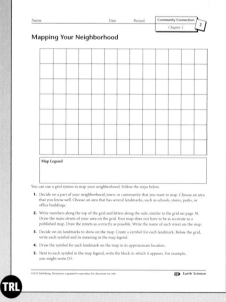

Community Connection 2

Chapter

2 Describing the Earth

If you looked down on the earth from space, what would you see? This photo was taken from the space shuttle *Atlantis*. It shows a mountain range in Southeast Asia. It shows ocean water and a coastline. There is smoke from a forest fire. The photo was placed on top of a map of the same area. What does the map have that the photo doesn't? Besides contour lines, the map has straight lines that intersect. In Chapter 2, you will learn about this grid system and other ways to describe the earth.

Organize Your Thoughts

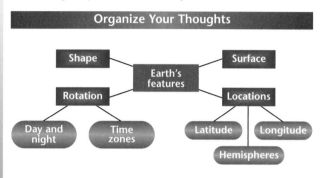

Goals for Learning

◆ To describe the earth's shape, continents, and oceans
◆ To explain what causes day and night
◆ To explain the earth's time zones
◆ To interpret a block grid on a map
◆ To use latitude and longitude to locate points on the earth

25

Introducing the Chapter

Use a globe and the Organize Your Thoughts chart on page 25 to find out what students already know about some of the physical attributes of the planet on which they live. On an overhead transparency, allow volunteers to define or describe each of the terms in the chart. Accept any responses at this point. However, to expel misconceptions, put question marks near incorrect responses or constructively rephrase the errors.

Notes and Technology Notes

Ask volunteers to read the notes that appear in the margins throughout the chapter. Then discuss them with the class.

TEACHER'S RESOURCE

The AGS Teaching Strategies in Science Transparencies may be used with this chapter. The transparencies add an interactive dimension to expand and enhance the *Earth Science* program content.

CAREER INTEREST INVENTORY

The AGS Harrington-O'Shea Career Decision-Making System-Revised (CDM) may be used with this chapter. Students can use the CDM to explore their interests and identify careers. The CDM defines career areas that are indicated by students' responses on the inventory.

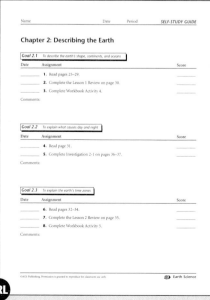

Chapter 2 Self-Study Guide

Chapter 2 Lesson 1

Overview In this lesson, students are introduced to features of the earth's surface—continents and oceans. Students also learn about the shape of the earth and how it rotates on an axis.

Objectives

- To describe the earth's shape
- To locate the seven continents
- To name the four major oceans
- To explain rotation

Student Pages 26–30

Teacher's Resource Library (TRL)

Workbook Activity 4

Alternative Workbook Activity 4

Lab Manual 5

Resource File 3

Vocabulary

axis
continent
North Pole
rotation
South Pole

Science Background

Approximately 30 percent of the earth's surface is land: Asia, Africa, North America, South America, Antarctica, Europe, and Australia. Most of the earth's landmasses are located in the Northern Hemisphere. Less than one-third of the earth's land surface lies in the Southern Hemisphere.

While the earth appears nearly spherical when viewed from space, it is, in fact, an oblate spheroid. This means that the poles are slightly flattened. The flattening is caused by the earth's rotation.

Objectives

After reading this lesson, you should be able to

- ◆ describe the earth's shape.
- ◆ locate the seven continents.
- ◆ name the four major oceans.
- ◆ explain rotation.

At one time, many people believed that the earth was flat. They thought that if they walked past its edge, they would fall off the earth! Of course, the earth is not flat and you cannot fall off.

The Earth's Shape

If you could view the earth from the moon, you would see that it has a shape like a ball. Most balls are perfectly round. If you measured the distance around the widest part of a ball in any direction, you would find that all the measurements would be equal. Compare the shape of the earth with the perfect circle below. You can see that the earth is not perfectly round. The distance around the earth in two different directions is given below. How do the measurements compare?

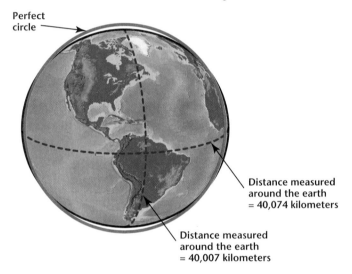

Perfect circle

Distance measured around the earth = 40,074 kilometers

Distance measured around the earth = 40,007 kilometers

The Earth's Surface

The earth's surface includes areas of land and water. The land areas make up about 30 percent of the earth's surface. Look at the circle graph. How much of the earth's surface is water?

Water area 70%

Land area 30%

The land on the earth's surface is divided into seven major areas called **continents**. Find the continents of the earth on the map. Which continent do you think is the largest? Which is the smallest? Check your answers in the table below.

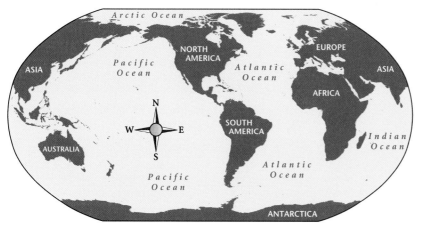

The Seven Continents		
Continent	Area (square kilometers)	Percent of Earth's Land Area
Asia	44,614,000	29.9
Africa	30,355,000	20.3
North America	24,208,000	16.2
South America	17,819,000	11.9
Antarctica	14,200,000	9.5
Europe	10,498,000	7.0
Australia	7,682,000	5.2

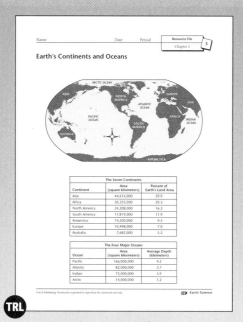

Resource File 3

1 Warm-Up Activity

Because we live on land, many students may be unaware that about 70 percent of our planet is covered with water. Ask a dozen volunteers to close their eyes as you spin a globe. Ask each volunteer, one by one, to stop the rotating globe with an index finger. Help students conclude that their fingers usually touched water rather than land because more of the earth's surface is covered with water.

2 Teaching the Lesson

Have students rephrase the lesson objectives as questions and write them down. As students read the text, allow sufficient time for them to answer each of the questions, using complete sentences.

To help students visualize how much more area of the earth is covered by water than land, call students' attention to the Pacific Ocean on a map or globe. Explain that this ocean alone covers more of the earth's surface than all the continents put together. In fact, the Pacific covers nearly one-third of the earth's surface. This huge ocean is about twice the size of the Atlantic.

After students read page 29, ask them to hypothesize which part of the earth is traveling the fastest. Guide students to conclude that the area around the equator—the middle—travels slightly faster than the areas near the poles. Reinforce this concept by spinning the globe, allowing students to see how the speed varies at different points on the globe.

3 Reinforce and Extend

LEARNING STYLES

Auditory/Verbal

Set up a tape recorder and record the following. Read aloud the first boldfaced vocabulary term in the lesson. Give a brief definition of this term, then have volunteers explain the term. Continue this process, recording each term in the lesson. Do this for each lesson in the chapter. Allow students to use the tape to review terms.

History

Students may incorrectly assume that most people believed the world was flat in the late 1400s when Christopher Columbus sailed to the Americas. Actually, most educated people knew the world was round by this time. The ancient Greeks theorized that the earth was round, and the mathematician Eratosthenes calculated the earth's circumference in 250 B.C. His calculation was nearly accurate. Interested students can find out more about the history of knowledge about the earth by researching the history of mapmaking and navigation.

LEARNING STYLES

Logical/Mathematical

Provide students with protractors and mathematical compasses. Have them use the information on page 27 to make a circle graph showing the percentage of the earth's land area covered by each of the seven continents.

GLOBAL CONNECTION

Have students find out the population of each continent. Then have them calculate the percentage of the world's population on each continent. Have them compare this percentage to the percentage of the earth's land area that each continent covers. Encourage students to discuss these comparisons. For example, Asia covers 30 percent of the earth's land area but contains 60 percent of its population.

Some scientists refer to the earth's water as one big ocean. They call it the world ocean or the global ocean. Other scientists break up the earth's water into five oceans instead of four. They include the Southern Ocean or Antarctic Ocean, referring to the water that moves around Antarctica.

Look again at the map on page 27. The major areas of water connect with each other and form one huge, continuous ocean. The earth's ocean, however, is usually divided into four major bodies of water: the Pacific Ocean, Atlantic Ocean, Indian Ocean, and Arctic Ocean. Locate each of these on the map. There are smaller bodies of water, too. Among them are lakes, bays, gulfs, and seas. Oceans are much larger than any of these.

You cannot see across an ocean to land on the other side. The diagram shows why. Just like you cannot see around a ball, the earth's curve keeps you from seeing across an ocean.

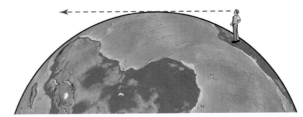

Use the table below to compare the sizes of the four major oceans. Which ocean is the largest? Which is the smallest?

The Four Major Oceans		
Ocean	Area (square kilometers)	Average Depth (kilometers)
Pacific	166,000,000	4.2
Atlantic	82,000,000	3.7
Indian	73,000,000	3.9
Arctic	14,000,000	1.2

To find out more about the earth's land and water, look at Appendixes G and H. Appendix G is a map showing the countries that make up the earth's continents. It also shows major seas, gulfs, and bays of the world. Appendix H is a map of North America.

SCIENCE INTEGRATION

Technology

Point out that because of its severe weather conditions, Antarctica has no permanent population. However, it does have a changing population, made up mostly of scientists. Have groups of students find out about the tools and equipment scientists need to survive in and communicate from this environment. Ask them to prepare a written report for presentation to the class.

The Earth's Rotation

Rotation

Spinning of the earth

Axis

Imaginary line through the earth that connects the North and South Poles

North Pole

Point farthest north on the earth

South Pole

Point farthest south on the earth

If you spin a top, at first it stands upright, turning around and around. After a while, friction slows down the top. It begins to wobble and stops spinning. Like a top, the earth also spins around. But unlike a top, the earth does not stop—it keeps on spinning. The spinning of the earth is called **rotation**.

As shown below, the earth spins, or rotates, from west to east around an imaginary line that passes through the center of the earth. This line is called the **axis** of the earth. The axis passes through two points called poles. The **North Pole** is the point farthest to the north on the earth. The **South Pole** is the point farthest to the south.

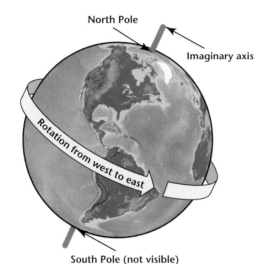

North Pole

Imaginary axis

Rotation from west to east

South Pole (not visible)

Science Myth

You may have heard that the sun "rises" and "sets." Some people may think this means the sun moves around the earth.

Fact: The sun does not move around the earth "rising" and "setting." Day and night occur because the earth rotates on its axis. As it rotates, one part of the earth moves into the sun's light. As this happens, another part of the earth turns away from the sun's light.

IN THE ENVIRONMENT

 Point out that pollution of our oceans is a major environmental concern. Have students explain why using information in this chapter. (*The oceans cover 70 percent of the earth's surface; we need healthy oceans to support ocean life and to provide a healthy environment for the entire planet.*) Ask students to describe kinds of ocean pollution. (*oil pollution from oil spills on land and from tankers, and industrial waste dumping*)

Science Myth

Have one student read the myth portion and one the fact portion of the feature on page 29. Have students tell in which directions the sun rises and sets. Have them explain how this illustrates the fact discussed in the feature.

SCIENCE INTEGRATION

 Physical Science

Students may be curious about how the geographic North and South Poles compare to the magnetic poles. Explain that the earth is surrounded by a magnetic field. This is strongest at the north and south magnetic poles. However, these poles are not exactly the same as the geographic North Pole and South Pole. The magnetic north pole is located in Canada. It is about 1,500 kilometers from the geographic North Pole. The magnetic south pole is located in Antarctica. It is about 2,900 kilometers from the geographic South Pole. Both magnetic poles continue to move.

Lesson 1 Review Answers

1. rounded, but not perfectly round
2. Asia, Africa, North America, South America, Antarctica, Europe, Australia
3. Atlantic, Pacific, Indian, Arctic 4. the spinning of the earth on its axis 5. The earth rotates from west to east.

Achievements in Science

Have students take turns reading paragraphs of the feature. Ask a student to trace the trip route on a globe and answer the question at the end of the feature. *(Fossett's route was quite far south of the equator, where the earth's circumference is smaller than at the equator.)*

Portfolio Assessment

Sample items include:
• Lesson objective questions and answers from Teaching the Lesson
• Lesson 1 Review answers

Write your answers to these questions on a sheet of paper.

1. Describe the earth's shape.

2. What are the seven continents?

3. What are the four major oceans?

4. What is rotation?

5. Use compass directions to describe how the earth rotates.

Achievements in Science

A Trip Around the World

In July 2002, Steve Fossett, an athlete and adventurer, achieved what no other human had ever done alone. After four failed attempts, he flew a hot-air balloon completely around the earth. The successful trip took Fossett about 14 days and 20 hours.

Fossett's balloon, the *Spirit of Freedom*, contained about 165,000 cubic meters of helium and 30,000 cubic meters of hot air. The capsule Fossett traveled in during the flight was just big enough for him to stretch out. There was also a special heating system to keep him warm.

Fossett navigated the flight using a global positioning system (GPS). During the trip, he used a laptop computer and satellite e-mail to communicate with his control center in St. Louis, Missouri.

The *Spirit of Freedom* started its flight in Australia. It flew east across the South Pacific Ocean, the tip of South America, across the Atlantic and Indian Oceans, then back to Australia. That's 34,000 kilometers! Trace this trip on the map on page 27. Why was Fossett's trip shorter than the distances shown on page 26?

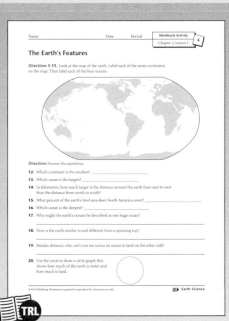

Lab Manual 5, pages 1–2

Workbook Activity 4

Objectives

After reading this lesson, you should be able to

◆ explain what causes day and night.

◆ describe the standard time zones.

What determines when you go to school, eat lunch, or get ready for bed? More than likely, what you are doing depends on what time of day it is. The time of day depends on the earth's rotation.

Day and Night

You have learned that the earth rotates on its axis. The earth takes 24 hours, or 1 day, to rotate once on its axis. Notice in the diagram how the sun shines on the earth as the earth rotates. The sun can shine on only one side at a time. As a result, one side of the earth is light and has daytime. The opposite side is dark and has nighttime.

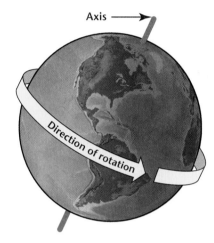

Axis

Sunlight

Direction of rotation

Because the earth continues to rotate, the places on the earth that have daytime keep changing. In other words, the time of day keeps changing everywhere on the earth. The time of day depends on where the sun appears to be in the sky. The sun does not really move across the sky, but the rotating earth makes the sun appear to move. As the earth turns from west to east, the sun appears to rise in the east in the morning. Then it appears to move across the sky and set in the west at night.

Chapter 2 Lesson 2

Overview In this lesson, students learn that day and night are caused by the rotation of the earth on its axis. They also learn that the world is divided into 24 time zones, reflecting the fact that different places experience daylight at different times.

Objectives

■ To explain what causes day and night

■ To describe the standard time zones

Student Pages 31–37

Teacher's Resource Library

Workbook Activity 5

Alternative Workbook Activity 5

Lab Manual 6

Resource File 4–5

....

Vocabulary

international date line
standard time zone

....

Science Background

The earth moves in two ways. It revolves around the sun, which takes about 365.25 days, or one year. It is the revolution around the sun, combined with the tilt of the earth's axis, that causes seasons to change on the earth. As it orbits the sun, however, the earth also rotates on its axis, an imaginary line that extends between the earth's poles. It is the earth's rotation, which takes just under 24 hours, or one day, that creates day and night. As the earth rotates, the part of the earth facing the sun experiences daylight, while the part facing away from the sun experiences nighttime. This chapter discusses the earth's rotation. The earth's orbit around the sun is covered in Chapter 3.

Warm-Up Activity

Display several small clocks, each representing the time in a different time zone. One of the clocks should show your local time. Another might show the time in Berlin, Germany, while a third might show the time in Beijing, China. Tell students that each clock shows the correct time for these areas. Have students use a globe to locate Berlin and Beijing. Ask them to suggest why the time in Berlin is different from their own time. *(The rotation of the earth causes the sun to light up different parts of the earth at different times.)*

 2

Teaching the Lesson

As students read each section, have them write a few sentences to summarize the information presented under each subhead.

Make sure students realize that the illustration on page 32 is a view from space, looking down onto the earth's North Pole. Some students might be able to better visualize time zones by observing a globe from the North Pole end.

 3

Reinforce and Extend

Did You Know?

Ask a student to read the feature aloud. Point out that time zone discrepancies still exist in some locations. For example, a U.S. state does not have to change to Daylight Saving Time if its legislature so chooses. The state of Indiana chose not to do so. So while most of this state's time is the same as the Eastern time zone in the winter, it is the same as the Central time zone in the summer.

CROSS-CURRICULAR CONNECTION

History

 The first transcontinental railroad was completed in the United States in 1869. Railroads had to set up schedules, but the varying times in communities made this difficult. Ask students to investigate what roles the railroads played in establishing time zones.

Standard Time Zones

Standard time zone
Area that has the same clock time

Compare the diagram on page 31 with the one below. Both show areas of daytime and nighttime. The diagram below shows the earth as seen from above the North Pole. Notice how time varies around the earth.

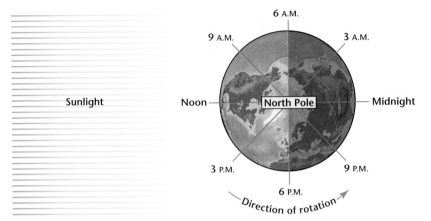

? Did You Know?

Standard time zones were set up in 1883. Until then, most places set their own time zones. For example, Philadelphia's clocks were 5 minutes behind New York's and 19 minutes ahead of Pittsburgh's. Confusing to travelers? You bet.

When it is noon at one point on the earth, it is midnight at a point that is halfway around the earth. The remaining hours of the day are equally spread around the earth between noon and midnight.

All 24 hours in the day are occurring somewhere on the earth right now. The earth has been divided into 24 **standard time zones**, one for each hour of the day. A standard time zone is an area of the earth that has the same clock time.

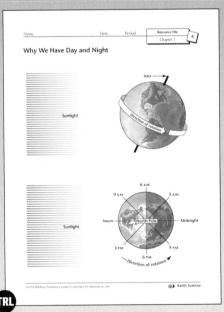

 TRL

Resource File 4

The map below shows the world's standard time zones. The boundaries of the time zones do not exactly follow straight lines. Over land areas, the zones usually follow borders of countries, states, counties, and towns. How many time zones are there across North America?

Find the **international date line** on the map. It is an imaginary line that defines the start of a day. When you cross it going west, you move to the next calendar day. When you cross it going east, you move to the previous calendar day.

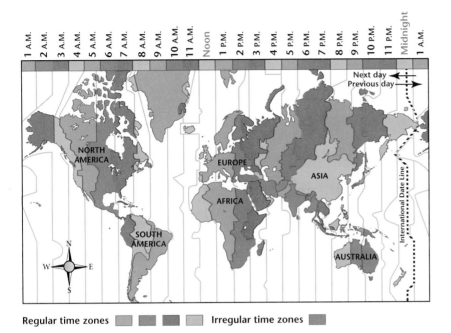

Regular time zones   Irregular time zones

CROSS-CURRICULAR CONNECTION

Language Arts

Point out that there are many stories and movies, such as *Back to the Future*, based on the science-fiction concept of time travel. Have students write a story in which time is treated unrealistically.

AT HOME

Remind students that many places in North America observe Daylight Saving Time, changing their clocks twice a year. On the first Sunday in April, Americans turn their clocks ahead one hour to Daylight Saving Time. In October, they turn their clocks back one hour to Standard Time. Most places in the United States, Mexico, and Canada observe these changes. However, certain places, such as Hawaii, Arizona, parts of Indiana, and Saskatchewan, do not. Have students discuss reasons for Daylight Saving Time. Point out that, when clocks change, students probably experience a form of jet lag. Have them discuss how their sleeping and waking patterns are affected during these time changes.

SCIENCE JOURNAL

Ask students to write their thoughts on why standardized time zones are helpful and what daily life might be like without them.

The map below shows the time zones for Hawaii and parts of North America. Notice that the time on the West Coast of the United States is 3 hours earlier than on the East Coast. So the time gets earlier as you travel westward.

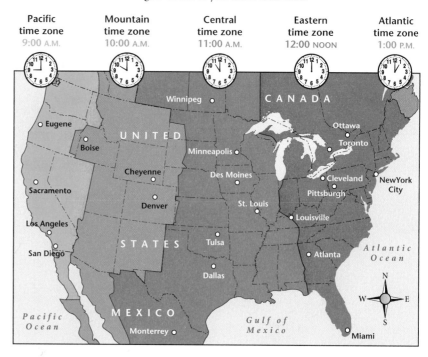

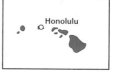

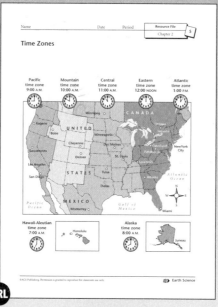

Resource File 5

Use the map on page 34 to answer these questions on a sheet of paper.

1. In what time zone is your home located? What time zone is 1 hour ahead of yours?

2. If it is 10:00 A.M. in Tulsa, what time would it be in Juneau?

3. If it is noon in New York City, what time would it be in Monterrey?

4. If it is 11:00 P.M. in Sacramento, what time would it be in Honolulu?

5. If you were to travel from Toronto to Eugene, would you move your watch forward or backward?

Science in Your Life

New York   Tokyo

Local

Zurich   London

Time Zones

You deal with time zones in your daily life. You may have noticed that when a TV show is advertised, more than one time is given for its airing. For example, a show might air at 8:00 P.M. Eastern Standard Time (EST) and 7:00 P.M. Central Standard Time (CST).

Let's say you live on the East Coast of the United States and want to call someone on the West Coast. Think about time zones before you place the call. If you call at 9:00 A.M. your time, it's only 6:00 A.M. on the West Coast. The person you called may still be asleep!

Now consider different time zones around the world. Find your time zone on the map on page 33. Then count 12 time zones to the right to see what time zone is a half day (exactly 12 hours) ahead of your time. What continent is shown within that time zone? What might people there be doing now?

International airports often have clocks showing the time in different cities or zones. Travelers use them to set their watches. Suppose you are catching a flight to London. You could look at the clocks shown here and set your watch from local time to London time, which is 8 hours ahead.

Describing the Earth   Chapter 2   **35**

Lesson 2 Review Answers

1. Answers will vary based on your location. **2.** 7:00 A.M. **3.** 11:00 A.M. **4.** 9:00 P.M. **5.** backward

Science in Your Life

Have a volunteer read the feature on page 35. Ask students if they have ever traveled to another time zone. Use an overhead transparency marker to draw their trip routes on a laminated map. Discuss the time change associated with each trip. Encourage students to relate any jet lag or car lag experiences, such as being hungry or sleepy at unusual times.

Portfolio Assessment

Sample items include:
• Section summaries from Teaching the Lesson
• Lesson 2 Review answers

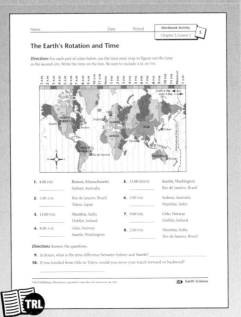

Workbook Activity 5

Investigation 2-1

The Purpose portion of the student investigation begins with a question to draw students into the activity. Encourage students to read the investigation steps and formulate their own questions before beginning the investigation. This investigation will take approximately 30 minutes to complete. Students will use these process and thinking skills: formulating and interpreting models, recognizing spatial relationships, and communicating.

Preparation

- Check all batteries before class. Keep extra batteries on hand in case some wear down.

- If several groups will be doing this investigation at the same time, be sure to set up work stations so that the flashlight used in each group does not interfere with the models of other groups.

- If available, reflecting masking tape will be easier for students to observe on the dark side of the globe. Be sure to use tape that will easily peel off the globe afterward.

- Students may use Lab Manual 6 to record their data and answer the questions.

Procedure

- This investigation is best done with students working in pairs. Assign one student to gather the equipment and the other student to return the equipment.

- Direct students to the Safety Alert and remind them about careful flashlight use around other people.

- For best results, instruct students to aim the flashlight so that its beam hits the globe at the equator. This will provide an even lighting effect.

- If only one globe is available, this activity can be done as a class.

Modeling the Earth's Rotation

Purpose

How would you create a model explaining day and night? In this investigation, you will model the earth's rotation.

Materials
- globe
- masking tape
- flashlight

Procedure

1. Work with a partner in this investigation. Copy the data table on your paper.

Step 5 Observations	Step 7 Observations

2. On the globe, find the approximate spot where your home is located. Place a piece of masking tape over the spot.

3. On the globe, find the North and South Poles. Imagine that the globe is the earth and that its axis runs through the poles. Place the globe on a table, with the South Pole toward the table. Practice rotating it slowly on its axis. Remember to rotate it from west to east (or counterclockwise, as seen from above the North Pole).

4. Darken the room. Have your partner hold the flashlight and stand at one end of the table. The flashlight represents the sun. Have your partner turn on the flashlight and shine it at the globe. Position the globe so that the masking tape is facing the flashlight. **Safety Alert: Do not shine the flashlight into the eyes of others.**

5. Observe what part of the globe is in light and what part is in shadow. Record your observations in the data table, noting the position of the masking tape.

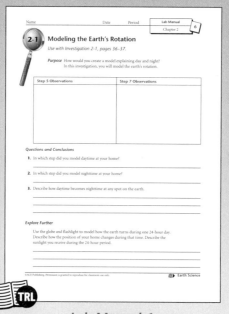

Lab Manual 6

6. Slowly rotate the globe on its axis from west to east. Stop when the masking tape has moved halfway around the globe.

7. Repeat step 5.

8. Switch places with your partner and repeat steps 4 through 7.

Questions and Conclusions

1. In which step did you model daytime at your home?

2. In which step did you model nighttime at your home?

3. Describe how daytime becomes nighttime at any spot on the earth.

Explore Further

Use the globe and flashlight to model how the earth turns during one 24-hour day. Describe how the position of your home changes during that time. Describe the sunlight you receive during the 24-hour period.

Results

If the flashlight is held in a stationary position, the model will demonstrate how the rotation of the earth causes a point on the earth to move from light (daytime) to darkness (nighttime).

Questions and Conclusions Answers

1. step 4

2. step 6

3. Answers will vary, but should reflect that a given point turns slowly eastward as the earth rotates. Because of this rotation, an area facing the sun slowly moves out of the sunlight and eventually experiences nighttime.

Explore Further Answers

Answers should include that the position of their home changes, not in relation to other points on the earth, but in relation to the sun. As the earth rotates, their home passes through day, dusk, night, dawn, and back to its original position in a 24-hour period.

Assessment

Check that students understand that the earth rotates. Check that they rotate the globe from west to east. Verify that they know which side of the globe represents day and which represents night. You might include the following items from this investigation in student portfolios:

• Data table

• Answers to Questions and Conclusions and Explore Further sections

Lesson at a Glance

Chapter 2 Lesson 3

Overview In this lesson, students learn to locate places on a map by using block grids.

Objectives

- To explain what a block grid is
- To use a block grid to locate a point on a map

Student Pages 38–41

Teacher's Resource Library

Workbook Activity 6

Alternative Workbook Activity 6

Lab Manual 7

Vocabulary

grid

 Warm-Up Activity

Use a checkerboard to introduce the concept of map grids. Place a few checkers inside squares on the board. Have volunteers locate the checkers by rows and columns, such as "fourth row from the top, third column from the left." Explain to students that they can use this technique to locate points on a map.

2 Teaching the Lesson

Ask students to list examples of grids. Responses might include graph paper grids, a crossword puzzle, or football field grids. Encourage students to use the examples to form a working definition of the term grid. *(a set of evenly spaced horizontal and vertical lines that can be used as a reference system)*

After students have mastered locating points on the map on page 38, provide them with a local map. Pairs of students can locate major cities, historic landmarks, or other points of interest. One partner should call out a block number and letter. The other partner should identify a feature that appears in that block. Partners can then switch roles.

Objectives

After reading this lesson, you should be able to

- explain what a block grid is.
- use a block grid to locate a point on a map.

Grid

Set of horizontal and vertical lines on a map

Locating places on a small, simple map is quick and easy. You simply search the map for the place name. Searching for places on a large, complex map, like a state or world map, is not as quick or easy. A better way to locate places on a complex map is to use a **grid**. A map grid is a set of horizontal and vertical lines drawn on a map.

The map below shows an example of one kind of grid called a block grid. The lines on a block grid divide a map into blocks. Each block is numbered and lettered. The numbers and letters help you to quickly locate the blocks and the places inside them.

Notice in the map that each letter represents a row and each number represents a column. Block C3 is highlighted in gray. It is located in row C and column 3. To find block C3, look across row C and down column 3. The city of Morris is in this block.

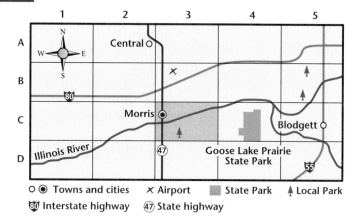

Now, use the same method to locate block B3 on the map. Look across row B and down column 3. What features are located in block B3? Refer to the map legend. If you said highways and an airport, you are correct.

Use the map on page 38 to answer these questions on a sheet of paper.

1. Which highway is located in column 5?

2. In which block is Central located?

3. In which block does Highway 80 cross Highway 55?

4. Which block includes two parks?

5. In which block is Goose Lake Prairie State Park located?

Achievements in Science

Global Positioning Systems

Global positioning systems (GPSs) are computers that can tell you exactly where you are. GPSs use signals from satellites to locate objects on the earth's surface. These tools were first used by astronauts and airline pilots to help them steer, or navigate. Today GPSs are used in a variety of ways. They are even found in many current-model cars.

Imagine getting into your car, fastening your seatbelt, starting the engine, and then entering an address into your car's GPS. A friendly voice guides you to your destination. It tells you when to turn right or left. You can even watch your progress on a colorful, on-screen map. If you miss a turn, the GPS figures out a new route for you to take.

Some GPS models are equipped with voice recognition. If you need help but cannot take your eyes off the road, you can simply talk to the GPS and it will respond.

Describing the Earth   Chapter 2   39

| Name | Date | Period | **Workbook Activity** |
| | | | Chapter 2, Lesson 3 6 |

A Grid System on a Map

Directions Use the map to answer the questions below.

1. In which block is most of Echo Lane? _____
2. In which block is the school that is closest to Mountain Drive? _____
3. In which block does Pine Trail cross Highway 42? _____
4. In which block is City High School? _____
5. In which block does Echo Lane meet James Street? _____
6. In which block is Rose Circle? _____
7. In which block is Bay Mall? _____
8. Which blocks contain parts of Bell Street? _____
9. What school is located in block B7? _____
10. In which block is the zoo? _____
11. To get to the corner of Barn Street and James Street from the corner of Echo Lane and James Street, what blocks would you travel through? _____
12. In which block does James Street cross Bell Street? _____
13. Michael wants to open a restaurant on a main street close to Bay Mall. Identify two areas by block names that would fit this description. _____
14. Jackie lives on Pine Trail near the zoo. What blocks would she travel through to take Highway 42 and Barn Street to City High School? _____
15. The Perezes are considering buying one of two houses. One is on Barn Street. The other is at the corner of Lake Street and Windy Circle. Which is closer to Wilson School? _____

Earth Science

---

3 Reinforce and Extend

LEARNING STYLES

Body/Kinesthetic

Set up a section of the classroom as a life-size map. Lay construction paper signs, labeled A, B, C, and D, along one side of the area. Lay signs labeled 1, 2, 3, and 4 along an adjacent side. Then tape down lengths of masking tape on the floor between the rows and columns to divide the area into grid squares. Place objects, such as books or pencils, in various squares. Then ask students to move an item from a particular grid square to another, such as from A3 to C2.

IN THE COMMUNITY

Have each student use a community map that has a grid. Provide a list of important community landmarks, such as schools, parks, and public buildings. Have students find each place on their map and mark it. Discuss how students used the map's grid system to find each place.

Lesson 3 Review Answers

1. Interstate Highway 55 2. A2 3. A5 4. B5 5. C4

Achievements in Science

Have students take turns reading aloud the feature on page 39. GPSs depend on 24 satellites that orbit 19,000 kilometers above the earth at 11,000 kilometers per hour. This satellite system was originally created by the U.S. Department of Defense for military use. It was made available to the general public in the 1980s. The satellites are powered by solar energy.

Portfolio Assessment

Sample items include:
• List of grids and definitions from Teaching the Lesson
• Lesson 3 Review answers

CROSS-CURRICULAR CONNECTION

Geography

Emphasize that grid systems, such as the one on page 38, are arbitrary designations that make map reading easier. Grid systems are not connected to the actual geographical area. To demonstrate, bring in two or more maps of the same area that are produced by different publishers. While many maps start with block A1 in the upper left corner, the exact area covered by A1 will vary among the maps, as will the scale and the size of the blocks.

Investigation 2-2

The Purpose portion of the student investigation begins with a question to draw students into the activity. Encourage students to read the investigation steps and formulate their own questions before beginning the investigation. This investigation will take approximately 40 minutes to complete. Students will use these process and thinking skills: making and using models, recognizing spatial relationships, and communicating.

Preparation

• Have extra balloons available.

• Have students work independently to complete steps 1 to 3. Then have students pair up to complete step 4. Step 5 can be done independently, and step 6 can be done with a different partner than the one in step 4. Interested students could also try methods devised by others.

• Students may use Lab Manual 7 to record their data and answer the questions.

Procedure

• If students are having a hard time describing the location of the X they've marked, encourage them to describe the location with respect to the neck or top of the balloon.

• Students can work in pairs for steps 4 and 6. For step 4, students should try to pinpoint their partner's X based only on the description.

• Pose questions during the investigation that will help students recognize the need for a standard way to locate points on the earth. For example, ask why someone would want to describe a location on a round surface.

• As students work on step 5, ask them to suggest ways to improve the accuracy and precision of their method. They might suggest using a tape measure, marking additional reference points, or superimposing a grid system to facilitate locating the X.

INVESTIGATION 2-2

Materials
◆ 2 round balloons
◆ marker

Describing Location on a Round Surface

Purpose
Can you think of a good way to describe a certain location on a round balloon? In this investigation, you will explore ways to describe a location on a round surface.

Procedure

1. Copy the data table on your paper.

Location of the X	Method for Locating the X

2. Blow up two balloons until they have a rounded shape. They should also be the same size. With the marker, make a small **X** on one of the balloons. **Safety Alert: Do not overfill balloons. They can burst and cause injury.**

3. In the data table, describe the location of the **X** on the balloon. Be as accurate and clear as possible.

4. Set aside the marked balloon. Show your description to another student. Then have the student point to the location on the unmarked balloon. See if he or she can use your description to tell where the **X** is.

5. Think about how you might improve your description. Then think of the best method you can for clearly describing the location of the **X**. In the data table, write the steps for your method. If possible, include diagrams.

SAFETY ALERT

◆ Be sure that students do not overfill balloons, causing them to burst. You might blow one up ahead of time and show it as an example of the size that students should aim for in blowing up their balloons.

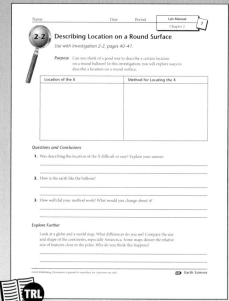

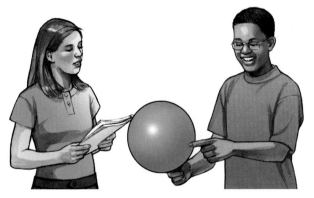

6. To test your method, trade methods with another student. See how well you can follow each other's steps and how well each method works.

7. If necessary, rewrite your steps.

Questions and Conclusions

1. Was describing the location of the **X** difficult or easy? Explain your answer.

2. How is the earth like the balloon?

3. How well did your method work? What would you change about it?

Explore Further

Look at a globe and a world map. What differences do you see? Compare the size and shape of the continents, especially Antarctica. Some maps distort the relative size of features close to the poles. Why do you think this happens?

Results

Because of the balloon's shape and lack of reference points, students might have a hard time describing the position of the X. They should realize that finding a location would be easier if they added reference points such as a grid system.

Questions and Conclusions Answers

1. Most students will find it difficult to describe the location of the X because of the balloon's uniformity and lack of edges or other reference points.

2. Both are rounded.

3. Most methods will be only partly successful. Adding other points of reference and/or a grid system would improve the location descriptions.

Explore Further Answers

The land areas near the poles seem smaller on the globe. Some maps make the areas around the poles appear larger because the map is a stretched-out picture of the globe: if the areas around the equator are accurate, those at the poles will not be accurate. It is impossible to picture accurately all the features of a sphere on a flat map, unless the map is split into many connected sections.

Assessment

Check not only students' approach to the problem but also their effectiveness in communicating it. Pay special attention to how they would modify their method, reflecting what they learned in the activity. You might include the following items from this investigation in student portfolios:

• Data table

• Answers to Questions and Conclusions and Explore Further sections

Lesson at a Glance

Chapter 2 Lesson 4

Overview This lesson introduces students to the concept of a global grid. They learn about lines of latitude, the imaginary east-west grid lines that mark off intervals between the North and South Poles.

Objectives

- To explain what a global grid is
- To define latitude
- To estimate a point's latitude

Student Pages 42–45

Teacher's Resource Library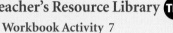

Workbook Activity 7

Alternative Workbook Activity 7

Resource File 6

Vocabulary

degree	latitude
equator	parallel

Science Background

Lines of latitude and longitude are imaginary lines around the earth that help pinpoint location. Lines of latitude, also called parallels, run east-west, measuring how far a point is from the equator. Lines of longitude, also called meridians, run north-south from pole to pole and measure how far a point is from the prime meridian, the longitude line that passes through Greenwich, England. Together, these lines are known as the geographic grid system. Lines of latitude and longitude are found on both globes and maps.

 Warm-Up Activity

Using a map of the world, have a volunteer make a tracing of the latitude and longitude lines that crisscross North America. Take the grid and attempt to superimpose it onto the same area on a globe. Point out that maps are two-dimensional models of our three-dimensional planet. Tell students that they will be learning about the grid lines that are used to locate places on the earth.

Objectives

After reading this lesson, you should be able to

- ◆ explain what a global grid is.
- ◆ define latitude.
- ◆ estimate a point's latitude.

Latitude

Angle that describes the distance north or south of the equator

Equator

Line of 0° latitude halfway between the poles

Parallel

Line of latitude

Degree

Unit for measuring angles in a circle or sphere

In Investigation 2-2, you may have discovered that a grid can be laid over a round object to locate points on the object. This grid is a global grid. Like other grids, it consists of two sets of lines. The first set of lines are lines of **latitude**. These are imaginary lines that run in an east-west direction around the earth. Latitude describes the distance north or south of the **equator**. The equator is the line of latitude halfway between the North and South Poles. Find the lines of latitude on the map on page 43. Lines of latitude are also called **parallels**.

Notice the two parallels called the tropic of Cancer and the tropic of Capricorn. The sun is directly over the tropic of Cancer on the first day of summer north of the equator. It is directly over the tropic of Capricorn on the first day of summer south of the equator. You will learn more about these parallels and the seasons in Chapter 3.

On the map, you can see that parallels are numbered, beginning at the equator and ending at each of the poles. The parallels are numbered in **degrees**. Degrees are used to measure angles in circles and spheres. A complete circle has 360 degrees. The symbol for degrees is a small circle. For example, 90 degrees is written as 90°.

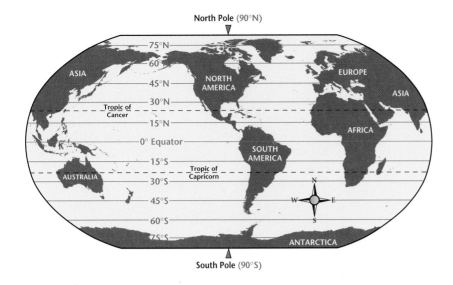

North Pole (90°N)

North Pole (90°N)
South Pole (90°S)

A *degree* can refer to two very different measurement units in science. Degrees are used to measure angles in a circle or sphere. Latitude is an example of this. Degrees are also used to measure temperature. For example, water freezes at 0°C. Both of these measurement units have the same symbol. But they are not related at all.

Notice that the latitude numbers begin at 0° at the equator and increase to 90° at the North Pole. All latitude numbers north of the equator are followed by the letter *N*.

The latitude numbers also begin at 0° at the equator and increase to 90° at the South Pole. South of the equator, all latitude numbers are followed by the letter *S*.

No line of latitude is greater than 90°. What happens if you try to go to a latitude that is higher than 90°N or 90°S? Trace an imaginary trip on a globe. Start at the equator and go north. From the equator to the North Pole, the number of degrees of latitude increases. If you continue your path past the pole, you will find yourself on the other side of the earth. You will be heading back toward the equator, and the number of degrees of latitude will be decreasing.

Describing the Earth Chapter 2 **43**

2 ▶ Teaching the Lesson

Have students copy the boldfaced words in this lesson. As they read, students should define each term and use it in an original sentence that accurately reflects its meaning.

Have students closely examine a globe to observe that lines of latitude are parallel. That is, the north-south distance between any two adjacent lines of latitude is always the same.

Direct students to study the map on page 44. Review the steps for estimating latitude. Then display a map of North America that includes boundary lines. Have students estimate the northern and southern extent of several states or provinces using lines of latitude.

3 ▶ Reinforce and Extend

CROSS-CURRICULAR CONNECTION

Geography

A map projection shows the round earth on a flat map. Many different projections for showing the earth have been developed. Each distorts distance, size, or shape in some way. The map shown here is a Robinson projection. The lines of latitude are drawn straight across the map from left to right. This projection makes places near the poles look larger than they really are.

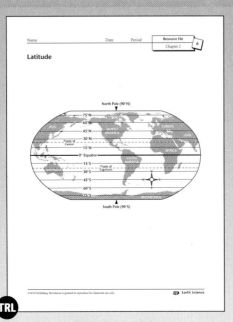

Resource File 6

Have students find a map of North America that shows latitude and longitude lines. Ask them to place a sticky note where your community is located. Then have students estimate the latitude of your community. They can check the latitude by using an atlas or by accessing an Internet place locator.

LEARNING STYLES

LEP/ESL

Refer students to the Note on page 43. The English language is full of multiple-meaning words. For English language learners, this can be very confusing. For example, when someone says "I want to get a college degree," he or she is not referring to degrees on a map or a thermometer. Help students begin a list of multiple-meaning words for reference and vocabulary development. Include the multiple meanings of *degree*. Each entry should include the word, its various meanings, and an example sentence for each meaning.

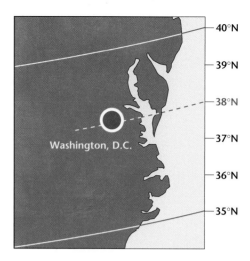

When a map, such as the one above, does not show every parallel, the person using the map must estimate the parallels that are not shown. To do that, the person must divide the space that is between the parallels that are shown. The divisions should be equal.

To find the latitude of Washington, D.C., on the map, use the following procedure.

1. Find the two parallels on either side of Washington, D.C. (35°N and 40°N).

2. In your mind or on paper, put in the latitude lines between 35°N and 40°N that are missing (36°, 37°, 38°, and 39°). Divide the space equally.

3. Use the divisions you added to estimate the latitude of Washington, D.C., to the nearest degree. The correct latitude is 38°N.

Use the map on page 43 to answer these questions on a sheet of paper.

1. What is the latitude of the equator?

2. What is the latitude of the South Pole?

3. Which two continents extend both north and south of 0° latitude?

4. Estimate the latitude of the northern tip of South America.

5. Estimate the latitude where you live.

▼◀▲▼◀▲▼◀▲▼◀▲▼◀▲▼◀▲▼◀▲▼◀▲▼◀▲▼◀▲▼◀▲▼◀▲▼◀▲▼◀▲▼

Science at Work

Air-Traffic Controller

Air-traffic controllers are responsible for directing millions of aircraft flights around the world. Their job is to keep the sky safe by preventing aircraft collisions. To do this, they communicate with pilots using a radio. They tell pilots how high to fly and when and where to land or take off. They use special maps to keep track of the positions of aircraft.

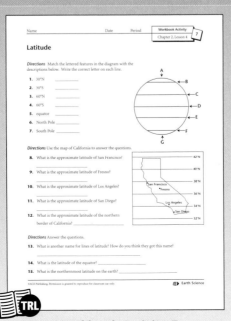

To apply for the position of air-traffic controller, a person must have a degree from a 4-year college or at least 3 years of related work experience. The applicant must also pass a written test.

Good air-traffic controllers are calm and able to make snap decisions in emergencies. They must have excellent vision and hearing. For example, in a single glance, they must memorize the positions of several aircraft. Air-traffic controllers must have another special skill. Since their air-traffic maps are flat, they must be able to visualize this information in three dimensions.

Where can you find an air-traffic controller? Every airport that has regularly scheduled flights has an air-traffic control tower where controllers work. From this tower, they can see planes coming in and taking off. Look for the air-traffic control tower the next time you visit an airport.

Lesson 4 Review Answers

1. 0° 2. 90°S 3. South America, Africa 4. about 12°N 5. Answers will vary based on your location.

Science at Work

Have students take turns reading the paragraphs in the feature on page 45. Explain that air-traffic controllers use radar screens that show the location of each plane in the area they are watching. If possible, invite an air-traffic controller to speak to the class.

Portfolio Assessment

Sample items include:
- Sentences from Teaching the Lesson
- Lesson 4 Review answers

Workbook Activity 7

Lesson at a Glance

Chapter 2 Lesson 5

Overview In this lesson, students learn that lines of longitude are the global grid lines that run north and south. They learn how these lines differ from lines of latitude. Students also describe location by longitude.

Objectives

- To define longitude
- To estimate a point's longitude

Student Pages 46–47

Teacher's Resource Library
  Workbook Activity 8
  Alternative Workbook Activity 8
  Resource File 7

....

Vocabulary

longitude
meridian
prime meridian

....

 Warm-Up Activity

Display a globe and point out the lines of longitude. Encourage students to trace the lines with their fingers. Ask students to describe what they notice about the lines—how they are like lines of latitude and how they are different. Accept any reasonable responses, such as that lines of longitude are not parallel like lines of latitude or that both sets of lines circle the globe.

 Teaching the Lesson

Direct students to write the title "Lines of Latitude and Lines of Longitude" at the top of a sheet of paper. Below the title, they should make two columns, entitled "How They Are Alike" and "How They Are Different." As students read this lesson, they should fill in the columns.

If necessary, review the concept that there are 360 degrees in a circle or a sphere. Then have a volunteer begin at the prime meridian and count off, in degrees, each line of longitude.

Objectives

After reading this lesson, you should be able to

- define longitude.
- estimate a point's longitude.

Longitude
Angle that describes the distance east or west of the prime meridian

Meridian
Line of longitude

Prime meridian
Line of 0° longitude

You have learned about global grid lines of latitude, which run east and west. The second set of lines making up a global grid are lines of **longitude**. These are imaginary lines that run in a north-south direction from pole to pole. Longitude lines are also called **meridians**. Longitude describes the distance east or west of the **prime meridian**. The prime meridian is the line of 0° longitude. It is sometimes called the Greenwich meridian because it passes through the town of Greenwich, England.

Like parallels, meridians are numbered in degrees. Numbering begins with 0° at the prime meridian and ends at 180°. The 180° line is on the opposite side of the earth from the prime meridian. Numbers east of the prime meridian are followed by the letter *E*. Numbers west of the prime meridian are followed by a *W*. The line that is 180°W is also 180°E. As you can see on the map below, meridians are not spaced equally at all points. They come together at the poles and are farthest apart at the equator.

Do you remember the steps used to estimate the latitude of Washington, D.C.? Review page 44. To estimate meridians that are not shown on a map, follow a similar procedure.

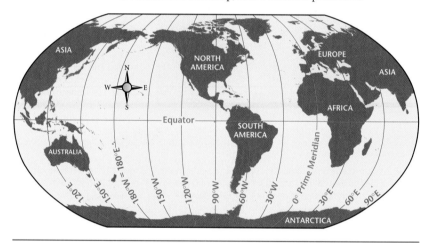

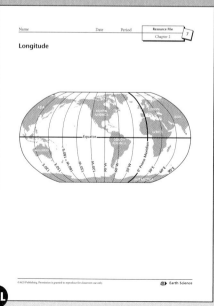

Resource File 7

Use the map on page 46 to answer these questions on a sheet of paper.

1. What is the longitude of the prime meridian?

2. What is the highest numbered meridian?

3. Estimate the longitude of the eastern edge of South America.

4. Estimate the longitude where you live.

5. Compare latitude and longitude lines. How are they different?

Technology Note

Through history, mapmakers, or cartographers, have used a variety of tools to create maps. Today cartographers use mathematics, computers, and photos taken from aircraft or satellites.

Imagine cutting open a hollow ball and taping it on a flat piece of paper. That's a bit like what cartographers do to make a map of the world. The result is called a map projection. There are many kinds. Three map projections are shown here.

A Mercator projection is a rectangle-shaped map. Its lines of latitude and longitude are equally spaced. These projections are useful for navigating the oceans. However, the true area of water and land near the poles is distorted on a Mercator projection.

An orthographic projection shows the earth as it might look from space. Because this kind of map is a globe shape, it can only show one half of the earth at a time. Areas at the edge of the map are distorted.

Robinson projections are frequently used for world maps. These kinds of maps are oval shaped. Lines of latitude appear as straight lines. Lines of longitude increase in curvature from the center of the map to the outer edges. Area near the poles is still distorted, but less than on a Mercator projection.

Look at the world maps in this chapter. What kinds of map projections are used?

Mercator projection

Orthographic projection

Robinson projection

Describing the Earth   Chapter 2   **47**

Ask a volunteer to locate the prime meridian on a globe. Have the student also find the international date line, which is approximately the 180° meridian.

Have students take turns estimating the longitude of various locations on the globe. If necessary, review the process for estimating latitude outlined on page 44. Then help students transfer this process to longitude estimation.

3   Reinforce and Extend

CROSS-CURRICULAR CONNECTION

 Math

When reading a map grid or a bar or line graph, students often have to estimate values. The estimation processes for maps and graphs are similar. On graphs, a bar may fall between two given scale values. To estimate the bar's value, the missing values on the scale need to be mentally added, evenly dividing the space between the two given values. A straightedge is often used to help estimate graph values by lining up a graph point with a side scale. If a map's global gridlines are not too curved, encourage students to use straightedges to help estimate latitude and longitude. Try this method by finding the location of San Francisco, which is at 37°N, 122°W on the map on page 50.

Lesson 5 Review Answers

1. 0° 2. 180° 3. about 35°W 4. Answers will vary based on your location. 5. Both are part of the global grid and are imaginary lines encircling the earth. Latitude lines are parallel lines that circle the globe from east and west, while longitude lines are lines that meet at the poles, run north and south, and are not parallel.

Portfolio Assessment

Sample items include:
• Compare-and-contrast activity from Teaching the Lesson
• Lesson 5 Review answers

Workbook Activity 8

TEACHER ALERT

When discussing the map projections detailed in the Technology Note, students may ask about the projections in this book. The flat-topped oval maps are Robinson projections; globes are various orthographic projections; rectangular maps such as the world time zone map on page 33 are Mercator projections.

Chapter 2 Lesson 6

Overview In this lesson, students use latitude and longitude to locate points on a map. They are also introduced to the four hemispheres.

Objectives

- To use latitude and longitude to find a point on the earth
- To explain what hemispheres are

Student Pages 48–50

Teacher's Resource Library

Workbook Activity 9

Alternative Workbook Activity 9

Lab Manual 8

Vocabulary

hemisphere

Warm-Up Activity

Ask: What if I told you to meet me at noon exactly one and a half blocks from the corner of Fifth and Main? Would you know where to meet me? Lead students to reason that the description is neither exact nor unique. There are probably four corners at the intersection, the block and a half could be measured in any direction, and many cities and towns have intersections of Fifth and Main.

Teaching the Lesson

Have students write a main-idea sentence for each of the subheads in this lesson. Students could find them in the book or write their own, but the sentences they choose should reflect the most important material in each section.

Provide students with clear metric rulers to help them estimate latitude and longitude. Have students trace the grid on page 48 and construct the missing lines at 5° intervals. Pairs of students can add more lettered points to their grids and challenge each other to describe the points by latitude and longitude.

You might point out that the map grids that students learned about in Lesson 3 are simply tools for reading maps and that they change from map to map. Parallels and meridians, on the other hand, are always the same wherever they are shown. For example, Chicago may appear in block D6 on one map and A3 on another. But it is *always* located at 42°N, 87°W.

Objectives

After reading this lesson, you should be able to

◆ use latitude and longitude to find a point on the earth.

◆ explain what hemispheres are.

Technology Note

Photogrammetry is a process used to make accurate maps. First, photos of the area to be mapped are taken from two locations above the earth. Then a computer called a stereoplotter creates a three-dimensional image using the photos.

Intersecting parallels and meridians form a global grid for the entire earth. Two intersecting lines meet only at one point. So intersecting parallels and meridians make it possible for you to locate a single point anywhere on the earth.

Locating Points by Latitude and Longitude

To locate any point on the surface of the earth, you need to know both the latitude and longitude of that point. When stating any point's location, the latitude is written before the longitude. For example, find point A on the map below. Point A lies on the 45°N parallel and the 30°W meridian. Its location is written as 45°N, 30°W. This means point A is 45° north of the equator and 30° west of the prime meridian.

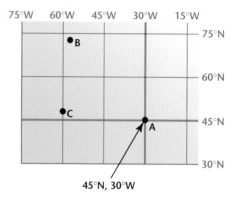

By estimating the position of any missing grid lines, you should be able to locate point C at about 48°N, 60°W. What is the location of point B? It is about 72°N, 57°W.

Hemispheres

The equator is the line of latitude halfway between the North and South Poles. This line divides the earth into two **hemispheres**. A hemisphere is half of the earth. Two equal-sized hemispheres make up the whole earth. The half of the earth north of the equator is called the Northern Hemisphere. The half south of the equator is the Southern Hemisphere. In which of these hemispheres do you live?

If the earth were cut in half through the prime meridian, it would be divided into another set of hemispheres. These two halves are known as the Eastern Hemisphere and the Western Hemisphere. Which hemisphere includes most of Africa?

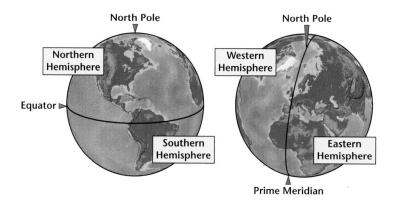

North Pole

Northern Hemisphere

Equator ▶

Southern Hemisphere

North Pole

Western Hemisphere

Eastern Hemisphere

Prime Meridian

TEACHER ALERT

Students may incorrectly conclude that a location can lie in only one of the following: the Northern, Southern, Eastern, or Western Hemisphere. Because each hemisphere covers one-half of the earth, not one-quarter, every location actually lies in two hemispheres—the Northern or Southern *and* the Eastern or Western.

LEARNING STYLES

Visual/Spatial

Use a sharp paring knife and two large oranges to model parallels and meridians. To demonstrate that lines of latitude are parallel, carefully cut an orange in half through its "equator." Make additional cuts through each half, parallel to the first cut, producing even slices. Reassemble the orange. To illustrate meridians, carefully cut a second orange into segments from "pole" to "pole." Reassemble the orange. Convey the difference between parallels and meridians.

CAREER CONNECTION

A cartographer makes maps. Today, cartographers use information provided by many others, including surveyors, who measure distances and elevations, and photogrammetrists, who get precise measurements from aerial photographs. A cartographer decides what a map's focus should be and then chooses a projection, scale, and symbols for the map. Computers help in mapmaking. Cartographers must have good math and computer skills and be able to visualize spatial relationships. Have students discuss reasons new maps must be made or old maps must be revised.

SCIENCE JOURNAL

Ask students to think back to Investigation 2-2 and their method for describing locations on a round object. Ask students to write a paragraph about how lines of latitude and longitude can help describe a location and how this system compares with their method. This activity provides a starting point for Lesson 6.

CROSS-CURRICULAR CONNECTION

Social Studies

Explain that the Eastern Hemisphere, made up of Europe, Asia, Africa, and Australia, is sometimes known as the Old World. The Western Hemisphere, made up of North America and South America, is known as the New World. Have students discuss reasons for this. Have them share information, including names of explorers and dates of exploration, about the "discovery" by Europeans of the New World.

Lesson 6 Review Answers

1. New Orleans 2. Philadelphia 3. Denver
4. about 47°N, 113°W 5. about 50°N, 97°W

Portfolio Assessment

Sample items include:

• Main-idea sentences from Teaching the Lesson
• Modified grid from Teaching the Lesson
• Lesson 6 Review answers

Use the map below to answer these questions on a sheet of paper.

1. What city is located at 30°N, 90°W?

2. What city is located at 40°N, 76°W?

3. What city is located at 39°N, 105°W?

4. What is the latitude and longitude of Helena?

5. What is the latitude and longitude of Winnipeg?

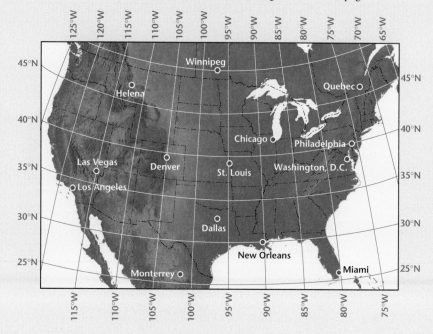

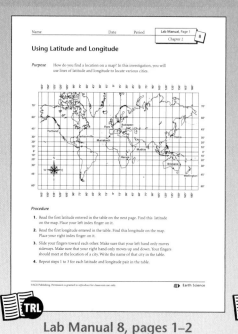

Lab Manual 8, pages 1–2

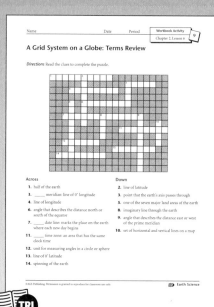

Workbook Activity 9

- The earth has a rounded shape, but it is not perfectly round.

- About 30 percent of the earth's surface is land, which is broken up into seven continents.

- About 70 percent of the earth's surface is water, most of which is divided into four oceans.

- Rotation is the spinning of the earth on its axis. The earth rotates from west to east.

- The turning of the earth on its axis results in day and night.

- The earth is divided into 24 standard time zones. Within a given zone, the clock time is the same.

- A grid is a set of horizontal and vertical lines on a map. A grid is used to locate places on a map.

- Latitude lines are imaginary lines that run east and west around the earth. Latitude lines are called parallels.

- Latitude is an angle that describes the distance from the equator.

- Longitude lines are imaginary lines that run north and south from pole to pole. Longitude lines are called meridians.

- Longitude is an angle that describes the distance from the prime meridian.

- Intersecting parallels and meridians make it possible to locate a single point anywhere on the earth.

- A hemisphere is half of the earth.

- The equator divides the earth into the Northern and Southern Hemispheres. The prime meridian divides the earth into the Western and Eastern Hemispheres.

Science Words

axis, 29	hemisphere, 49	meridian, 46	South Pole, 29
continent, 27	international date	North Pole, 29	standard time
degree, 42	line, 33	parallel, 42	zone, 32
equator, 42	latitude, 42	prime meridian, 46	
grid, 38	longitude, 46	rotation, 29	

Chapter 2 Summary

Have volunteers read aloud each Summary item on page 51. Ask volunteers to explain the meaning of each item. Direct students' attention to the Science Words box on the bottom of page 51. Have them read and review each word and its definition.

Chapter 2 Review

Use the Chapter Review to prepare students for tests and to reteach content from the chapter.

Chapter 2 Mastery Test

The Teacher's Resource Library includes two parallel forms of the Chapter 2 Mastery Test. The difficulty level of the two forms is equivalent. You may wish to use one form as a pretest and the other form as a posttest.

Review Answers
Vocabulary Review

1. grid 2. hemisphere 3. prime meridian
4. standard time zone 5. axis 6. parallel
7. continents 8. rotation 9. equator
10. longitude

Concept Review

11. **A** axis; **B** North Pole; **C** South Pole;
D latitude line or parallel; **E** meridian or longitude line 12. rounded 13. about
30 percent 14. noon 15. degree 16. the equator 17. 92°W 18. Eastern and Western Hemispheres 19. C 20. A 21. B
22. D 23. D

TEACHER ALERT

In the Chapter Review, the Vocabulary Review activity includes a sample of the chapter's vocabulary terms. The activity will help determine students' understanding of key vocabulary terms and concepts presented in the chapter. Other vocabulary terms used in the chapter are listed below:

degree
international date line
latitude
meridian
North Pole
South Pole

Vocabulary Review

Word Bank
axis
continents
equator
grid
hemisphere
longitude
parallel
prime meridian
rotation
standard time zone

Choose the word or phrase from the Word Bank that best completes each sentence. Write the answer on your paper.

1. The set of horizontal and vertical lines on a map is its _____.
2. One half of the earth is a(n) _____.
3. The line of 0° longitude is the _____.
4. An area that has the same clock time is a(n) _____.
5. The imaginary line through the earth connecting the North and South Poles is the _____.
6. A line of latitude is a(n) _____.
7. The seven major land areas of the earth are _____.
8. The spinning of the earth is _____.
9. The line of latitude halfway between the North and South Poles is the _____.
10. The angle that describes the distance east or west of the prime meridian is _____.

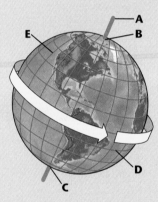

Concept Review

Write the answer to each of the following questions.

11. Name each of the lettered features in the diagram.
12. Describe the shape of the earth.
13. What percentage of the earth's surface do the continents represent?
14. When it is midnight at one point on the earth, what time is it at a point exactly halfway around the earth?

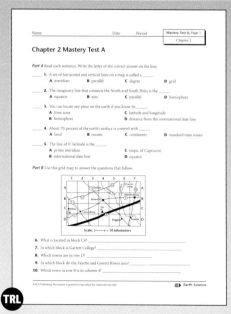

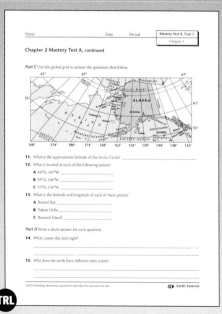

Chapter 2 Mastery Test A

15. What is the measurement unit for latitude and longitude?

16. What is the line of 0° latitude called?

17. On which line of longitude does a point at 31°S, 92°W lie?

18. Which hemispheres lie on either side of the prime meridian?

Choose the word or phrase that best completes each sentence. Write the letter of the answer on your paper.

19. The earth rotates from _____.
- **A** east to west
- **B** north to south
- **C** west to east
- **D** south to north

20. The earth rotates once every _____.
- **A** day **B** week **C** month **D** year

21. The time in Europe is _____ the time in North America.
- **A** behind
- **B** ahead of
- **C** the same as
- **D** 1 hour different from

22. A point at 80°N latitude is located near the _____.
- **A** equator
- **B** South Pole
- **C** tropic of Capricorn
- **D** North Pole

23. The entire continent of Antarctica is located in the _____ Hemisphere.
- **A** Northern **B** Eastern **C** Western **D** Southern

Critical Thinking

Write the answer to each of the following questions.

24. How are latitude and longitude alike and different?

25. How would day and night be different if the earth did not rotate?

Test-Taking Tip Answer all questions you are sure of first, then go back and answer the others.

24. Answers will vary. Both are measures of distance given in degrees, used to locate points on the earth. Lines of latitude are parallel and circle east-west around the earth. Lines of longitude run north-south and converge at the poles. **25.** Day and night would change gradually as the earth revolved around the sun. Day and night would each be six months long.

ALTERNATIVE ASSESSMENT

Alternative Assessment items correlate to the student Goals for Learning at the beginning of this chapter.

n Ask students to draw two diagrams—one of a baseball and one of the earth. The diagrams should show how the shapes of the two objects differ. If they wish, students could use a compass or a round object, such as a jar lid, to help them.

n Have students hold a tennis ball or other small ball and imagine it is the earth. Have them demonstrate the motion of the earth that causes day and night. Then have them tell what time of day it is in New York City if it is night on a point on the opposite side of the earth.

n Ask students to imagine they are hosting a party in Houston, Texas, for the World Cup soccer championship. If the games will be televised live from Buenos Aires, Argentina, at 12:30 P.M. and from Great Britain at 3:30 P.M., when should the party begin? *(9:30 A.M. Houston time)*

n Provide students with small index cards and detailed road maps of your community. Have each student locate five points of interest, using the map grid. Have students record the name of each site on one side of a card and the block location on the other side. Small groups can use the flash cards to quiz each other.

n Provide students with copies of a U.S. map showing lines of latitude and longitude. Have students determine the city at each location: 40°N, 75°W *(Philadelphia, PA)*; 35°N, 107°W *(Albuquerque, NM)*; 47°N, 117°W *(Spokane, WA)*; 31°N, 31°W *(Baton Rouge, LA)*

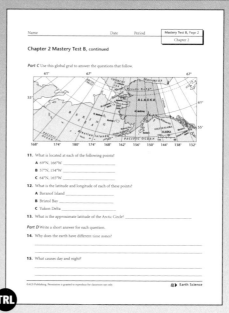

Chapter 2 Mastery Test B

Chapter 3

Planning Guide

The Earth and Moon System

	Student Text Lesson		
	Student Pages	Vocabulary	Lesson Review
Lesson 1 The Effect of Gravity	56–59	✔	✔
Lesson 2 The Earth's Movement in Space	60–64	✔	✔
Lesson 3 The Moon's Movement in Space	65–69	✔	✔
Lesson 4 The Moon's Surface	70–72	✔	✔

Chapter Activities

Student Text
Science Center
Teacher's Resource Library
Community Connection 3:
   Seasonal Changes

Assessment Options

Student Text
Chapter 3 Review
Teacher's Resource Library
Chapter 3 Mastery Tests A and B

	Student Text Features								Teaching Strategies						Learning Styles						Teacher's Resource Library				
Achievements in Science	Science at Work	Science in Your Life	Investigation	Science Myth	Note	Technology Note	Did You Know	Science Integration	Science Journal	Cross-Curricular Connection	Online Connection	Teacher Alert	Applications (Home, Career, Community, Global, Environment)	Auditory/Verbal	Body/Kinesthetic	Interpersonal/Group Learning	Logical/Mathematical	Visual/Spatial	LEP/ESL	Workbook Activities	Alternative Workbook Activities	Lab Manual	Resource File	Self-Study Guide
57			58						57	56		56			56					10	10	9		✔
	62		63	61				61		61		60	62						62	11	11	10	8	✔
		69			✔		65	66		67, 68	68		66, 68	67			67	66	67	12	12	11	9, 10	✔
						✔	71	71, 72	72	71	71	71	72			71				13	13	12		✔

Pronunciation Key

a	hat	e	let	ī	ice	ô	order	ù	put	sh	she		a in about
ā	age	ē	equal	o	hot	oi	oil	ü	rule	th	thin	ə	e in taken
ä	far	ėr	term	ō	open	ou	out	ch	child	ᵀH	then		i in pencil
â	care	i	it	ȯ	saw	u	cup	ng	long	zh	measure		o in lemon
													u in circus

Alternative Workbook Activities

The Teacher's Resource Library (TRL) contains a set of lower-level worksheets called Alternative Workbook Activities. These worksheets cover the same content as the regular Workbook Activities but are written at a second-grade reading level.

Skill Track Software

Use the Skill Track Software for Earth Science for additional reinforcement of this chapter. The software program allows students using AGS textbooks to be assessed for mastery of each chapter and lesson of the textbook. Students access the software on an individual basis and are assessed with multiple-choice items.

Chapter 3:
The Earth and Moon
System pages 54–75
Lessons

1. **The Effect of Gravity**
   pages 56–59

   Investigation 3-1 pages 58–59

2. **The Earth's Movement in Space**
   pages 60–64

   Investigation 3-2 pages 63–64

3. **The Moon's Movement in Space**
   pages 65–69

4. **The Moon's Surface** pages 70–72

Chapter 3 Summary page 73

Chapter 3 Review pages 74–75

Skill Track Software
for Earth Science

Teacher's Resource Library

Workbook Activities 10–13

Alternative Workbook Activities
10–13

Lab Manual 9–12

Community Connection 3

Resource File 8–10

Chapter 3 Self-Study Guide

Chapter 3 Mastery Tests A and B

(Answer Keys for the Teacher's
Resource Library begin on page 400
of the Teacher's Edition. The
Materials List for the Lab Manual
activities begins on page 415.)

Science Center

Have students prepare a display titled
"Eclipses." Provide foam balls or other
balls of appropriate sizes to show the
positions of the sun, the earth, and the
moon during a solar eclipse and a lunar
eclipse. Have students label each of the
models. This will reinforce the difference
between the two kinds of eclipses.

Community Connection 3

Chapter 3

The Earth and Moon System

Looking up at a full moon on a clear night, it might be hard to believe that the moon is about 400,000 kilometers away from us. It seems closer! Even though the earth and moon are far apart, they affect each other in many ways. Ocean tides, lunar eclipses, the phases of the moon—these all happen because of the interaction between the earth and moon. In Chapter 3, you will find out about the earth and moon system.

Organize Your Thoughts

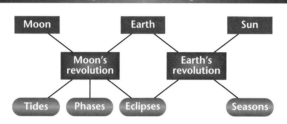

Goals for Learning

◆ To define gravity and understand its effects

◆ To describe how the earth and moon move in space

◆ To explain how the earth's revolution and the tilt of its axis cause seasons

◆ To describe the four major phases of the moon

◆ To explain how an eclipse happens

◆ To explain how the moon causes tides

◆ To describe features of the moon's surface

55

Introducing the Chapter

Ask students to describe what is shown in the photo on page 54. Have them guess how and from where the photo was taken. Have volunteers tell what they know about each object's position and movement in space. *(Possible responses: The earth and moon are closer together than the earth and sun. The earth moves around the sun; the moon moves around the earth as well as the sun. Both the earth and the moon spin on their axes.)*

Read the Goals for Learning together. Discuss what students already know about these topics. Help them formulate questions about what they do not know and want to learn more about. For example, students might ask: What causes days, nights, and seasons? What causes phases of the moon? What is the difference between an eclipse of the sun and an eclipse of the moon? Ask students to write down their questions and keep them on hand as they read the chapter.

Notes and Technology Notes

Ask volunteers to read the notes that appear in the margins throughout the chapter. Then discuss them with the class.

TEACHER'S RESOURCE

The AGS Teaching Strategies in Science Transparencies may be used with this chapter. The transparencies add an interactive dimension to expand and enhance the *Earth Science* program content.

CAREER INTEREST INVENTORY

The AGS Harrington-O'Shea Career Decision-Making System-Revised (CDM) may be used with this chapter. Students can use the CDM to explore their interests and identify careers. The CDM defines career areas that are indicated by students' responses on the inventory.

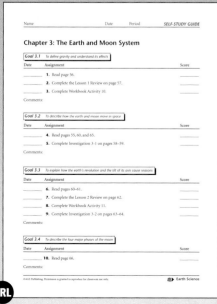

Chapter 3 Self-Study Guide

Lesson at a Glance

Chapter 3 Lesson 1

Overview In this lesson, students learn about the force of gravity and why it causes the moon to orbit the earth and the earth to orbit the sun.

Objectives

- To explain what gravity is
- To name the factors that affect the strength of gravity
- To describe how gravity affects the moon and the earth

Student Pages 56–59

Teacher's Resource Library

Workbook Activity 10

Alternative Workbook Activity 10

Lab Manual 9

Vocabulary

gravity   orbit
mass

 Warm-Up Activity

Roll a ball off the edge of a table, then toss the ball into the air and catch it. Have students tell why the ball fell toward the floor in each case. (Some students may know that gravity pulls objects toward the earth.) Have students read to find out how gravity affects the movement of the earth and the moon.

 Teaching the Lesson

Ask students to use each vocabulary word in a sentence that shows its meaning.

Draw the earth, moon, and sun on the board. Ask students to draw the orbit path of the earth and moon, using arrows to show the direction of movement.

 Objectives

After reading this lesson, you should be able to

- explain what gravity is.
- name the factors that affect the strength of gravity.
- describe how gravity affects the moon and the earth.

Gravity

Force of attraction between any two objects

Mass

Amount of matter that an object contains

Orbit

Curved path that an object follows as it revolves around another object

When you throw a ball into the air, it eventually falls. It falls because of **gravity**. Gravity is a force of attraction between any two objects, caused by those objects pulling on each other. The strength of this force depends on two factors:

- The distance between the two objects
- The **mass** of each object, or how much matter each object contains

The closer the objects are to each other, the stronger the gravity between them. Objects with greater mass have greater gravitational pull. For example, when you throw a ball, the ball and the earth pull on each other. The earth and the ball are very close to each other, and the earth's mass is much greater than the ball's mass. Therefore, the earth's gravitational pull brings the ball back toward the earth, and the ball falls.

The diagram shows how gravity affects the earth and moon. The earth has more mass than the moon. So the gravity between the earth and moon pulls the moon into a curved path around the earth. This curved path is an **orbit**. The sun has more mass than the earth. Gravity pulls the earth, with its moon, into an orbit around the sun. Notice that the shape of an orbit is not an exact circle. It is an ellipse, which is an oval shape.

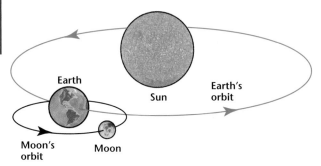

TEACHER ALERT

 Students may think that gravity is a force that causes objects to fall *downward*. Emphasize that the term *gravity* applies to the force that pulls two objects together. Objects fall to the ground because the mass of the earth exerts a much greater gravitational pull than an object such as a book or ball.

 Reinforce and Extend

CROSS-CURRICULAR CONNECTION

Language Arts
Copy the complete dictionary entry for *orbit* on an overhead transparency. Have students find the word's etymology and explain its history. (*Orbit* comes from the Latin word *orbita*, which means "path," "track," or "rut.") Have students explain how the meaning of *orbit* fits this history. (*An orbit is the path a satellite makes as it revolves around a larger object such as a planet.*)

Write your answers to these questions on a sheet of paper.

1. What is gravity?

2. What factors affect the strength of gravity?

3. What is an orbit?

4. How does gravity affect the motion of the earth?

5. Explain the relationships between the earth, moon, and sun in terms of orbits.

Achievements in Science

Almanacs

An almanac is a book of information organized by the days of a year. Almanacs are updated and published each year. They predict moon phases, times of sunrise and sunset, weather, and much more. These predictions are based on carefully recorded facts from previous years.

In 1476, a German astronomer wrote one of the first almanacs to be printed on a printing press. Almanacs became important resources, especially for farmers and ship navigators. The early almanacs were often one of the few books in a home.

The most famous almanac in the American colonies was *Poor Richard's Almanack*. Benjamin Franklin wrote and published this almanac from 1732 to 1757. He did all of his own calculations for the data in his almanacs. Benjamin Banneker was another American inventor who wrote almanacs. He started studying math and astronomy when he was 40. By teaching himself, he accurately predicted solar eclipses, tides, and weather. He published his almanac from 1792 to 1802.

In 1886, Joseph Pulitzer began publishing *The World Almanac*. This was the first almanac to include a wider range of topics, such as sports records and facts about countries. During World War II, copies of *The World Almanac* were given to soldiers overseas. It is still produced every year, but now it is called *The World Almanac and Book of Facts*.

There are many kinds of almanacs published today. The next time you visit a library, look in the reference section. Find an almanac and page through this handy book.

The Earth and Moon System Chapter 3 **57**

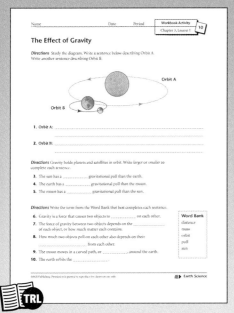

Workbook Activity 10

PRONUNCIATION GUIDE

Use the pronunciation shown below to help students pronounce *ellipse*. Refer to the pronunciation key on the Chapter Planning Guide for the sounds of the symbols.

ellipse (i lips´)

SCIENCE JOURNAL

 Ask students to imagine what it might be like to live without gravity (or to live in a place where gravity is much stronger). Ask them to describe how their daily lives would be affected. Journal entries should reflect students' understanding of gravity and its effects on the behavior of objects.

Lesson 1 Review Answers

1. the force of attraction between two objects, causing them to be pulled toward each other **2.** Gravity's force depends on how close the two objects are to each other and how much mass each object has. **3.** the curved path of an object as it revolves around another object **4.** Gravity pulls the earth into orbit around the sun. **5.** The moon orbits the earth; the earth, with the moon, orbits the sun.

Achievements in Science

After students read the feature on page 57, ask them to explain why Banneker's achievements in science are so outstanding. *(As an African American in eighteenth-century America, he would have lacked educational and economic opportunities, so he was largely self-taught.)* Explain that Banneker taught himself astronomy. His calculations about stars and constellations enabled him to predict eclipses, weather, hours of sunrise and sunset, and so on, which he published in his almanacs. Discuss how navigators and farmers could have made use of this information.

Portfolio Assessment

Sample items include:
- Vocabulary sentences and drawings from Teaching the Lesson
- Lesson 1 Review answers

LEARNING STYLES

Body/Kinesthetic

Have students work in groups of three to model the earth's revolution around the sun and the moon's revolution around the earth. One student represents the sun, one represents the earth, and a third represents the moon. Each group's movements should show the moon orbiting the earth and the earth, with the moon, orbiting the sun.

The Purpose portion of the student investigation begins with a question to draw students into the activity. Encourage students to read the investigation steps and formulate their own questions before beginning the investigation. This investigation will take approximately 30 minutes to complete. Students will use these process and thinking skills: making models, recognizing patterns and relationships, and communicating.

Preparation

• To save time, cut strings into 25-centimeter lengths and tie the ends to form loops.

• Be sure the cardboard is thick enough so that the pushpins do not scratch desks or tables.

• Demonstrate the procedure to give students a feel for how hard they need to pull on the pencil to keep the string taut.

• Students may use Lab Manual 9 to record their data and answer the questions.

Procedure

• This investigation can be done individually or in small groups. Group members should work cooperatively to record their observations and clean up. Assign one student to gather equipment and another to set up the paper, cardboard, and pushpins. Students can take turns drawing the ellipses and repositioning the pins. Larger groups can repeat the procedure so that all members have a chance to draw an ellipse.

• Students might need help in keeping the string taut while they draw ellipses. Have them practice a few times using their fingers instead of a pencil to get the feel of the procedure.

SAFETY ALERT

◆ Have students wear safety glasses to protect their eyes from dislodged pins.

◆ Caution students to handle pushpins carefully. In trying to keep the string taut, they might pull too hard and dislodge a pin.

3-1 INVESTIGATION

Materials
◆ sheet of paper
◆ piece of corrugated cardboard
◆ safety glasses
◆ 2 pushpins
◆ centimeter ruler
◆ scissors
◆ string

Making a Model of an Orbit

Purpose
How might you model an orbit? In this investigation, you will construct a device that helps you draw an ellipse.

Procedure

1. Place the sheet of paper over the piece of cardboard.

2. **Safety Alert: Put on safety glasses.**

3. Stick two pins near the center of the paper so they are 7 centimeters apart. Stick the pins through both the paper and the cardboard. **Safety Alert: Use care with pins. The points are sharp.**

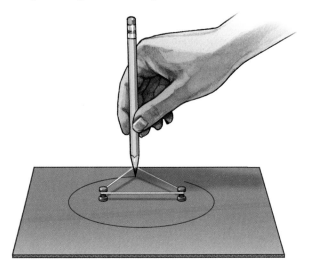

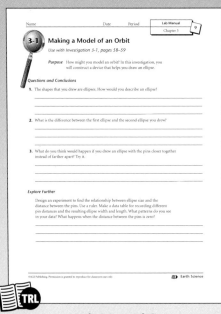

Lab Manual 9

4. Cut a piece of string about 25 centimeters long. Tie the ends together to form a loop. Place the loop of string over both pins. The loop should be about 5 centimeters longer than the distance between the pins.

5. Place a pencil inside the loop and pull it gently away from the pins so the string straightens out.

6. Keeping the string fairly tight, draw a curving line all the way around both pins. **Safety Alert: Avoid pulling the string too tight and pulling out the pins.**

7. Remove the pins and place them a little farther apart. Repeat steps 5 and 6.

Questions and Conclusions

1. The shapes that you drew are ellipses. How would you describe an ellipse?

2. What is the difference between the first ellipse and the second ellipse you drew?

3. What do you think would happen if you drew an ellipse with the pins closer together instead of farther apart? Try it.

Explore Further

Design an experiment to find the relationship between ellipse size and the distance between the pins. Use a ruler. Make a data table for recording different pin distances and the resulting ellipse width and length. What patterns do you see in your data? What happens when the distance between the pins is zero?

Results

The farther apart the students place the pushpins, the more elongated the ellipses will be. The closer together the pushpins, the more circular the ellipse. If the pushpins are placed right next to each other, students may not be able to distinguish the ellipse from a circle.

Questions and Conclusions Answers

1. Answers will vary, but may include an oval, an egg shape, or a "stretched" circle.

2. The second ellipse is longer but not as wide. It is more elliptical.

3. The ellipse would be more circular and less elongated than the others.

Explore Further Answers

Data tables should show ellipse width decreasing and length increasing as distance between pins increases. Length should equal width when the distance between the pins is zero (a circle is drawn when only one pin is used).

Assessment

Check students' ellipses to see that they become more elongated as the pins are placed farther apart, but also check their answers to questions. Students may understand the concept even if they are unable to draw smooth ellipses. Note whether they have constructed logical data tables and recorded reasonable patterns of length and width. Include the following items from this investigation in student portfolios:

• Ellipse drawings

• Data table from the Explore Further section

• Answers to Questions and Conclusions and Explore Further sections

Lesson at a Glance

Chapter 3 Lesson 2

Overview In this lesson, students learn how the earth revolves around the sun and is tilted on its axis, resulting in four seasons.

Objectives

- To describe the movement of the earth around the sun
- To explain how the earth's revolution and the tilt of its axis cause seasons

Student Pages 60–64

Teacher's Resource Library (TRL)

Workbook Activity 11

Alternative Workbook Activity 11

Lab Manual 10

Resource File 8

Vocabulary

revolution

Science Background

Because the earth's axis is tilted 23.5°, the region between the tropic of Cancer (23.5°N latitude) and the tropic of Capricorn (23.5°S latitude) receives the most intense sunlight during the entire year. The North and South Poles receive the least intense sunlight, so they are the coldest regions on the earth.

1 Warm-Up Activity

Have two volunteers model the sun and earth. As the earth walks around the sun, have students explain the term *revolution*. Have the earth spin slowly while walking around the sun. Ask students to review the term *rotation* from Chapter 2. Tell them that they will read to learn about the earth's movement in space.

2 Teaching the Lesson

As they read the lesson, have students draw diagrams to illustrate the difference between the earth's revolution and rotation.

To model the earth, have pairs of students push a pencil through the center of a foam ball and draw the equator on the ball. Darken the room. Ask one student

to shine a flashlight at the equator as the other holds the ball. The student holding the ball tilts the North Pole away from the flashlight. Have students explain which hemisphere gets more direct light when the earth's axis is pointed in this direction. *(the Southern Hemisphere)* Repeat the procedure when the North Pole is tilted toward the flashlight. Ask students to name the season in the Northern Hemisphere at this position. *(summer)*

Objectives

After reading this lesson, you should be able to

- describe the movement of the earth around the sun.
- explain how the earth's revolution and the tilt of its axis cause seasons.

Revolution

Movement of one object in its orbit around another object in space

Why is a year about 365 days? Why do seasons change throughout the year? You can answer these questions once you know how the earth moves in space.

Revolution and Rotation

The movement of the earth in its orbit around the sun is the earth's **revolution**. A single revolution of the earth takes about 365 days, which is one year.

While the earth is revolving around the sun, it is also rotating on its axis. As discussed in Chapter 2, the earth rotates once every day, or every 24 hours.

Seasons

As the earth revolves around the sun, the earth's axis always stays tilted at $23\frac{1}{2}°$, as shown below. The tilt causes sunlight to fall more directly on different parts of the earth throughout its orbit. The diagram on the next page shows how this causes seasons. Notice that when it is summer in the Northern Hemisphere, that hemisphere is tilted toward the sun. When it is winter in the Northern Hemisphere, that hemisphere is tilted away from the sun.

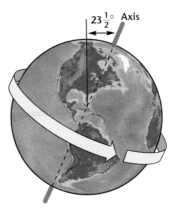

$23\frac{1}{2}°$ Axis

TEACHER ALERT

Remind students that the earth's rotation is responsible for intervals of day and night, each 24 hours in duration. The tilt of the earth, however, is responsible for the varying lengths of daylight and darkness. When the Northern Hemisphere is tilted toward the sun, in summer, light rays reach the earth for a longer period each day, and we experience more hours of daylight.

When it is summer in the Northern Hemisphere, it is winter in the Southern Hemisphere. For example, July is a summer month in the United States, but it is a winter month in Argentina. In the Northern Hemisphere, October is a fall month. In the Southern Hemisphere, October is in springtime.

No matter where you live, in the summer, the noontime sun appears at its highest in the sky. During the winter, it appears at its lowest. The sun's rays strike the earth more directly in the summer than in the winter. The more direct the sunlight is, the more it heats up the ground. Thus, it is warmer in the summer than it is in the winter.

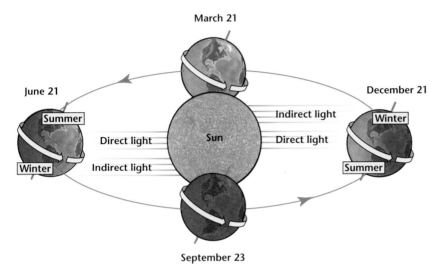

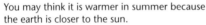

Science Myth

You may think it is warmer in summer because the earth is closer to the sun.

Fact: Actually, in the Northern Hemisphere, the distance between the earth and the sun is slightly greater during the summer months. It is the tilt of the earth toward the sun that causes summer sunlight to hit the earth directly. This results in the warmer temperatures of summer.

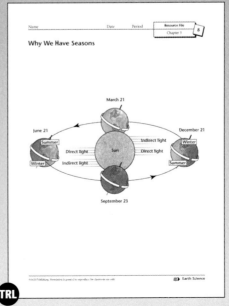

Resource File 8

SCIENCE INTEGRATION

Biology

Lead a class discussion about how the seasons affect living things. Ask students to name things that change as seasons change. *(temperature, length of daylight, quantity and form of precipitation)* Have students name ways living things react to such changes. *(Trees may drop leaves. Some animals hibernate, some migrate, some store fat, some change color. Mating seasons are timed to take advantage of mild temperatures and plentiful food supplies.)*

Science Myth

Ask students to predict why temperatures are warmer in summer months. Then have them read the Science Myth feature on page 61. Explain that it is the angle at which sunlight strikes the earth that causes the change in temperature. More direct light is more intense.

CROSS-CURRICULAR CONNECTION

Drama

Model the revolution of the earth around the sun or reproduce the diagram from page 61 on the board. Work through each season by moving the earth model to a different position in its revolution or by pointing to a part of the diagram. Pause at each season and have students act out how plants, animals, and people respond to the changes that occur in that season. For example, students might pantomime a plant growing taller and blooming in summer or an animal going into hibernation in winter.

LEARNING STYLES

LEP/ESL

Have students who are learning English write the terms *revolution* and *rotation* on index cards. They can write the definition in their own words on the reverse side of each card. Spin a globe and have students hold up the card that fits this action. Ask two volunteers to use the globe to demonstrate revolution.

IN THE ENVIRONMENT

Have students research the concept of biological clocks. Lead a discussion about how the hours of daylight affect activities of various plants and animals in your community.

Lesson 2 Review Answers

1. This is how long it takes the earth to revolve once around the sun. 2. $23\frac{1}{2}°$ 3. summer 4. fall 5. Direct sunlight strikes the earth head-on, at an angle close to 90°; indirect sunlight strikes the earth at a lesser angle.

Science at Work

Display photos or illustrations that show the shape and layout of the International Space Station. Read aloud statistics and facts about the station, and have students compare its size to the classroom size. Have volunteers read the feature aloud.

Discuss the living quarters in space. How must astronauts adapt to space travel? What effects would the weak gravity conditions have on astronauts' daily lives? Ask students to list qualities that a person would need to live, work, and cooperate in close quarters with other people for weeks and months at a time.

Portfolio Assessment

Sample items include:
• Diagrams from Teaching the Lesson
• Lesson 2 Review answers

Write your answers to these questions on a sheet of paper.

1. Why is a year about 365 days long?

2. How far is the earth tilted on its axis?

3. When the Northern Hemisphere is tilted toward the sun, what season is it in that hemisphere?

4. When it is spring in the Northern Hemisphere, what season is it in the Southern Hemisphere?

5. Explain the difference between indirect and direct sunlight.

▼◄▲▼◄▲▼◄▲▼◄▲▼◄▲▼◄▲▼◄▲▼◄▲▼◄▲▼◄▲▼◄▲▼◄▲▼◄▲▼◄▲▼

Science at Work

Space Shuttle and International Space Station Crews

The International Space Station (ISS) is a big research laboratory orbiting the earth. Many countries, including the United States, Canada, and Russia, use and contribute to the ISS. Space shuttles are launchable spacecraft designed to shuttle, or go back and forth, between the earth and the ISS.

Space shuttle crew members fly shuttle missions to maintain and supply the ISS. Astronaut and pilot Pamela Ann Melroy was part of a 2002 crew that carried equipment to the ISS and installed it. The entire mission took 11 days.

In addition to space shuttle crews, there are ISS crews. They live and work on the ISS for months at a time.

Space shuttle and ISS crew members help construct, maintain, and repair the ISS. Sometimes crew members go on space walks to perform these tasks. Crew members also perform scientific experiments to test the effects of the space environment on human beings, animals, and diseases. Some experiments test properties of matter in space.

Space shuttle and ISS crew members come from several countries. They must have a bachelor's degree in engineering, biological science, physical science, or mathematics. At least three years of related job experience is also required. An applicant must pass a physical exam that tests vision and blood pressure, among other things. An astronaut must have strong science and math skills and be physically strong and healthy.

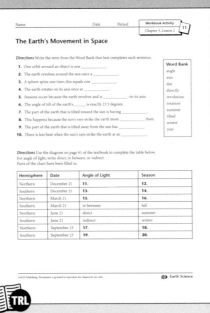

Workbook Activity 11

Exploring Light Angle

Purpose

How does the angle of a light affect its brightness on an object? In this investigation, you will model how the angle of sunlight affects its strength.

Materials
◆ two sheets of graph paper
◆ flashlight
◆ centimeter ruler

Procedure

1. Copy the data table on your paper.

Light Spot	Number of Squares Lit
1	
2	

2. Place a sheet of graph paper on a flat surface.

3. Holding the flashlight 20 centimeters directly above the paper, shine the light on the paper, as shown. Trace the spot of light. Label it Spot 1. **Safety Alert: Do not shine the flashlight into the eyes of others.**

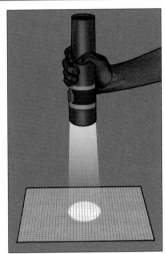

Lab Manual 10

Investigation 3-2

The Purpose portion of the student investigation begins with a question to draw students into the activity. Encourage students to read the investigation steps and formulate their own questions before beginning the investigation. This investigation will take approximately 30 minutes to complete. Students will use these process and thinking skills: making models, measuring, observing, and recognizing patterns and relationships.

Preparation

• Check flashlight batteries to be sure they are working. Have extra batteries on hand to replace those that run down.

• Place work stations far enough apart so that light from one group will not interfere with other groups.

• Students may use Lab Manual 10 to record their data and answer the questions.

Procedure

• Students may work alone or in small groups. As a group, students should work cooperatively to make and record observations and clean up. Assign jobs to individual students, such as gathering equipment, holding the flashlight, measuring the distance from the flashlight to the paper, tracing the spots of light, and counting the squares.

• Darken the room so that students can see the shapes formed by the flashlight beams more easily.

• Remind students to count only whole squares within their tracings.

• Remind students to keep the flashlight the same distance from the paper in both trials.

SAFETY ALERT

◆ Point out the Safety Alert in the text. Students should not shine flashlights into the eyes of others.

Continued on page 64

Continued from page 63

Results

The flashlight beam should light more squares when the flashlight is held at an angle to the paper. Students should observe that the light is brighter when shining straight down onto the paper.

Questions and Conclusions Answers

1. Spot 1
2. Spot 1. The flashlight shined more directly on the paper, creating brighter, more intense light.

Explore Further Answers

The thermometer should register a slightly higher temperature when the flashlight is directly above it. Relate this result to the position of the sun during summer.

Assessment

Check students' drawings to see that Spot 1 is circular and Spot 2 is oval. Also check results in the data table: Spot 1 should have fewer squares than Spot 2 and should have been brighter. Verify that students answered the questions correctly. You might want to include the following items from this investigation in student portfolios:

• Data table

• Answers to Questions and Conclusions and Explore Further sections

4. Now use a second sheet of graph paper. Hold the flashlight at the same distance from the paper, but at an angle, as shown. Trace the spot of light. Label it Spot 2.

5. Count the whole graph squares in each spot you traced. Record your data.

Questions and Conclusions

1. Which light spot seemed brighter?

2. Which spot represents sunlight during the summer season? Why?

Explore Further

Design an experiment to compare the temperature of direct light with the temperature of angled light. Use a thermometer and a flashlight. You may have to leave the light shining for several minutes to get an accurate measurement. What differences do you observe?

Objectives

After reading this lesson, you should be able to

◆ describe the rotation of the moon.
◆ explain the phases of the moon.
◆ explain why eclipses occur.
◆ explain how the moon helps cause tides.

Did You Know?

The first photos of the far side of the moon were taken by robotic spacecraft in 1959. Astronauts saw the far side of the moon for the first time during the Apollo flights of the late 1960s.

Revolution and Rotation

It takes the moon about 29 days to complete its revolution around the earth. From the earth, we can see only one side of the moon as it travels around us. The moon always keeps the same side toward the earth.

You might think that the moon does not rotate on its axis. It does rotate, but the rotation is unusual. It takes the moon the same amount of time to rotate once as it takes to revolve once around the earth. If the moon rotated slower or faster, you would be able to see its other side, too.

The figure below shows how you can make a model of the moon's movement. Hold your left fist in front of you. This is the earth. Hold your right fist at its side. This is the moon. Move the "moon" in a half circle around the "earth." Do not change the position of your right fist. Notice how you can see different parts of your right fist as it orbits your left fist. You did not rotate your right fist. Now move the "moon" again. This time, keep the same part of your right fist facing your left fist, as shown. In order to do that, you have to rotate your right fist.

Lesson at a Glance

Chapter 3 Lesson 3

Overview This lesson explores the moon's revolution and rotation and how its movement causes phases of the moon, eclipses, and tides.

Objectives

■ To describe the rotation of the moon
■ To explain the phases of the moon
■ To explain why eclipses occur
■ To explain how the moon helps cause tides

Student Pages 65–69

Teacher's Resource Library

Workbook Activity 12
Alternative Workbook Activity 12
Lab Manual 11
Resource File 9–10

Vocabulary

full moon   phases of the moon
lunar eclipse   solar eclipse
new moon   tides

Science Background

Tides are caused mainly by the gravitational pull of the moon, which makes the water bulge on the side of the earth closest to the moon as well as on the opposite side. The sun's gravitational pull also causes tides, but because the sun is so much farther away from the earth, its tidal effects are less than half those of the moon. The maximum tides occur when the earth, sun, and moon line up, adding together the gravitational forces of the moon and sun. When the sun and moon are about 90° apart, as seen from the earth, tides are at their minimum.

 Warm-Up Activity

Ask a volunteer to stand before the class and rotate in one spot. Have students explain how they know the student rotated. *(They saw the front, back, and both sides of the student.)* Have another student sit in a chair and a second student slowly walk around the chair, always facing the chair. Discuss why this

Continued on page 66

Did You Know?

Have a volunteer read aloud the feature on page 65. If possible, show pictures of the far side of the moon and the side visible from the earth. Have students predict differences in the sides. Ask an interested student to research and report on any differences.

Continued from page 65

modeled both revolving and rotating. *(Students should have seen the front, back, and both sides of the revolving student.)* Point out that this dual movement meant that the seated student saw only the revolving student's front. Explain that this illustrates the movement of the moon around the earth. Then have students model this movement with their fists, as shown on page 65.

 2 Teaching the Lesson

As they read, have students write a sentence or two summarizing the most important ideas in each section of the lesson.

Use a volleyball and flashlight in a darkened room to model phases of the moon. A student holds the ball over his or her head while you shine the flashlight on the ball. Have students observe the shapes of the lighted portion of the ball as they look at it from different positions.

Display photographs showing the same stretch of shoreline at high tide and at low tide. You may also show students almanac data relating changes in tides over a period of time. In most parts of the earth, two high tides and two low tides occur each day. Discuss how tides might affect coastal residents.

 3 Reinforce and Extend

LEARNING STYLES

Visual/Spatial

Give each student a copy of the month's calendar that shows the dates of the phases of the moon. In the appropriate boxes on the calendar, have students draw pictures of what the moon would look like in the sky. Encourage them to observe the moon at night.

AT HOME

 Have students observe the moon several times over a two-week period, recording the phase changes they observe.

Phases of the moon

Changes in the moon's appearance as it orbits the earth

Full moon

Phase of the moon when the earth is between the sun and the moon

New moon

Phase of the moon when the moon is between the sun and the earth

The Phases of the Moon

The moon is the brightest object in the night sky. It shines by reflecting light from the sun. The side of the moon facing the sun is always lit up. Notice in the diagram below that not all of the sunlit side can be seen from the earth at all times. For this reason, the moon's appearance changes as it orbits the earth. These changes are known as the **phases of the moon**.

The bottom diagram shows how each phase looks from the earth. When the earth is between the sun and the moon, the side of the moon facing the earth is completely lit. You see a **full moon**. When the moon is between the earth and the sun, the side of the moon facing the earth is dark and cannot be seen. This is called the **new moon** phase. As the moon moves around the earth from phase to phase, you can see different amounts of the sunlit side. The full moon and the new moon phases are about two weeks apart.

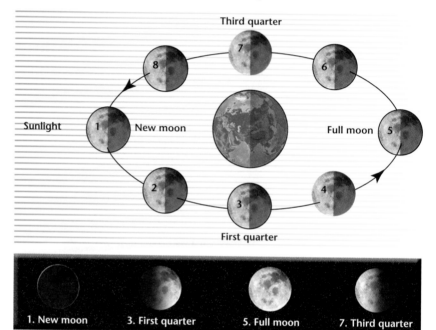

SCIENCE INTEGRATION

Physical Science

Explain that two forces must be in balance to keep a satellite in orbit: gravitational pull and inertia. Inertia is the property that tends to make a moving object travel in a straight line at a constant speed. Have students conclude how the two forces combine, resulting in an orbit. *(The opposing forces are balanced; that is, the pull toward space equals the pull toward the earth.)*

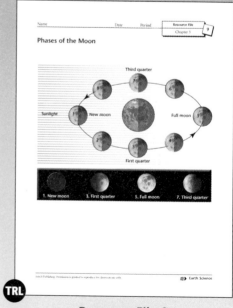

Resource File 9

Eclipses

Lunar eclipse

Passing of the moon through the earth's shadow

Solar eclipse

Passing of the moon between the earth and the sun

Sometimes the earth, the moon, and the sun line up together. When they line up exactly, there is an eclipse. An eclipse is either the earth blocking sunlight from reaching the moon or the moon blocking sunlight from reaching part of the earth.

A **lunar eclipse** happens when the earth is between the moon and the sun. The earth casts a shadow on the moon, as shown in the diagram below. As the earth moves between the sun and the moon, the moon darkens. A total lunar eclipse occurs when the shadow covers the entire surface of the moon. If the shadow does not cover the moon completely, then there is a partial lunar eclipse.

When the moon is between the earth and the sun, there is a **solar eclipse**. The moon casts a shadow on the earth, as shown below. People in the dark, central part of the moon's shadow cannot see the sun. For those people, the moon is in just the right position to hide the sun completely. They are seeing a total solar eclipse. Viewers who are in the outer part of the shadow see a partial eclipse. People who are outside the shadow do not see a solar eclipse at all.

Looking directly at the sun is dangerous, even during an eclipse. The sun's rays can burn the retina of the eye. To look at a solar eclipse safely, you need to use an eclipse viewer. You can make an eclipse viewer yourself. Simply make a pinhole in a small sheet of paper and hold it about 15 centimeters in front of a larger sheet of paper. First, face away from the eclipse. Next, line up the two sheets of paper until you can see the outline of the eclipse on the larger sheet.

Lunar eclipse

Sun — Moon — Earth

Solar eclipse

Sun — Moon — Earth

The Earth and Moon System   Chapter 3   **67**

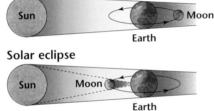

Resource File 10

Name   Date   Period   Resource File   10   Chapter 3

Lunar and Solar Eclipses

Lunar Eclipse

Moon
Earth

Solar Eclipse

Moon
Earth

Earth Science

TRL

Tides

Tides
Regular rising and falling of the earth's major bodies of water

Other factors besides gravity affect tides. Some of these factors are wind, ocean temperature, and rainfall or river water flowing into an ocean.

Tides

Recall from Lesson 1 that the gravity between the earth and moon pulls on the moon, keeping it in its orbit.

As the earth pulls on the moon, the moon also pulls on the earth. The moon pulls on the land and the water. The continents are too solid for the moon's pull to move them very much. But the pull on the earth's oceans is noticeable. This pull is the main cause of **tides**. Tides are the regular rising and falling of the major bodies of water on the earth.

Look at the diagram below. The moon's pull causes ocean water to pile up on the side of the earth facing the moon. The water also piles up on the side opposite the moon. These bulges are high tides. Low tides happen between the bulges. What is the difference between high tides and low tides? Compare the photos to find out.

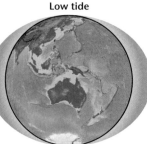

Low tide

Moon's gravitational pull

High tide   High tide

Moon

Low tide

The difference between high and low tide can be 16 meters in the Bay of Fundy in New Brunswick, Canada.

Lesson 3   R E V I E W

Write your answers to these questions on a sheet of paper.

1. Why do we see the same side of the moon?

2. Why does the moon shine?

3. Describe the phases of the moon.

4. How is a solar eclipse different from a lunar eclipse?

5. What is the main cause of tides?

Science in Your Life

Natural and Artificial Satellites

A natural satellite is a naturally occurring object that revolves around a larger object, usually a planet. The moon is the earth's only natural satellite.

There are artificial satellites, too. These are human-made objects that are sent into space, then continuously orbit. Some artificial satellites orbit the earth, the moon, or another planet.

Many forms of communication rely on signals from artificial satellites. These signals are received by satellite dishes. Cable television and cellular telephones require artificial satellites. Global positioning systems track and locate people and things by using satellite signals. Emergency radio signals given off by lost ships are transmitted by artificial satellites. Weather information is gathered using instruments on satellites. Then this information is sent by way of satellite across the world. Meteorologists use this information to prepare weather forecasts. You probably rely on artificial satellites more than you think!

Lab Manual 11, pages 1–2

Workbook Activity 12

Lesson 3 Review Answers

1. The moon rotates once in the same amount of time that it revolves once around the earth. Therefore, the same side always faces the earth. **2.** It reflects light from the sun. **3.** A full moon occurs when the side of the moon facing the earth is fully lit by the sun. A new moon occurs when the moon is between the sun and the earth; the side of the moon facing the earth appears dark. Other phases occur as the moon moves around the earth, showing different amounts of its sunlit side. **4.** A solar eclipse occurs when the moon is between the earth and the sun. A lunar eclipse occurs when the earth is between the moon and the sun. **5.** the moon's gravitational pull on the earth's water

Science in Your Life

Read the title of the feature on page 69 and ask students to give an example of a natural satellite and an artificial satellite. *(the moon; the International Space Station)* Ask students if they know of any ways that satellites affect their lives. Read the feature together. Then brainstorm as a class to make a list of ways that your community depends on artificial satellites.

Discuss any problems students can see with placing so many artificial satellites in orbit around the earth. *(As they become obsolete or unusable, the artificial satellites continue to orbit as "space junk," which can present a hazard to space explorers and spacecraft. In addition, when they fall from orbit, they may cause damage or injury.)*

Portfolio Assessment

Sample items include:
- Summary sentences from Teaching the Lesson
- Lesson 3 Review answers

Lesson at a Glance

Chapter 3 Lesson 4

Overview In this lesson, students learn about the craters and maria on the moon's surface and about space missions to the moon.

Objectives

- To describe physical features of the moon
- To tell when astronauts visited the moon and what their missions accomplished

Student Pages 70–72

Teacher's Resource Library

Workbook Activity 13

Alternative Workbook Activity 13

Lab Manual 12

Vocabulary

crater	meteorite
maria	telescope

Science Background

The craters of the moon are its dominant feature. Other moons and planets, including the earth, also have craters. However, unlike the earth, the moon lacks a protective atmosphere, so all objects headed for the moon strike it, creating craters. The earth's craters are less conspicuous because they are diminished by erosion and sedimentation over time.

1 Warm-Up Activity

Display a detailed map of the moon. Ask volunteers to locate Mare Imbrium, Mare Tranquillitatis, and Mare Orientale. Ask other volunteers to locate the Tycho, Copernicus, and Korolev craters. Explain that these names refer to features on the moon's surface, just as Pike's Peak and Lake Michigan refer to features on the earth's surface. Tell students that they will be reading about the moon's surface.

2 Teaching the Lesson

As they read the first section, have students make an illustration showing features of the moon's surface, including a diagram of a crater and its rim. For the second section

of the lesson, students can write summary sentences for each paragraph.

Divide students into small groups and provide each with an aluminum pie pan about three-quarters full of fine, damp sand. Have them smooth the surface, then drop stones of various sizes into the pan from shoulder height. Students should carefully remove the stones and describe the surface of the sand. *(Stones will form craters similar to those on the moon's surface.)*

If possible, allow students to use binoculars or a small telescope to look at the moon when it is visible during daylight hours. Ask them to compare how the moon looks through the instrument and without it.

---

70 Chapter 3 The Earth and Moon System

Objectives

After reading this lesson, you should be able to

- describe physical features of the moon.
- tell when astronauts visited the moon and what their missions accomplished.

Telescope
Instrument that collects light, making faint objects easier to see and enlarging distant objects

Maria
Low, flat plains on the moon's surface that appear as dark areas

Crater
Circular low area surrounded by a rim, usually caused by an object hitting the ground

Meteorite
Piece of rock that hits the surface of a planet or moon after traveling through space

---

For hundreds of years, scientists could only study the moon by using **telescopes**. A telescope is an instrument that makes the moon and stars appear much brighter. Telescopes can also make objects look closer and larger.

Maria and Craters

If you look at the moon without using a telescope, among the first things you may notice are the light and dark areas of the moon's surface. The dark areas of the moon are low, flat plains called **maria**. *Maria* is the Latin word for "seas." But the moon does not have water. The maria are places where melted rock flowed onto the surface and hardened billions of years ago. The lighter areas are mountains and other highlands.

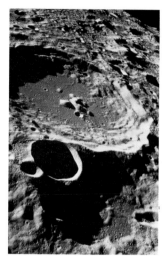

The surface of the moon is covered with craters and plains called maria.

If you use binoculars or a telescope to look at the moon, you will see many **craters**. The craters are circular areas with rims around them. These rims form many of the mountains on the moon.

Craters are caused by rocks called **meteorites**. A meteorite is a piece of rock traveling through space that hits the surface of a planet or moon. A meteorite may be as small as a sand grain or as large as a boulder. The impact of a meteorite causes an explosion. Rocky material is blasted away, forming a crater. Most of the rocky material settles around the crater, forming a rim. You can make a model of a moon crater by dropping a marble onto a pile of sand or mud.

Did You Know?

Astronauts left behind on the moon an American flag, pieces of equipment, four mirrors, and a camera.

Apollo Missions

After a decade of space flights in the 1960s, people were finally able to study the moon "up close." On July 20, 1969, *Apollo 11* astronauts Neil Armstrong and Buzz Aldrin became the first people to walk on the moon.

Between 1969 and 1972, six more Apollo missions carried astronauts almost 400,000 kilometers to the moon. They took thousands of photographs and brought back nearly 400 kilograms of rocks to study. The astronauts also set up equipment to carry out many scientific experiments.

Some equipment left on the moon measured moonquakes, which are like earthquakes. Other equipment was used to learn about the inside of the moon and the environment on the surface of the moon. By studying moon rocks, scientists discovered that the moon is about 4.6 billion years old, the same as the earth. They also learned that the moon rocks were melted at one time, erupting through volcanoes. The moon's rocks and dust have even provided information about the sun's history.

In 1972, Apollo 17 astronauts Eugene Cernan, above, and Harrison Schmitt were the last to walk on the moon.

TEACHER ALERT

Students might think craters are found only on the moon. Point out that craters have been found on other moons and planets, including the earth.

3 Reinforce and Extend

Did You Know?

Read the feature on page 71 to students. Ask them why they think each item was left on the moon's surface.

CROSS-CURRICULAR CONNECTION

History

Display a large map of the moon on a bulletin board. Groups of students can use reference books to locate the landing sites of the Apollo missions. Students can mark the sites with pushpins and run a string from each site to an index card with information about that flight.

LEARNING STYLES

Interpersonal/ Group Learning

Have students review the history of space exploration outlined in Appendix D on pages 366–367. They can point out principal missions and achievements. Then ask each student to research one topic listed in the appendix timeline. Work together to integrate their research results into one visual display. All students should have input into the design and content of the display.

ONLINE CONNECTION

Students can log on to kids.msfc.nasa.gov/ Rockets to find information on the International Space Station, space shuttles, satellites, and other space research.

SCIENCE INTEGRATION

Technology

Ask several students to explore the technology that had to be developed before astronauts could reach the moon. The group might make a poster showing the stages of the Apollo spacecraft and the lunar module. Invite them to explain how the astronauts were able to return to the earth.

Lesson 4 Review Answers

1. Dark areas are plains called maria; light areas are highlands. 2. Rocks called meteorites hit the surface, causing an explosion that blasts away rocky material, leaving a rimmed depression. 3. July 20, 1969 4. 400,000 kilometers 5. From the photos, moon rocks, and experiment results the missions brought back, scientists learned about the moon's surface and interior, calculated the moon's approximate age, and learned about the geologic and radiation history of the moon.

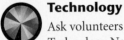
Write your answers to these questions on a sheet of paper.

1. What are the dark and light areas on the moon's surface?

2. How are craters formed on the moon?

3. When did the first person walk on the moon?

4. About how far away is the moon from the earth?

5. What did the Apollo space missions accomplish?

Technology Note

There are two kinds of telescopes: refracting and reflecting. Most telescopes used by astronomers are reflecting telescopes.

In a refracting telescope, light enters the telescope, is bent by a convex lens, and then forms an image. A second lens in the eyepiece makes the image appear larger when you look through the telescope. A convex lens is a glass lens that is thicker in the middle. Most refracting telescopes are used for observing small areas in space.

In a reflecting telescope, light enters the telescope, is reflected off a concave mirror, and then is reflected off a flat mirror to the eyepiece lens. A concave mirror is curved inward like a bowl. Reflecting telescopes tend to be larger than refracting telescopes and can collect more light. They are used to look far into space.

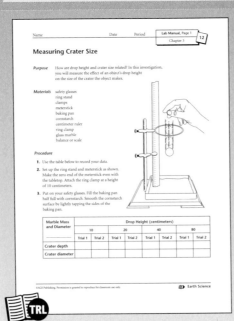

Lab Manual 12, pages 1–2

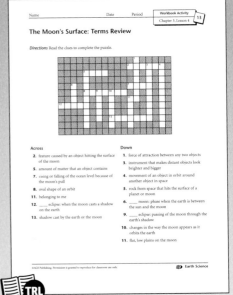

Workbook Activity 13

- Gravity is a force of attraction between any two objects, caused by those objects pulling on each other.

- Gravity between the earth and moon pulls the moon into an orbit around the earth.

- The earth revolves around the sun once about every 365 days.

- The tilt of the earth's axis causes sunlight to fall more directly on different parts of the earth throughout its orbit. This causes seasons.

- The moon revolves around the earth once about every 29 days.

- Because it takes the moon the same amount of time to rotate as it does to orbit the earth, we always see the same side of the moon.

- The changes in the moon's appearance are the phases of the moon.

- A lunar eclipse happens when the earth is between the moon and the sun. The moon passes through the earth's shadow.

- A solar eclipse happens when the moon is between the earth and the sun. The moon's shadow falls on the earth and blocks out part or all of the sun.

- Gravity between the earth and moon is the main cause of tides on the earth. Tides are the regular rising and falling of major bodies of water.

- The moon's surface has dark areas called maria and light areas that are highlands.

- The highlands are mountainous areas including the rims of craters. Craters are caused by rocks, such as meteorites, hitting the moon's surface.

- During the 1960s and 1970s, astronauts walked on the moon, collecting information about it.

Science Words			
crater, 70	maria, 70	orbit, 56	solar eclipse, 67
full moon, 66	mass, 56	phases of the	telescope, 70
gravity, 56	meteorite, 70	moon, 66	tides, 68
lunar eclipse, 67	new moon, 66	revolution, 60	

Chapter 3 Summary

Have volunteers read aloud each Summary item on page 73. Ask volunteers to explain the meaning of each item. Direct students' attention to the Science Words box on the bottom of page 73. Have them read and review each word and its definition.

Chapter 3 Review

Use the Chapter Review to prepare students for tests and to reteach content from the chapter.

Chapter 3 Mastery Test

The Teacher's Resource Library includes two parallel forms of the Chapter 3 Mastery Test. The difficulty level of the two forms is equivalent. You may wish to use one form as a pretest and the other form as a posttest.

Review Answers
Vocabulary Review

1. revolution 2. mass 3. solar eclipse 4. gravity 5. tides 6. crater 7. orbit 8. meteorite 9. lunar eclipse 10. maria

Concept Review

11. The earth rotates, or spins, on its axis. One rotation takes about 24 hours, or one day. The earth revolves in an orbit around the sun. One revolution takes about 365 days, or one year. 12. the earth 13. A third quarter, B full moon, C new moon, D first quarter 14. Apollo 15. A 16. D 17. C

Critical Thinking

18. It always faces away from the earth, so it is less protected and more vulnerable to asteroids coming from beyond the earth's orbit. 19. A lunar eclipse occurs because the earth is between the moon and the sun, and the earth casts a shadow on the moon. A new moon occurs because the moon is between the sun and the earth. Therefore, the side of the moon lit by the sun is turned away from the earth and cannot be seen. 20. The moon might orbit at a greater distance from the earth, or if the force were reduced enough, the moon would fly off into space.

TEACHER ALERT

In the Chapter Review, the Vocabulary Review activity includes a sample of the chapter's vocabulary terms. The activity will help determine students' understanding of key vocabulary terms and concepts presented in the chapter. Other vocabulary terms used in the chapter are listed below:

full moon   phases of the moon
new moon   telescope

Word Bank
crater
gravity
lunar eclipse
maria
mass
meteorite
orbit
revolution
solar eclipse
tides

Vocabulary Review

Choose the word or phrase from the Word Bank that best completes each sentence. Write the answer on your paper.

1. The movement of the earth in its path around the sun is the earth's _____.

2. The amount of matter in an object is its _____.

3. When the moon casts a shadow on the earth, there is a(n) _____.

4. The moon stays in its orbit because of _____.

5. The earth's oceans rise and fall because of _____.

6. A(n) _____ is caused by the impact of a meteorite.

7. The curved path of the moon around the earth is called its _____.

8. A piece of rock that hits a moon or planet after traveling through space is called a(n) _____.

9. When the earth casts a shadow on the moon, there is a(n) _____.

10. The dark areas on the moon's surface are low, flat plains called _____.

A

B

C

D

Concept Review

Follow the directions for each of the questions below.

11. Explain the difference between the earth's rotation and the earth's revolution.

12. Which of the following spins on its axis faster: the earth or the moon?

13. Identify each lettered phase of the moon shown in the photos on the left.

14. What was the name of the missions to the moon in the 1960s and 1970s?

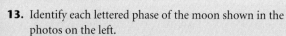

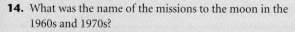

Choose the phrase that best answers each question. Write the letter of the answer on your paper.

15. What is the main cause of the earth's seasons?
  A the earth's tilt
  B the earth's tides
  C the moon's revolution around the earth
  D the gravity between the moon and earth

16. What is the main cause of ocean tides?
  A the earth's tilt
  B the earth's revolution around the sun
  C the moon's revolution around the earth
  D the moon's gravitational pull

17. If it is winter in the Northern Hemisphere, which statement is true?
  A The noontime sun is high in the sky there.
  B It is winter in the Southern Hemisphere.
  C It is summer in the Southern Hemisphere.
  D The Northern Hemisphere is tilted toward the sun.

Critical Thinking

Write the answer to each of the following questions.

18. The far side of the moon has more craters than the near side has. Why?

19. The moon looks dark during a lunar eclipse. The moon also looks dark during a new moon. What is the difference? You may make a drawing to help explain.

20. If the force of gravity between the earth and moon were reduced, how might the moon's orbit change?

 **Test-Taking Tip** When studying for a test, use a marker to highlight important facts and concepts in your notes. For a final review, read what you highlighted.

The Earth and Moon System Chapter 3 **75**

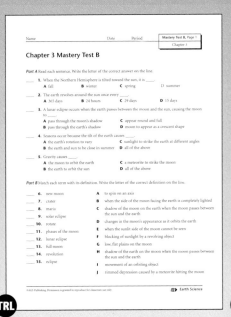

Chapter 3 Mastery Test B

ALTERNATIVE ASSESSMENT

Alternative Assessment items correlate to the student Goals for Learning at the beginning of this chapter.

■ Have students draw a diagram of the moon orbiting the earth. Have them add two arrows to show the gravitational pull between these objects. Ask students to write a caption explaining what holds the moon in orbit.

■ Have three students hold balls of three different sizes representing the sun, earth, and moon. Help them position themselves to model the revolution and rotation of the earth and moon.

■ Refer students to the diagram on page 61. Point out the two parts of the diagram that represent summer. Ask students to indicate which hemisphere is experiencing summer for each. Then ask them to explain how the angle of the sun's rays affects temperatures on the earth.

■ Provide students with a diagram like the one on page 66, but with no labels. Have them write *full moon, new moon, first quarter,* and *third quarter* on sticky notes and place them in the appropriate places on the diagram as they explain each phase of the moon.

■ Have three students position themselves with a flashlight, a tennis ball, and a golf ball in the correct order to demonstrate a lunar eclipse. Ask them to explain a lunar eclipse. Three more students can demonstrate and explain a solar eclipse.

■ Show pictures of high and low tide in the same location and ask students to explain these sea level changes.

■ Display a map of the moon that shows craters and maria. Point to various craters and have students explain what they are and how they formed. Repeat the process for maria.

The Earth and Moon System Chapter 3 **75**

4

Planning Guide
The Solar System

	Student Text Lesson		
	Student Pages	Vocabulary	Lesson Review
Lesson 1 The Solar System	78–85	✔	✔
Lesson 2 The Inner Planets	86–91	✔	✔
Lesson 3 The Outer Planets	92–99		✔
Lesson 4 Other Objects in the Solar System	100–102	✔	✔

Chapter Activities

Student Text
Science Center
Teacher's Resource Library
Community Connection 4: Observing
Your Night Sky

Assessment Options

Student Text
Chapter 4 Review

Teacher's Resource Library
Chapter 4 Mastery Tests A and B

Student Text Features								Teaching Strategies						Learning Styles						Teacher's Resource Library				
Achievements in Science	Science at Work	Science in Your Life	Investigation	Science Myth	Note	Technology Note	Did You Know	Science Integration	Science Journal	Cross-Curricular Connection	Online Connection	Teacher Alert	Applications (Home, Career, Community, Global, Environment)	Auditory/Verbal	Body/Kinesthetic	Interpersonal/Group Learning	Logical/Mathematical	Visual/Spatial	LEP/ESL	Workbook Activities	Alternative Workbook Activities	Lab Manual	Resource File	Self-Study Guide
		83	84	80	✔		81	80	79	81, 82	80		82		79			81	79	14	14	13	11	✔
91					✔		89, 90	90	89	88, 90		87, 89	89			90				15	15	14		✔
	97	98					94, 96		96	95	96		94, 95, 97			94	95		93	16	16	15, 16		✔
					✔	✔	101	102		101	101			101						17	17			✔

Pronunciation Key

a	hat	e	let	ī	ice	ô	order	u̇	put	sh	she	ə	a in about
ā	age	ē	equal	o	hot	oi	oil	ü	rule	th	thin		e in taken
ä	far	ėr	term	ō	open	ou	out	ch	child	₮H	then		i in pencil
â	care	i	it	ȯ	saw	u	cup	ng	long	zh	measure		o in lemon
													u in circus

Alternative Workbook Activities

The Teacher's Resource Library (TRL) contains a set of lower-level worksheets called Alternative Workbook Activities. These worksheets cover the same content as the regular Workbook Activities but are written at a second-grade reading level.

Skill Track Software

Use the Skill Track Software for Earth Science for additional reinforcement of this chapter. The software program allows students using AGS textbooks to be assessed for mastery of each chapter and lesson of the textbook. Students access the software on an individual basis and are assessed with multiple-choice items.

Chapter 4:
The Solar System
pages 76–105

Lessons

1. **The Solar System** pages 78–85

Investigation 4-1 pages 84–85

2. **The Inner Planets** pages 86–91

3. **The Outer Planets** pages 92–99

Investigation 4-2 pages 98–99

4. **Other Objects in the Solar System** pages 100–102

Chapter 4 Summary page 103

Chapter 4 Review pages 104–105

Skill Track Software for Earth Science

Teacher's Resource Library (TRL)

Workbook Activities 14–17

Alternative Workbook Activities 14–17

Lab Manual 13–16

Community Connection 4

Resource File 11

Chapter 4 Self-Study Guide

Chapter 4 Mastery Tests A and B

(Answer Keys for the Teacher's Resource Library begin on page 400 of the Teacher's Edition. The Materials List for the Lab Manual activities begins on page 415.)

Science Center

Have students begin a display of the solar system by cutting out a drawing or picture of the sun and affixing it to the center of a poster board. Be sure the sun image is small enough so that students can add to the display. As students learn about the other bodies in the solar system, they can add those elements to the display, along with index cards giving information about each one.

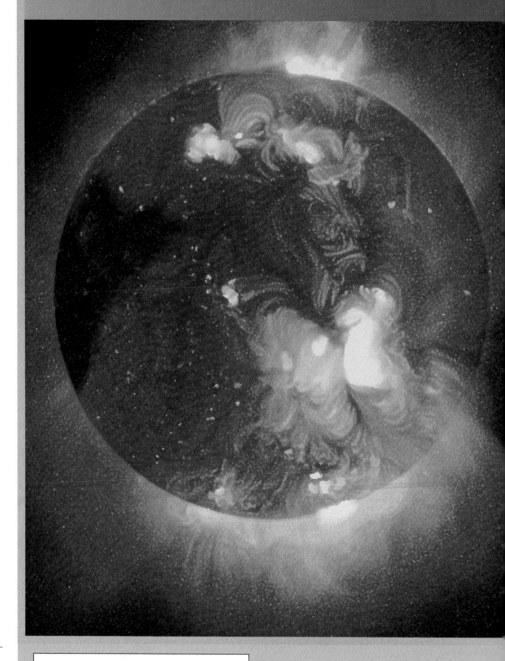

Community Connection 4

4 The Solar System

The center of the solar system is the sun. Even though it is 150 million kilometers away, the sun affects us in many ways. For example, huge explosions, called solar flares, sometimes move outward from the sun's surface. Solar flares send electrically charged particles into space. Some of these particles reach the earth and cause static on radios. The particles can also change the amount of power in electric lines. In Chapter 4, you will learn more about the sun, planets, and other objects in the solar system.

Organize Your Thoughts

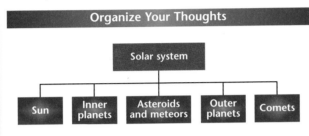

Solar system

- Sun
- Inner planets
- Asteroids and meteors
- Outer planets
- Comets

Goals for Learning

◆ To explain what the solar system is

◆ To identify the four inner planets

◆ To identify the five outer planets

◆ To tell something about each planet

◆ To describe the motions and positions of the planets

◆ To compare comets and asteroids

77

Introducing the Chapter

Ask students to examine the photograph on page 76. Have them write one fact they know about the sun. Have volunteers share these observations with the class. Use students' statements as a starting point for assessing their knowledge of the solar system. Make a list of the shared observations and post it on a bulletin board. Encourage students to reread the list frequently and add information or corrections to the statements.

Notes and Technology Notes

Ask volunteers to read the notes that appear in the margins throughout the chapter. Then discuss them with the class.

TEACHER'S RESOURCE

The AGS Teaching Strategies in Science Transparencies may be used with this chapter. The transparencies add an interactive dimension to expand and enhance the *Earth Science* program content.

CAREER INTEREST INVENTORY

The AGS Harrington-O'Shea Career Decision-Making System-Revised (CDM) may be used with this chapter. Students can use the CDM to explore their interests and identify careers. The CDM defines career areas that are indicated by students' responses on the inventory.

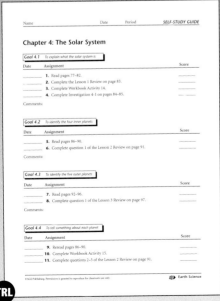

Chapter 4 Self-Study Guide

Lesson at a Glance

Chapter 4 Lesson 1

Overview This lesson introduces students to the sun and the objects that revolve around it in the solar system. Students learn how stars, planets, and moons are alike and different.

Objectives

- To explain the difference between stars, planets, and moons
- To identify objects of the solar system
- To describe the sun

Student Pages 78–85

Teacher's Resource Library

Workbook Activity 14

Alternative Workbook Activity 14

Lab Manual 13

Resource File 11

....

Vocabulary

atmosphere	solar system
moon	star
planet	sunspot

....

Science Background

Some scientists believe that about 4.6 billion years ago, a cloud of gas and dust collapsed into a spinning disk. Gravity pulled so much material into the center of the disk that the sun was formed. In fact, there is so much matter in the sun that its mass is 99 percent of the entire solar system. The tremendous gravitational pull from all this mass created so much heat and pressure that a nuclear reaction began. The sun began to give off light and heat.

1 Warm-Up Activity

Show students a grapefruit, a large orange, two plums, two peas, and three peppercorns. Then arrange the items in the following order on a table: peppercorn, pea, pea, peppercorn, grapefruit, orange, plum, plum, peppercorn. Label the items Mercury, Venus, Earth, Mars, Jupiter, Saturn, Uranus, Neptune, and Pluto. Ask students what large object is missing from this

---

Objectives

After reading this lesson, you should be able to

◆ explain the difference between stars, planets, and moons.

◆ identify objects of the solar system.

◆ describe the sun.

Star

Glowing ball of hot gas that makes its own energy and light

Planet

Large object in space that orbits a star such as the sun

Moon

Natural satellite that orbits a planet

Stars, Planets, and Moons

If you stand outside on a clear night, away from bright city lights, you should be able to see hundreds of shining objects in the sky. Most of the objects are **stars**. These glowing balls of hot gas shine because they make their own light. A few of the objects you might see are **planets**. Planets are large objects in space that orbit the sun. You will likely see the earth's **moon**, although there are other moons in space. A moon is an object that orbits a planet. Another name for a moon is a satellite. Later you will read about some moons of other planets.

Planets and moons do not make their own light. They shine because they reflect the light of the sun, our closest star. Stars are the source of light for all objects in space. The diagram shows how a star like the sun can cause a planet to shine. You can see the ball because it reflects light from the flashlight. You can see a planet or moon because it reflects light from the sun.

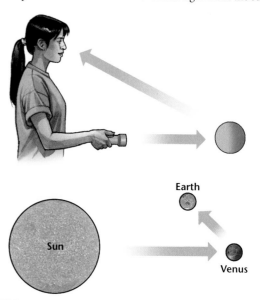

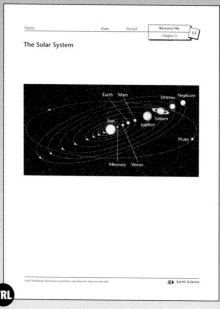

Resource File 11

The motion of the solar system has a regular pattern to it. This means you can predict where in space a planet will be on your next birthday! You can even predict where it will be several years from now.

The stars, planets, and moons in the sky are moving. The word *planet* comes from a Greek word meaning "wanderer." Because planets change their position in the sky from day to day, ancient stargazers thought of planets as wandering stars.

In Chapter 3, you read about the movement of the earth and its moon. Planets, with their moons, revolve around the sun in what is known as the **solar system.** *Solar* refers to the star in the center of the system: the sun.

The stars in the night sky are not part of the solar system. But they do move. Planets seem to move across the sky faster than stars do. Why? Think about riding in a car and looking out the window. Have you ever noticed that objects closer to the car seem to go by faster than objects farther away? The more distant something is, the more slowly it seems to move. Stars are much, much farther away from the earth than the planets are. Therefore, stars appear to move very slowly in the sky.

Objects in the Solar System

The solar system contains many objects. Nine of these objects are planets. Each planet travels in a fixed orbit around the sun. Look at the diagram to find the name and path of each planet. Most of the planets do not orbit in an exact circle, but in an ellipse.

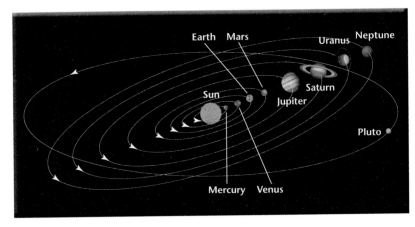

model of the solar system. Students should mention the sun. Have students suggest evidence from their own experience that the sun is very hot. (*It feels hot on the skin. It melts ice and snow. Objects—especially metal ones—get hot if left in the sun.*)

 Teaching the Lesson

Before students read the lesson, have them write on paper each vocabulary word and what they think it means. As students read, have them review what they wrote and add notes to correct or extend information about the words.

Direct students to the diagram on page 79. Ask them to name the planets beginning with the one closest to the sun. (*Mercury, Venus, Earth, Mars, Jupiter, Saturn, Uranus, Neptune, Pluto*) Explain that one way to remember the order of the planets is to use a memory aid. For example, the words in the sentence "My very eager mother just served us nine pizzas" begin with the same letters as the names of the planets.

 Reinforce and Extend

SCIENCE JOURNAL

Students can draw their own diagram of the nine planets in the solar system and create their own memory aid to help them recall the order of the planets.

LEARNING STYLES

 LEP/ESL

Take the index cards with the planet names from the previous activity. Mix the cards and lay them in random order on a table. Ask students to put the cards in the correct order, from the planet closest to the sun to the planet farthest from the sun. When students have finished arranging the cards, let them check their order against the diagram on page 79.

LEARNING STYLES

 Body/Kinesthetic

Ask for nine volunteers and give each an index card with the name of one of the planets in the solar system. Have the nine students stand in a row in the order of the planets, beginning with Mercury on the left and continuing to Pluto on the right. Darken the room. Have another student stand to the left of "Mercury" and shine a flashlight onto the "planets." Ask students why they are able to see the planets. (*Light from the flashlight reflects from them.*) Ask what object the person with the flashlight represents. (*the sun*) Ask what the whole model represents. (*the solar system*) Finally, ask why some planets are visible in the night sky. (*Light from the sun reflects from them.*)

Have students read the first sentence in the Science Myth feature on page 80. Ask them whether they agree with this statement: There is no gravity in space. Encourage them to give reasons for their answer. Then have them read the Fact section.

SCIENCE INTEGRATION

Technology

Point out that the lack of gravity poses a problem for space travelers. Have groups of students find out about the equipment and technology scientists are working on to help astronauts live and work in space. Ask them to prepare a written report for presentation to the class.

ONLINE CONNECTION

Students can use this site to add to their information about the solar system: starchild. gsfc.nasa.gov/docs/StarChild/ StarChild.html.

The following NASA Web site shows student drawings of the solar system. Students might enjoy discussing these drawings and creating drawings of their own: sseforum.jpl.nasa.gov/community/ index.cfm?Display=Gallery.

This Web site uses cartoons to present a summary of facts about the solar system: www.astronomy. com/content/static/AstroForKids/ default.asp.

This Web site is a particularly good resource for teachers: stardate.org/ resources/ssguide/earth.html.

Imagine tracing the paths of these nine planets in space. You would see that most of the orbits could be traced on a flat plane or on a giant piece of paper. One planet orbits a little outside of this flat plane. Look at the diagram on page 79 to see which one it is.

All of the planets move around the sun in the same direction. However, the planets don't orbit together as a group. Each planet moves along its path at its own speed. Mercury orbits the fastest. In general, the farther away a planet is from the sun, the bigger its orbit and the slower its speed. Besides planets, smaller objects in space orbit the sun, too.

The entire solar system holds together because of gravity. There is gravity between every object in the solar system, attracting these objects to each other. Because the sun has much more mass than the objects orbiting it, the objects are pulled toward the sun. This pull of gravity is balanced by the speed and motion of the objects. This balance keeps the objects in orbit. Without this perfect balance, an orbiting planet could fly off in a straight line or fall toward the sun.

Science Myth

Since astronauts float in outer space, some people may think this means that there is no gravity there.

Fact: Gravity is everywhere. It holds our solar system together. Astronauts appear to float because they are in orbit. The orbital force pulling them away from the earth is balanced by the force of gravity pulling them toward the earth. Because of this, astronauts weigh less in space than at home.

The Sun

The largest object in the solar system is the sun. In fact, the sun is larger than all of the planets put together. Its mass, the amount of matter it contains, is 99 percent of the entire solar system. So 99 percent of the "stuff" in the solar system is in the sun! The diagram compares the size of the earth and the sun.

The sun is made mostly of two gases: hydrogen and helium. The sun also contains very small amounts of the elements found on the earth. Because the sun is mostly gas, it has no solid surface.

The sun is not fixed in space. It rotates on an axis like a planet. Because it is mostly gas, parts of the sun rotate at different rates. On average, the sun rotates once a month.

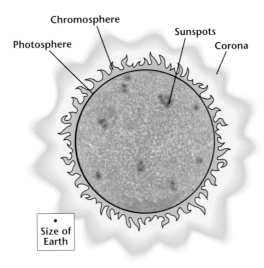

Chromosphere

Photosphere

Sunspots

Corona

Size of Earth

Literature

Have students look up and read myths about the sun, such as those found in ancient Greek, ancient Egyptian, Japanese, or American Indian cultures. Discuss with students how these myths reflected people's observations of the sun. For example, in Greek mythology, the sun god Helios drives a fiery chariot across the sky every day because people thought that the fiery sun moved across the sky every day. Ask volunteers to share the stories they found.

IN THE ENVIRONMENT

Invite an amateur astronomer or someone who uses a telescope to visit your class. Ask the speaker to explain the difficulties of viewing stars and planets from sites in or near cities. Then have students research causes of air and light pollution and write a brief summary of their findings.

Atmosphere

Envelope of gas surrounding an object in space

Sunspot

Dark area on the sun's surface that gives off less energy than the rest of the sun

The outer temperature of the sun is about 5,500°C. This high temperature is caused by nuclear reactions inside the sun. In the sun's center, temperatures of 15,000,000°C cause hydrogen particles to fuse and form helium. These nuclear reactions produce energy that we see as light and feel as heat. Later you will learn how the sun's energy is important for many processes on the earth, such as wind and rainfall.

The only part of the sun that can be seen is its **atmosphere**. An atmosphere is an envelope of gas surrounding an object in space. The sun's atmosphere consists of three layers, as shown in the diagram on page 81. The inner layer is called the photosphere. This is the layer of gas that gives off light. Just outside of this layer is another layer of gas called the chromosphere. The gas of the chromosphere can sometimes be seen during a total solar eclipse, when the photosphere is blocked. The outer layer of the sun's atmosphere is the corona. It is a layer of gas thicker than the chromosphere. The corona can also be seen during a solar eclipse.

Notice in the diagram that the photosphere contains dark areas called **sunspots**. Sunspots give off less energy and are, therefore, cooler than the rest of the sun. But they are still about 4,000°C. Sunspots move in groups across the face of the sun. This shows that the sun rotates.

Many spacecraft and satellites have photographed the sun and measured its surface activity. The satellite SOHO was launched in 1995 to study the sun. It contains 12 instruments. Besides taking photos, it measures corona activity, vibrations in the sun, and space conditions. SOHO stands for Solar and Heliospheric Observatory.

Write your answers to these questions on a sheet of paper.

1. What is the difference between a star and a planet?

2. Why do the moon and planets shine in the night sky?

3. What makes up our solar system? What holds it together?

4. Compare the sun and the earth in terms of size, makeup, and temperature.

5. Describe the layers of the sun's atmosphere.

Science in Your Life

A Solar House

The sun not only warms our planet, but it also provides us with energy. Solar energy is energy that comes from the sun.

Solar energy can be used in many ways. For example, a solar house is specially built to capture solar energy. Solar panels are mounted on the roof of the house. The panels collect radiant energy from the sun and change it to heat energy. This heat energy is used to run electric appliances and heat water.

The main benefit of using solar energy is that it saves our natural resources. Oil, gas, and coal are natural resources that are burned for energy. These resources are limited and will run out someday. But the sun's energy is unlimited. The sun will keep producing energy for about another 5 billion years.

Are there any solar houses or solar panels in your neighborhood? To learn about other ways to save our natural resources, read Appendix B: Alternative Energy Sources.

The Solar System   *Chapter 4*   **83**

Lesson 1 Review Answers

1. A star is made of hot gas and creates its own light. A planet is an object that orbits a star; a planet doesn't make its own light. **2.** The moon and planets reflect the light of the sun. **3.** The solar system is made up of the sun and all of the objects that revolve around it in space. Gravity holds the solar system together. **4.** The sun is many, many times larger than the earth. The sun is composed of gases. Due to nuclear reactions inside the sun, its inner temperature reaches 15 million °C. Earth is composed of land, water, and air. Earth revolves around the sun and is held in place by gravity. Earth's warmth comes from the sun. **5.** The sun's atmosphere is made up of three layers of gases. The inner layer is the photosphere; the next layer is the chromosphere; the outer layer is the sun's corona.

Science in Your Life

Ask volunteers to read the feature on page 83 describing one use of solar energy. Ask students why this form of energy should be studied. Have groups of students investigate the use of solar energy in their local community. Suggest that each group think of three questions they would like to answer. Encourage students to use the Internet, books, and magazine articles as well as an interview with a local builder, government official, or scientist. Have the groups share their questions and answers with the class.

Portfolio Assessment

Sample items include:
- Vocabulary notes from Teaching the Lesson
- Summary from In the Environment activity
- Lesson 1 Review answers

Workbook Activity 14

*The Solar System   Chapter 4   **83***

Investigation 4-1

The Purpose portion of the student investigation begins with a question to draw students into the activity. Encourage students to read the investigation steps and formulate their own questions before beginning the investigation. This investigation will take approximately 30 minutes to complete. Students will use these process and thinking skills: observing, using scientific equipment, recognizing time and space relationships, recording data, comparing, and drawing conclusions.

Preparation

- Before setting up this activity, be sure the sun is visible in the sky and not obscured by clouds or buildings.

- If more than one pair of students is performing this investigation at the same time, make sure that the pairs are far enough apart to avoid bumping each other or casting shadows on other clipboards.

- Students may use Lab Manual 13 to record their data and answer questions.

Procedure

- This investigation is best done with students working in pairs. Student A sets up the telescope or binoculars and then holds the clipboard. Student B traces the outline of the sun and the sunspots and labels the drawing with the date and time.

- This activity is to be repeated four more times over the next four days. Be sure partners switch roles so that both have a chance to draw the sunspots.

Materials
- telescope or binoculars
- clipboard

Observing Sunspots

Purpose

What does a telescope image of the sun look like? In this investigation, you will observe sunspots.

Procedure

1. Work with a partner in this investigation. Set up a telescope aimed in the direction of the morning sun. If you use binoculars, cover one of the large lenses. **Safety Alert: Never look at the sun, especially through a telescope or binoculars.**

2. Place a sheet of paper on the clipboard and position it 20 to 30 centimeters behind the eyepiece of the telescope. Without looking through the telescope, aim the telescope so that the sun causes a light spot to appear on the paper.

Name ___ **Date** ___ **Period** ___ **Lab Manual** **Chapter 4** **13**

4-1 **Observing Sunspots**
Use with Investigation 4-1, pages 84–85

Purpose What does a telescope image of the sun look like? In this investigation, you will observe sunspots.

Questions and Conclusions

1. Can you see the same sunspot two days in a row? How do you know?

2. Does the position of a sunspot change? If so, in what direction does the sunspot seem to move?

Explore Further

Try tracking sunspot changes over a longer period of time. Repeat this investigation for a week or longer. Keep a record of the sunspot changes you observe. What patterns do you see?

©AGS Publishing. Permission is granted to reproduce for classroom use only.   **Earth Science**

Lab Manual 13

3. Move the clipboard back and forth behind the eyepiece until the light spot is brightest. This is the sun's image.

4. While your partner holds the clipboard steady, trace the outline of the sun's image. Trace any spots you see on the image. These are sunspots.

5. Write the date and the time at the top of the paper.

6. Repeat the procedure on the next four mornings. Each time, take turns tracing the sun's image.

Questions and Conclusions

1. Can you see the same sunspot two days in a row? How do you know?

2. Does the position of a sunspot change? If so, in what direction does the sunspot seem to move?

Explore Further

Try tracking sunspot changes over a longer period of time. Repeat this investigation for a week or longer. Keep a record of the sunspot changes you observe. What patterns do you see?

Results

Sunspots will probably be visible. They will most likely move, change shape, and grow, shrink, or disappear over a period of five days.

Questions and Conclusions Answers

1. If a sunspot is visible, it is likely to be seen on consecutive days. The position and shape of the sunspot suggest that it is the same one as previously viewed.

2. Students may observe that sunspots move, change shape, and grow, shrink, or vanish over the course of days. Sunspots will seem to move west to east. With an inverted image, they will seem to move east to west.

Explore Further Answers

Patterns over a longer period of time may include the changing of shape and location of sunspots and the disappearance and/or appearance of other sunspots.

Assessment

Neatness and precision are important skills in carrying out this activity. Students should be assessed mainly on their ability to make clear records of sunspots viewed over the assigned period. You might include the following items from this investigation in student portfolios:

• Dated tracings

• Answers to Questions and Conclusions and Explore Further sections

Lesson at a Glance

Chapter 4 Lesson 2

Overview In this lesson, students learn about the four planets closest to the sun. They compare the planets' locations, sizes, movements, atmospheres, and surface features.

Objectives
- To identify the four inner planets
- To describe the four inner planets
- To explain what the greenhouse effect is and how it affects Venus

Student Pages 86–91

Teacher's Resource Library **TRL**

Workbook Activity 15

Alternative Workbook Activity 15

Lab Manual 14

Vocabulary
Greenhouse effect

Science Background

The inner planets—Mercury, Venus, Earth, and Mars—are small, rocky worlds with metal cores and, except for airless Mercury, shallow atmospheres.

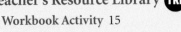

1 Warm-Up Activity

Fill a baking dish half-full of sand. Rinse a small piece of steel wool with vinegar. Snip the steel wool into tiny pieces and mix it with the sand. Pour enough water into the dish to cover the mixture and allow the dish to sit for a while. This will model the Martian landscape. Explain that steel wool contains iron compounds and that iron reacts with water to form a reddish rust. Tell students that iron compounds in the soil of Mars give the soil a reddish color, indicating that there was once water on Mars.

Objectives

After reading this lesson, you should be able to
- identify the four inner planets.
- describe the four inner planets.
- explain what the greenhouse effect is and how it affects Venus.

The planets of the solar system are divided into two groups: the inner planets and the outer planets. The inner planets are the ones that are closest to the sun. They are Mercury, Venus, Earth, and Mars. All of the inner planets are solid and similar in size. But these rocky worlds are also very different from one another. Read about each one below. Then look at Appendix C to learn more facts about the planets.

Mercury

The planet closest to the sun is Mercury. Because it is so close to the sun, Mercury is not easy to see in the sky. Named after the Roman god of speed, Mercury is the fastest-moving planet. Its average speed as it orbits the sun is about 50 kilometers per second. Mercury completes an entire revolution of the sun in 88 Earth days. It rotates slowly though. One day on Mercury lasts about 59 Earth days.

In 1974 and 1975, a spacecraft called *Mariner 10* passed close by Mercury three times. It photographed about half of its surface. These photos show that Mercury is covered with craters and flat areas, like those on the moon.

Of all the planets, Mercury's surface temperature changes the most. This is because Mercury has almost no atmosphere to hold in or keep out the sun's heat. The side of Mercury facing the sun reaches 427°C. The side away from the sun drops to −183°C.

This image is actually many small photos put together. The smooth band and patches are areas that Mariner 10 *did not photograph.*

Venus

The planet that is next closest to the sun is Venus. It was named after the Roman goddess of love and beauty. Venus is the hottest planet at 460°C. It is also the brightest planet in the sky. Like the moon, you can sometimes see Venus during the day. Depending on the time of year, Venus is known as the "morning star" or the "evening star."

Venus is different from most of the other planets because it rotates in the opposite direction. Earth and the other inner planets rotate from west to east. Venus rotates from east to west. That means the sun rises in the west on Venus. Also, it takes a long time for Venus to rotate. A day on Venus is 243 Earth days.

This radar image of Venus shows surface features that are visibly hidden by clouds.

2 Teaching the Lesson

Have students locate the headings in the lesson and list the names of the four inner planets on four sheets of paper. Tell students that as they read they should list facts about each planet on its sheet. Have them save their work for use in the next lesson.

Explain to students that a greenhouse is a building with glass sides and a glass roof. It is used to grow and protect young plants. The glass lets in the sunlight that plants need and keeps out the cold and the wind, which can damage the plants. The glass also holds in the heat that the sunlight generates. Ask students to think about what it is like inside a car on a hot summer day. The glass windows in the car work the same way as the glass in the greenhouse: they let in the light and hold in the heat. A planet's atmosphere acts like glass windows: it lets in the light and holds in the heat.

TEACHER ALERT

Students may assume that the greenhouse effect is entirely a bad thing. Explain that we need the greenhouse effect; without it, Earth would be too cold for people to live on. But there can be too much of a good thing: if too much heat is trapped in Earth's atmosphere, the planet's overall temperature will begin to rise. Some scientists fear this global warming could cause polar ice caps to melt and sea levels to rise. Then Earth might become too hot and too wet for people to live on.

Music

Pythagoras was a Greek philosopher and mathematician who lived around the 6th century B.C. Pythagoras and his followers, called Pythagoreans, believed there was harmony all around them, starting with relationships (ratios) among numbers. A stringed instrument, for example, was built using a certain mathematical ratio to place the strings on the frame. It seemed clear to the Pythagoreans that the distances between the planets would have the same ratios as those that produced harmonious sounds in a plucked string. Pythagoreans believed the solar system consisted of ten spheres revolving about a central fire. Each sphere gave off a sound the way a projectile makes a sound as it swishes through the air. The closer spheres gave low tones. The farther spheres moved faster and gave high-pitched sounds. All combined into a beautiful harmony, *the music of the spheres.*

Although people today do not accept this theory of Pythagoras, many musicians have been inspired by the idea of the music of the spheres. Suggest that each student find a piece of music—a song or an instrumental piece—that they could use as background music for a project that describes the movement of the solar system. Encourage students to share their choices with the class.

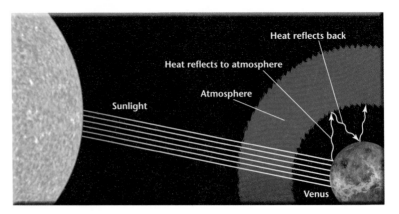

Heat reflects back

Heat reflects to atmosphere

Atmosphere

Sunlight

Venus

Greenhouse effect

Warming of the atmosphere because of trapped heat energy from the sun

The average temperature on Earth's surface is 15°C (59°F). The coldest temperature on record is −89°C (−128°F). The hottest temperature on record is 58°C (136°F). Earth is the only planet that has the right temperature range for life.

Unlike Mercury, Venus has an atmosphere. It contains great amounts of the gas carbon dioxide. Carbon dioxide in the atmosphere traps heat energy from the sun. As a result, the atmosphere heats up. This warming, shown above, is called the **greenhouse effect**. The clouds of Venus's atmosphere are made of tiny drops of sulfuric acid. These clouds trap heat and add to the greenhouse effect. Because of the greenhouse effect, the surface temperature of Venus is very high. The surface of the planet would be much cooler without this effect.

We cannot see through Venus's thick clouds with our eyes. However, in the 1990s, a spacecraft called *Magellan* used radar to penetrate the clouds and make images of the planet's surface. These images show areas of rolling plains, towering highlands, and craters.

Earth

Our own planet, Earth, is the third planet from the sun. It is about the same size as Venus. But Earth has several differences from the other inner planets:

◆ Earth has a mild surface temperature that changes very little.
◆ It has a dense, protective atmosphere.
◆ It is the only planet to have liquid water on its surface.

Because of these unique features, Earth can support life. There is no evidence of life on the other planets. Earth is also the closest planet to the sun that has a moon.

The greenhouse effect occurs on Earth as well as on Venus. Without an atmosphere that traps heat, Earth would be an icy planet with temperatures no warmer than −10°C.

Mars

Mars, the fourth planet from the sun, is named for the Roman god of war. Its reddish color in the night sky may have reminded ancient people of blood. Mars has two small moons.

The rotation period of Mars is about the same as that of Earth. Mars rotates once every 24 hours and 38 minutes. It takes the planet 687 Earth days to complete one revolution around the sun. So, a Martian day is similar to an Earth day, but its year is almost twice as long as ours.

The atmosphere on Mars is much less dense than on Earth. The atmosphere is mostly carbon dioxide. Mars is colder than Earth because it is farther from the sun and has a thinner atmosphere. Little heat can be trapped by a thin atmosphere.

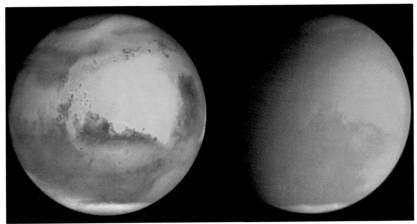

These Hubble Space Telescope photos show Mars before a global dust storm (left) and during the storm (right).

Have students read the Did You Know? feature on page 89. Discuss with them ways that people can stop adding carbon dioxide to the atmosphere and prevent global warming. Refer to the alternative energy sources listed in Appendix B on pages 358–363.

TEACHER ALERT

 Some students, particularly science-fiction fans, may think that when scientists look for life on other planets, they are looking for highly advanced, humanlike species with which we can communicate. Explain that life forms may be as simple as bacteria or other microscopic organisms.

SCIENCE JOURNAL

 Ask students to suppose they could live on Mercury, Venus, or Mars. Have them use the information in this lesson to write a description of how their new environment would change their lives.

AT HOME

 Have students ask family members what they know about the four inner planets. Students might make a chart with the planets' names as headings and write family members' answers under each planet. As an alternative, students might write a series of true/false statements about the planets and ask family members to respond. Encourage students to share their findings, especially any common misconceptions.

Have students read the Did You Know? feature on page 90. Discuss with them why it is important that scientists found water in any form on Mars.

CROSS-CURRICULAR CONNECTION

Literature

Read to students the short science-fiction story "All Summer in a Day" by Ray Bradbury, or show the film based on the story. The story's setting highlights an important part of imagining life on another planet: the length of a season or a day. After reading the story, ask students if the length of summer described in the story matches the revolution time of any of the inner planets. (*It is not a realistic description, but is used to strengthen the plot of the story.*)

SCIENCE INTEGRATION

Biology

Remind students that scientists tested Martian soil for signs of life. You can model their experiments by filling two glass jars one-third full of sand. In the first jar, mix in two spoonfuls of salt. In the second, mix in two spoonfuls of yeast. In a third container, mix a half cup of sugar in warm (not hot) water. Add half the sugar solution to each of the two jars. Set the jars aside and have students observe them periodically. After an hour, ask students which jar they think contains life. (*the one with the yeast*) Ask them how they can tell. (*As the yeast feeds on the sugar water, it should begin to bubble.*) Point out to students that yeasts are living cells.

Did You Know?

Although no liquid water exists on Mars, frozen water does. The polar regions contain frozen water and frozen carbon dioxide. During spring and summer, some of the ice turns directly to water vapor—a gas.

Several space missions have landed on Mars. In 1997, the Mars Pathfinder lander visited Mars. Cameras on board sent many photographs back to Earth. One of them is shown below. The lander also brought a robotic rover to Mars. The rover rolled across the surface, testing the rocks, soil, and air. Iron in the rocks and soil makes the surface look red. Winds blow dust in the air, making the sky look pink.

Since 1960, many American and Russian spacecraft without crews have tried to orbit or land on Mars. Many did not succeed. But successful missions like Mars Pathfinder have sent back thousands of photos and other data.

In 2001, the *Odyssey* orbiter was launched. It took six months to travel the 459 million kilometers to Mars. The *Odyssey* is studying the minerals and chemicals on Mars. It will also test for hazards for future human explorers.

The two hills shown in this Martian landscape are called the Twin Peaks. They are about 30 to 35 meters tall.

LEARNING STYLES

Interpersonal/ Group Learning

Divide students into groups of four or five. Each student should take about five minutes to review the lesson and write two questions about the information in the lesson. Students then take turns asking a question of their group. The person who answers the question reads aloud the part of the lesson in which the answer is found. If no one can answer the question correctly, the writer of that question reads from the lesson the information on which the question was based.

Lesson 2 REVIEW

Write your answers to these questions on a sheet of paper.

1. What are the names of the inner planets?

2. How would you describe Mercury?

3. Which planet has a reddish surface?

4. What does the greenhouse effect do to the temperature on a planet's surface?

5. How is Earth unique?

Achievements in Science

The Struggle to Accept the Solar System

In the early 1500s, a Polish astronomer named Nicolaus Copernicus had a new idea. Using careful observations and mathematics, he concluded that the sun must be at the center of all the planets. In such a system, Earth and the other planets revolve around the sun. Other astronomers at the time thought that Earth was at the center of everything. They believed Earth didn't move. They rejected Copernicus's idea of a sun-centered, or solar, system.

Copernicus's idea was not picked up again until almost 100 years later. In the early 1600s, an Italian astronomer named Galileo Galilei concluded that not all objects in space revolve around Earth. Galileo was one of the first astronomers to use a telescope. The more he observed the moon and the planets, the more convinced he became that Copernicus's idea was correct. Galileo published a book explaining the idea of a solar system. Still, this idea was very unpopular.

In the late 1600s, Isaac Newton, an English scientist, took a serious look at Galileo's idea. He was able to prove that Copernicus and Galileo were right. People finally accepted the fact that Earth revolves around the sun. Newton became a hero and was knighted by the queen of England.

The Solar System Chapter 4 **91**

Lesson 2 Review Answers

1. Mercury, Venus, Earth, Mars **2.** closest planet to sun, both hot and cold temperature extremes, fast moving, almost no atmosphere **3.** Mars **4.** It increases the atmospheric temperature because of trapped heat. **5.** Earth has a mild surface temperature, a dense atmosphere, and liquid water. Only Earth can support life.

Achievements in Science

Ask volunteers to read aloud the feature on page 91. Discuss with students why Copernicus's and Galileo's theories about the solar system were not accepted, while Newton's theory was accepted. Point out that, in part, it was because of changes in people's thinking and attitudes over time. By the 17th century, science was more widely practiced and understood than in earlier times. Also, people wanted to know why they didn't fall off Earth if it was moving as Copernicus and Galileo claimed. Newton's explanation of gravity answered that question.

Portfolio Assessment

Sample items include:
- Planet fact sheets from Teaching the Lesson
- Lesson 2 Review answers

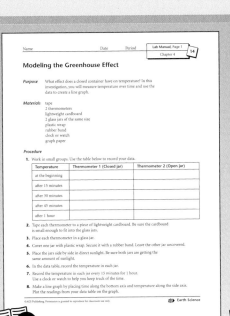

Lab Manual 14, pages 1–2

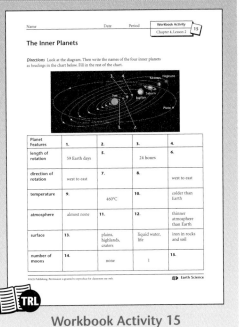

Workbook Activity 15

The Solar System Chapter 4 **91**

Lesson at a Glance

Chapter 4 Lesson 3

Overview This lesson focuses on the five outer planets. Students learn about the relative sizes of the planets as well as distinguishing features of each, such as composition, atmosphere, ring systems, and number of moons.

Objectives

- To identify the five outer planets
- To describe the five outer planets

Student Pages 92–99

Teacher's Resource Library **TRL**

Workbook Activity 16

Alternative Workbook Activity 16

Lab Manual 15–16

Science Background

The four large outer planets—Jupiter, Saturn, Uranus, and Neptune—are referred to as the gas giants. None of them seems to have a solid surface. Their deep atmospheres thicken from gas to hot liquid, which reaches all the way to their small, rocky cores. Pluto, the fifth outer planet, is a tiny, frozen world.

 Warm-Up Activity

Pour about a cup of milk into a clear glass bowl. Add one drop of yellow and one drop of red food coloring. Gently spin the bowl to start the milk moving. Then place one drop of dishwashing liquid on top of each drop of food coloring. Continue to spin the bowl gently. Let students observe what happens to the colors. Then have them look at the photograph of Jupiter on page 92. Ask them to compare the picture with what they saw in the bowl. Explain that the milk and food coloring mixture is a model of the surface of Jupiter.

Objectives

After reading this lesson, you should be able to

- ◆ identify the five outer planets.
- ◆ describe the five outer planets.

Except for Pluto, the outer planets have rings and are much larger than the inner planets. The outer planets are mostly frozen gas and liquid, with a small, solid core. Over the last 25 years, *Voyager* and *Galileo* spacecraft have collected much information about these planets. Look at Appendix D to learn more about space exploration.

Jupiter

Jupiter is the largest planet in the solar system. In fact, all of the other planets in the solar system could fit inside Jupiter. The diameter of Jupiter is more than 11 times larger than Earth's. It's no wonder Jupiter was named for the Roman king of the gods.

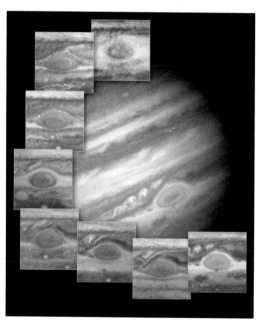

The Great Red Spot rotates in a counterclockwise direction. Wind speeds inside this storm reach 400 kilometers per hour.

Among the most noticeable features of Jupiter are its colorful bands. These bands are clouds of gases where storms are taking place. The bands change shape every few days but generally run in the same direction. Jupiter's fast rotation might cause these bands. It takes Jupiter only 10 hours to rotate once.

A large red oval appears on the surface of Jupiter. This area is called the Great Red Spot. It is more than twice as wide as Earth. This spot is actually a spinning windstorm. It is the largest known storm in the solar system, and it has lasted at least 300 years! The Great Red Spot changes its shape and color, as shown in the photo.

When two Voyager spacecraft flew by Jupiter in 1979, astronomers discovered faint rings around the planet. Astronomers also discovered more moons than they had thought existed. At least 60 moons orbit this giant planet.

Shown below is one of Jupiter's moons, Io. This moon has active volcanoes that erupt constantly. Io's volcanoes spew out sulfur, which colors the surface yellow, orange, and green.

The largest of Jupiter's moons is Ganymede. It is bigger than the planet Mercury. The smallest moon is only about 2 kilometers in diameter. A moon called Europa is an icy world with a smooth, cracked surface. It has been described as a giant, cracked cue ball.

The spacecraft Galileo *flew close to Io in 1999 and photographed its colorful surface.*

 2 Teaching the Lesson

Before beginning this lesson, have students look at the facts they wrote about the inner planets. Then have them locate the headings in this lesson and list the names of the five outer planets on five sheets of paper. Tell students that as they read they should list facts about each planet on its sheet. When they finish the lesson, they should compare the outer planets with the inner planets and make a list of differences.

Ask students to flip ahead to page 228 to see a photo of a hurricane in Earth's atmosphere. Ask them to compare it with the images of the Great Red Spot in Jupiter's atmosphere shown on page 92.

Point out that the rings of Saturn reach far out into space. Their distance from Saturn's surface is almost the distance from Earth's surface to the moon. However, Saturn's rings are only about 1 kilometer thick.

 3 Reinforce and Extend

LEARNING STYLES

 LEP/ESL

Use facts from Appendix C and Lessons 2 and 3 to make up questions you can use to quiz students about the nine planets in the solar system. Focus on the main features that distinguish the planets from one another. Ask questions such as these:

Which is the largest planet in the solar system? *(Jupiter)*

Which planet rotates on its side? *(Uranus)*

Which planet takes the longest to revolve around the sun? *(Pluto)*

Which planet is closest to the sun? *(Mercury)*

Which planet has been explored by an exploration robot? *(Mars)*

Did You Know?

One of Saturn's moons, Mimas, has a crater so huge that scientists think the object that caused the crater came close to destroying this moon.

Saturn

You are probably familiar with the rings of Saturn. Saturn, the sixth planet from the sun, was named for the Roman god of agriculture. Saturn is the second largest planet in the solar system. It revolves around the sun once every 29 years.

About 1,000 individual rings orbit Saturn's equator. They are mostly ice particles and dust. When you look at Saturn through a telescope, you can see the rings only at certain times during Saturn's orbit. That is because the rings are very thin, and Saturn rotates on a tilted axis. When the edge of the ring system is pointed toward Earth, the rings disappear from view. The images below were taken between 1996 and 2000. They show how Saturn nods as it revolves.

Like Jupiter, Saturn is a giant planet of gases with stormy bands of clouds running along its surface. Winds in these storms reach speeds of 1,800 kilometers per hour. Also like Jupiter, Saturn spins very fast. One day is about 11 hours.

Saturn has at least 31 moons, the largest of which is Titan. Titan is the only moon in the solar system that is known to have an atmosphere of its own. This atmosphere is mostly nitrogen. Titan may also have active volcanoes.

The *Cassini* spacecraft, launched in 1997, is scheduled to put a probe on Titan in 2004. Then the spacecraft will orbit Saturn for four years, studying its atmosphere, rings, and moons.

We see Saturn's rings at different angles during its revolution around the sun.

Uranus

The seventh planet from the sun is Uranus. This greenish-blue planet was named for the Greek god of the sky. One unusual thing about Uranus is the tilt of its axis. Uranus rotates on its side. During some parts of its revolution, one pole of Uranus points directly at the sun. Because of this, astronomers disagree about which of Uranus's poles is its north pole.

In 1977, astronomers discovered that Uranus has a faint, dark ring system. They were using a telescope to observe Uranus as it passed in front of a star. They noticed that the star dimmed briefly many times. Each dimming occurred as another ring passed in front of the star. In 1986, the *Voyager 2* spacecraft studied the rings and moons of Uranus up close. Since then, more rings and moons have been discovered. Uranus has at least 11 rings and 22 moons.

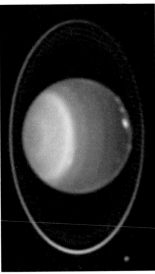
The outer planets are very cold. The cloud tops of Uranus are −200°C.

Because Uranus is so far out in the solar system, it takes 84 Earth years to complete a single orbit of the sun. Uranus rotates on its axis once every 17 hours.

Neptune

Neptune is the eighth planet from the sun. Named after the Roman god of the sea, Neptune cannot be seen without a telescope. Like Uranus, Neptune appears greenish blue because of methane gas in its atmosphere. Neptune has four rings: two thin and two thick. Like Jupiter, Neptune has a big spot in its atmosphere. The Great Dark Spot seen at the center of the photo is about as wide as Earth. The wispy, white streaks are clouds.

The Great Dark Spot is a storm system spinning counterclockwise.

It takes Neptune 164 Earth years to complete a revolution around the sun. The planet rotates once on its axis every 16 hours.

The Solar System   Chapter 4   **95**

LEARNING STYLES

Logical/Mathematical

Have students work in pairs to create a dialogue between a politician who thinks that NASA should send a space vehicle to land on an outer planet and a scientist who thinks that would not be wise. Remind students that exact facts must be used to convince their opponent. Pairs of students may perform their dialogues for the class.

CROSS-CURRICULAR CONNECTION

Literature

Suggest that students read *Voyager: An Adventure to the Edge of the Solar System* by Sally Ride and Tam O'Shaughnessy. Then ask students to prepare an oral or a written report on what additional information they learned from this book about the four giant outer planets.

GLOBAL CONNECTION

The International Space Station is the first multinational cooperative space project. The United States and 16 other nations, including Canada, Russia, and Japan, are contributing money, equipment, people, and technical expertise. But the project is costing billions of dollars, with most of the money coming from the United States. Should the United States continue to support the International Space Station? Have students take a side on this issue, write their opinion, and support it with facts. Allow time for students on both sides of the issue to give their arguments.

Did You Know?

Have students read the Did You Know? statement on page 96. Add that the planet was first seen by astronomer Clyde Tombaugh in 1930, but the planet's existence was predicted earlier by astronomer Percival Lowell. Pluto's moon, Charon, was discovered in 1978.

Science Journal

Ask students to imagine that it is 500 years in the future and that people travel to the outer planets for vacations. Have students create an advertisement that encourages people to travel to one of the outer planets. Students might describe interesting features to see on the planet or suggest side trips to its moons or rings. Their journal entry should reflect facts presented in the lesson.

Online Connection

Students as well as teachers can find a wealth of information by taking *The Nine Planets: A Multimedia Tour of the Solar System* at this Web site: seds.lpl.arizona.edu/nineplanets/nineplanets/nineplanets.html.

Did You Know?

Pluto was not discovered until 1930.

Until 1989, astronomers thought Neptune had two moons. Later, nine more moons were found. One of Neptune's 11 moons is unusual. It rotates in the opposite direction from Neptune's rotation. This moon, named Triton, also has active volcanoes.

Pluto

Pluto is the coldest, outermost planet of the solar system, but it is not always the farthest from the sun. It has a tilted, stretched-out orbit that sometimes falls inside the orbit of Neptune, as shown below. Even so, if you were to stand on Pluto, the sun would appear only as a bright star in the sky. Pluto has not yet been visited by a spacecraft.

Pluto is the smallest planet. It is the only outer planet without a ring system and a thick atmosphere. Pluto has one known moon, Charon. Even with powerful telescopes, Pluto and Charon are hard to see. At an average distance from the sun of almost 6 billion kilometers, Pluto takes 248 Earth years to make one revolution. Pluto seems to rotate about once every 6 days.

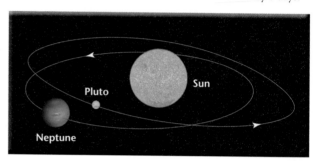

Write your answers to these questions on a sheet of paper.

1. What are the five outer planets of the solar system?

2. What are the large outer planets made of?

3. Which outer planets have rings?

4. Besides on Earth, where could you find active volcanoes?

5. How is Pluto different from the other outer planets?

▼◄ ▲ ▼◄ ▲ ▼◄ ▲ ▼◄ ▲ ▼◄ ▲ ▼◄ ▲ ▼◄ ▲ ▼◄ ▲ ▼◄ ▲ ▼◄ ▲ ▼◄ ▲ ▼◄ ▲ ▼◄ ▲ ▼◄ ▲ ▼◄ ▲ ▼◄ ▲ ▼

Science at Work

Astronomer

Astronomers study stars, planets, and other objects in space. Most astronomers do research by analyzing large amounts of data. The data are collected from satellites and powerful telescopes. Some astronomers try to solve problems with space flight or satellite communications.

The usual education needed to be an astronomer is a doctoral degree, or Ph.D. An astronomer needs to have a strong background in physics and mathematics.

Besides science skills, a successful astronomer needs to be a problem-solver. A curious mind and an active imagination are also helpful.

Many astronomers teach at colleges or universities. Other astronomers are planetarium directors. They may also be members of a research team that operates large telescopes on Earth or in space.

The Solar System *Chapter 4* **97**

Lab Manual 15, pages 1–2

Workbook Activity 16

Lesson 3 Review Answers

1. Jupiter, Saturn, Neptune, Uranus, Pluto **2.** frozen gas and liquid, with a small, solid core **3.** Jupiter, Saturn, Neptune, Uranus **4.** Io (one of Jupiter's moons) and Triton (one of Neptune's moons) **5.** Pluto is very small compared to the other four outer planets. Pluto is the only outer planet without a thick atmosphere or a ring system.

Science at Work

Have students read the feature on page 97. Ask them whether or not they would be interested in a career in astronomy and why. Interested students might enjoy visiting NASA's site for young astronomers: starchild.gsfc.nasa.gov/docs/StarChild/Starchild.html.

CAREER CONNECTION

Students who are interested in how to prepare for a career in astronomy can visit the following Web sites:

www.aas.org/education/career.html

curious.astro.cornell.edu/careers.php

astronsun.tn.cornell.edu/~brs/faq.html

Have students write a summary of the education and training an astronomer needs and the places where an astronomer might work.

Portfolio Assessment

Sample items include:
• Planet fact sheets from Teaching the Lesson
• Diary, dialogue, and opinion writing from other activities
• Lesson 3 Review answers

The Purpose portion of the student investigation begins with a question to draw students into the activity. Encourage students to read the investigation steps and formulate their own questions before beginning the investigation. This investigation will take approximately 45 minutes to complete. Students will use these process and thinking skills: making models, measuring, sequencing, and recognizing patterns and relationships.

Preparation

• Measure and cut a strip of adding machine paper for each student or group. Cut extra strips or keep the roll on hand.

• Consider the placement of work stations so that students do not interfere with one another.

• Students may use Lab Manual 16 to record their data and answer the questions.

Procedure

• Students may work individually or in groups. For group work, assign one student to gather equipment and another to tape the paper to the floor. All of the students in the group should take turns measuring, marking, calculating, and labeling.

4-2 INVESTIGATION

Modeling Distances in the Solar System

Purpose
What kind of model might show how far the planets are from the sun? In this investigation, you will use a scale to show distances in the solar system.

Procedure

1. Tape the strip of adding machine paper to the floor. Draw a circle at one end of the paper. The circle represents the sun.

2. The table on the next page shows the relative distances of the planets from the sun. Use this table and a meterstick to mark the location of each of the planets on the adding machine paper. Label the position of each planet with its name.

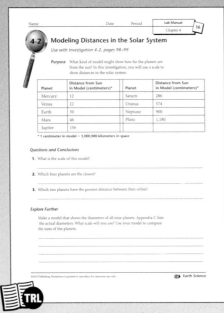

Name _____ Date _____ Period _____   Lab Manual
                                                  Chapter 4   16

4-2   **Modeling Distances in the Solar System**
      Use with Investigation 4-2, pages 98–99

Purpose   What kind of model might show how far the planets are from the sun? In this investigation, you will use a scale to show distances in the solar system.

Planet	Distance from Sun in Model (centimeters)*	Planet	Distance from Sun in Model (centimeters)*
Mercury	12	Saturn	286
Venus	22	Uranus	574
Earth	30	Neptune	900
Mars	46	Pluto	1,180
Jupiter	156		

* 1 centimeter in model = 5,000,000 kilometers in space

Questions and Conclusions

1. What is the scale of this model?

2. Which four planets are the closest?

3. Which two planets have the greatest distance between their orbits?

Explore Further

Make a model that shows the diameters of all nine planets. Appendix C lists the actual diameters. What scale will you use? Use your model to compare the sizes of the planets.

isGES Publishing. Permission is granted to reproduce for classroom use only.   Earth Science

Lab Manual 16

Planet	Distance from Sun in Model (centimeters)*
Mercury	12
Venus	22
Earth	30
Mars	46
Jupiter	156
Saturn	286
Uranus	574
Neptune	900
Pluto	1,180

*1 centimeter in model = 5,000,000 kilometers in space

3. Each centimeter on the strip of paper represents 5 million kilometers in space. Next to each planet on the paper, record its actual distance in kilometers from the sun.

Questions and Conclusions

1. What is the scale of this model?

2. Which four planets are closest together?

3. Which two neighboring planets have the greatest distance between their orbits?

Explore Further

Make a model that shows the diameters of all nine planets. Appendix C lists the actual diameters. What scale will you use? Use your model to compare the sizes of the planets.

Results

Planet distances should be labeled on the paper as follows:

Mercury: 60 million kilometers
Venus: 110 million kilometers
Earth: 150 million kilometers
Mars: 230 million kilometers
Jupiter: 780 million kilometers
Saturn: 1,430 million kilometers
Uranus: 2,870 million kilometers
Neptune: 4,500 million kilometers
Pluto: 5,900 million kilometers

Questions and Conclusions Answers

1. 1 centimeter = 5,000,000 kilometers

2. Mercury, Venus, Earth, Mars

3. Uranus and Neptune

Explore Further Answers

Students' models should show an understanding and use of a realistic scale based on diameters of the planets listed in Appendix C.

Assessment

Check to see that students are measuring accurately. Be sure they understand the concept of scale—that each centimeter actually represents 5 million kilometers and that the model represents the *relative* distances of the planets from the sun. Make sure that students accurately translate their model data into answers to the questions. You might include the following items from this investigation in student portfolios:

• Adding machine paper with distances marked

• Answers to Questions and Conclusions section

• Scale model from Explore Further section

Lesson at a Glance

Chapter 4 Lesson 4

Overview This lesson explores asteroids, meteors, meteorites, and comets. Students learn what these objects are made of, how they travel through the solar system, and how they differ from one another.

Objectives

- To describe asteroids and comets
- To identify the position of the asteroid belt
- To explain the difference between meteors and meteorites

Student Pages 100–102

Teacher's Resource Library (TRL)

Workbook Activity 17

Alternative Workbook Activity 17

Vocabulary

asteroid	meteor
asteroid belt	meteorite
comet	

Science Background

An old theory suggested that asteroids were pieces of a tenth planet that broke apart between Mars and Jupiter, but current theories state that Jupiter's great mass caused asteroids to clump together in an orbit. Ancient astronomers believed that comets appeared by chance, but English astronomer Edmond Halley proved that comets, like planets, follow constant, predictable paths. Halley calculated the path of a comet that was later named for him: Halley's comet.

1 Warm-Up Activity

Fill a disposable pan with plaster of paris about 7 centimeters deep. Before the material hardens, have a volunteer measure the diameter of a marble, using calipers. Then drop the marble into the pan. Ask students to measure the crater left when the marble is removed and compare the two dimensions. *(The crater will be larger than the marble.)* Have students look at the photograph at the top of page 101. Explain that the crater in the picture was formed when a meteorite struck the earth.

Objectives

After reading this lesson, you should be able to

- ◆ describe asteroids and comets.
- ◆ identify the position of the asteroid belt.
- ◆ explain the difference between meteors and meteorites.

Asteroid

Rocky object, smaller than a planet, that orbits a star

Asteroid belt

Region between Mars and Jupiter where most asteroids orbit the sun

Meteor

Brief streak of light seen when an asteroid enters the earth's atmosphere and burns up

Asteroids

The solar system has other objects besides the sun, the planets, and their moons. Some of these objects are **asteroids**. An asteroid is a rocky object smaller than a planet that has its own orbit around the sun. Most asteroids are smaller than a kilometer in diameter, but a few are 1,000 kilometers across.

As the diagram shows, a large number of asteroids lie between the orbits of Mars and Jupiter. This area is known as the **asteroid belt**. As many as a million asteroids make up this belt, orbiting the sun. The belt may have formed as gravity between Jupiter and much smaller matter pulled the matter into this region of space.

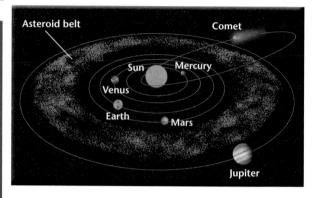

Not all of these asteroids stay in their orbits. Sometimes they are pulled out of orbit by the gravity of other planets. Asteroids may also be pulled in toward the sun.

A few asteroids come close to Earth and, at times, are captured by Earth's gravity. If an asteroid enters Earth's atmosphere, it heats up and becomes a ball of glowing gases. This brief streak of light seen in the sky is called a **meteor**. You probably know meteors as "shooting stars" or "falling stars." When many shooting stars occur, they are referred to as a "meteor shower."

2 Teaching the Lesson

Before beginning this lesson, have students write down the lesson title and objectives. As they read the lesson, students can write a sentence that meets each of the lesson's objectives.

Tell students that the word *comet* comes from a Greek word that means "wearing long hair." Ask students to examine the photograph at the bottom of page 101 and explain why that comparison is appropriate.

Have students mix dirt or sand with crushed ice. Instruct them to pack the mass into a ball. Ask students what object in the solar system this "dirt snowball" represents. *(a comet)*

Meteorite

Asteroid that hits the surface of a planet or moon after traveling through space

Comet

Ball of ice, rock, frozen gases, and dust that orbits the sun

If an asteroid is big enough and does not completely burn up, it may hit Earth. The part that actually strikes Earth is called a **meteorite**. Large meteorites can leave craters. About 50,000 years ago, a meteorite created Meteor Crater in Arizona, shown in the photo.

Meteor Crater in Arizona is more than a kilometer across.

One of the most well-known comets is Hale-Bopp. It was discovered in 1995 by two astronomers named Alan Hale and Thomas Bopp. The comet's closest approach to Earth was on March 22, 1997.

Comets

Other objects of the solar system include **comets**. Most of these objects follow large orbits. Most comets are not on the same orbital plane as the planets. A comet's orbit may take it far beyond the orbit of Pluto.

Scientists have found that comets are made of ice, rock, frozen gases, and dust. When a comet approaches the sun, the comet begins to warm up. Some of the ice turns to gas, and dust is also released. The gas and dust reflect sunlight, making the comet visible. A stream of particles from the sun, called the solar wind, pushes the gas and dust away from the head of the comet. This gas and dust form a tail that points away from the sun.

Did You Know?

When comets come close to Earth, they can be seen for days or weeks. They do not streak across the sky like meteors.

Comet Hale-Bopp, seen in 1997, has a very long orbit. It will not be seen again until the year 4377!

The Solar System   *Chapter 4*   **101**

---

3 **Reinforce and Extend**

Did You Know?

Have students read the Did You Know? feature on page 101. Explain that asteroids enter Earth's atmosphere at very high speeds—between 10 and 70 kilometers per second, but friction causes them to heat up and slow down. If they don't burn up, they usually hit Earth without causing much damage.

CROSS-CURRICULAR CONNECTION

Math

Another famous comet is Halley's comet. The orbit of Halley's comet causes it to pass near Earth every 76 years. The last time the comet was visible from Earth was in 1986. Ask students to calculate in which century Halley's comet will appear twice. (*The comet will appear one time in each century until the 23rd century when it will be visible from Earth in 2214 and 2290.*)

LEARNING STYLES

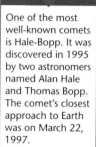
Auditory/Verbal

Write the Lesson 4 vocabulary terms on large index cards. Hold up two of the cards at a time. Have volunteers tell first what the two terms have in common and then how the two terms are different. For example, if you hold up *asteroid* and *meteorite*, students might say, "They are both asteroids. But a meteorite is an asteroid that strikes the surface of a planet."

ONLINE CONNECTION

Students can get answers to many of their questions about asteroids and comets, as well as other space objects, at this Web site: curious.astro.cornell.edu/careers.php.

The Solar System   *Chapter 4*   **101**

Lesson 4 Review Answers

1. a rocky object, smaller than a planet, that orbits a star 2. between Mars and Jupiter 3. A meteor is the streak of light made by an asteroid as it burns up in Earth's atmosphere, and a meteorite is an asteroid that hits Earth or another planet. 4. ice, rock, frozen gases, dust 5. When a comet nears the sun, some of its ice turns to gas and some dust is released. The solar wind pushes this material away from the comet's head. The gas and dust reflect sunlight and form a tail visible from Earth.

SCIENCE INTEGRATION

Technology

Ask three volunteers to read a paragraph each in the Technology Note on page 102. Have students name and list on the board as many forms of power or energy as they can think of. (*gas, wood burning, sun, wind, water, muscle, etc.*) Then skim Appendix B: Alternative Energy Sources on pages 358–363, asking students to note the headings in the text. Have small groups of students research one of these energy sources and how it is used today. (You might suggest the Web site www.miltonhydro.com/Kids.html, which explores and evaluates a wide variety of energy sources.) Have students share what they learned with the class.

Portfolio Assessment

Sample items include:
- Sentences for lesson objectives from Teaching the Lesson
- Lesson 4 Review answers

Write your answers to these questions on a sheet of paper.

1. What is an asteroid?
2. Where is the asteroid belt located?
3. What is the difference between a meteor and a meteorite?
4. What are comets made of?
5. How does the tail of a comet form?

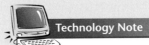

Technology Note

A photovoltaic (PV) cell, or solar cell, uses the sun's energy to produce electricity. The biggest advantage to this kind of energy is that it's free. Since PV cells have no moving parts, they require very little maintenance and are clean and quiet.

The basic idea of a PV cell was discovered in 1839. But the details of the technology were not worked out until about 100 years later. PV cells were first used in space. In fact, PV cells are still used to power most of the satellites orbiting Earth. PV cells are especially useful in remote places where regular power lines are not available.

PV cells also have more common applications. Simple PV systems power wristwatches and solar calculators. More complicated PV systems produce electricity for water pumps and communications equipment. PV systems even provide electricity for some homes and appliances.

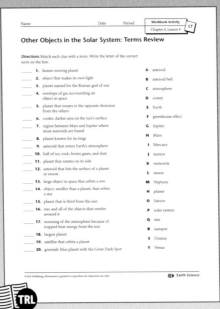

Workbook Activity 17

- Stars shine because they give off their own light. Planets and moons shine because they reflect light from the sun.

- The solar system is made of the sun, the planets and their moons, and other objects that revolve around the sun.

- The sun is a star. It is mostly hydrogen and helium gas. The sun's atmosphere has three layers: the photosphere, the chromosphere, and the corona.

- The inner planets are Mercury, Venus, Earth, and Mars. They are all solid, rocky worlds.

- Mercury has craters and almost no atmosphere.

- Venus rotates in the opposite direction from most other planets, has an atmosphere of carbon dioxide, and is very hot.

- Earth has one moon, moderate temperatures, a dense atmosphere, and much water. It is the only planet known to have life on it.

- Mars has a thin atmosphere, a reddish surface, and two moons.

- The outer planets are Jupiter, Saturn, Uranus, Neptune, and Pluto. Pluto is small and solid. The others are large and mostly gas.

- Jupiter is the largest planet and has 60 moons. A giant storm, called the Great Red Spot, can be seen in its atmosphere.

- Saturn has a big ring system and 31 moons.

- Uranus rotates on its side. It has a ring system and 22 moons.

- Neptune has a ring system and 11 moons.

- Pluto has a tilted, stretched-out orbit and one moon.

- Asteroids are small objects that orbit the sun between Mars and Jupiter. A meteor is the streak of light seen when an asteroid enters Earth's atmosphere.

- Comets are made of ice, rock, frozen gases, and dust.

Science Words

asteroid, 100	greenhouse	moon, 78	sunspot, 82
asteroid belt, 100	effect, 88	planet, 78	
atmosphere, 82	meteor, 100	solar system, 79	
comet, 101	meteorite, 101	star, 78	

Chapter 4 Summary

Have volunteers read aloud each Summary item on page 103. Ask volunteers to explain the meaning of each item. Direct students' attention to the Science Words box on the bottom of page 103. Have them read and review each word and its definition.

Chapter 4 Review

Use the Chapter Review to prepare students for tests and to reteach content from the chapter.

Chapter 4 Mastery Test

The Teacher's Resource Library includes two parallel forms of the Chapter 4 Mastery Test. The difficulty level of the two forms is equivalent. You may wish to use one form as a pretest and the other form as a posttest.

Review Answers
Vocabulary Review

1. solar system 2. star 3. atmosphere
4. sunspot 5. greenhouse effect
6. asteroid belt 7. planet 8. meteor
9. comet 10. moon 11. asteroid

Concept Review

12. A sun; B Mercury; C Venus; D Earth; E Mars; F Jupiter; G Saturn; H Uranus; I Neptune; J Pluto 13. stars, planets, moons, asteroids, comets 14. Earth has a mild surface temperature, a dense atmosphere, and liquid water on its surface. Earth alone can support life. 15. They are made up of gas and liquid. They have small, solid cores. They are relatively large. They have ring systems and thick, cloudy atmospheres. 16. B 17. A 18. C

TEACHER ALERT

In the Chapter Review, the Vocabulary Review activity includes a sample of the chapter's vocabulary terms. The activity will help determine students' understanding of key vocabulary terms and concepts presented in the chapter. Another vocabulary term used in the chapter but not in the Vocabulary Review is *meteorite*.

Vocabulary Review

Word Bank
asteroid
asteroid belt
atmosphere
comet
greenhouse effect
meteor
moon
planet
solar system
star
sunspot

Choose the word or phrase from the Word Bank that best completes each sentence. Write the answer on your paper.

1. The planets, moons, and sun are part of the _____.

2. The sun is the _____ that the planets orbit.

3. The gases around a planet make up its _____.

4. A dark area that appears on the sun is called a(n) _____.

5. Venus has a hot surface temperature because of the _____.

6. The _____ is between Mars and Jupiter.

7. A(n) _____ is a large object that orbits a star.

8. A shooting star is a(n) _____.

9. A(n) _____ is made of ice, rock, frozen gases, and dust.

10. Another name for a natural satellite is a(n) _____.

11. A rocky object smaller than a planet is called a(n) _____.

Concept Review

Write the answer to each of the following questions.

12. Identify each member of the solar system shown in the diagram below. On your paper, write the name after each letter.

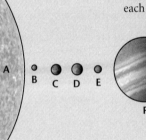

Chapter 4 Mastery Test A

13. Name five different kinds of objects that make up the solar system.

14. What makes Earth unique compared to other planets?

15. Four of the outer planets are very similar. Give two features that they share.

Choose the word or phrase that best completes each sentence. Write the letter of the answer on your paper.

16. The sun is mostly _____.
   A helium and oxygen
   B helium and hydrogen
   C hydrogen and nitrogen
   D hydrogen and oxygen

17. The solar system is held together by _____.
   A gravity   C energy
   B mass   D gases

18. The moon shines in the sky because _____.
   A the moon is very hot
   B the moon produces its own light
   C the sun lights up part of the moon
   D the moon is a close star

Critical Thinking

Write the answer to each of the following questions.

19. What is the difference between a star and a planet?

20. One of Jupiter's moons is as big as the planet Mercury. If this moon is so big, why is it a moon and not a planet?

Test-Taking Tip | When studying for a test, you will remember facts and definitions more easily if you write them down on index cards. Practice with a partner, using these as flash cards.

Review Answers
Critical Thinking

19. A star, made up of hot gases, makes its own light. A planet does not make its own light. **20.** It is a moon because it orbits a planet, not a star.

ALTERNATIVE ASSESSMENT

Alternative Assessment items correlate to the student Goals for Learning at the beginning of this chapter.

■ Ask students to make a network tree (see page xvii) with the term *solar system* in the center circle. Add the objects that make up the solar system in circles around it.

■ Have students draw and label the four inner planets in order and explain why they are called inner planets.

■ Have students draw and label the five outer planets in order and explain why they are called outer planets.

■ Have students make a chart for the nine planets and list facts that they know about each planet. Suggest that they refer to the solar system chart on page 364 to help them get started.

■ Ask two students to act out a planet's orbit around the sun. Then have another student enter the model as a second planet. Continue adding students until all nine planets are orbiting the sun. Remind students that the planets orbit the sun in the same direction. Also remind them that revolution speed generally decreases with increasing distance from the sun.

■ Have students make a Venn diagram (see page xvii) for comets and asteroids, filling in details about how the two are alike and different.

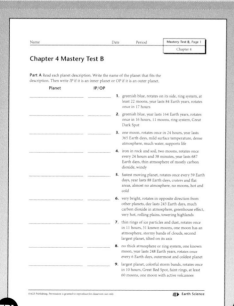

Chapter 4 Mastery Test B

The Solar System Chapter 4 **105**

Planning Guide

Stars and Galaxies

| | Student Text Lesson | | |
	Student Pages	Vocabulary	Lesson Review
Lesson 1 Stars	108–113	✔	✔
Lesson 2 Distances to Stars	114–116	✔	✔
Lesson 3 The Life of a Star	117–120	✔	✔
Lesson 4 Groups of Stars	121–126	✔	✔

Chapter Activities

Student Text
Science Center
Teacher's Resource Library
Community Connection 5: Local
   Opportunities to Study Stars

Assessment Options

Student Text
Chapter 5 Review

Teacher's Resource Library
Chapter 5 Mastery Tests A and B

	Student Text Features								Teaching Strategies						Learning Styles						Teacher's Resource Library				
	Achievements in Science	Science at Work	Science in Your Life	Investigation	Science Myth	Note	Technology Note	Did You Know	Science Integration	Science Journal	Cross-Curricular Connection	Online Connection	Teacher Alert	Applications (Home, Career, Community, Global, Environment)	Auditory/Verbal	Body/Kinesthetic	Interpersonal/Group Learning	Logical/Mathematical	Visual/Spatial	LEP/ESL	Workbook Activities	Alternative Workbook Activities	Lab Manual	Resource File	Self-Study Guide
		111		112		✔			110	110	109		110, 111	110							18	18	17		✔
			114				✔	114	116		115			115							19	19	18		✔
	120										119	118	118	119			119		119	118	20	20	19	12	✔
			124	125				122		124	123			123, 124	123	122		122			21	21	20		✔

Pronunciation Key

a	hat	e	let	ī	ice	ô	order	ù	put	sh	she		a	in about
ā	age	ē	equal	o	hot	oi	oil	ü	rule	th	thin	ə	e	in taken
ä	far	ėr	term	ō	open	ou	out	ch	child	ᵺ	then		i	in pencil
â	care	i	it	ȯ	saw	u	cup	ng	long	zh	measure		o	in lemon
													u	in circus

Alternative Workbook Activities

The Teacher's Resource Library (TRL) contains a set of lower-level worksheets called Alternative Workbook Activities. These worksheets cover the same content as the regular Workbook Activities but are written at a second-grade reading level.

Skill Track Software

Use the Skill Track Software for Earth Science for additional reinforcement of this chapter. The software program allows students using AGS textbooks to be assessed for mastery of each chapter and lesson of the textbook. Students access the software on an individual basis and are assessed with multiple-choice items.

Chapter 5:
Stars and Galaxies
pages 106–129

Lessons

1. Stars pages 108–113

Investigation 5-1 pages 112–113

2. Distances to Stars
pages 114–116

3. The Life of a Star pages 117–120

4. Groups of Stars pages 121–126

Investigation 5-2 pages 125–126

Chapter 5 Summary page 127

Chapter 5 Review pages 128–129

Skill Track Software
for Earth Science

Teacher's Resource Library

Workbook Activities 18–21

Alternative Workbook Activities
18–21

Lab Manual 17–20

Community Connection 5

Resource File 12

Chapter 5 Self-Study Guide

Chapter 5 Mastery Tests A and B

(Answer Keys for the Teacher's Resource Library begin on page 400 of the Teacher's Edition. The Materials List for the Lab Manual activities begins on page 415.)

Science Center

Have students prepare a display entitled "How Stars Have Been Used to Help People." Instruct groups of students to research a cross-staff, an astrolabe, a Viking solar stone, a medicine wheel, and a Polynesian calabash. Have students construct models or draw pictures of these devices and then write on index cards how the devices worked. A good reference book for this display is *The Night Sky Book: An Everyday Guide to Every Night* by Jamie Jobb.

Community Connection 5

Chapter

5

Stars and Galaxies

The sun is the closest star to Earth. It seems big, but it's an average-sized star. On a clear night, you can see many more stars in the sky. The sun is just one of at least 100 billion stars in our galaxy, the Milky Way. Beyond what you can see, there are millions of other galaxies in space. That's a lot of stars! The photo shows a star cluster found in a neighboring galaxy. This kind of star cluster isn't found in the Milky Way. In Chapter 5, you will learn about different kinds of stars and galaxies. You will discover how stars change as they grow old. You also will learn about constellations such as the Big Dipper and how far away those stars are.

Organize Your Thoughts

Stars

- **Characteristics**
  - Brightness
  - Distance
  - Age
  - Color
- **Groups**
  - Galaxies
  - Constellations

Goals for Learning

◆ To identify characteristics of stars

◆ To define a light-year

◆ To describe the life of a star

◆ To recognize constellations and explain what they are

◆ To explain what galaxies are

107

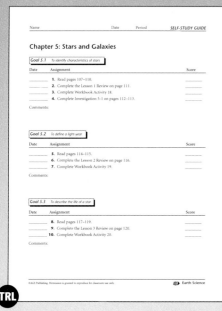

Introducing the Chapter

Ask students to compare the photo of a star cluster on page 106 to what they see when they look up at the night sky. Ask them to name the star that is closest to Earth. *(the sun)* Encourage volunteers to describe the sun and offer any information they already know about it. Ask students how they think the sun compares with other stars. *(Although it appears very large and bright because of its closeness to Earth, it is actually similar in size and composition to many of the stars we see at night.)* Then have students suggest ways in which all stars might be alike and how some might be different from others. *(Stars are all hot balls of gas that produce light. They go through a life cycle and eventually die out. However, they differ in size, temperature, and color as well as location. Their life cycles end in different ways, depending on their size.)*

Notes and Technology Notes

Ask volunteers to read the notes that appear in the margins throughout the chapter. Then discuss them with the class.

TEACHER'S RESOURCE

The AGS Teaching Strategies in Science Transparencies may be used with this chapter. The transparencies add an interactive dimension to expand and enhance the *Earth Science* program content.

CAREER INTEREST INVENTORY

The AGS Harrington-O'Shea Career Decision-Making System-Revised (CDM) may be used with this chapter. Students can use the CDM to explore their interests and identify careers. The CDM defines career areas that are indicated by students' responses on the inventory.

Lesson at a Glance

Chapter 5 Lesson 1

Overview This lesson explores why all stars do not look the same. Students learn that the brightness of stars is affected by the energy they give off and by their distance from Earth. Students also learn about the colors of stars.

Objectives

- To explain why stars shine
- To explain why some stars are brighter than others
- To determine a star's temperature by its color

Student Pages 108–113

Teacher's Resource Library **TRL**

Workbook Activity 18

Alternative Workbook Activity 18

Lab Manual 17

Vocabulary

absolute magnitude fusion
apparent magnitude magnitude

Science Background

Stars are large balls of hot gases, thousands to millions of kilometers in diameter. They form as gravity pulls together particles of dust and gas, packing them so tightly that the increased temperature causes nuclear fusion to occur. These nuclear reactions cause stars to radiate heat and light. The color of that light depends on how hot the surface of the star is, just as heated steel changes from red to yellow to white to blue-white as its temperature increases.

 Warm-Up Activity

Ask students if they have ever noticed stars twinkling when they watched them in the night sky. Explain to students that the twinkling is caused by the movement of Earth's atmosphere between the star and the viewer. To demonstrate this phenomenon, darken the room and stand at one end, holding a flashlight. Have students view the flashlight from at least 5 meters away. Hold a piece of bubble wrap in front of the flashlight and move it back and forth to simulate Earth's atmosphere.

Objectives

After reading this lesson, you should be able to

- explain why stars shine.
- explain why some stars are brighter than others.
- determine a star's temperature by its color.

Fusion

Process by which particles combine to form a new particle

People have studied stars since ancient times. Ancient Egyptians, Greeks, Chinese, American Indians, and other civilizations were able to predict the movements of stars in the sky. We now know much more about stars than the first stargazers did. Scientific instruments, such as powerful telescopes, have allowed us to search farther and farther into the sky.

Why Stars Shine

A star is made mostly of hydrogen and helium gas particles. Deep inside the star, temperatures of 15,000,000°C make these particles move at incredible speeds. When moving at high speeds, the particles collide and combine, or fuse. This process is called **fusion**. The figure shows that four hydrogen particles in a star can fuse to form one helium particle plus energy. Continuous fusion produces a constant supply of energy. This energy makes its way to the star's surface. Gas particles on the surface become very hot and radiate light. We see this as a shining star.

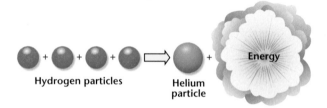

Hydrogen particles   Helium particle   Energy

Magnitude

Brightness of a star

Apparent magnitude

How bright a star looks

Absolute magnitude

How bright a star actually is

The Brightness of Stars

The first thing that you notice when you look at stars is that some of them are brighter than others. A star's brightness depends on two things:

◆ The star's distance from Earth
◆ The amount of energy that the star gives off

The closer a star is, the brighter it appears. Also, if two stars are the same distance from Earth, the star that gives off more energy will appear brighter.

To understand these ideas better, compare the brightness of stars to the flashlights in the figures below. In the first figure, both flashlights give off the same amount of light. But one looks brighter because it is closer. In the second figure, both flashlights are the same distance away. But one looks brighter because it gives off more light.

Scientists use the term **magnitude** to describe the brightness of a star. How bright a star looks is its **apparent magnitude**. The **absolute magnitude** is how bright a star really is. Absolute magnitude measures how bright the star would be if all stars were the same distance from Earth.

The brighter light is closer.

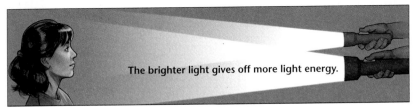

The brighter light gives off more light energy.

Stars and Galaxies   Chapter 5   **109**

Students should observe that the brightness of the light varies. Ask students if the amount of light that the flashlight gave off changed or if it only appeared to change. *(only appeared to change)*

 Teaching the Lesson

Tell students that when they finish reading the lesson, they will write a brief explanation of why stars look different from one another to observers on Earth.

To model the nuclear fusion that takes place inside stars, use four small balls of clay. Explain that the clay balls represent hydrogen particles. Combine the four balls into one larger ball. Explain that the heat inside stars causes the hydrogen particles to collide and fuse, resulting in one helium particle (the new clay ball). Tell students that a great deal of energy is also produced.

Have students refer to the star color and temperature chart on page 110. Ask the following questions: Are blue-white stars cooler or hotter than red stars? *(hotter)* What color star is our sun? *(yellow)* Is the sun cooler or hotter than a red star? *(hotter)* Than a white star? *(cooler)* What would you expect the temperature of the sun's surface to be? *(about 5,500°C)*

 Reinforce and Extend

CROSS-CURRICULAR CONNECTION

 History

The first methods of navigation, used by sailors in ancient times, were based on observing the positions of stars, constellations, and other celestial bodies. In celestial navigation, sailors relied on their observations plus an almanac that listed the position of these bodies throughout the year. Two early navigational instruments were the astrolabe and the octant. Both measured the angle between the horizon and a celestial body such as a star. The sextant developed from these early instruments. Have students research one of these instruments or the navigation methods of European explorers in the 16th and 17th centuries.

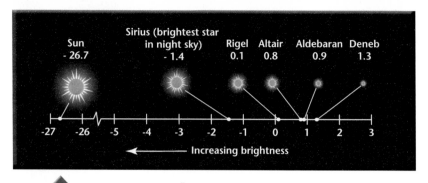

TEACHER ALERT

Students may find it illogical, and therefore difficult to remember, that the lower the number of a star's magnitude, the brighter the star. Explain that the system of classifying star magnitude comes from the Greek astronomer Hipparchus. He described stars of the *first magnitude,* which were brighter than stars of the *second magnitude.* Later scientists created a scale on which first magnitude stars were given the number 1, second magnitude stars the number 2, and so on. Stars brighter than first magnitude stars were given a number smaller than 1. Magnitude values are not necessarily whole numbers; they can be decimals, zero, or negative numbers.

SCIENCE JOURNAL

Ask students to study the sky on a clear night and write down their observations. They might notice that the stars are twinkling, as in the Warm-Up Activity, or that they can or cannot notice stars of different colors. Encourage students to include any impressions or feelings they have while stargazing. If they have access to a telescope or binoculars, students could compare observations of the sky with and without the instrument.

IN THE ENVIRONMENT

Explain that fusion, which produces energy in stars, is also the basis of energy in a nuclear power plant. Nuclear energy supplies great quantities of electricity without the air pollution caused by burning fossil fuels. However, nuclear energy has its own drawbacks: radiation released by nuclear fusion is a health danger. Have students research nuclear energy and then decide if its advantages outweigh its risks.

You may have heard the expressions "red hot" and "white hot." As a piece of metal is heated, it will first glow red. As the temperature increases, the metal will eventually turn white. In the same way, white stars are hotter than red stars.

The brightness of a star is represented by a number. The apparent magnitudes of some stars are shown on the scale above. Notice that the largest negative numbers are the brightest stars.

Sirius is the brightest star in the night sky. As you can see on the scale, the apparent magnitude of Sirius is -1.4. The sun's apparent magnitude is -26.7. Of course, the sun is much brighter to us. But the absolute magnitude for Sirius is $+1.4$. By comparison, the sun's absolute magnitude is $+4.7$. This means that the sun is actually a dimmer star. If the sun and Sirius were the same distance from Earth, Sirius would shine brighter.

The Color of Stars

At first glance, you might think that all stars are white. Many of them are. But if you observe stars carefully, you will see that some are red, some are yellow, and others are blue-white. The color of a star depends on its temperature. The following table shows the temperature of stars of each color.

The sun's surface temperature is about 5,500°C. Looking at the table, you can see that the sun is a yellow star.

Star Color and Temperature	
Color	Average Surface Temperature (°C)
blue-white	35,000
white	10,000
yellow	5,500
red	3,000

SCIENCE INTEGRATION

Biology

Remind students that the sun enables life to exist on Earth. Have them explain how this is so. (*The sun's light provides energy for photosynthesis, which generates oxygen. The sun provides warmth. The sun's energy produces winds and ocean currents. It also drives the water cycle of evaporation and precipitation.*)

Write your answers to these questions on a sheet of paper.

1. Describe the process of fusion in stars.

2. What two factors affect a star's brightness?

3. Explain a star's apparent magnitude and absolute magnitude.

4. Which star is brighter: a star with a magnitude of 1 or a star with a magnitude of 0?

5. Which is hotter: a red star or a blue-white star?

▼◄▲▼◄▲▼◄▲▼◄▲▼◄▲▼◄▲▼◄▲▼◄▲▼◄▲▼◄▲▼◄▲▼◄▲▼◄▲▼◄▲▼◄▲▼◄▲▼◄▲▼

Science at Work

Telescope Technician

Telescope technicians help operate, maintain, repair, and program optical, radio, or X-ray telescopes. They often work closely with astronomers at observatories.

Technicians working at the National Radio Astronomy Observatory in New Mexico help operate a set of 27 radio telescopes. Each telescope is the size of a house and can be moved on tracks. The telescopes send and receive radio waves. Telescope technicians collect and organize this information. Astronomers use this information to map distant galaxies.

Telescope technicians need either two years of vocational training or a bachelor's degree in astronomy, mathematics, or engineering. They must have a thorough knowledge of the type of telescope they work with. Telescope technicians need to be precise and detail-oriented.

Stars and Galaxies   Chapter 5   **111**

Workbook Activity 18

Lesson 1 Review Answers

1. The hydrogen and helium particles in a star move at incredible speeds due to the star's high temperature. The moving particles collide and fuse, producing constant energy that makes the stars hot and glowing. **2.** the amount of energy it gives off and its distance from Earth **3.** A star's apparent magnitude is how bright it looks to an observer on Earth. Its absolute magnitude is how bright it really is. **4.** a star with a magnitude of 0 **5.** a blue-white star

Science at Work

Have volunteers read the feature aloud. Ask pairs of students to find out more about the world's most important observatories and their telescopes. For example, the world's largest radio telescope, with a 300-meter-diameter reflector, is located at the Arecibo Observatory in Puerto Rico. The largest reflecting optical telescope in the United States is at the Palomar Observatory in California.

TEACHER ALERT

Students may think that the higher the magnification, the better the telescope. While magnification makes it easier to see detail in faraway objects, it also makes it harder to find and focus on a specific object. Explain that, besides magnification, telescopes are useful because they gather light, making faint objects appear much brighter than they would appear to the naked eye. Some very large telescopes can make a star appear about a million times brighter than it would appear without a telescope.

Portfolio Assessment

Sample items include:
• Explanations from Teaching the Lesson
• Lesson 1 Review answers

The Purpose portion of the student investigation begins with a question to draw students into the activity. Encourage students to read the investigation steps and formulate their own questions before beginning the investigation. This investigation will take approximately 40 minutes to complete. Students will use these process and thinking skills: observing, making models, measuring, recognizing space relationships, comparing, drawing conclusions, and recognizing cause and effect.

Preparation

- Check the batteries in all flashlights. Be sure both flashlights in a pair are equally bright. Have extra batteries on hand in case some start to wear down.

- Check how dark you can make your classroom. Make sure the investigation will work in this amount of darkness.

- Have plenty of extra tissue paper—students can easily tear it while affixing it to the flashlights.

- Be sure that work stations are far enough apart so that the flashlights from each group do not interfere with the results of other groups.

- Students may use Lab Manual 17 to record their data and answer the questions.

Procedure

- You may want to do a practice run with the class as a whole. Have two volunteers hold flashlights at very different distances from the class so that students can observe the differences in brightness. Have students predict which flashlight in the investigation will look brighter.

- This investigation is best done with students working in groups of three. Assign one student to gather equipment. The other two can label the flashlights and cover them with tissue paper. Student A holds and moves flashlight A. Student B holds and moves flashlight B. Student C observes and describes the brightness of the light from the flashlights. Students will repeat the observation part of the activity twice so each student has a turn as the observer.

INVESTIGATION

5-1

Materials

- ◆ masking tape
- ◆ marker
- ◆ 2 identical flashlights
- ◆ 2 sheets of tissue paper
- ◆ meterstick

Observing Brightness

Purpose

Does distance affect the brightness of a light source? In this investigation, you will demonstrate the different brightnesses of stars.

Procedure

1. Work with two partners in this investigation. Copy the data table on a sheet of paper.

Step	Observations
5	
6	
7	

2. Use masking tape and a marker to label one flashlight *A* and one flashlight *B*. **Safety Alert: Do not shine the flashlights into the eyes of others.**

3. Tape one layer of tissue paper over the front of each flashlight.

4. Darken the room.

5. Have each partner turn on a flashlight and stand together about 3 meters away from you. As they shine their flashlights toward you (but not into your eyes), compare the brightness of each light. Record your observations in the data table.

6. Have the partner holding flashlight A move about 4 meters away from you. Compare the brightness of each light. Record your observations.

Lab Manual 17

7. Have the partner holding flashlight A move about 2 meters away from you. Compare the brightness of each light. Record your observations.

8. Repeat steps 5 to 7 two times, giving each partner a turn as the observer.

Questions and Conclusions

1. When did both flashlights have the same brightness?

2. Explain what you observed in steps 6 and 7.

3. In this investigation, did you change the apparent magnitude or the absolute magnitude of the flashlights?

4. How are the flashlights like stars?

Explore Further

Make one flashlight dimmer by covering it with two layers of tissue paper. Repeat the procedure. Move the flashlights until they have the same brightness. Measure the distances. Look at your results. Then, make up a system to describe the brightness of the flashlights. Consider distance and number of tissue layers. Explain your results using this system.

- Before they do the Explore Further activity, have students predict how they will need to position the flashlights so that they look equally bright.

Results

When two flashlights give off the same amount of energy, the flashlight that is closer to the observer will look brighter.

Questions and Conclusions Answers

1. when they were the same distance away

2. First, flashlight B looked brighter. Then flashlight A looked brighter. In each case, the flashlight that was nearer was brighter.

3. apparent magnitude

4. They make light; their apparent brightness depends on observation distance.

Explore Further Answers

Students should find that the flashlight with the additional tissue layers will shine more dimly. It will, therefore, need to be closer for the lights to appear equally bright. Students' systems will vary, but should indicate that more tissue layers require shorter observation distances in order to achieve equal apparent brightness.

Assessment

Check that students are measuring the distances correctly and that they are able to discern which flashlight is brighter. Check that students understand what causes one light to look brighter and how the flashlights model the appearance of stars. You might include the following items from this investigation in student portfolios:

- Data table
- Answers to Questions and Conclusions section
- Explore Further results

Lesson at a Glance

Chapter 5 Lesson 2

Overview In this lesson, students learn that the distance to stars is measured in light-years, or the distance that light travels in a year.

Objectives

- To define a light-year
- To explain how far away stars are

Student Pages 114–116

Teacher's Resource Library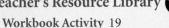

Workbook Activity 19

Alternative Workbook Activity 19

Lab Manual 18

Vocabulary

light-year

Science Background

The sun is our nearest star. From Earth, all stars except the sun look like tiny points of light because of their great distances from Earth. Astronomers measure distances in space in units called light-years. A light-year is the distance light will travel in one year. It is important to remember that the term *light-year* refers to a distance, not a period of time. There are approximately 1,000 stars within 55 light-years of the sun. About 950 of them are smaller and dimmer than the sun. The nearest star visible from North America is Sirius, the brightest star in the night sky. Sirius is 8.6 light-years from Earth. It is 23 times as bright and twice as big as the sun.

1 Warm-Up Activity

Show students a picture of a family taking a trip in a car loaded with baggage. Write the following sentence on the board: *Our vacation spot is three days away.* Point out to students that three days is a period of time, even though you just used it to describe a distance. Ask students to give examples of how people use time to measure distances. (*Examples might include "My house is 15 minutes from school" or "The airport is an hour away from the hotel."*) Point out that when we use time to describe how far away something is, we are assuming travel at a

certain speed. For example, the vacation spot that is three days away by car might be only four hours away by plane because a plane travels much faster than a car.

Science Myth

Have one student read aloud the myth portion of the feature on page 114 and another student read aloud the fact portion. Explain that a light-year is a measure of distance, like a foot, mile, or kilometer. Explain that light, unlike cars or planes, always travels at the same speed. Because light travels at a constant speed, it covers a fixed distance in a given time period.

Objectives

After reading this lesson, you should be able to

- ◆ define a light-year.
- ◆ explain how far away stars are.

Light-year

Distance that light travels in one year

? Did You Know?

In order to see an object, light from that object must reach your eyes. Suppose you are looking at a star that is 10 light-years away. The starlight that you see left that star 10 years ago. If that star exploded tonight, you would not see the flash for 10 years. Therefore, when you look at the stars, you are really looking back in time.

When you look at the night sky, you see some stars that seem to be closer to Earth and some that seem to be farther away. It is hard to imagine how far away stars really are.

Light-Years

Distances to stars are not expressed in kilometers or miles. Such numbers are so large that they are difficult to read and work with. Instead, scientists use a unit of length called the **light-year**. A light-year is the distance that light travels in one year.

1 light-year = 9.5 trillion kilometers

The speed of light is 300,000 kilometers per second. If a spaceship could travel at this speed, it would be going over 1 billion kilometers an hour. Moving as fast as light, this ship could travel from Earth to the moon in just over a second. The sun would be only 8 minutes and 20 seconds away. But the brightest star in the night sky, Sirius, would be almost 9 years away. That's because Sirius is 85.5 trillion kilometers, or 9 light-years, from Earth.

The distances between stars are much greater than distances between objects in our solar system. The distance between the sun and its nearest neighbor star, Proxima Centauri, is 4.2 light-years. That is more than 40 trillion kilometers.

Science Myth

Because of its name, people may assume that a light-year measures time.

Fact: A light-year is a measure of distance, not time. It is the distance light travels in one year, or about 9.5 trillion kilometers.

Did You Know?

Ask a student to read aloud the Did You Know? feature on page 114. Explain that in the 1600s, Galileo tried to determine the speed of light. He created an experiment in which he and an assistant stood on distant hills where they could see one another. Galileo instructed the other man to open the shutter on his lantern when he saw Galileo open his shutter. Galileo thought he would be able to measure the speed of light based on how long it took the assistant to open the shutter of his lantern. Of course, he did not realize that light traveled so swiftly that he would be unable to measure such a short time.

Sometimes, stars that look like they are near one another in space are actually very far from one another. Have you ever seen the Big Dipper? The stars in this familiar group all look like they are near one another in space. But, as the photo below shows, the stars of the Big Dipper are separated from one another by many light-years.

In this photo of a Canadian summer sky, the stars of the Big Dipper are highlighted. Each star's distance from Earth is given in light-years.

Measuring Star Distances

Astronomers determine distances to stars in different ways. One way begins by observing a star's position in the sky compared to more distant stars. Astronomers wait a few months while Earth moves in its orbit. Then they observe the star's position again. The star will appear to have shifted its position compared to the more distant stars. Closer stars appear to shift more than distant stars.

Very distant stars have shifts too small to measure. For these stars, astronomers compare their absolute and apparent magnitudes. If two stars have the same absolute magnitude, the dimmer star is farther away.

2 Teaching the Lesson

As students read about how astronomers measure distances, review the information in Lesson 1 about the apparent and absolute magnitudes of stars.

To help students conceptualize the great distance of a light-year, ask them to recall how far away Proxima Centauri is. *(4.3 light-years)* Then use the following comparison: Our current space probes would take 80,000 years to reach Proxima Centauri; a jet plane would take 5 million years to cover the same distance; an automobile would take 48 million years; and a person walking would take 720 million years.

Students might have difficulty visualizing how a nearer star seems to move relative to a more distant star. Demonstrate by placing a ball or other object at the back edge of a table. Place another ball near the front edge of the table, lined up with the first ball. Have students one by one pass along the front of the desk, observing how the front object seems to change position with regard to the back object. Point out that the movement of each student is like Earth in its orbit. Astronomers use this apparent shift in position to determine how far away a star is.

3 Reinforce and Extend

CAREER CONNECTION

Scientists who study stars and other objects in space are astronomers. They use powerful telescopes, observatories, and their knowledge of astronomy and physics to make new discoveries in space. Point out that though most astronomers have a Ph.D. and often work as university professors, amateur astronomers have also made many exciting discoveries. For example, in 1995, two amateurs, Alan Hale of New Mexico and Thomas Bopp of Arizona, discovered the comet that would become known as Hale-Bopp.

CROSS-CURRICULAR CONNECTION

Math

Tell students that an airplane can travel at a speed of 800 kilometers per hour. Have them calculate the number of kilometers the plane could travel in one day without stopping if it flew at that constant speed. *(800 × 24 = 19,200 kilometers)* Ask students to calculate how many days it would take the plane to travel 150 million kilometers to the closest star, the sun. *(150,000,000 ÷ 19,200 = about 7,812 days)* Have students calculate how many years that would be. *(7,812 ÷ 365 = more than 21 years)* An "airplane-year" might be defined as the distance this airplane can travel in a year. Have students calculate what that distance would be. *(19,200 × 365 = 7,008,000 kilometers)* Ask students to compare an airplane-year and a light-year. *(Students might note that light travels to the sun in 8 minutes and 20 seconds, while the plane would take more than 21 years to travel the same distance. A light-year is more than a million times longer than an airplane-year.)*

Lesson 2 Review Answers

1. distance 2. If distances to stars were measured in kilometers, the numbers would be very large and difficult to read and work with. 3. A 4. Stars are much, much farther apart than planets are. A spaceship going as fast as light could travel between planets in minutes. If the spaceship traveled between stars, it would take years. 5. They measure how much a nearer star's position seems to shift in relation to a more distant star over a few months' time. They compare the absolute and apparent magnitudes of two stars, knowing that if two stars have the same absolute magnitude, the dimmer one is farther away.

SCIENCE INTEGRATION

Technology

Have a volunteer read the first paragraph in the feature on page 116. Then ask a volunteer to summarize the main ideas in the paragraph in a sentence or two. *(The Hubble Space Telescope is a reflecting telescope that orbits the Earth.)* Continue in the same way with the other paragraphs.

Encourage students to check out some of the astounding pictures that the Hubble Space Telescope has taken. Have them visit www.hubblesite.org and click on "NewsCenter" or "Gallery."

Portfolio Assessment

Sample items include:
• Lesson 2 Review answers

Write your answers to these questions on a sheet of paper.

1. What does a light-year measure?

2. Why do scientists use light-years instead of kilometers to describe some distances?

3. Which of the following describes a light-year?
   A trillions of kilometers
   B millions of kilometers
   C hundreds of kilometers
   D a tiny part of a kilometer

4. Compare the distance between two stars and the distance between two planets.

5. Describe two ways astronomers measure distances to stars.

Technology Note

The Hubble Space Telescope was launched in 1990. This telescope orbits Earth about every 97 minutes at 600 kilometers above its surface. The Hubble Space Telescope is a reflecting telescope with a main mirror that is 2.4 meters wide. The telescope is about as big as a bus. It is maintained regularly by NASA astronauts who travel to the telescope. NASA stands for the National Aeronautics and Space Administration, a U.S. agency.

Why did NASA launch a telescope into space? Telescopes on the ground have to "see" through Earth's dense atmosphere. This can distort and blur telescope images. Because the Hubble Space Telescope orbits above the atmosphere, it can capture sharp images that cannot be seen from the ground.

The Hubble Space Telescope has taken more than 330,000 images. It has observed at least 25,000 different objects in space.

Thanks to the Hubble Space Telescope, astronomers have learned much about the structure and evolution of our universe. This amazing telescope will continue exploring space until it retires in 2010.

Lab Manual, Page 1
Chapter 5 **18**

Observing Distant Objects

Purpose How does an observer's position affect where a star appears to be? In this investigation, you will model how a star can seem to move as the earth moves.

Materials notebook paper
transparent tape
marker
meterstick
masking tape
small object such as a pen or a quarter

Procedure

1. Work with a partner in this investigation. Use the table below to record your data.

Distance Between Observer and Object	Number Position Seen by Left Eye	Number Position Seen by Right Eye	Difference
1 meter			
2 meters			
3 meters			

2. Tape pieces of notebook paper together to form a strip 1 meter long. Mark it into sections 10 centimeters long. Number the marks from 0 to 10. Tape the strip horizontally along a wall at eye level.

3. Place the meterstick on the floor beneath the paper strip. One end should be against the wall, directly under the mark numbered 5 (50-centimeter mark). On the floor, place a piece of masking tape 1 meter from the wall. Continuing in a straight line, place another piece of tape 2 meters from the wall. Place a piece of tape 3 meters from the wall, and another one 4 meters from the wall.

4. Stand at the 4-meter mark. Have your partner hold the object at eye level, directly over the 3-meter mark.

5. Close your right eye. Look at the object and the paper strip behind it. Notice what part of the paper strip appears to be behind the object. Remember the number.

Lab Manual 18, pages 1–2

Workbook Activity
Chapter 5, Lesson 2 **19**

Distances to Stars

Directions Write the answer to each question.

1. What is the speed of light?

2. Does a light-year measure time, brightness, or distance?

3. What measurement does 1 light-year equal?

4. The star Procyon is 11 light-years away. What is its distance in kilometers?

5. The star Betelgeuse is 2,850 trillion kilometers away. What is its distance in light-years?

6. If you look at a star that is 14 light-years away, how long ago did the light you are seeing leave the star?

7. When you see light from the sun, how long ago did the light leave the sun?

8. How do astronomers determine how far away a star is by observing it once and then a few months later?

9. How do astronomers figure out the distance of stars that have shifts too small to measure?

Directions Look at the table of stars and their distances from Earth. List the stars in order of distance, from closest to farthest, on the lines.

Star	Distance from Earth
Aldebaran	646 trillion kilometers
Pollux	35 light-years
Vega	26 light-years
Alpha Centauri	41 trillion kilometers
Sirius	8.8 light-years
Capella	46 light-years

10. _____
11. _____
12. _____
13. _____
14. _____
15. _____

Workbook Activity 19

Objectives

After reading this lesson, you should be able to

◆ describe how a star forms.

◆ describe the life cycle of a star.

Nebula
Cloud of gas and dust in space

As a star shines, fusion changes hydrogen into helium and energy. This energy is given off as light and heat. Eventually, the star's hydrogen is used up, fusion stops, and the star dies. This process takes billions of years. By studying different stars, astronomers can piece together the complete life cycle of a star.

The Birth of a Star

A star's life begins when a cloud of gas and dust is drawn together by its own gravity. This cloud is a **nebula**. The photo shows the Little Ghost Nebula. Within a nebula, gravity continues to pull gas and dust into a spinning ball. As the gas and dust pack tighter, the temperature of the ball increases. When the temperature gets high enough, fusion begins. A star is born.

Stars rotate on an axis, like planets. Stars are born rotating very fast. As stars grow old, they rotate slower and slower.

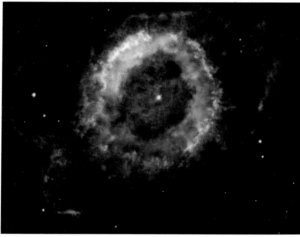

This nebula is about a light-year wide. It is more than 2,000 light-years from Earth.

Chapter 5 Lesson 3

Overview In this lesson, students learn how stars form, how they change over time, and the different ways in which they end their lives as stars.

Objectives

■ To describe how a star forms

■ To describe the life cycle of a star

Student Pages 117–120

Teacher's Resource Library TRL

Workbook Activity 20

Alternative Workbook Activity 20

Lab Manual 19

Resource File 12

Vocabulary

black hole	red giant
nebula	supergiant
neutron star	supernova
nova	white dwarf

Science Background

The sun, composed primarily of hydrogen and helium, will follow the same pattern of life and death as other stars that have about the same mass. Astronomers calculate that in about 5 billion years the sun will use up all its hydrogen. When fusion stops, the sun will begin to collapse inward. Then helium nuclei will begin to fuse to form heavier elements, such as carbon. The energy from this fusion will cause the sun to expand and become a red giant. As a red giant, the sun will be 100 times larger than it is now, expanding beyond the orbits of Mercury and Venus. Its outer layers will then drift into space, leaving a collapsed white dwarf.

 Warm-Up Activity

Display pictures of people at various stages of life: an infant, a toddler, a child, a teenager, a young adult, a middle-aged adult, and an older adult. Ask students to use the pictures to describe the changes that people undergo as they pass through life. *(Students might suggest that people*

Continued on page 118

Continued from page 117

grow larger and mature, their appearance changes, their levels of energy and activity change, and they eventually die.)

2 Teaching the Lesson

As they read, students can write a few sentences in response to each lesson objective. They should meet the first objective before moving on to the second.

Tell students that the word *nebula* comes from the Latin word for "cloud." Have students look at the picture of the nebula on page 117. Then ask them to tell how a nebula is like a cloud and how it is different from a cloud. *(From far away, a nebula looks like a cloud. But a nebula is made of dust and gas, held together by gravity; a cloud is made of tiny water droplets or crystals. A nebula spins and is very hot; a cloud usually doesn't spin and is about the same temperature as the surrounding air.)*

Explain to students that one of the most famous supernovas was the exploding star seen by astronomers in China in 1054. The astronomers had no idea that they were seeing the death of a star. They reported that for several weeks the star was so bright it could be seen during daylight. The explosion produced what is today called the Crab Nebula, which is expanding into space at a rate of 4 million kilometers per hour. The Crab Nebula now covers an area of space 15 light-years across. Remind students that, as they learned in Lesson 2, the astronomers did not see the death of the star when it happened, but long afterward.

3 Reinforce and Extend

TEACHER ALERT

Because of its closeness and importance to Earth, students might think that the sun is a large star. Emphasize that the sun is average in size and temperature when compared with other stars.

Red giant
Star that has expanded after using up its hydrogen

Supergiant
One of the largest stars, formed when a star expands after using up its hydrogen; larger than a red giant

Nova
Brilliant explosion of a collapsed red giant

White dwarf
Small, white, hot, dense star that remains after a nova

The Death of a Star

The stages of a star's life depend on the balance between gravity and fusion. Gravity causes collapse, but fusion causes heat and expansion. Look at the diagram below as you read about these two forces.

Once a star uses up its hydrogen, the outer layers of the star begin to collapse toward the center. As the star collapses, particles of helium fuse. This fusion gives off energy, which expands the surface of the star. If the original star was a small- or medium-sized star, like the sun, it swells to about 100 times its size to become a **red giant**. If the star was larger and more massive than the sun, it swells even more to become a **supergiant**. These are the largest stars. Betelgeuse is the name of one supergiant. If it were placed where our sun is, Earth's orbit would be inside the star.

As the diagram shows, gravity pulls the outer parts of a red giant toward its center. It collapses. Then, its temperature increases once again, and the outer layer blows off, forming a **nova**. The center of the nova becomes a white, hot, dense star called a **white dwarf**. When the white dwarf uses up its energy, it becomes a dark, dense star that no longer shines.

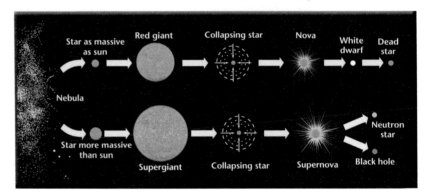

Supernova
Brilliant explosion of a collapsed supergiant

Neutron star
Very small, very dense star that remains after a supernova

Black hole
Region in space with tremendous gravity, caused by the collapse of a huge star

A star that becomes a supergiant has a more dramatic end. Gravity makes the supergiant collapse. Particles smashing into the center of the star make it so hot that a huge explosion occurs—a **supernova**. A supernova sends gas and dust into space and forms a nebula. After the explosion, a tiny **neutron star** may remain. A neutron star is only about 20 kilometers wide but has about as much mass as the sun. Therefore, a neutron star is very dense. One teaspoonful of a neutron star would weigh a billion tons. After a very large supernova, astronomers think the remaining star continues to collapse. The star's gravity becomes so great that light cannot escape. Thus, this region of space is called a **black hole**.

Scientists cannot visibly see black holes like they can see stars. However, black holes give off X rays, which scientists can measure. These X-ray "fingerprints" are often spotted in the centers of galaxies.

The photo on the left was taken by a camera aboard the Hubble Space Telescope. It shows a distant galaxy that formed when two smaller galaxies collided. This is what we would see if we were space observers. The image on the right was taken by an X-ray telescope in space. This X-ray image of the same galaxy shows two large black holes at the galaxy's center. The black holes appear as bright white spots, but they would not look this way to us. They are "bright" on an X-ray image because they are sending out X rays. Astronomers believe that, millions of years from now, these two black holes will combine to form one even larger black hole.

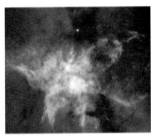 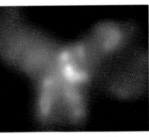

Stars can be seen on the optical image (left). Black holes and other X-ray sources can be seen on the X-ray image (right).

Stars and Galaxies Chapter 5 **119**

120 *Chapter 5 Stars and Galaxies*

Lesson 3 Review Answers

1. A swirling cloud of dust and gas is drawn together by gravity and, when it gets hot enough, gives off energy from fusion. **2.** Gravity causes collapse, but fusion causes heat and expansion. **3.** larger than **4.** Gravity makes a supergiant collapse. Particles colliding in the center of the star make it so hot that a huge explosion occurs, which is a supernova. **5.** A small star swells into a red giant, explodes as a nova, and leaves a white dwarf, which finally becomes a dead star. A large star becomes a supergiant, explodes as a supernova, and leaves either a neutron star or a black hole.

Achievements in Science

Have volunteers read aloud the feature on page 120. Explain that new facts about black holes continue to emerge. Scientists now believe that most galaxies have a black hole at their center. The closest one to Earth, discovered in 1971, is in the Cygnus constellation. Encourage students to learn more about Stephen Hawking's accomplishments and about black holes.

Portfolio Assessment

Sample items include:
• Objective sentences from Teaching the Lesson
• Lesson 3 Review answers

Write your answers to these questions on a sheet of paper.

1. How does a star's life begin?

2. Explain how gravity and fusion have opposite effects on a star.

3. Is a supergiant larger than, smaller than, or about the same size as a red giant?

4. Describe how a supergiant becomes a supernova.

5. What happens to a star when its life ends?

Achievements in Science

Black Holes

Black holes are not really holes. They are collapsed objects that are extremely heavy, yet very tiny. Because of this, they have a huge gravitational pull on objects close to them. An object on a black hole would have to go faster than the speed of light to escape this pull. Black holes are invisible because no light can escape from them.

Although black holes cannot be seen, astronomers know they exist. When gas and dust wander too close to a black hole, these particles are pulled into an orbit around it. This kind of orbit creates heat, and X rays are given off. Astronomers use powerful telescopes to measure the speed and heat of the orbiting material. From this information, they can tell that a black hole is at the center.

Stephen Hawking is a scientist who studies black holes. One of his theories is that mini black holes exist. Over time, these small black holes lose energy and mass and eventually disappear. Hawking also has shown that black holes produce their own radiant energy particles. Scientists previously thought that nothing could escape a black hole.

Hawking teaches mathematics at Cambridge University in England. He has the same teaching position as Sir Isaac Newton had 300 years ago. Hawking has amyotrophic lateral sclerosis (ALS), a disease of the nervous system. He uses a wheelchair and speaks with the aid of a computer-synthesized voice.

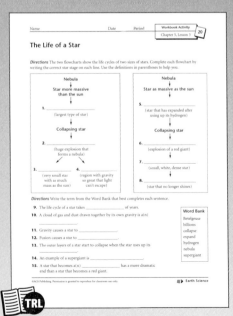

Lab Manual 19, pages 1–2

Workbook Activity 20

Objectives

Constellation
Pattern of stars seen from Earth

Constellations

When ancient people looked at the sky, they imagined the stars formed the shapes of people, animals, and objects. They related these shapes to myths, or stories. Today, we still use these groups of stars, called **constellations**, to describe parts of the sky.

The ancient Greeks named 48 constellations. Today, astronomers divide the sky into 88 constellations, including the ones named by the ancient Greeks. You have probably recognized part of a constellation many times. The Big Dipper is the rump and tail of the constellation Ursa Major, also called the Great Bear.

Shown below are some constellations that can be seen from the Northern Hemisphere. Appendix E contains two sets of constellation maps: a summer set and a winter set. By comparing them, you can see that stars change position.

One star that doesn't appear to move much is Polaris. It is also called the North Star because it is located above the North Pole. During the year, the constellations appear to move in a circle around this star. To find the North Star in the sky, use the pointer stars in the Big Dipper, as shown.

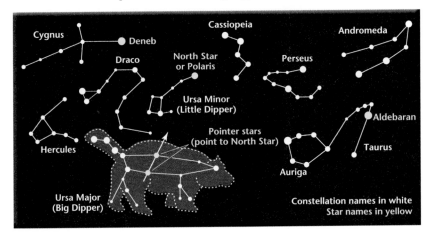

Constellation names in white
Star names in yellow

Lesson at a Glance

Chapter 5 Lesson 4

Overview In this lesson, students learn that groups of stars form galaxies within the universe. Students also learn that, through the ages, people have grouped stars together in patterns called constellations.

Objectives

- To explain what a constellation is
- To identify some constellations
- To explain what a galaxy is
- To identify the galaxy that includes our solar system

Student Pages 121–126

Teacher's Resource Library (TRL)

Workbook Activity 21
Alternative Workbook Activity 21
Lab Manual 20

Vocabulary

| constellation | Milky Way galaxy |
| galaxy | universe |

Science Background

All around the world, people have invented constellations, imagining that groups of stars depict animals, people, or other shapes. The particular star groupings, as well as the shapes they are said to form, vary from culture to culture. However, the use of constellations has helped people through the ages recognize and remember stars that are visible in the night sky.

Stars are gathered in groups called galaxies. Each galaxy contains billions of stars and planets, plus gas and dust between the stars. Millions of galaxies are spread throughout the universe. Most galaxies are tens of thousands of light-years across. Galaxies belong to still larger groups and clusters. Some parts of the universe contain several giant clusters of galaxies, while other parts of the universe contain very little matter. Galaxies are classified as spiral, elliptical, or irregular, based on their shapes. Our solar system is located in one of the spiral arms of the Milky Way galaxy.

Warm-Up Activity

Ask students to draw 8 to 12 random dots on a sheet of paper. Then ask them to connect the dots in some way to form a simple picture. Have students name the picture and share them with the class. Explain that, in ancient times, people believed the stars were arranged in patterns that represented people, animals, or objects.

Teaching the Lesson

Before they read this lesson, have students scan the lesson for unfamiliar words. Students can work in pairs to define each word on their list.

Explain to students that thousands of years ago people had no idea what the patchy band of light across the sky was. They thought it looked like a flowing river of milk and called it the Milky Way. Tell students that the word *galaxy* comes from the Greek word *gala*, meaning "milk."

Reinforce and Extend

Did You Know?

Have students read the Did You Know? feature on page 122. Explain that Ferdinand Magellan and his crew made their observations during the first circumnavigation of the earth in 1519–1522. They were able to see the fuzzy cloudlike areas because they were traveling in the Southern Hemisphere. These galaxies are not visible to observers in the Northern Hemisphere. The Large and Small Magellanic Clouds are actually satellites of the Milky Way; they travel in orbits around it.

LEARNING STYLES

Logical/Mathematical

Point out that the lesson includes several statistics about the Milky Way and other galaxies. Have students find and discuss these statistics. Then have them research additional interesting statistics about galaxies and share them with the class. For example, our solar system is located about 25,000 light-years away from the galaxy's center.

Galaxy
Group of billions of stars

Did You Know?

While sailing in the South Pacific in the 1500s, the crew of the explorer ship *Magellan* observed two fuzzy regions in the night sky. They were called the Large and Small Magellanic Clouds. These regions are actually irregular galaxies. They are the closest galaxies to our own—about 175,000 light-years away.

Galaxies

The sun is part of a large group of stars called a **galaxy**. A galaxy may contain many billions of stars. Galaxies can be divided into three different groups, based on their shape. The three shapes are elliptical, spiral, and irregular, as shown in the photos.

An elliptical galaxy is shaped like an oval, or ellipse. Most galaxies are elliptical. An irregular galaxy has no regular shape. These galaxies look like fuzzy clouds in space.

The stars in elliptical galaxies are close together. These galaxies contain very little gas or dust.

The Large Magellanic Cloud, an irregular galaxy, can be seen from the Southern Hemisphere.

LEARNING STYLES

Body/Kinesthetic

Explain that it is easier to locate constellations in the night sky if you know in which direction to look. Take students outside on a sunny day and show them how to make a shadow stick. Anchor a straight, 30-centimeter-long stick in the ground so that it doesn't cast any shadows. The stick should point straight at the sun. Check the stick in an hour or so, when the shadow is about 15 centimeters long. The shadow points to the east, allowing you to determine north, south, and west. Tell students they can do this at home, during the day, to help them locate constellations at night using star charts like the ones in Appendix E.

A spiral galaxy might remind you of a pinwheel. Spiral galaxies are the least common, but they are very bright. Therefore, we can see many of them from Earth.

This spiral galaxy is about the same size as the Milky Way galaxy. Named M74, it is 30 million light-years away.

Most of the stars that you can see without a telescope belong to the **Milky Way galaxy**. The Milky Way galaxy is a spiral galaxy that is about 100,000 light-years wide. This galaxy contains at least 100 billion stars. The sun is one of these stars. Our solar system is a small part of one swirling arm of this galaxy.

On some nights, you can see a faint band of light across the sky. This band is called the Milky Way. It is the light from the distant stars of our galaxy. The Milky Way forms a band of light because you are looking toward the center of the galaxy. This view is like looking at a dinner plate from its side. You see only a thin portion of the plate.

There are millions of galaxies moving through space. Spiral galaxies rotate as they move. All of the galaxies together are called the **universe**. The word *universe* refers to everything that exists. The best telescopes built so far have not found an end to the universe.

Lesson 4 Review Answers

1. a pattern of stars 2. elliptical, spiral, irregular 3. the Milky Way galaxy 4. the light from the distant stars of our galaxy as it is viewed from the thin side (like looking at the edge of a plate) 5. all of the galaxies together; everything that exists

Science in Your Life

Light pollution is greatest in the northeastern United States. The sites that students choose for their stargazing should be ones that would minimize light pollution. Students might choose an elevated place, such as a large hill, if there is one in your area.

AT HOME

Have students observe the night sky outside their homes for several nights. Beforehand, discuss conditions such as light pollution that make viewing stars easy or difficult. Then have students draw diagrams of what they see for several nights. Hold a class discussion about the results. If students come from a variety of rural and urban locations, discuss how these differences affected their viewing.

SCIENCE JOURNAL

Ask students to observe and write about the constellations that they can see from outside their homes. Students should record observations of constellations with which they are already familiar, as well as any they can identify with the aid of a star chart or Appendix E. Students should also describe how much their viewing area is affected by light pollution.

Portfolio Assessment

Sample items include:
• Definitions from Teaching the Lesson
• Lesson 4 Review answers

Lesson 4   R E V I E W

Write the answers to these questions on a sheet of paper.

1. What is a constellation?

2. What are three kinds of galaxies?

3. To what galaxy does our solar system belong?

4. When you view the Milky Way in the night sky, what are you seeing?

5. What is the universe made of?

Science in Your Life

Light Pollution

If you step outside your front door and look up at the sky on a clear night, what do you see? If you live in or near a city, you might just see a dark sky. The farther away from city lights you live, the easier it is to see the stars. If you cannot see the stars, the problem is nighttime light, or light pollution. The sun's light blocks your view of the stars in the daytime sky. At night, other lights can block your view. Even light from cities you can't see may cause light pollution. Observatories are located in places far away from sources of light pollution. That way, telescopes get a clearer view of objects in the sky.

For hundreds of years, stargazers have tried to solve the problem of light pollution. Some ancient stargazers looked at the sky from dark holes dug in the earth. Most simply went to places away from lights to look at stars. A mountaintop is a good place because it is usually away from cities and the air is thinner. It is easier for starlight to get through.

The satellite image shows what North America looks like at night. Where does light pollution seem greatest on this map?

On the map, locate where you live. What sources of light pollution are near your home? (Don't forget street lights.) Try viewing the stars from a few different locations. How does light pollution affect your observations?

124   *Chapter 5   Stars and Galaxies*

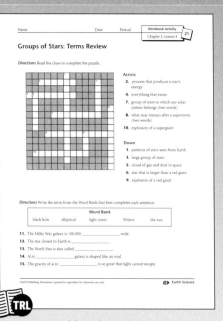

Workbook Activity 21

5-2 INVESTIGATION

Materials

◆ star guide showing constellations
◆ tissue paper
◆ black construction paper
◆ pin
◆ flashlight
◆ blackboard and chalk

Making a Constellation Model

Purpose

How could you model a constellation of stars? In this investigation, you will make a constellation projection.

Procedure

1. Work with a partner in this investigation. Copy the data form on a sheet of paper.

Constellation Data
Name of constellation:
Number of stars:
Reasons for choosing:
Description of pattern:

2. Choose a picture of a constellation from a star guide.

3. Trace the constellation onto a piece of tissue paper. Use a dot to mark the position of each star in the constellation.

4. Place the tracing over a sheet of black construction paper.

5. Use a pin to make a hole through both sheets of paper at each dot. Set the tissue paper aside. **Safety Alert: Use care with pins. The points are sharp.**

Stars and Galaxies   Chapter 5   **125**

Investigation 5-2

The Purpose portion of the student investigation begins with a question to draw students into the activity. Encourage students to read the investigation steps and formulate their own questions before beginning the investigation. This investigation will take approximately 45 minutes to complete. Students will use these process and thinking skills: making models, observing, recognizing patterns and relationships, comparing, and communicating.

Preparation

• Check all batteries before class. Keep spare batteries on hand in case some wear down.

• You may want to make photocopied enlargements of constellations from a star guide or Appendix E so that they will be easier for students to trace and project.

• Assign each group a specific section of the board on which to shine and draw its constellation.

• Students may use Lab Manual 20 to record their data and answer the questions.

Procedure

• Students can work in pairs or larger groups. Assign one student to gather equipment. All students should complete their own data table and clean up when finished.

• If possible, use very large pins so the holes will be larger. Suggest that students wiggle the pin in each hole to be sure the hole is big enough for the light to shine through.

• Be sure all groups have completed step 5 of the procedure before darkening the room.

• After students complete step 7, you may want to ask them to draw lines connecting the stars in their constellation. This will help the class recognize the shape of each constellation.

Continued on page 126

Lab Manual 20

Stars and Galaxies   Chapter 5   **125**

Continued from page 125

Results

Projected constellations should look like those in the star guide.

Questions and Conclusions Answers

1. Both are patterns of lights; people recognize the patterns.
2. Answers may include that the model is much smaller; stars are themselves a light source, while the model uses a flashlight; the stars in the model are arranged in a flat plane, while real stars in a constellation are varying distances from Earth; the model stars are all the same color.
3. Model larger or brighter stars by using bigger pinholes; show additional stars; use appropriate colors for different stars.

Explore Further Answers

The location of the constellation and the season when it is most visible will vary. You might select a few student constellations that should be visible at this time of year and ask students to locate them at night.

Assessment

Check that student constellations match the configurations in the star chart. Verify that students understand how their models are like and unlike the constellations they represent. You might include the following items from this investigation in student portfolios:

• Data table
• Construction paper constellations
• Answers to Questions and Conclusions and Explore Further sections

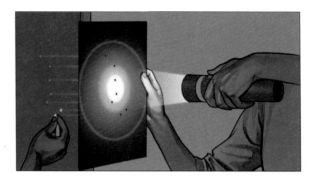

6. Darken the room. Hold the black paper in front of a blackboard. Turn on the flashlight and shine it at the paper as shown. Move the flashlight until it shines through all of the pinholes. **Safety Alert: Do not shine the flashlight into the eyes of others.**

7. Have your partner use the chalk to mark the stars in your constellation projection. Write the name of your constellation on the board.

8. Record the data about your constellation on the data form.

Questions and Conclusions

1. How is your model like an actual constellation?

2. How is your model different from a constellation?

3. How could you try to make your model better?

Explore Further

Locate the actual constellation. Use a star guide or Appendix E to find out when the constellation is in your night sky. Also, find out where to look in the sky for the constellation.

- Stars shine because of fusion. In this process, hydrogen particles combine to form helium particles plus energy. The energy makes the stars shine.

- A star's brightness depends on its distance from Earth and the amount of energy the star gives off.

- How bright a star looks is its apparent magnitude. The star's absolute magnitude is how bright it really is.

- The color of a star depends on its temperature.

- A light-year is the distance light travels in one year. Distances of stars are expressed in light-years.

- Even though stars seem to be near one another in the sky, they are far apart in space.

- Astronomers determine star distances by comparing the positions of stars and their absolute and apparent magnitudes.

- A star is created when fusion begins inside a nebula.

- A star shines until its hydrogen is used up. This process usually takes billions of years.

- The way a star dies depends on its size. A small- or medium-sized star swells to become a red giant, collapses, then explodes as a nova. A white dwarf remains.

- A massive star swells and becomes a supergiant, collapses, then explodes as a supernova. A tiny, dense neutron star may remain, or a black hole may develop.

- Constellations are groups of stars that form a pattern in the sky.

- A galaxy is a group of billions of stars. The sun is a star in the Milky Way galaxy.

- Galaxies are grouped by their shapes. The Milky Way galaxy is shaped like a spiral.

Science Words

absolute magnitude, 109	constellation, 121	Milky Way galaxy, 123	red giant, 118
apparent magnitude, 109	fusion, 108	nebula, 117	supergiant, 118
black hole, 119	galaxy, 122	neutron star, 119	supernova, 119
	light-year, 114	nova, 118	universe, 123
	magnitude, 109		white dwarf, 118

Chapter 5 Summary

Have volunteers read aloud each Summary item on page 127. Ask volunteers to explain the meaning of each item. Direct students' attention to the Science Words box on the bottom of page 127. Have them read and review each word and its definition.

Chapter 5 Review

Use the Chapter Review to prepare students for tests and to reteach content from the chapter.

Chapter 5 Mastery Test

The Teacher's Resource Library includes two parallel forms of the Chapter 5 Mastery Test. The difficulty level of the two forms is equivalent. You may wish to use one form as a pretest and the other form as a posttest.

Review Answers
Vocabulary Review

1. absolute magnitude 2. supergiant
3. white dwarf 4. light-years 5. supernova
6. constellations 7. galaxy 8. apparent magnitude 9. Milky Way galaxy
10. nebula 11. fusion 12. universe

Concept Review

13. A. 14. B 15. A 16. B 17. D 18. C 19. A
20. B 21. D 22. B

TEACHER ALERT

In the Chapter Review, the Vocabulary Review activity includes a sample of the chapter's vocabulary terms. The activity will help determine students' understanding of key vocabulary terms and concepts presented in the chapter. Other vocabulary terms used in the chapter are listed below:

black hole
magnitude
neutron star
nova
red giant

Word Bank
absolute magnitude
apparent magnitude
constellations
fusion
galaxy
light-years
Milky Way galaxy
nebula
supergiant
supernova
universe
white dwarf

Vocabulary Review

Choose the word or phrase from the Word Bank that best completes each sentence. Write the answer on your paper.

1. The actual brightness of a star is called its _____.

2. One of the largest stars that forms after using up its hydrogen is a(n) _____.

3. A small, hot, dense star is a(n) _____.

4. Distances to stars are measured in units called _____.

5. An explosion of a large star is a(n) _____.

6. Patterns of stars seen from Earth are called _____.

7. A group of billions of stars is called a(n) _____.

8. How bright a star looks is its _____.

9. Our solar system belongs to the _____.

10. The cloud of gas and dust in which a star is born is a(n) _____.

11. Stars shine because of a process called _____.

12. Everything that exists is called the _____.

Concept Review

Choose the word or phrase that best answers each question. Write the letter of the answer on your paper.

13. Which star magnitude is the brightest?
    A −0.1   **B** 0.5   **C** 0.1   **D** 1.5

14. Which star color is the hottest?
    A red   **B** blue-white   **C** yellow   **D** white

15. Which star color is the coolest?
    A red   **B** blue-white   **C** yellow   **D** white

16. A light-year measures _____.
    A time   **B** distance   **C** light   **D** brightness

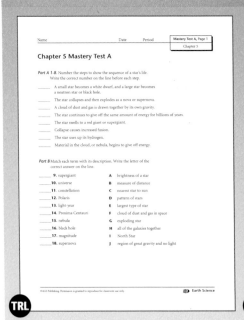

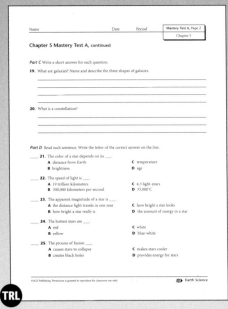

Chapter 5 Mastery Test A

17. A star's brightness depends on which two things?
- **A** distance and color
- **B** shape and age
- **C** age and energy given off
- **D** distance and energy given off

18. Which pair of objects is farthest apart?
- **A** Earth and the moon
- **C** Earth and night star
- **B** Earth and the sun
- **D** Earth and Mars

19. During fusion in stars, hydrogen particles combine to form helium and _____.
- **A** energy
- **B** water
- **C** neutron stars
- **D** oxygen

20. Galaxies are divided into groups by _____.
- **A** temperature
- **B** shape
- **C** color
- **D** size

21. A star that is the size of the sun will swell and become a _____ toward the end of its life.
- **A** supergiant
- **C** nebula
- **B** supernova
- **D** red giant

22. Light cannot escape from _____.
- **A** white dwarfs
- **C** neutron stars
- **B** black holes
- **D** novas

Critical Thinking

Write the answer to each of the following questions.

23. Explain what happens when a star uses up its hydrogen.

24. Order the following six objects by size, from smallest to largest: Milky Way galaxy, Earth, supergiant, white dwarf, solar system, and universe.

25. Why do Alaskans and Australians see different stars?

Test-Taking Tip When studying for a test, learn the most important points. Practice writing this material or explaining it to someone.

Review Answers
Critical Thinking

23. The outer layers of the star begin to collapse toward the center, and particles of helium fuse, causing the star to expand. It becomes a red giant or a supergiant. Gravity pulls the outer parts of this swollen star toward its center, and it collapses again. When its temperature increases, the collapsed star explodes, forming a nova or supernova. What remains is a white dwarf, a neutron star, or a black hole, depending on original star size. **24.** Earth, white dwarf, supergiant, solar system, Milky Way galaxy, universe **25.** Alaska is in the Northern Hemisphere and Australia is in the Southern Hemisphere. The two hemispheres look toward space in opposite directions. The tilt of Earth, combined with its revolution around the sun, causes these views to change over the course of the year, just as it causes seasons to change.

ALTERNATIVE ASSESSMENT

Alternative Assessment items correlate to the student Goals for Learning at the beginning of this chapter.

- Ask students to draw four circles in a vertical column on a sheet of paper. Explain that the circles represent different colored stars. Ask students to label these stars with their color and temperature, starting with the hottest.

- Ask students to explain why spacecraft have not been sent to study other stars. (*The distances the spacecraft would have to cover are so great that they would not be able to reach the stars for thousands of years.*)

- Ask students to draw two flowcharts that illustrate the stages in the life of a large and small star.

- Display a photo of a constellation. Have students write a paragraph explaining what a constellation is.

- Have students draw and label the three different shapes of galaxies.

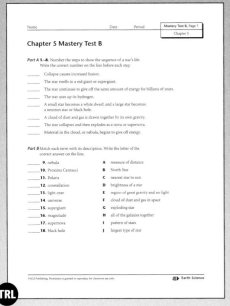

Chapter 5 Mastery Test B

Chapter

6

Planning Guide
Earth Chemistry

	Student Text Lesson		
	Student Pages	Vocabulary	Lesson Review
Lesson 1 Matter	132–136	✔	✔
Lesson 2 The Smallest Parts of Matter	137–140	✔	✔
Lesson 3 Compounds and Mixtures	141–148	✔	✔

Chapter Activities

Student Text
Science Center
Teacher's Resource Library
Community Connection 6: Using States
  of Matter

Assessment Options

Student Text
Chapter 6 Review

Teacher's Resource Library
Chapter 6 Mastery Tests A and B

130A

Achievements in Science	Science at Work	Science in Your Life	Investigation	Science Myth	Note	Technology Note	Did You Know	Science Integration	Science Journal	Cross-Curricular Connection	Online Connection	Teacher Alert	Applications (Home, Career, Community, Global, Environment)	Auditory/Verbal	Body/Kinesthetic	Interpersonal/Group Learning	Logical/Mathematical	Visual/Spatial	LEP/ESL	Workbook Activities	Alternative Workbook Activities	Lab Manual	Resource File	Self-Study Guide
		134	135				132		133	133		133	133, 134					133		22	22	21		✔
140					✔		138, 139	139		139	139	138			139		138		139	23	23	22		✔
	146	147		145	✔	✔	143	144	142	143, 145	145		143, 144	144		144	145	142		24	24	23, 24	13	✔

Pronunciation Key

a	hat	e	let	ī	ice	ô	order	ù	put	sh	she
ā	age	ē	equal	o	hot	oi	oil	ü	rule	th	thin
ä	far	ėr	term	ō	open	ou	out	ch	child	ⱦH	then
â	care	i	it	ȯ	saw	u	cup	ng	long	zh	measure

ə { a in about / e in taken / i in pencil / o in lemon / u in circus }

Alternative Workbook Activities

The Teacher's Resource Library (TRL) contains a set of lower-level worksheets called Alternative Workbook Activities. These worksheets cover the same content as the regular Workbook Activities but are written at a second-grade reading level.

Skill Track Software

Use the Skill Track Software for Earth Science for additional reinforcement of this chapter. The software program allows students using AGS textbooks to be assessed for mastery of each chapter and lesson of the textbook. Students access the software on an individual basis and are assessed with multiple-choice items.

Chapter 6:
Earth Chemistry

pages 130–151

Lessons

1. **Matter** pages 132–136

   Investigation 6-1 pages 135–136

2. **The Smallest Parts of Matter**
   pages 137–140

3. **Compounds and Mixtures**
   pages 141–148

   Investigation 6-2 pages 147–148

Chapter 6 Summary page 149

Chapter 6 Review pages 150–151

**Skill Track Software
for Earth Science**

Teacher's Resource Library

Workbook Activities 22–24

Alternative Workbook Activities
22–24

Lab Manual 21–24

Community Connection 6

Resource File 13

Chapter 6 Self-Study Guide

Chapter 6 Mastery Tests A and B

(Answer Keys for the Teacher's
Resource Library begin on page 400
of the Teacher's Edition. The
Materials List for the Lab Manual
activities begins on page 415.)

Science Center

Have students prepare a three-section
display on the three states of matter.
Ask them to find pictures of or objects
representing solids, gases, and liquids.
For each picture or object, students can
prepare an index card listing some of the
properties of that type of matter.

Community Connection 6

Chapter

6 Earth Chemistry

There are many different objects in this photo of a winter scene. But they all have at least one thing in common. Everything is made of matter. Matter can take the form of a solid, liquid, or gas. The river water is in a liquid state. The snow is a solid form of water. The water that evaporates into the air is a gas. In Chapter 6, you will learn about matter and its properties. You will find out about the elements that make up matter and their atoms. You also will learn how matter combines to form mixtures and compounds.

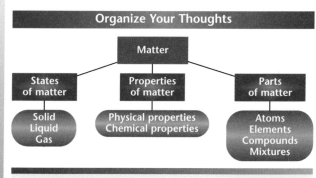

Organize Your Thoughts

Matter

States of matter	Properties of matter	Parts of matter
Solid Liquid Gas	Physical properties Chemical properties	Atoms Elements Compounds Mixtures

Goals for Learning

◆ To define matter

◆ To identify the states of matter

◆ To identify properties of matter

◆ To locate on a diagram the parts of an atom

◆ To compare and contrast elements, compounds, and mixtures

131

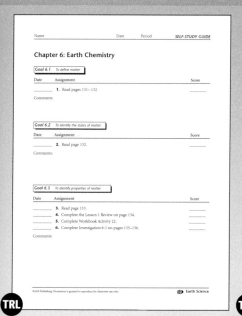

Chapter 6 Self-Study Guide

Introducing the Chapter

Ask students to give a definition of matter in their own words. Have them point out examples of matter in the picture on page 130. If students do not mention it, ask if air is matter. *(yes; some students may believe it is not because air is hard to observe with the senses.)* As they progress through the chapter, have students change or expand on their definition of matter and point out other examples of matter in the photo.

Have students read the Organize Your Thoughts chart and Goals for Learning. They can point out concepts that are new to them and make questions they would like to answer as they read.

Notes and Technology Notes

Ask volunteers to read the notes that appear in the margins throughout the chapter. Then discuss them with the class.

TEACHER'S RESOURCE

The AGS Teaching Strategies in Science Transparencies may be used with this chapter. The transparencies add an interactive dimension to expand and enhance the *Earth Science* program content.

CAREER INTEREST INVENTORY

The AGS Harrington-O'Shea Career Decision-Making System-Revised (CDM) may be used with this chapter. Students can use the CDM to explore their interests and identify careers. The CDM defines career areas that are indicated by students' responses on the inventory.

Chapter 6 Lesson 1

Overview This lesson explores what matter is, what states it can take, and how it can be identified by its properties.

Objectives

- To define matter
- To recognize three states of matter
- To identify properties of matter
- To measure properties of matter

Student Pages 132–136

Teacher's Resource Library

Workbook Activity 22

Alternative Workbook Activity 22

Lab Manual 21

Vocabulary

chemical property   property
matter   states of matter
physical property

Science Background

The way its particles are arranged gives matter its state. In solids, particles are tightly packed and linked. Thus, a solid keeps its shape and volume. Particles in a liquid move easily. They are not linked as firmly as particles in solids, allowing the substance to flow. Thus, a liquid takes the shape of its container but maintains a constant volume. Particles in a gas move freely and quickly. Thus, a gas assumes the shape and volume of its container. Heat can be applied to change the state of matter. The added energy makes the particles move more freely, changing a solid to a liquid and a liquid to a gas.

1 Warm-Up Activity

Place some crushed ice in a beaker and heat the beaker on a burner. As the ice is being heated, write the words *solid*, *liquid*, and *gas* on the board. Ask students to identify the term that describes the ice. *(solid)* Have them observe and describe what happens as the ice melts, then boils until most of it has evaporated. Encourage students to use the terms on the board in their descriptions. Explain that in this lesson, they will learn about the changing states of matter.

Objectives

After reading this lesson, you should be able to

- define matter.
- recognize three states of matter.
- identify properties of matter.
- measure properties of matter.

Matter

Anything that has mass and takes up space

States of matter

Basic forms in which matter exists, including solid, liquid, and gas

A house is made of many parts. Not all the parts are made of the same material. For example, the lumber inside the walls is different from the shingles that cover the roof. Some parts of the house are held together with nails. The lumber, the shingles, and the nails have different characteristics. But they are all examples of **matter**.

Matter is anything that has mass and takes up space. That includes a lot of different things. Land, water, and air are matter. In fact, except for energy, everything the earth is made of is matter. Understanding some basic ideas about matter will help you understand how land, water, and air change.

States of Matter

Matter usually exists on the earth in three basic forms, or states. These **states of matter** are solid, liquid, and gas. Below are examples of these three states. What other examples can you think of?

You can describe matter by identifying it as a solid, a liquid, or a gas. The state of matter is only one way to describe something. There are many other ways.

Did You Know?

Matter can exist in a fourth state called plasma. This is a very hot gas made of electrically charged particles. Plasma is rare on the earth. It occurs in lightning and in stars.

Solid

Liquid

Gas

---

2 Teaching the Lesson

Have students write each vocabulary word on a sheet of paper, leaving space between terms. As they read about each word, they can write their own examples.

Have students take turns naming something in the classroom that is matter. Then have them identify the item's state of matter and describe some of its properties.

Display two objects at a time, each with some similar and some different properties (for example, milk and water, gravel and sand, an orange and an onion). Have students compare and contrast the pair's physical and chemical properties.

Give each student three index cards and have students label the cards *solid*, *liquid*, and *gas*. As you show pictures of different states of matter, ask students to identify the state illustrated by holding up the correct card.

Did You Know?

Invite students to brainstorm ideas about a fourth type of matter that might exist in outer space. Then have a volunteer read the feature on page 132. Assign an interested student to research and report more information on plasma to the class.

Properties of Matter

How would you describe salt? It is white, solid, and made of small grains. This description is a list of three **properties** of salt. A property is a characteristic that describes matter. Properties help you identify matter.

The following table lists some properties of salt and sugar. Compare the properties to see how the two substances differ. You can use these properties to tell whether a substance is salt or sugar.

Physical Properties of Salt and Sugar		
Property	Salt	Sugar
color	white	white
state	solid	solid
size	small grains	small grains
taste	salty	sweet

The properties of salt and sugar listed above are **physical properties**. These properties can be observed without changing the substance into a different substance. Below are some common physical properties you can use to identify matter.

color	shape	size	feel
weight	smell	taste	state

To identify a substance, scientists often need to know more than just its physical properties. In such cases, scientists may use chemical tests to describe **chemical properties**. A chemical property describes how a substance changes into a different substance. For example, wood burns to form ashes and gases. A chemical property of wood, then, is that it changes to ashes and gases when burned.

Reacting with air and water is another chemical property. For example, a can left in water turns into rust because iron in the can reacts with oxygen and water. So a chemical property of iron is that it reacts with oxygen and water to form rust. A complete description of matter, then, includes both chemical and physical properties.

 Students should be aware that the three states of matter occur as energy is added. Applying heat to a solid causes it to turn into a liquid; heating a liquid causes it to turn into a gas. Various kinds of matter change their states at predictable energy levels. Melting point and boiling point properties are used by chemists to identify specific elements, compounds, and mixtures.

3 Reinforce and Extend

AT HOME

 Explain that, because of their chemical properties, some cleaning chemicals should not be combined. The resulting substance is dangerous. Ask students to read caution labels on containers of household products that contain chemicals such as ammonia or chlorine. Suggest that they make a list of household products that should not be mixed together and discuss their list with family members.

SCIENCE JOURNAL

 Have students select a common substance and describe its properties. They should include enough physical and chemical properties that classmates can identify the substance without being given the name.

LEARNING STYLES

 Visual/Spatial
Place a spoonful of baking soda in a beaker. Ask students to describe its physical properties. *(solid, white, powder)* Then ask them to describe the physical properties of vinegar. *(liquid, sharp smell, clear or colored)* Add a small amount of vinegar to the beaker. Now have students describe a chemical property of the substances. *(Vinegar and baking soda foam when they contact each other.)* One of the products of this acid-base reaction is carbon dioxide gas.

CROSS-CURRICULAR CONNECTION

 Art
Provide old magazines and calendars. Have students cut out pictures that show matter in a solid, liquid, or gaseous state. They can create a collage to illustrate one state of matter or one type of matter in different states.

Lesson 1 Review Answers

1. anything that has mass and takes up space **2.** Answers will vary. Sample answers: salt, milk, air **3.** Answers will vary. Sample answers: solid, hard, shiny, round, flat, sinks in water, silver-colored **4.** Physical properties are observable in a substance as it is. Chemical properties can only be observed by changing a substance into a different substance. **5.** Answers will vary. Sample answer: Iron rusts.

Science in Your Life

Invite a volunteer to read aloud the feature on page 134. Have students look around the room and find plastic items. List these on the board. Invite volunteers to explain why they think we use so much plastic. Have students note and list the plastic items they find in their trash at home. Discuss how students might reduce the amount of plastic they throw away.

Explain that plastics are compounds made from resins, most derived from oil. Plastics consist of chains of molecules called polymers, which combine hundreds, thousands, or millions of smaller molecules. The length, arrangement, and types of molecules in these chains give plastics their properties.

IN THE ENVIRONMENT

 Have small groups of students explore the impact of plastics on the environment. Ask them to find out what is being done and what can be done to recycle various plastics, both in their community and around the world.

Portfolio Assessment

Sample items include:
- Vocabulary examples from Teaching the Lesson
- Lesson 1 Review answers

Write your answers to these questions on a sheet of paper.

1. What is matter?

2. Give an example of a solid, a liquid, and a gas.

3. Name three physical properties of a dime.

4. How is a physical property different from a chemical property?

5. Give an example of a chemical property.

Science in Your Life

Lasting Plastic

For the past 70 years, plastic has been a useful invention. It bends. It bounces. It protects from the cold. Plastic is cheap to make and easy to mold. Because of these properties, people use a lot of plastic. But people also throw away a lot of it. Plastic has another property: it is not biodegradable. This means it does not break down in the environment. Plastic lasts and lasts, whether it is dumped in a landfill or carelessly thrown in a lake.

Recycling is one way to reduce the amount of plastic thrown away. Many cities have recycling programs for plastic and other materials. Another way to reduce plastic garbage is to use less of it. For example, when you are shopping, pick products with little plastic packaging or none at all.

You might be surprised to discover how much plastic you throw away every day. What can you do in your home to reduce plastic garbage?

Workbook Activity 22

Materials
- assortment of objects
- centimeter ruler
- balance

Measuring Physical Properties of Objects

Purpose
What are ways of describing and identifying objects? In this investigation, you will measure the physical properties of some objects.

Procedure
1. Copy the data table on a sheet of paper.

Object	State of Matter	Color	Shape	Size	Mass	

2. List each object in the first column of your data table.

3. Describe the physical properties of each object. First, describe the properties that you can observe without making measurements (state, color, and shape). Record your observations. **Safety Alert: Use care with liquids. Wipe up any spills immediately.**

4. Use the ruler to describe the size of each object. Record these measurements.

5. Use the balance to measure the mass of each object. Record these measurements.

6. Think of another physical property that helps identify the objects. Add this property to your data table. Then, record your observations for each of the objects. **Safety Alert: Do not choose taste as a physical property. Never taste any substances used in a science investigation.**

Earth Chemistry Chapter 6 **135**

The Purpose portion of the student investigation begins with a question to draw students into the activity. Encourage students to read the investigation steps and formulate their own questions before beginning the investigation. This investigation will take approximately 45 minutes to complete. Students will use these process and thinking skills: observing, collecting data, measuring, and applying information to new situations.

Preparation
- Gather an assortment of objects for students to use. The objects should vary widely in physical properties. They might include a large rubber band, a walnut, a spoon, some sand, coins, seashells, a cotton ball, and a variety of minerals. Include some water or another liquid in a container, but be sure to also provide an identical, empty container so that students can determine the liquid's mass.
- You might provide a magnet so that students could choose "attracted by a magnet" as a property if they wish.
- Students may use Lab Manual 21 to record their data and answer the questions.

Procedure
- This investigation may be done individually or in small groups. If you choose small groups, be sure that each student in the group measures and describes the properties of some objects.
- Demonstrate how to use a balance so that students will be confident when they calculate the mass of their objects.
- Some students may need guidance to determine the mass of the liquid sample. (They can measure the empty container, then the filled one, and subtract.)
- Discuss ideas for the extra property students will choose in step 6. Explain that it should be one that will help distinguish an object from some others that are similar.

Continued on page 136

Lab Manual 21

Name	Date	Period	Lab Manual 21 Chapter 6

6-1 Measuring Physical Properties of Objects
Use with Investigation 6-1, pages 135–136

Purpose What are ways of describing and identifying objects? In this investigation, you will measure the physical properties of some objects.

Object	State of Matter	Color	Shape	Size	Mass	

Questions and Conclusions
1. Is it hard to describe some properties? Why?
2. Which of your descriptions are the same?
3. What property did you add to your data table? Why did you choose that property?

Explore Further
Cover the first column of your data table with a sheet of paper, or fold your data table so the first column doesn't show. Now, exchange your data table of physical properties with a classmate. Can you identify each other's objects based only on their physical properties? If not, what other properties might be helpful?

©AGS Publishing. Permission is granted to reproduce for classroom use only.   **Earth Science**

SAFETY ALERT
- Explain that, although taste is a physical property, students should never taste any substance in an investigation. It might be poisonous or unclean.
- Use plastic or paper containers for liquid samples. Remind students to clean up spills immediately.

Continued from page 135

Results

Properties described will vary according to the objects used. Note whether students' data agree with actual properties of the objects.

Questions and Conclusions Answers

1. Answers will vary. Sample answer: Yes, finding precise words to describe objects can be difficult. Some objects seem to have more specific properties than others.

2. Examples should match actual data in the table. For example, two metal objects might both be described as "silver-colored" and "attracted to a magnet."

3. Properties will vary. Sample answer: Feel, because each object had a unique texture.

Explore Further Answers

First, remove objects from sight and see if students can identify objects only by the properties listed. Students may find that more descriptive clues are needed to identify some objects. For example, a solid might also be described as plastic, very lightweight, and shiny.

Assessment

Check that students find the mass of objects accurately and that descriptions match the physical properties of objects. Verify that the extra property is one that students could determine using available tools and could use to differentiate at least some of the objects. Include the following items from this investigation in student portfolios:

• Data table

• Answers to Questions and Conclusions and Explore Further sections

Questions and Conclusions

1. Is it hard to describe some properties? Why?

2. Which of your descriptions are the same?

3. What property did you add to your data table? Why did you choose that property?

Explore Further

Cover the first column of your data table with a sheet of paper, or fold your data table so the first column doesn't show. Now, exchange your data table of physical properties with a classmate. Can you identify each other's objects based only on their physical properties? If not, what other properties might be helpful?

Objectives

After reading this lesson, you should be able to

◆ explain what an element is.

◆ explain what an atom is.

◆ describe how the parts of an atom are arranged.

◆ identify some common elements.

Element

Substance that cannot be changed or separated into other kinds of substances

Elements

All words in the English language are made from combinations of just 26 letters. In the same way, all matter is made from combinations of 109 known **elements**.

An element is a substance that cannot be changed or separated into other kinds of substances. For example, the rock shown in the photo contains the element gold. But the gold is mixed with a mineral called quartz. You could smash the rock to separate the gold from the quartz. You could then smash the gold into tiny specks. Are the specks different elements? No, they are tiny pieces of gold, but they are still gold. What if you melted the specks? Would you have a different element? No, you would have liquid gold. You can change the physical state of an element, but it is still the same element.

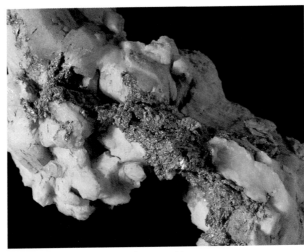

This quartz rock contains the element gold.

Chapter 6 Lesson 2

Overview In this lesson students learn about atoms as the smallest unit of matter. They explore atomic structure and learn that elements are composed of a single kind of atom.

Objectives

■ To explain what an element is

■ To explain what an atom is

■ To describe how the parts of an atom are arranged

■ To identify some common elements

Student Pages 137–140

Teacher's Resource Library

Workbook Activity 23

Alternative Workbook Activity 23

Lab Manual 22

Vocabulary

atom   nucleus
element

Science Background

Atoms actually contain a number of subatomic particles, but the principal ones are protons, neutrons, and electrons. The protons in the nucleus of an atom are positively charged; the neutrons have no charge. The nucleus is a tiny portion of the atom, but it contains most of the mass. Much larger is the electron cloud in which electrons, negatively charged particles, whirl around the nucleus in various energy-level orbits. Atoms are held together by various forces. An electromagnetic force causes the negative electrons to be attracted to the positively charged protons, thus holding them in orbit.

 Warm-Up Activity

Introduce the idea of divisibility of matter by holding up a sheet of paper and asking students how many times it can be divided into smaller pieces. Use scissors to cut it in half, then to cut one of the halves in half again, and so on, until you can no longer practically subdivide

Continued on page 138

Continued from page 137

the paper into smaller pieces. Ask: Are these the smallest pieces of paper we can make? If we had a tool that could make very small cuts, how many subdivisions might be possible? *(Students may say an infinite number are possible, or that if the paper is subdivided too far, it might no longer have the properties that make it paper.)* Explain to students that they will read about the smallest particles of matter.

 2 Teaching the Lesson

Read together the definitions for the vocabulary terms in this lesson. Have students write a few sentences telling how the three terms are related to each other.

Display samples of pure elements, such as carbon (charcoal or pencil lead), aluminum (foil), iron (nail), and copper (a pan bottom). Ask students to compare and contrast the properties of these elements. *(For example, aluminum and copper are both shiny; copper is reddish while aluminum is silver.)* Stress that each sample contains only atoms of that element: the foil contains only aluminum atoms, the carbon sample contains only carbon atoms.

3 Reinforce and Extend

Did You Know?

Show examples or pictures of diamond and graphite. Ask students to name properties these two substances have in common. Ask a volunteer to read the feature on page 138. Explain that carbon has several forms (coal and charcoal are two others). The properties of these forms are determined by the way in which atoms are joined. Diamond is the densest form of carbon; its atoms are joined in a rigid structure that gives the material its hardness. Graphite, which is easily crumbled and feels greasy, is made of carbon atoms joined in thin layers. Bonds between these layers are weak, so they are easily rubbed off, as when you write with pencil lead.

Atom

Smallest particle of an element that has the characteristics of that element

Nucleus

Atom's center, which is made of protons and neutrons

 Did You Know?

Diamond—the hardest substance known—is made of pure carbon. Graphite, or pencil lead, is also made of pure carbon. The difference is how the carbon atoms are arranged and held together.

Atoms and Elements

Suppose you could continue to break the gold into smaller and smaller particles. Eventually you would break the gold into individual **atoms**. An atom is the smallest particle of an element that has the characteristics of that element. An element is made of only one kind of atom. For example, a chunk of pure gold is made of only gold atoms.

What makes the element gold different from any other element? The answer is in the atoms. Look at the model of a carbon atom below. An atom is made of three kinds of particles. In its center are protons and neutrons. The protons and neutrons make up the **nucleus** of an atom. Moving around the outside of the nucleus are electrons.

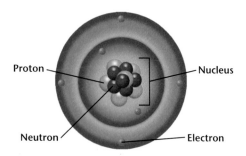

Carbon atom

Elements are different from one another because their atoms have different numbers of protons, neutrons, and electrons. However, it is the number of protons that makes each element unique. The carbon atom above has 6 protons. Each atom of gold has 79 protons. An atom of silver has 47 protons. Each copper atom has 29 protons.

TEACHER ALERT

 Students may think that atoms and elements are two different objects. Stress that an element is a substance made of only one kind of atom, although there may be billions of these atoms in a sample of the element. Students might think of atoms as building blocks. Every element is constructed of a different type of building block.

LEARNING STYLES

 Logical/Mathematical

Draw models for a hydrogen atom, a helium atom, and a carbon atom on the board. Together identify the neutrons, protons, and electrons in each atom. Have students work in pairs to count the number of each type of particle and record the data in a table. After they study the data, ask them to draw a conclusion about atomic construction. *(A stable atom has equal numbers of negative electrons and positive protons. The oppositely charged particles are attracted to each other, helping to hold the atom together.)*

The atoms in a solid are packed tightly and don't move much. The atoms in a liquid are packed tightly too, but they move freely. The atoms in a gas move very fast and spread out to fill the container they are in.

Scientists have discovered and officially named 109 elements. They have organized these elements into a chart called the Periodic Table of Elements. It is shown in Appendix E. For each element, this table gives the atomic weight and number of protons in an atom. It also lists each element's scientific symbol. Ninety-two of these elements are found in nature. For example, oxygen and nitrogen are two elements found in the air. Water contains oxygen and hydrogen.

The following table lists the 10 most common elements found in the earth's rocks. Which of these elements has the greatest number of protons? Which has the least? Notice the scientific symbol for each element. Most of these symbols are the first letter or the first two letters of the element's name. But some symbols may seem odd. For example, why is iron's symbol *Fe*? This symbol and some others are based on the element's Latin name. The Latin name for iron is *ferrum*.

Most Common Elements in Earth's Rocks		
Element	**Symbol**	**Number of Protons**
oxygen	O	8
silicon	Si	14
aluminum	Al	13
iron	Fe	26
calcium	Ca	20
sodium	Na	11
potassium	K	19
magnesium	Mg	12
titanium	Ti	22
hydrogen	H	1

LEARNING STYLES

LEP/ESL

Have students who are learning English write the words *atom, proton, neutron, electron, nucleus,* and *element* on index cards. Create a larger diagram of the carbon atom from page 138 on a bulletin board. Have students label the parts of the atom using the cards and some string. As each student provides a new label, he or she can explain its meaning.

LEARNING STYLES

Body/Kinesthetic

Assign students to be electrons, protons, or neutrons in a carbon atom. Make a tape or chalk circle on the floor to represent the nucleus. Draw two larger circles to represent the two electron levels for carbon. Have each student wear a label with a −, +, or 0. Explain that protons have a positive charge, electrons have a negative charge, and neutrons have no charge. Using the diagram on page 138, students can arrange themselves to show the atom's structure. Electrons should "orbit" the nucleus at their respective levels.

SCIENCE INTEGRATION

Biology

Have students use reference materials to find out how the human body uses the elements calcium, iron, zinc, and potassium. Ask students to share their information.

ONLINE CONNECTION

TrackStar is a site where teachers have listed and annotated sites about specific subjects. The resource list remains visible as students explore, allowing them to easily stay on track. The page titled Learning About Atoms links users to basic information, interactive diagrams, an opportunity to build an atom, and an interactive Periodic Table of Elements. This page can be found at http://trackstar.hprtec.org/main/track_frames.php3?option=nav&track_id=102924.

CROSS-CURRICULAR CONNECTION

Geography

Have students work in small groups to discover which elements are found in useful quantities in your state or region. Tell students to find out how these elements are obtained and how they are used. Ask students to share their information with the class.

Lesson 2 Review Answers

1. the smallest particle of an element that has the characteristics of the element
2. an element 3. protons and neutrons
4. Their atoms have differing numbers of protons, neutrons, and electrons.
5. Answers will vary. Students may include the elements listed in the table on page 139, those mentioned in the text, or any others with which they are familiar.

Achievements in Science

Have volunteers read the Achievements in Science feature on page 140. Using the pronunciations listed in the box below, repeat each element name. Then ask volunteers to practice reading the list aloud. Tell students that these elements do not occur in nature, but are produced from other, naturally occurring elements by nuclear reactions. Point out that natural elements may be found either in a pure form or combined with other elements or compounds.

Display a Periodic Table of Elements or refer students to Appendix F. Have students find the elements discovered by Seaborg and his team. Point out the atomic number of each of these elements and explain that this number represents the number of protons in each atom.

Pronunciation Guide

Use this list to help students pronounce difficult words in this lesson. Refer to the pronunciation key on the Chapter Planning Guide for the sounds of these symbols.

plutonium (plü tō′ nē əm)

americium (am ə rish′ ē əm)

curium (kyür′ ē əm)

berkelium (bėr′ klē əm)

californium (kal ə fôr′ ne əm)

einsteinium (īn stī′ nē əm)

fermium (fėr′ mē əm)

mendelevium (men dl ē′ vē əm)

nobelium (nō bē′ lē əm)

Portfolio Assessment

Sample items include:
• Sentences from Teaching the Lesson
• Lesson 2 Review answers

140   *Chapter 6   Earth Chemistry*

Write your answers to these questions on a sheet of paper.

1. What is an atom?

2. What kind of matter is made of only one kind of atom?

3. What does an atom's nucleus contain?

4. How are elements different from one another?

5. Name five elements and give their symbols.

Achievements in Science

Creating New Elements

Several elements were discovered by creating them in a laboratory. The nine elements below were discovered by a research team led by Glenn Seaborg. This American nuclear chemist was awarded the Nobel Prize for Chemistry in 1951.

plutonium (Pu)   einsteinium (Es)
americium (Am)   fermium (Fm)
curium (Cm)   mendelevium (Md)
berkelium (Bk)   nobelium (No)
californium (Cf)

The best known of these elements is plutonium. It is an important source of nuclear energy. Traces of plutonium are found in the earth, but this element is usually made artificially. The other elements listed have not been found in nature. Locate each one in the bottom row of the Periodic Table of Elements (Appendix E).

Seaborg made other significant discoveries. He noticed that certain heavy elements have similar properties. Because of this, the Periodic Table of Elements was reorganized. Seaborg also helped discover many isotopes. Isotopes are atoms with the same number of protons but with different numbers of neutrons. Isotopes are used to treat cancer patients.

As a tribute to Seaborg's contributions to chemistry, the element seaborgium (Sg) was named after him. Seaborg taught at the University of California at Berkeley. Look again at the list of elements he discovered. What or who are they named after?

140   *Chapter 6   Earth Chemistry*

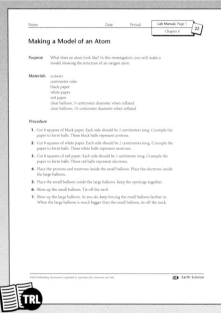

Lab Manual 22, pages 1–2

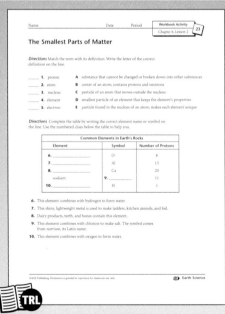

Workbook Activity 23

Objectives

After reading this lesson, you should be able to

◆ explain the differences among compounds, elements, and mixtures.

◆ identify some common compounds.

◆ recognize the formula for a compound.

Compound

Substance formed when the atoms of two or more elements join chemically

Since there are only 92 natural elements, how can the earth contain so many different kinds of matter? This variety is possible because the atoms of elements combine to make different substances.

Compounds

When the atoms of two or more elements combine, a **compound** forms. Compounds have properties that are different from the elements that make them up, just as a cake is different from the eggs, flour, and milk that go into it. The example below shows this idea dramatically.

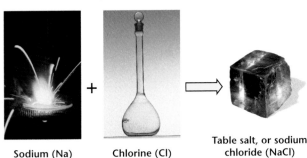

Sodium (Na)   Chlorine (Cl)   Table salt, or sodium chloride (NaCl)

Sodium is a metal. It explodes in water. Chlorine is a poisonous, greenish gas. You may have noticed the smell of this gas in a bottle of household bleach. When these two extremely dangerous elements combine, they form a compound called sodium chloride. You probably know this compound by its common name—table salt.

Chapter 6 Lesson 3

Overview In this lesson, students learn that elements combine to form compounds. They learn how to read formulas for compounds. They also contrast compounds with mixtures.

Objectives

- To explain the differences among compounds, elements, and mixtures
- To identify some common compounds
- To recognize the formula for a compound

Student Pages 141–148

Teacher's Resource Library

Workbook Activity 24

Alternative Workbook Activity 24

Lab Manual 23–24

Resource File 13

Vocabulary

compound
mixture

Science Background

When two or more elements combine *chemically,* they form a compound whose properties may be very different from those of the elements that make it up. For example, hydrogen and oxygen gas combine to form water, a liquid. A compound cannot be separated into elements by physical means. However, two or more elements or compounds may combine *physically* to form a mixture. The parts retain their own identities and properties. They may be separated by physical means.

Warm-Up Activity

Allow students to inspect samples of sulfur and iron filings. Test both elements with a magnet. *(The iron is attracted to the magnet, but the sulfur is not.)* Then mix some sulfur and iron together in a test tube and heat it over the flame of a Bunsen burner. After the elements have combined, allow the compound to cool.

Continued on page 142

Continued from page 141

Explain that the elements sulfur and iron have combined chemically to form the compound iron sulfide. Ask students to devise a way to test the properties of the compound and contrast them with the properties of sulfur and iron. *(The compound is gray and is not attracted to the magnet.)*

 2 **Teaching the Lesson**

After reading, have students make a Venn diagram to compare and contrast mixtures and compounds.

Have students choose a compound, such as Fe_2O_3, from the table on page 143. Provide students with a simple atomic diagram of their compound. Then have them title it and label the parts.

Have students compare several recipes for the same food, such as fruit salad or punch. Ask them to list ways the recipes differ. *(different ingredients and amounts)* Have students identify the food as a mixture or a compound and explain why. *(mixture; a mixture may contain different substances in different proportions, while a compound must always have the same "ingredients" in the same proportion.)*

 3 **Reinforce and Extend**

LEARNING STYLES

Visual/Spatial

 Ask students to use the diagram of water on page 142 to point out the two kinds of atoms *(oxygen and hydrogen)*, the parts of each atom *(nucleus, protons, neutrons, electrons)*, and the parts that are shared *(electrons)*. Note that hydrogen atoms have no neutrons. Provide each student with a copy of the diagram on Resource File 13 and ask students to color electrons red, protons blue, and neutrons black. Using their diagrams, students can explain how atoms of hydrogen and oxygen combine to form the compound water.

There is a fixed amount of matter in the universe. Matter can only be created from existing matter. Atoms can rearrange and take a different form. But the new form is still made of the same atoms.

What does it mean to say that two or more elements combine? If a bit of sodium was placed in a container of chlorine gas, you would not suddenly have sodium chloride. To form a compound, the elements must join chemically. This means the atoms must undergo a change, such as sharing electrons. For example, the figure shows how the elements oxygen and hydrogen join chemically to form the compound water. The atoms share electrons. This sharing holds the atoms together.

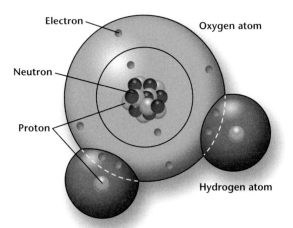

The compound water

Once elements are combined chemically, they are not easily taken apart. You cannot separate the sodium from the chlorine in salt by breaking the salt into tiny bits. You cannot separate the oxygen and the hydrogen in water by pouring it through a strainer. Usually, heat or electricity is needed to separate a compound into its elements.

SCIENCE JOURNAL

Have students write a paragraph describing how the atoms of a compound are joined. Encourage them to include the term *electrons* and to add a diagram to illustrate.

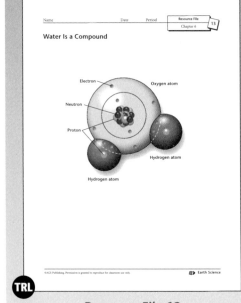

Resource File 13

Formulas for Compounds

Scientists use chemical formulas to represent compounds. Here is a list of some common compounds and their formulas. Notice how each formula includes the symbols of the elements that make up the compound.

Some Common Compounds		
Common Name	Compound Name	Formula
water	hydrogen oxide	H_2O
salt	sodium chloride	$NaCl$
rust	iron oxide	Fe_2O_3
baking soda	sodium bicarbonate	$NaHCO_3$
chalk	calcium carbonate	$CaCO_3$
carbon dioxide	carbon dioxide	CO_2

Besides including the symbols of the elements, a formula also tells you how many atoms of each element join to form the compound. Here's how to understand a chemical formula:

1. Identify the elements in the compound by their symbol.

   For example, water has the formula H_2O, so it contains the elements hydrogen (H) and oxygen (O).

2. Determine the number of atoms of each element. Look for a number that follows an element's symbol. This tells how many atoms of that element are in the compound. If there is no number, it means there is 1 atom of that element.

   The formula for water shows that there are 2 atoms of hydrogen and 1 atom of oxygen. In other words, the smallest unit of the compound water is formed by 2 atoms of hydrogen joined to 1 atom of oxygen.

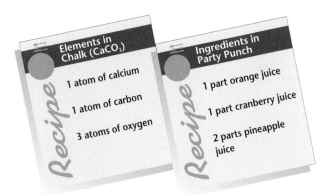

Recipe
Elements in Chalk (CaCO₃)
1 atom of calcium
1 atom of carbon
3 atoms of oxygen

Recipe
Ingredients in Party Punch
1 part orange juice
1 part cranberry juice
2 parts pineapple juice

Mixture

Two or more elements or compounds mixed together, but not joined chemically

Mixtures

The photo shows a type of matter called a **mixture**. A mixture is made of two or more elements or compounds. But a mixture is different from a compound. The substances that form a mixture do not join chemically. They are simply mixed together. The soil shown here is a mixture of dead plants, sand, clay, water and other matter. The atoms of these substances are not joined.

This garden soil is a mixture called compost.

Can you name some other mixtures? Air is a mixture of gases. Some of the gases, such as oxygen, are elements. Other gases, such as carbon dioxide, are compounds. Most rocks are mixtures of compounds. A river is a mixture of water, oxygen, soil, pebbles, and other substances that move along a riverbed. Even the taco salad you might have had for lunch is a mixture.

The parts in a mixture can vary. You can take out the dead plant material in soil and it is still a mixture of soil. You can add more oxygen atoms to air and it is still a mixture of air. Compounds, however, have a fixed recipe or formula. You cannot simply add more oxygen atoms to water. Water must have exactly one oxygen atom for every two hydrogen atoms.

Unlike a compound, you can easily separate the parts of some mixtures. For example, you can separate the dead plant material in the soil just by picking it out with your fingers. Can you think of a way to separate the salt from a mixture of salt water? You will learn how in the investigation on pages 147 and 148.

Science Myth

Some people may think that air and oxygen are the same thing.

Fact: Air is a mixture of gases. We need to breathe in oxygen, but oxygen is only about 21 percent of air. Most of the air we breathe is nitrogen gas. Air also contains small amounts of carbon dioxide, water vapor, and other gases. This mixture varies. For example, air contains more water vapor on humid days.

Science Myth

Ask students to cover the Science Myth feature on page 145. Then read aloud the first sentence to the class. Ask for a show of hands from those who agree with the statement and from those who do not. Then have students uncover the feature and read the fact section.

CROSS-CURRICULAR CONNECTION

Home Economics
Ask students to bring in boxes of prepackaged mixes, such as cake mix, pancake mix, or dried potato products. They can work in pairs to read the ingredients label on one box and then list the elements and compounds in that mix.

LEARNING STYLES

Logical/Mathematical
Provide small groups of students with 8 washers, 8 bolts, and 8 nuts. Ask them to find a way to show the difference among elements, compounds, and mixtures using these items. You may want to have students refer to the list of compound formulas on page 143 and think of how they might represent each. For example, CO_2 could be modeled using a bolt and two nuts. Invite groups to explain how they decided to represent a mixture. For example, they might mix several kinds of "atoms" (individual bolts, nuts, and washers) with one or more "compounds" (combinations of nuts and bolts, washers and bolts, or nuts, bolts, and washers).

ONLINE CONNECTION

This site gives links to a number of science resources on mixtures: www.scienceteacherstuff.com/mixtures.html.

Lesson 3 Review Answers

1. An element is a substance made of only one type of atom. A compound is made of two or more types of atoms chemically combined. The properties of a compound are unlike those of the atoms from which it was made. **2.** Answers will vary. Sample answer: water—clear liquid; chalk—white solid. **3.** hydrogen and oxygen **4.** One atom of silicon and two atoms of oxygen combine to form one particle of silicon dioxide. **5.** The elements that make up a compound are joined chemically. The elements and compounds that make up a mixture are mixed together physically, but not joined chemically. A compound has a specific "recipe," while the amounts of substances in a mixture can vary. The substances in a mixture can be separated physically, while the elements in a compound must be separated chemically.

Science at Work

Read together the Science at Work feature on page 146. Ask students to summarize the tasks that chemical engineers might do on the job. Invite a chemical engineer to class to talk about how they use the properties of elements, compounds, and mixtures.

Portfolio Assessment

Sample items include:
- Venn diagram and compound diagram from Teaching the Lesson
- Lesson 3 Review answers

Write your answers to these questions on a sheet of paper.

1. What is the difference between an element and a compound?

2. Name two compounds. Describe one physical property of each.

3. The formula for water is H_2O. What kinds of atoms combine to make water?

4. The formula for silicon dioxide is SiO_2. How many atoms of silicon (Si) and oxygen (O) combine to form this compound?

5. How is a mixture different from a compound?

▼◄▲▼◄▲▼◄▲▼◄▲▼◄▲▼◄▲▼◄▲▼◄▲▼◄▲▼◄▲▼◄▲▼◄▲▼◄▲▼

Science at Work

Chemical Engineer

Engineers use science and mathematics to solve practical problems. Chemical engineers solve problems that involve chemicals.

Some chemical engineers design and test better ways to manufacture products. Others develop equipment to prevent pollution. Chemical engineers improve the ways chemicals are stored and moved. In all of these tasks, chemical engineers aim for better quality and lower cost.

Since the use of chemicals is so widespread, chemical engineers work in various fields. They develop many products, such as food, gasoline, and medical devices. They work with many materials, such as plastic cooling in a mold and liquid flowing through a pipe. They test processes to develop film and make synthetic fabric.

Chemical engineers need a bachelor's degree in chemical engineering. They also need a strong background in mathematics. Chemical engineers must be skilled problem solvers. They often work as part of a team. Good planning and communicating skills also are important.

Name _____ Date _____ Period _____ | Lab Manual, Page 1
Chapter 6 | 23

Testing Solutions

Purpose What substances dissolve most easily and least easily in water? In this investigation, you will find out more about solutions: mixtures in which one substance is dissolved in another.

Materials
drinking glass | salt
measuring cup | sugar
water | instant coffee
stirring spoon | powdered detergent
measuring tablespoon | sand
flour | clock or stopwatch

Procedure

1. Use the table below to record your data.

Substance	Did It Dissolve Completely?	How Long to Dissolve?	Appearance of Solution
flour			
salt			
sugar			
instant coffee			
detergent			
sand			

2. Put a cup of water in the glass. Add 1 tablespoon of flour.
3. Stir the mixture. As you do so, use a clock or stopwatch to measure how long it takes for the substance to dissolve. Stop after 2 minutes.
4. Observe the solution. Did the substance dissolve entirely? If so, how long did it take? What does the solution look like? Record your observations in the data table. Discard the mixture and rinse the glass with water.
5. Repeat steps 2 to 4 with each of the other substances.

©AGS Publishing. Permission is granted to reproduce for classroom use only.   Earth Science

Lab Manual 23, pages 1–2

Name _____ Date _____ Period _____ | Workbook Activity
Chapter 6, Lesson 3 | 24

Compounds and Mixtures: Terms Review

Directions When you compare and contrast things, you tell how they are alike and different. Compare and contrast each pair of terms.

compound—element

1. Alike _____

2. Different _____

compound—mixture

3. Alike _____

4. Different _____

Directions Salt is sodium chloride, NaCl. A common type of sand is silicon dioxide, SiO_2. Use this information to answer the questions.

5. What elements make up salt? _____

6. In silicon dioxide, how many atoms of silicon combine with two oxygen atoms? _____

7. Are NaCl and SiO_2 examples of compounds or mixtures? _____

Directions Match each term with its definition. Write the letter of the correct definition on the line.

_____ 8. atom | A anything that has mass and takes up space
_____ 9. chemical property | B two or more substances mixed but not chemically combined
_____ 10. compound | C characteristic that describes matter
_____ 11. matter | D property observed when matter is chemically changed
_____ 12. mixture | E property observed without having to change matter
_____ 13. nucleus | F smallest unit of an element that keeps the element's properties
_____ 14. physical property | G part of an atom; contains neutrons and protons
_____ 15. property | H what forms when atoms of two or more elements combine chemically

©AGS Publishing. Permission is granted to reproduce for classroom use only.   Earth Science

Workbook Activity 24

Separating a Mixture

Purpose

How would you separate a mixture of sand, salt, and water? In this investigation, you will use different methods to separate mixtures.

Materials

- clean sheet of paper
- 2 teaspoons of sand
- 2 teaspoons of salt
- spoon
- 2 beakers
- 10 tablespoons of warm water
- filter paper
- funnel

Procedure

1. Copy the data table on your paper.

Mixture	Description
salt and sand, dry	
salt and sand in water	
contents in beaker after filtering	
contents on filter paper after filtering	
contents in beaker after 1 day	
contents on filter paper after 1 day	

Fold once.

Fold twice.

Open to make a cone.

2. Use the spoon to stir the salt and sand together on a sheet of paper. Describe this dry mixture in your data table.

3. Pour the dry mixture into a beaker. Add the water. Stir the mixture well. Describe the new mixture. **Safety Alert: Never taste any substances used in a science investigation. Wipe up any spills immediately.**

4. Make a cone with the filter paper as shown. Place the cone in the funnel. Put the funnel in the empty beaker. Pour the mixture into the funnel. Describe the mixture that dripped into the beaker.

5. Describe the contents on the filter paper.

Earth Chemistry Chapter 6 **147**

Lab Manual 24

The Purpose portion of the student investigation begins with a question to draw students into the activity. Encourage students to read the investigation steps and formulate their own questions before beginning the investigation. This investigation will take approximately 45 minutes on Day 1 and 10 minutes on Day 2. Students will use these process and thinking skills: observing, inferring, interpreting data, and applying information to new situations.

Preparation

- The funnel chosen for this activity must be large enough to rest on top of the beaker. Otherwise, students will have to hold the funnel as it is draining.

- Two clear, plastic cups may be substituted for the beakers.

- Prepare a place where students can leave their beakers and filter paper undisturbed until the next day.

- Be sure students label their materials so they can identify them easily the next day.

- Students may use Lab Manual 24 to record their data and answer the questions.

Procedure

- Students may perform this investigation individually or in small groups. In groups, students should work cooperatively to record results and clean up. Assign jobs to individual students. For example: Student A mixes the salt and sand and pours it into the beaker, Student B adds the water and mixes, Student C makes the filter paper cone and sets up the apparatus, and Student D pours the mixture into the funnel and removes the funnel and filter paper.

- In step 3, make sure students stir the mixture enough to dissolve the salt.

- Caution students to pour the mixture into the cone slowly so that it does not overflow.

Continued on page 148

SAFETY ALERT

- Point out the Safety Alert in the text. Students should not taste the mixture.

Continued from page 147

Results

The salt will dissolve in the water, but the sand will not. The dissolved salt will pass through the filter paper along with the water, while the sand will be trapped in the filter. When the water has evaporated, the salt will be left behind.

Questions and Conclusions Answers

1. The salt seemed to disappear. It dissolved. The sand got darker but did not dissolve.

2. sand

3. Most of the salt went through the filter. On the second day, all or most of the water was gone, but dried salt stayed on the bottom and sides of the beaker.

Explore Further Answers

Mixture A: Separate by adding water and swabbing the sawdust from the surface with the cotton square. Mixture B: Separate iron filings with a magnet. Mixture C: Separate by sifting the sand through a wire screen.

Assessment

Verify that students correctly infer what happened to the salt. Check that students' approaches to Explore Further are logical. You might want to include the following items from this investigation in student portfolios:

• Data table

• Answers to Questions and Conclusions and Explore Further sections

6. Remove the funnel. Place the filter paper on the paper sheet. Set the beaker containing its mixture on the paper, too. Observe both the next day. Describe what you find.

7. Clean your work space and wash the equipment.

Questions and Conclusions

1. What happened to the salt when you added water and stirred? What happened to the sand?

2. What was left on the filter paper?

3. What happened to the salt? How do you know?

Explore Further

A	sand; sawdust
B	sand; iron filings
C	sand; pebbles

Choose one of the lettered mixtures at the left. Describe a procedure for separating it. You may use water and any equipment used earlier. You also may use a magnet, a wire screen, and a cotton square.

■ Matter is anything that has mass and takes up space.

■ Matter usually exists on the earth in three states: solid, liquid, and gas.

■ A physical property can be observed without changing a substance into a different substance.

■ A chemical property describes how a substance changes into a different substance.

■ An element is made of only one kind of atom. An element cannot be changed or separated into other kinds of substances.

■ An atom is the smallest particle of an element that has the characteristics of that element.

■ Atoms are made of protons, neutrons, and electrons. The nucleus of an atom is made of protons and neutrons.

■ Elements differ from one another because their atoms have different numbers of protons.

■ Scientists have discovered and named 109 elements. Ninety-two of them are found in nature.

■ The scientific symbol for each element has one or two letters.

■ Compounds form when the atoms of two or more elements combine chemically.

■ Scientists use formulas to represent compounds.

■ Mixtures are made of two or more elements or compounds that are not combined chemically.

Science Words

atom, 138	element, 137	nucleus, 138	property, 133
chemical	matter, 132	physical	states of
property, 133	mixture, 144	property, 133	matter, 132
compound, 141			

Chapter 6 Summary

Have volunteers read aloud each Summary item on page 149. Ask volunteers to explain the meaning of each item. Direct students' attention to the Science Words box on the bottom of page 149. Have them read and review each word and its definition.

Chapter 6 Review

Use the Chapter Review to prepare students for tests and to reteach content from the chapter.

Chapter 6 Mastery Test

The Teacher's Resource Library includes two parallel forms of the Chapter 6 Mastery Test. The difficulty level of the two forms is equivalent. You may wish to use one form as a pretest and the other form as a posttest.

Review Answers
Vocabulary Review

1. state of matter 2. matter 3. element 4. atom 5. nucleus 6. compound 7. mixture 8. property

Concept Review

9. Answers will vary. Sample answer: liquid—water; gas—oxygen; solid—paper 10. Answers will vary. Sample answer: solid, cold, clear 11. They have different numbers of protons, neutrons, and electrons. 12. The elements or compounds in a mixture are just mixed together physically. The elements in a compound are joined chemically. Substances in a mixture can be separated physically. Elements in a compound must be separated chemically. The parts of a mixture can vary in type and amount. The elements in a compound combine in specific atomic ratios. 13. A 14. D 15. C 16. B

TEACHER ALERT

In the Chapter Review, the Vocabulary Review activity includes a sample of the chapter's vocabulary terms. The activity will help determine students' understanding of key vocabulary terms and concepts presented in the chapter. Other vocabulary terms used in the chapter are listed below:

chemical property
physical property

Chapter 6   REVIEW

Word Bank
atom
compound
element
matter
mixture
nucleus
property
state of matter

Vocabulary Review

Choose the word or phrase from the Word Bank that best matches each phrase. Write the answer on your paper.

1. solid, liquid, or gas
2. anything that takes up space and has mass
3. substance made of only one kind of atom
4. smallest particle of an element
5. center of an atom
6. NaCl, water, or calcium carbonate
7. soil, air, or salad
8. characteristic of something

Concept Review

Write the answer to each of the following questions.

9. Name three states of matter and give an example of each.
10. Describe three physical properties of an ice cube.
11. What is the difference between the atoms of two different elements?
12. Explain how a mixture is different from a compound.

Choose the word or phrase that best answers each question. Write the letter of the answer on your paper.

13. Which parts of atoms are outside the nucleus?
   A electrons   C neutrons
   B protons   D elements

14. Which of the following is a chemical property?
   A large size
   B round shape
   C salty taste
   D black compound formed when burned

Chapter 6 Mastery Test A

15. Which compound is formed from three elements?
A H_2O **B** CO_2 **C** $CaCO_3$ **D** $NaCl$

16. Which statement is true about the compound carbon dioxide (CO_2)?
A It contains 2 carbon atoms.
B It contains 1 carbon atom.
C It contains 2 carbon atoms and 2 oxygen atoms.
D It contains 2 oxygen atoms and no carbon atoms.

Critical Thinking

Write the answer to each of the following questions.

17. How could you show someone that air is matter?

18. Iron atoms combine with oxygen atoms to form rust. Is this a physical property of iron or a chemical property? Why?

19. Compare and contrast the properties of each pair below.
A water; vinegar   **B** air; helium   **C** plastic; steel

20. Choose one of the lettered mixtures at the left. Explain how you would separate it. Use any of the tools shown.

A wood shavings; pebbles
B soil; water
C sand; iron filings

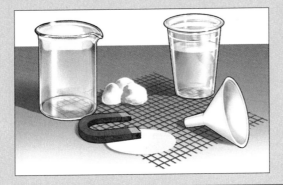

Test-Taking Tip When you review your notes to prepare for a test, use a marker to highlight key words and phrases.

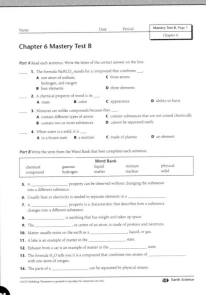

Chapter 6 Mastery Test B

Review Answers
Critical Thinking

17. Pump air into a balloon to show it takes up space. Calculate its mass by subtracting the mass of the deflated balloon from the mass of the inflated balloon. **18.** It is a chemical property because the iron and oxygen atoms combine to form a new substance, rust. **19. A** Both are liquids and can be colorless; water is tasteless and odorless while vinegar has a sharp taste and smell. **B** Both are colorless gases; at normal temperatures, helium makes a balloon float while air does not. **C** Both are solids that can block light; plastic is lighter, more flexible, and weaker than steel; steel is shiny, heavier, and rusts; plastic can be many colors and does not rust. **20. A** Wet the wood shavings and pebbles, then use the cotton square to gather the wooden shavings. **B** Line the funnel with filter paper and pour the mixture through it, catching the water in the empty beaker and the soil in the filter. **C** Use the magnet to remove the iron filings from the sand.

ALTERNATIVE ASSESSMENT

Alternative Assessment items correlate to the student Goals for Learning at the beginning of this chapter.

■ Have students list three examples of things that are matter and three that are not.

■ Fill a container with sand, another with water, and leave a third empty. Have students use an index card to label each container with the type of matter it contains and the state of that matter. Ask students to explain how they identified the states.

■ Have students observe the containers of sand, water, and air and list four physical properties of each type of matter on the index cards.

■ Ask students to draw a diagram of an atom and label these parts: nucleus, protons, neutrons, electrons.

■ Have students make a chart listing one way compounds and mixtures are alike and several ways they are different. Then have them make a diagram showing how elements and compounds are different.

Chapter

Planning Guide

Minerals

| | | Student Text Lesson | |
	Student Pages	Vocabulary	Lesson Review
Lesson 1 Minerals	154–156	✔	✔
Lesson 2 Properties Used to Identify Minerals	157–163	✔	✔
Lesson 3 Other Physical Properties of Minerals	164–169	✔	✔
Lesson 4 Common Uses of Minerals	170–172		✔

Chapter Activities

Student Text
Science Center

Teacher's Resource Library
Community Connection 7: A Mineral
   Museum at Home

Assessment Options

Student Text
Chapter 7 Review

Teacher's Resource Library
Chapter 7 Mastery Tests A and B
Chapters 1–7 Midterm Mastery Test

	Student Text Features								Teaching Strategies						Learning Styles						Teacher's Resource Library				
Achievements in Science	Science at Work	Science in Your Life	Investigation	Science Myth	Note	Technology Note	Did You Know	Science Integration	Science Journal	Cross-Curricular Connection	Online Connection	Teacher Alert	Applications (Home, Career, Community, Global, Environment)	Auditory/Verbal	Body/Kinesthetic	Interpersonal/Group Learning	Logical/Mathematical	Visual/Spatial	LEP/ESL	Workbook Activities	Alternative Workbook Activities	Lab Manual	Resource File	Self-Study Guide
156					✔					155			155	155		155		155		25	25			✔
		162	160			✔	158, 160	160, 161	159	159	159, 160	160						159		26	26	25, 26		✔
	167	168					164	166		166			165		165					27	27	27, 28	14	✔
			172		✔		171		172	171		171	171				171		172	28	28			✔

Pronunciation Key

a	hat	e	let	ī	ice	ô	order	ù	put	sh	she	
ā	age	ē	equal	o	hot	oi	oil	ü	rule	th	thin	
ä	far	ėr	term	ō	open	ou	out	ch	child	ŦH	then	
â	care	i	it	ȯ	saw	u	cup	ng	long	zh	measure	

ə { a in about / e in taken / i in pencil / o in lemon / u in circus }

Alternative Workbook Activities

The Teacher's Resource Library (TRL) contains a set of lower-level worksheets called Alternative Workbook Activities. These worksheets cover the same content as the regular Workbook Activities but are written at a second-grade reading level.

Skill Track Software

Use the Skill Track Software for Earth Science for additional reinforcement of this chapter. The software program allows students using AGS textbooks to be assessed for mastery of each chapter and lesson of the textbook. Students access the software on an individual basis and are assessed with multiple-choice items.

Chapter at a Glance

Chapter 7:
Minerals
pages 152–175

Lessons

1. Minerals pages 154–156

2. Properties Used to Identify Minerals pages 157–163

   Investigation 7-1 pages 162–163

3. Other Physical Properties of Minerals pages 164–169

   Investigation 7-2 pages 168–169

4. Common Uses of Minerals pages 170–172

Chapter 7 Summary page 173

Chapter 7 Review pages 174–175

Skill Track Software for Earth Science

Teacher's Resource Library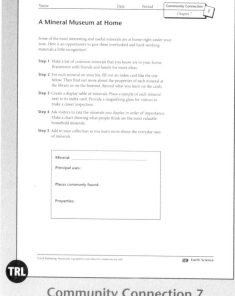

Workbook Activities 25–28

Alternative Workbook Activities 25–28

Lab Manual 25–28

Community Connection 7

Resource File 14

Chapter 7 Self-Study Guide

Chapter 7 Mastery Tests A and B

Chapters 1–7 Midterm Mastery Test

(Answer Keys for the Teacher's Resource Library begin on page 400 of the Teacher's Edition. The Materials List for the Lab Manual activities begins on page 415.)

Science Center

Display small, unlabeled specimens of some common minerals, such as quartz, calcite, pyrite, galena, copper, hematite, feldspar, halite, talc, gypsum, and fluorite. Have students compare and contrast the minerals often as they learn how physical properties can identify minerals.

Provide poster boards, markers, and magazines to cut up. As students learn about the uses of minerals in their lives, they can draw pictures or cut pictures from magazines to show examples of minerals being used by people. Students can use the pictures to create a poster or other kind of display.

Community Connection 7

Chapter

7 Minerals

inerals are all around us. We use them every day. Can you tell what mineral is shown in the photo? The long ropes you see are really copper wires braided into cable. Copper is a mineral that can carry an electric current. It is frequently used to make electrical wires and cables. These wires are braided so that the cable will not crack when it bends. In Chapter 7, you will learn what minerals are, how you can tell them apart, and how they are used today.

Organize Your Thoughts

- Crystal shape
- Hardness
- Luster
- Break pattern
- **Physical properties of minerals**
- Streak
- Color
- Specific gravity

Goals for Learning

- ◆ To explain what a mineral is
- ◆ To explain how minerals are located and mined
- ◆ To name familiar minerals
- ◆ To identify basic properties of all minerals
- ◆ To compare minerals by their properties
- ◆ To describe how minerals are used

153

Introducing the Chapter

Have students look at the photograph on page 152, and ask a volunteer to read aloud the opening paragraph. Say, "I thought copper was a metal. What do you think makes it a mineral?" Encourage students to discuss what they know and what they think they know about minerals. Make a three-column chart on the board with the headings *What I Know, What I Think I Know,* and *What I Want to Know.* Refer to this chart as students read the chapter.

Have students study the Organize Your Thoughts chart on page 153. Encourage them to write working definitions for the terms on the map. For example, students might define luster as the shininess of a mineral. Have them modify their definitions as they study the chapter.

Notes and Technology Notes

Ask volunteers to read the notes that appear in the margins throughout the chapter. Then discuss them with the class.

TEACHER'S RESOURCE

The AGS Teaching Strategies in Science Transparencies may be used with this chapter. The transparencies add an interactive dimension to expand and enhance the *Earth Science* program content.

CAREER INTEREST INVENTORY

The AGS Harrington-O'Shea Career Decision-Making System-Revised (CDM) may be used with this chapter. Students can use the CDM to explore their interests and identify careers. The CDM defines career areas that are indicated by students' responses on the inventory.

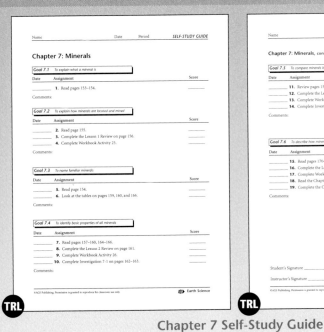

Chapter 7 Self-Study Guide

Lesson at a Glance

Chapter 7 Lesson 1

Overview In this lesson, students learn about the five features or criteria scientists use to classify an element or a compound as a mineral. Students identify some of the minerals that make up the earth's crust and learn how minerals are located and mined.

Objectives

- To explain what a mineral is
- To name some common minerals
- To explain how minerals are located and mined

Student Pages 154–156

Teacher's Resource Library

Workbook Activity 25

Alternative Workbook Activity 25

Vocabulary

mineral

Warm-Up Activity

Place a teaspoon of salt on a saucer. Have students describe what they observe. *(Students may mention that the salt is white and that it comes in small grains.)* Provide students with hand lenses. Guide them to see that the salt crystals are cubic and regular. Tell students that salt is a mineral. Explain that in this lesson they are going to learn why some substances are classified as minerals.

Teaching the Lesson

Have students rephrase the lesson objectives as questions. Allow sufficient time for them to answer the questions, using complete sentences.

You might want to review the difference between an element and a compound. An element is made of a single kind of atom, while a compound is made of two or more elements that have joined chemically to form a new substance.

Display samples of the common minerals listed on page 154. Give students hand lenses and allow them to observe the samples. Have them make a table to show

---

Objectives

After reading this lesson, you should be able to

- explain what a mineral is.
- name some common minerals.
- explain how minerals are located and mined.

Mineral

Element or compound found in the earth

The earth around you is a mixture of useful compounds and elements. Scientists classify some of these compounds and elements as **minerals**.

Features of Minerals

What do copper, quartz, and diamond have in common? They are all minerals. Elements or compounds are called minerals if they have these five features:

- They are solids.
- They are formed naturally in the earth.
- They have the same chemical makeup throughout.
- They are not alive or made of living things.
- They have definite atomic patterns.

About 3,000 different minerals are found in the earth. Some are common, but most are rare. In fact, only a small number of minerals make up most of the earth's surface. The most common minerals are aluminum, quartz, feldspar, mica, calcite, dolomite, halite, and gypsum.

Copper deposits often tarnish to a brown or green color.

Some minerals, such as gold (Au) and sulfur (S), are pure elements. Graphite and diamond are different forms of pure carbon. Most minerals, however, are compounds. They are made of two or more kinds of elements. For example, quartz (SiO_2) is made of the elements silicon (Si) and oxygen (O).

each mineral's physical properties. Explain to students that in later lessons they will learn how scientists use physical properties to classify minerals.

Locating and Mining Minerals

Minerals can be found in rocks, sand, soil, and seashells. Many minerals are found below the earth's surface. Minerals are mined, or dug out of the earth, so they can be used. People mine for minerals on every continent except Antarctica. Some minerals are found in pure forms. But most minerals are found mixed with other minerals in rocks.

Geologists locate rocks with certain minerals by looking for clues on the earth's surface. They observe the kinds of rocks and plants in an area. Geologists might test running water for traces of minerals.

Once minerals are located, they are either skimmed off the earth's surface or dug deep out of the ground. Minerals near the surface can be strip-mined. This means that long patches of soil are stripped off. Then the exposed minerals are scooped up. Another way to reach minerals near the surface is to dig open pits.

For minerals deep underground, long shafts are dug into the earth. These shafts are often as long as 1.6 kilometers. Mining tunnels branch off the shafts. In the tunnels, explosives are used to break apart rock so the mineral deposits can be collected.

After deposits are taken out of the earth, the minerals need to be separated from the rock, or purified. One way to do this is to melt the minerals in huge smelting ovens. Another method is to use chemicals to break apart the minerals.

The mineral quartz is silicon dioxide, SiO_2.

Graphite is a soft form of pure carbon.

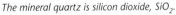

---

3 Reinforce and Extend

LEARNING STYLES

Interpersonal/ Group Learning

Have pairs of students rephrase the features of a mineral listed on page 154. For example, students might say that a mineral cannot be a gas or a liquid, minerals are not made by people, and so on. Encourage pairs to get together to check each other's work and provide constructive feedback if necessary. List their revised feature definitions on the board.

GLOBAL CONNECTION

Assign a continent to each of seven groups of students. Each group is responsible for finding out about the major mineral deposits on its continent. Allow time for each group to briefly relate its findings to the rest of the class.

LEARNING STYLES

Visual/Spatial

Encourage students to explore the amazing variety of minerals. Assign them each two or three minerals, and have them conduct an Internet search using the key words *minerals* and *photographs*. Ask students to print out images of their assigned minerals. Help them create a mineral photo gallery in the classroom.

IN THE ENVIRONMENT

Have students debate the pros and cons of mining the earth's minerals. Major points covered should include our dependence on the earth's resources, the pollution associated with mining, the importance of recycling, the economic aspects of mining, and the limited quantities of many of these minerals.

LEARNING STYLES

Auditory/Verbal

Point out that the names of minerals are sometimes challenging. Have small groups of students practice pronouncing common minerals such as aluminum, apatite, asbestos, cadmium, calcite, corundum, chromium, dolomite, feldspar, fluorite, gypsum, halite, hematite, mica, pyrite, quartz, and tourmaline. Invite groups to say the words for the class. Then have the whole class repeat the correct pronunciation.

CROSS-CURRICULAR CONNECTION

History

Explain that mining for minerals is an ancient—and a dangerous—occupation. Ask students to choose a mineral and learn how and why people began to extract it from the earth. Have them use Internet or print resources to find out about the purpose, the technology, and the hazards of early mining practices. Have students share their research in small groups or with the class.

Lesson 1 Review Answers

1. A mineral is a solid, formed naturally in the earth, having the same chemical makeup throughout, not made of living things, and having a definite atomic pattern. **2.** Answers will vary, but might include gold, quartz, diamond, carbon, feldspar, mica, calcite, dolomite, halite, or gypsum. **3.** Geologists look for clues on the earth's surface. These might include the kinds of rocks or plants in an area. Sometimes geologists test running water for traces of minerals. **4.** Minerals can be stripped off the earth's surface or dug out of open pits. People reach minerals far underground by digging long shafts. **5.** Minerals are purified either by melting them or by using chemicals to break them apart.

Achievements in Science

Read together the feature on page 156. Ask students to imagine human society thousands of years ago—before people learned how to extract metal from rocks. Then invite them to consider how the discovery that metals could be melted and shaped would have changed the way people lived. Point out that people knew about only seven metals—called the metals of antiquity—until the 13th century. These were gold, copper, silver, lead, tin, iron, and mercury. Ask students what they know about the qualities of these metals and how they might have been used.

Portfolio Assessment

Sample items include:
- Questions and answers from Teaching the Lesson
- Lesson 1 Review answers

Lesson 1   R E V I E W

Write your answers to these questions on a sheet of paper.

1. What are the five features of a mineral?

2. Name two common minerals.

3. How do geologists know where to find minerals deep in the earth?

4. How are minerals taken out of the earth?

5. How are minerals purified?

Achievements in Science

Working With Metals

Many minerals are metals. People have been making things out of metals for thousands of years. One of the first minerals to be used was copper. Copper was mined around 9000 B.C. on the island of Cyprus in the Mediterranean Sea.

By 3000 B.C., the Sumerians had discovered bronze. They heated rocks containing copper and tin ore to produce bronze for ornaments and weapons.

Around 1900 B.C., the Hittites of Turkey began making tools and weapons out of iron. Although these ancient people were mainly farmers, they developed metal-working techniques that were more advanced than others at the time.

In the 1850s, a process for making steel was invented in America and England. This process adds carbon to melted iron by forcing air through the iron. The steel that results is stronger than iron.

More than 90 percent of all metal used in the world today is iron. Almost all of this iron is in the form of steel. Steel costs much less than other metals. It is used in thousands of products, such as cars, buildings, and paper clips.

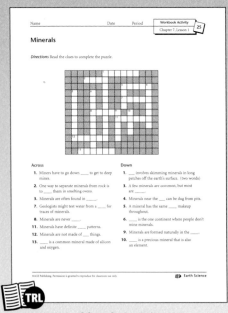

Workbook Activity 25

Objectives

After reading this lesson, you should be able to

◆ identify four properties of minerals.

◆ assess color as a way to identify minerals.

◆ define luster.

◆ describe a streak test.

◆ explain how to test the hardness of a mineral.

Pyrite is sometimes called fool's gold because people can easily mistake it for gold. However, no two minerals share the same physical properties. For example, pyrite is almost the same color as gold, but it is harder than gold. In this lesson, you will learn about four properties used for identifying minerals.

Color

Some minerals have a unique color. For example, sulfur is usually bright yellow, as you can see in the photo below. However, most minerals can be found in more than one color. For example, quartz might be clear, purple, pink, black, or white. The color varies because the mineral is not usually found in a pure form. It often contains tiny amounts of different minerals called impurities.

Many minerals are similar in color, such as pyrite and gold. Color is one clue to a mineral's identity, but color alone is usually not enough of a clue.

Sulfur is easy to recognize because of its bright yellow color.

Chapter 7 Lesson 2

Overview In this lesson, students explore color, luster, streak, and hardness as properties used to identify minerals.

Objectives

■ To identify four properties of minerals

■ To assess color as a way to identify minerals

■ To define luster

■ To describe a streak test

■ To explain how to test the hardness of a mineral

Student Pages 157–163

Teacher's Resource Library

Workbook Activity 26

Alternative Workbook Activity 26

Lab Manual 25–26

Vocabulary

hardness   streak
luster

Science Background

While most minerals are actually composed of elements that are colorless, colored varieties of minerals are quite common due to defects in crystal structure or small inclusions of other minerals. Color might be the first thing you notice when you pick up a mineral sample. More often than not, however, color cannot be used as a reliable identifier.

Minerals are also described by how they reflect light. The luster of minerals is divided into two broad categories—metallic and nonmetallic. Nonmetallic lusters can be further described as pearly, glassy, resinous, dull, greasy, silky, and adamantine. Pearly, glassy, and dull are self-explanatory. Lusters of minerals such as sulfur and opal are said to be resinous, or resembling resin. While clear quartz has a glassy luster, massive quartz appears as though it is covered with a thin layer of oil and its luster is described as greasy.

Continued on page 158

Continued from page 157

Fibrous minerals, such as certain types of gypsum, have a silky luster due to the reflection of light from the numerous fibers of the mineral. An adamantine luster is a hard, brilliant luster like that of a diamond.

 Warm-Up Activity

Obtain a variety of quartz crystals, such as rose, milky, amethyst, clear, smoky, and citrine quartz. Without revealing the identities of the samples, have students observe them with hand lenses. Challenge students to group the crystals based on their observations. They might classify the samples into light-colored groups, dark-colored groups, and so on. When they have finished, tell them that each sample is quartz. Help them conclude that, in many cases, we need to know more than one physical property to identify minerals.

 Teaching the Lesson

Have students write the words *color, luster, streak,* and *hardness* on a sheet of paper. Tell them that as they read, they are to explain, in their own words, the usefulness of each property in determining the identity of an unknown mineral.

If possible, obtain and display labeled mineral specimens that do have diagnostic colors, such as azurite (bright blue), malachite (bright green), sulfur (bright yellow), and native copper (bright copper color on a fresh surface; bright green, blue-green, or black on a tarnished surface).

Provide students with a streak plate and two different samples of hematite: the red, earthy form and the metallic form called specularite. Have students observe each sample with a hand lens. Ask if they think the samples are the same mineral. (They may think they are different minerals because of their different appearances.) Have students perform the streak test with each sample and observe the powdered residue on the plate with the lens. (Students should determine that the dark reddish-brown streak of both samples is the same.) Inform students that both samples are the mineral hematite.

Luster
How a mineral reflects light

Streak
Color of the mark a mineral makes on a white tile

 Did You Know?

Since ancient times, people have used minerals with metallic luster to make mirrors. The first mirrors were made of pyrite or polished metal. Today's mirrors are usually a glass plate painted with a film of aluminum or silver.

Luster

Some minerals are shiny, but others look dull. Different minerals reflect light differently. The way that a mineral reflects light is called **luster**. There are two main kinds of luster: metallic and nonmetallic. Shiny minerals, such as gold and silver, have a metallic luster.

Minerals with a nonmetallic luster can be described in several ways. For example, if a mineral looks like a pearl, its luster is described as pearly. A mineral that looks like glass is said to have a glassy luster. Compare the luster of the minerals shown here.

Talc has a pearly luster.   *Calcite has a glassy luster.*

Streak

When you rub a soft mineral across a tile, it leaves a mark. The color of the mark is the mineral's **streak**. A streak test helps you identify a mineral because a mineral usually has the same streak. The tile used in a streak test is called a streak plate. It is made of white, unglazed porcelain.

Did You Know?

Have a volunteer read aloud the Did You Know? feature on page 158. Ask students what metals they think might make the best mirrors. Point out that silver is the best reflector of light, but that it tarnishes easily and has to be polished. Glass mirrors backed with metal began to be produced about 1,000 years ago. For a long time they were luxury items. Until the 19th century, most people in Europe and North America could not afford a full-length mirror.

Hardness

Ability of a mineral to resist being scratched

The streak of a mineral may be different from the mineral's color. For example, chunks of gold and pyrite are both gold colored, but you can tell them apart with a streak test. Gold has a yellow streak, but pyrite has a black streak. Some minerals are so hard, however, that they will not leave a streak.

The table below gives the luster and streak of some minerals. Notice that quartz does not leave a streak.

The Luster and Streak of Some Minerals		
Mineral	Luster	Streak
gold	metallic	yellow
silver	metallic	silver-white
pyrite	metallic	gray to black
quartz	glassy	colorless
calcite	glassy	white
talc	pearly	white
hematite	metallic or dull	red to brown

Hardness

Suppose someone offers to sell you a diamond ring. How can you tell if the diamond is real? You could do a simple test. You could see if the diamond can scratch a piece of glass. A diamond will scratch glass because it is harder than the glass. Diamond is the hardest of all minerals. It will scratch any other material. But nothing will scratch diamond.

The **hardness** of a mineral describes how well the mineral resists being scratched. Geologists measure hardness on a scale of 1 to 10, called Mohs' scale of hardness. This scale is described in a table on the next page.

CROSS-CURRICULAR CONNECTION

 History

Explain that the mineral gold has been highly prized by many world civilizations throughout history. Point out that in 1849 many Americans traveled to the West during the Gold Rush. Suggest students look up and read first-person accounts of the Gold Rush. Ask students to research ways that Gold Rush miners distinguished real gold from fool's gold, or pyrite. What properties of gold were used? Have students write a report and present it to the class.

SCIENCE JOURNAL

 Ask students to imagine that they have discovered a new mineral. Have them write a description of this mineral's color, luster, streak, and hardness, including how they determined each property.

ONLINE CONNECTION

 Refer students with questions about geology to the U.S. Geological Survey's Ask-A-Geologist site. Have them go to walrus.wr.usgs.gov and click on "Education and Outreach" and then "Ask-A-Geologist Program." This site also refers users to other addresses where experts are available to answer questions online.

LEARNING STYLES

Visual/Spatial

Students may have a hard time visualizing such descriptions as pearly, glassy, or metallic. Show them actual samples of pyrite, talc, quartz, or other minerals that have these lusters. They might write their own descriptions of these lusters so that they better remember what each means.

Did You Know?

Ask a volunteer to read aloud the Did You Know? feature on page 160. Show students the label from a bottle of multivitamin pills. Compile two lists on the board: ingredients that students know are minerals and ingredients that they think might be. Have students use dictionaries or other reference works to identify the mineral ingredients.

ONLINE CONNECTION

Encourage students to learn more about essential minerals in our diet by going to www.nal.usda.gov/fnic. They should click on "Topics A–Z," then scroll down to "Vitamins and Minerals" for links to information about mineral nutrients. The site is run by the Food and Nutrition Information Center of the U.S. Department of Agriculture.

SCIENCE INTEGRATION

Biology

Point out that plants as well as people depend on mineral nutrients for healthy growth. Ask students to find out what important nutrients plant fertilizers contain and how each contributes to a plant's development.

Science Myth

Ask a volunteer to read the Science Myth feature. Make sure students understand the variety of forms minerals can take. Have them find illustrations in their textbook showing contrasting examples. Show students a silver chain and a piece of chalk. Point out that both are minerals: silver and calcite. If necessary, review the definition of a mineral on page 154.

TEACHER ALERT

Make sure students understand that most rocks are made of a variety of minerals and may therefore have several degrees of hardness. The hardness scale on page 160 applies to specimens of pure minerals.

Did You Know?

Minerals are good for you. They provide the calcium and phosphorus your body needs to make strong bones. Your body needs iron to make red blood cells. Zinc helps your body to heal. These and other minerals are in the food you eat. Do you know what foods contain calcium?

Science Myth

Some people may think that all minerals look about the same.

Fact: Although all minerals have some characteristics in common, there are great differences among them. Some minerals are soft enough to scratch with your fingernail. Some minerals are hard enough to scratch glass.

Mohs' Scale of Hardness		
Mineral	Hardness	Quick Test
talc	1	scratched easily by fingernail
gypsum	2	scratched by fingernail
calcite	3	barely scratched by copper penny
fluorite	4	scratched easily by steel
apatite	5	scratched by steel
feldspar	6	scratches glass easily
quartz	7	scratches both glass and steel easily
topaz	8	scratches quartz
corundum	9	no simple test
diamond	10	no simple test

The higher the number on Mohs' scale, the harder the mineral. A mineral will scratch any other mineral that has a lower number. In the table, the mineral fluorite has a hardness of 4. It scratches calcite but does not scratch apatite. Feldspar will scratch calcite, fluorite, and apatite.

You can use Mohs' scale to find the hardness of an unknown sample. Scratch the sample against each mineral on the scale, starting with the softest mineral. If the unknown sample scratches one mineral, test it with the next. Keep moving up the hardness scale, testing until the sample itself is scratched by one of the minerals. Its hardness is between that of the last two minerals tested. For example, a mineral that scratches feldspar but is scratched by quartz has a hardness of about 6.5.

If you do not have a set of minerals, you can use the "quick test" instead. The quick test shows how to use common materials to test hardness. For example, suppose you cannot scratch a mineral with your fingernail but you can easily scratch it with a penny. The mineral probably has a hardness between 2 and 3. Geologists working in the field usually use the quick test.

Write your answers to these questions on a sheet of paper.

1. Why might the same mineral be found in different colors?

2. Describe both the color and the luster of silver.

3. How do you determine a mineral's streak?

4. The hardness of quartz is 7. The hardness of topaz is 8. Will quartz scratch topaz? Explain.

5. What is the hardness of a mineral that is scratched by steel but does not scratch glass?

Technology Note

Gold isn't just for rings and earrings. This mineral has many useful properties besides being a popular metal for jewelry.

Gold doesn't tarnish or rust when exposed to air and water. It easily conducts, or carries, an electric current. These properties make it a good choice for use in electronic products. Examples of such products include computers, telephones, and home appliances.

Gold can reflect heat without becoming hot. In the industrial and medical fields, gold-coated reflectors are used to focus light energy. Some face shields for firefighters are coated with gold.

Gold is easily hammered into tiny wires or thin sheets without breaking. For example, 28 grams of gold can be drawn into a wire 8 kilometers long. Similarly, 28 grams of gold can be flattened into a single sheet that is 30 square meters. That's enough to cover the floor of a small bedroom.

Gold is also an excellent conductor of heat energy. The main engine nozzle on a space shuttle contains gold. Temperatures around a space shuttle can reach 3,300°C. The purpose of the gold is to draw this heat away from sensitive instruments.

Minerals   Chapter 7   **161**

Lesson 2 Review Answers

1. Tiny amounts of different minerals, called impurities, can give samples of the same mineral different colors. **2.** Silver has a white or gray color and a metallic luster. **3.** You determine streak by rubbing a soft mineral across a white porcelain tile. The color of the mark it leaves is the mineral's streak. **4.** No. On Mohs' hardness scale, a mineral with a higher number is harder than a mineral with a lower number. The softer mineral, quartz, will not scratch the harder mineral, topaz. **5.** between 5 and 6 on Mohs' hardness scale

SCIENCE INTEGRATION

Technology
Ask volunteers to each read one paragraph in the Technology Note on page 161. Explain that gold is an easy metal to work with because it can be pulled or hammered into different shapes. Ask students what disadvantages this quality might have. *(A gold ornament could easily be damaged.)* Point out that gold is often combined with other metals to strengthen it. These combinations, called alloys, sometimes have the added effect of changing gold's color. For example, adding copper gives gold a red tint, silver makes it green, and nickel makes it white.

Portfolio Assessment

Sample items include:
• Explanations from Teaching the Lesson
• Lesson 2 Review answers

Name _____ Date _____ Period _____ | Lab Manual, Page 1 / Chapter 7 | 25

Testing the Hardness of Minerals

Purpose Are some minerals harder than others? In this investigation, you will find and compare the hardness of several minerals.

Materials 2 mineral samples labeled 1 and 2 / copper penny / steel nail

Procedure

1. Use the table below to record your data.

Quick Test	Mineral Sample 1	Mineral Sample 2
scratched by fingernail?		
scratches fingernail?		
scratched by penny?		
scratches penny?		
scratched by steel nail?		
scratches steel nail?		
scratched by other sample?		
scratches other sample?		

2. Test mineral sample 1. Try to scratch it with your fingernail. Does it make a mark? Rub the mineral against your fingernail. Does it make a mark? Write your observation in the data table.

3. Scratch the mineral with the penny. Does it make a mark? Scratch the penny with the mineral. Does it make a mark? Write your observations in the data table.

4. Scratch the mineral with the steel nail. Does it make a mark? Scratch the steel nail with the mineral. Does it make a mark? Write your observations in the data table.

5. Scratch mineral sample 1 with mineral sample 2. Then scratch sample 2 with sample 1. Write your observations.

6. Repeat steps 2 to 5 using mineral sample 2 instead.

©AGS Publishing. Permission is granted to reproduce for classroom use only. | Earth Science

Lab Manual 25, pages 1–2

Name _____ Date _____ Period _____ | Workbook Activity / Chapter 7, Lesson 2 | 26

Properties Used to Identify Minerals

Directions Look at the concept map of mineral properties. Match each empty box in the map with an answer from the Answer Bank. Write the letter of the correct answer in the box.

Answer Bank
A which is found by making a mark on a tile
B luster
C color
D properties
E metallic
F which can be measured according to Mohs' scale

Directions Unscramble the word in parentheses to complete each sentence. Write the answer on the line.

7. _____ and pyrite may look alike, but their streaks are different. (dolg)

8. No other mineral is capable of scratching a _____. (donmaid)

9. One of the very softest minerals is _____. (lact)

10. Mohs' scale measures _____. (sendrash)

11. The _____ of quartz is described as glassy. (elrust)

12. A hard mineral can scratch a _____ one. (fots)

13. Sulfur is easy to recognize because it is bright _____. (wolley)

14. When doing a streak test, use a _____ tile. (thwse)

15. You can quickly test for hardness by using a copper _____. (nynep)

©AGS Publishing. Permission is granted to reproduce for classroom use only. | Earth Science

Workbook Activity 26

Investigation 7-1

The Purpose portion of the student investigation begins with a question to draw students into the activity. Encourage students to read the investigation steps and formulate their own questions before beginning the investigation. This investigation will take approximately 40 minutes to complete. Students will use these process and thinking skills: comparing and contrasting, estimating, observing, collecting and organizing data, communicating, and describing.

Preparation

- Have specimens of halite, galena, pyrite, mica (biotite or muscovite), hematite, and amphibole (hornblende) prepared for each student or group.

- Make sure all specimens are labeled correctly with permanent marker.

- You might want to prepare investigation kits before class. For each student or group, put a sample of each of the six minerals, a streak plate, a penny, and a steel spoon in a small container. You may substitute a steel paper clip or other steel object for the spoon.

- For the unknown mineral in the Explore Further activity, any of the minerals on Mohs' scale of hardness would be appropriate. Tell students if the unknown sample is not listed on the scale. Provide unlabeled samples of enough different minerals so that each student or group can test a different mineral.

- Students may use Lab Manual 26 to record their data and answer the questions.

Procedure

- Students may work individually or in cooperative groups. For group work, assign one student to gather equipment and another to clean up when finished. The students should take turns observing and testing the samples.

- Students may have difficulty doing a streak test. You might want to demonstrate once for the whole class.

- Hand lenses can be used to better observe streaks and mineral scratches.

7-1 INVESTIGATION

Observing Color, Streak, and Hardness

Purpose

How could you show that minerals have unique physical properties? In this investigation, you will describe the color, streak, and hardness of known mineral samples.

Materials
- labeled samples of minerals
- streak plate
- copper penny
- steel spoon

Procedure

1. Copy the data table on a sheet of paper.

Mineral Name	Color Observations	Streak Observations	Quick Test Observations	Hardness Estimate

2. Write the name of each mineral sample in the first column of the data table.

3. Observe the color of each sample. Record your observations in the data table.

4. Rub each sample across the streak plate, as shown here. Record your observations in the data table.

162   Chapter 7   Minerals

Lab Manual 26

5. Refer to the Quick Test column of Mohs' scale on page 160. Try to scratch each sample with your fingernail, the penny, and the spoon. Record your observations. Wash your hands and fingernails.

6. Using Mohs' scale and your observations from step 5, estimate the hardness number of each sample.

7. Return the samples and equipment.

Questions and Conclusions

1. Which property was the easiest to observe?

2. Which property was the hardest to observe?

3. How did the color of each mineral compare to its streak?

Explore Further

Ask your teacher for an unknown mineral sample. Identify it by finding its hardness. Use the materials and minerals you already have. Explain how you tested the sample.

• As an extension to this activity, you might have students add a column labeled Luster Observations to their data tables. Galena, pyrite, and specular hematite have metallic lusters. Halite, mica, amphibole, and earthy hematite have nonmetallic lusters.

SAFETY ALERT

◆ Be sure students wash their hands and fingernails after scratching the samples.

Results

Students should arrive at descriptions approximately as follows: halite: colorless, colorless, less than 3.0; galena: gray, gray, less than 3.0; pyrite: brassy, gray-black, more than 5.5; mica (biotite): black, gray to black, 2.5–3; or mica (muscovite): white to gray, no streak, 2.5–3.0; hematite: reddish brown to black, light to dark red, more than 5.5; amphibole (hornblende): dark green to black, no streak, 5.0–6.0.

Questions and Conclusions Answers

1. Answers will vary, but color is probably the most obvious property to observe.

2. Answers will vary. Students will probably find hardness to be the most difficult property to determine.

3. Mineral colors were the same as their streaks for all samples except hematite, pyrite, and mica.

Explore Further Answers

Students can identify the mineral sample by attempting to scratch it with their fingernails, the penny, the spoon, and the other known minerals. Answers will depend on the samples provided.

Assessment

Be sure that students have correctly filled in their data table. If their answers differ widely from the rest of the class, ask them to try the tests a second time. You might include the following items from this investigation in student portfolios:

• Data table

• Answers to Questions and Conclusions and Explore Further sections

Lesson at a Glance

Chapter 7 Lesson 3

Overview In this lesson, students learn about some additional physical properties that help identify minerals: crystal shape, the way minerals break, and their density compared to water.

Objectives

- To explain what a crystal is
- To recognize how minerals break
- To measure the specific gravity of mineral samples

Student Pages 164–169

Teacher's Resource Library

Workbook Activity 27

Alternative Workbook Activity 27

Lab Manual 27–28

Resource File 14

Vocabulary

cleavage   fracture

crystal   specific gravity

Science Background

All minerals can be described by color, luster, hardness, streak, break pattern, crystal shape, and specific gravity. However, some minerals also have other signature properties. For example, halite (salt) has a distinct salty taste and is soluble in water. Calcite exhibits double refraction—that is, an object placed behind a transparent piece of the mineral appears to double. Magnetite, an iron oxide mineral, is magnetic. Dolomite and calcite, which contain carbon and oxygen, will effervesce, or bubble, when hydrochloric acid is placed on them. Students might be interested in seeing demonstrations of some of these properties.

1 Warm-Up Activity

Display some large mica and quartz specimens. Allow students to observe similarities and differences between the two minerals. (*Students may not know the word* crystal, *but they should observe that the crystal forms of the two minerals are quite different.*) Allow students to separate sheets of mica along the flat

---

Objectives

After reading this lesson, you should be able to

- explain what a crystal is.
- recognize how minerals break.
- measure the specific gravity of mineral samples.

Crystal

Basic shape that a mineral tends to take

 Did You Know?

Scientists have grown crystals on several space shuttle missions. Nearly perfect crystals can be grown in weightlessness.

Lesson 2 explored some of the properties that can help you identify minerals: color, luster, streak, and hardness. In this lesson, you will learn about some other properties you can use.

Crystal Shape

The atoms of most minerals are arranged in an orderly, repetitive pattern. The arrangement of a mineral's atoms causes it to form in solid chunks with a characteristic shape, called **crystals**. The shape of a crystal depends on the arrangement of its atoms. For example, if you look at a few grains of salt through a magnifying glass, you will see that all the grains have the same shape. Each salt grain is a tiny cube. The cubes are salt crystals.

Crystal shapes can help you identify a mineral. For example, salt and quartz have the same color and luster. However, salt crystals always form cubes, but quartz crystals have six long sides. As you can see in the photos below, the shape of a quartz crystal is very different from the shape of a salt crystal.

Salt crystals are shaped like cubes.   *Quartz crystals have six sides.*

Most minerals form crystals. The crystals of some minerals are easily visible. Some crystals, however, are so small that they cannot be seen without a microscope.

---

cleavage planes. Encourage them to speculate why minerals have these different shapes. (*The characteristic shape of a mineral is determined by the arrangement of its atoms.*) Tell students they will learn about mineral shapes in this lesson.

2 Teaching the Lesson

Have students list the boldfaced terms in this lesson. Next to each term, have them write a definition of the term along with a sentence that correctly expresses the meaning of the term.

Display a small, irregularly shaped sponge, a plum-sized piece of quartz, a wadded-up sheet of notebook paper, and a small, hard rubber ball. All of these

items should be nearly the same size. Let students assess the density of the items by picking them up. Ask students to rank the items in order of increasing density. (*sponge, paper, ball, quartz*)

Emphasize that students could compare the densities of the items by their weight only because the objects are approximately the same size. A less dense object could weigh more than a more dense object if it were much larger.

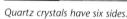 **Did You Know?**

Have a volunteer read the feature on page 164. Explain to students that the earth's gravitational pull can misshape crystals by disturbing the liquids in which they grow. In an orbiting space shuttle, gravity is one millionth that on the earth.

Break Pattern

Cleavage

Ability to split along flat surfaces

Fracture

Tendency to break with jagged edges

Specific gravity

Mineral's weight compared to the weight of water

The arrangement of atoms in a mineral also makes it break in a specific way. Some minerals tend to break along flat surfaces. That kind of break is called **cleavage**.

Other minerals do not leave flat surfaces when they break. Instead, they break unevenly, leaving jagged edges. A jagged break pattern is called **fracture**.

Cleavage break

Fracture break

Specific Gravity

You can compare the density of many materials just by picking them up. If you pick up a hammer, you can tell that the steel head is denser than the wooden handle. The steel feels heavier, as if more matter is packed into it.

Density can help you identify minerals. To measure the density of a mineral, you compare the weight of a sample to the weight of the same volume of water. This comparison is called **specific gravity**. It can be calculated using this formula:

$$\text{specific gravity} = \frac{\text{weight of sample}}{\text{weight of same volume of water}}$$

Water has a specific gravity of 1. A mineral that is twice as heavy as water has a specific gravity of 2. If a mineral has a specific gravity of 3.5, it is 3.5 times heavier than water.

Minerals   Chapter 7   **165**

Properties and Uses of Common Minerals

Name _____ Date _____ Period _____ | Resource File **14** Chapter 7 |

Mineral	Color and Luster	Streak	Hardness	Break Pattern	Specific Gravity	Uses
calcite	variety of colors, glassy	white	3	cleavage	2.7	cement, other building materials, chalk, fertilizers, metals, glass, rubber, paint
copper	copper, metallic	copper	2.5–3	fracture	8.8–8.9	wires, motors, electro-magnets, generators, communication devices, cookware, coins
corundum	variety of colors, glassy to adamantine	white	9	fracture	3.9–4.1	jewelry, abrasives
diamond	colorless to white, adamantine	white	10	cleavage	3.1–3.5	jewelry, abrasives, thermal insulators, optics, electronics, tools
fluorite	variety of colors, glassy	white	4	cleavage	3–3.2	lenses, toothpaste
gold	pale to deep yellow, metallic	yellow	2.5–3	fracture	15.5–19.3	jewelry, coins, medicines, photography, electronics
graphite	gray-black, metallic	gray to black	1–2	cleavage	1.9–2.3	pencil lead, lubricants, batteries
gypsum	clear to white, pearly	white	2	cleavage	2.3–2.4	plaster, wallboard
halite	variety of colors, glassy	white	2–2.5	cleavage	2.1–2.6	salt
hematite	black, gray, brown, or red; metallic to dull	red to brown	5–6	fracture	4.9–5.3	iron, jewelry
magnetite	black, metallic	black	5.5–6	fracture	4.9–5.2	source of iron, magnets
mica	variety of colors, glassy	colorless	2.5–3	cleavage	2.7–3.1	insulation, paint
pyrite	brassy yellow, metallic	gray to black	6–6.5	fracture	4.9–5.2	minor source of iron and sulfur
quartz	variety of colors, glassy	colorless	7	fracture	1.9–2.8	glass, jewelry, watches, radios, pressure gauges, abrasives, soaps, ceramics, computers
silver	white, metallic	silver-white	2.5	fracture	9.6–12	jewelry, coins, wires, trays, cutlery
sulfur	yellow, dull	white	1.5–2.5	fracture	2–2.5	medicine, rubber, pesticides, dyes, matches, explosives
talc	white to green, pearly	white	1	cleavage	2.7–2.8	talcum powder, cosmetics, paper

©AGS Publishing. Permission is granted to reproduce for classroom use only.

 Earth Science

TRL

---

3 **Reinforce and Extend**

LEARNING STYLES

Body/Kinesthetic

Display a variety of mineral samples with different crystal shapes. Provide students with toothpicks and colored clay. Have them use these materials to make models of crystal shapes based on the mineral samples.

AT HOME

To help students understand how crystals develop, have them perform the following experiment at home: Completely dissolve $\frac{1}{4}$ cup of salt in 1 cup of water. Pour the solution into a small, flat-bottomed glass bowl and let it sit uncovered until the water evaporates. (Depending on the shape of the bowl and the room temperature, this process may take up to a month.) Ask students to observe the results and compare notes in class. *(Salt crystals will form on the bowl's bottom. A fine salt deposit will be on the sides.)* Ask students why the salt might reappear in different forms. *(Salt ions in solution need time to form cubic crystals. The water on the bottom remained the longest.)* Challenge students to think of circumstances in the natural world in which a similar situation might occur. *(Students may have heard of rock salt formations in certain lakes or natural salt beds formed by slow-drying oceans.)*

CAREER CONNECTION

Explain that a gemologist examines gems, such as diamonds, emeralds, and rubies, to determine their value. To appraise a gem, a gemologist must look at many different properties, including luster, color, cut, weight, and rarity. Encourage students to research information about gemologists, their appraisal techniques, educational background, and career opportunities. Students might search online for information or arrange to interview a gemologist at a museum or college.

Minerals   Chapter 7   **165**

CROSS-CURRICULAR CONNECTION

History

Point out that gold has a specific gravity of 19.3. It is one of the densest minerals. Have students look up *placer mining* in a reference book or on the Internet and explain how miners used specific gravity to help them during the Gold Rush. (*Miners panned for gold, combining handfuls of dirt in a pan with water. The heavier gold sank to the bottom, while the lighter materials washed over the sides.*) Students can simulate the placer mining technique by using a metal pie plate, sand, water, and small ball bearings.

SCIENCE INTEGRATION

Technology

Point out that a revolution in timekeeping occurred during the 1970s with the development of accurate wristwatches regulated by common quartz crystals. Have students research the technology of measuring time, from primitive water clocks to atomic clocks. Have them share their findings in small groups or with the class. Bring to school a quartz watch or clock that no longer works. Allow students to disassemble it to locate the quartz crystal. Compare quartz mechanisms to those of mechanical clocks or watches.

The table lists the crystal shape, break pattern, and specific gravity of several minerals. Compare the properties of the metals copper, gold, and silver. What do you notice? Check the specific gravity of diamond and corundum. Do minerals with a high hardness have to be very dense?

Crystal Shape, Break Pattern, and Specific Gravity of Some Minerals			
Mineral	Crystal Shape	Break Pattern	Specific Gravity
calcite	6-sided	cleavage	2.7
copper	rarely forms crystals	fracture	8.8 to 8.9
corundum	6-sided	fracture	3.9 to 4.1
diamond	8-sided	cleavage	3.1 to 3.5
fluorite	cubed or 8-sided	cleavage	3 to 3.2
garnet	12-sided	fracture	3.5 to 4.3
gold	rarely forms crystals	fracture	15.5 to 19.3
graphite	rarely forms crystals	cleavage	1.9 to 2.3
gypsum	sword-shaped	cleavage	2.3 to 2.4
halite	cubed	cleavage	2.1 to 2.6
magnetite	8-sided	fracture	4.9 to 5.2
mica	6-sided	cleavage	2.7 to 3.1
pyrite	cubed	fracture	4.9 to 5.2
quartz	6-sided	fracture	1.9 to 2.8
silver	rarely forms crystals	fracture	9.6 to 12
sulfur	cubed	fracture	2 to 2.1
talc	not visible	cleavage	2.7 to 2.8

Lesson 3   REVIEW

Write your answers to these questions on a sheet of paper.

1. What determines a crystal's shape?

2. What is the difference between cleavage and fracture?

3. What does specific gravity measure?

4. If a mineral is 10 times heavier than water, what is its specific gravity?

5. What is the specific gravity of water?

▼◄▲▼◄▲▼◄▲▼◄▲▼◄▲▼◄▲▼◄▲▼◄▲▼◄▲▼◄▲▼◄▲▼

Science at Work

Jeweler

Jewelers design and manufacture, or make, pieces of jewelry. They cut, polish, and set stones and gems used in jewelry. Jewelers also repair jewelry. Some jewelers own or work in a small retail shop. Others own or work for a large manufacturing company.

To design a piece of jewelry, jewelers may use a computer. Then they shape a solid model or create a wax mold for pouring liquid metal. To finish a metal piece, jewelers may need to solder pieces together, polish it, mount a gem, or engrave a design. Lasers are often used in the process.

Most jewelers learn their trade in vocational or technical schools, or on the job. Some schools offer a bachelor's or master's degree in jewelry design.

Jewelers need to know the properties of the metals, stones, and gems they use. They must be precise in their work and give attention to detail. Hand and finger control is important, as well as creativity, patience, and concentration. Knowing how to use computer-aided design software is helpful.

Minerals   Chapter 7   **167**

Lesson 3 Review Answers

1. the arrangement of its atoms
2. Cleavage is a mineral's tendency to break along flat surfaces. A mineral that fractures leaves a jagged edge. **3.** density, or a mineral's weight compared to the weight of the same volume of water
4. 10 **5.** 1

Science at Work

Ask for four volunteers to each read one paragraph in the Science at Work feature on page 167. Invite volunteers to describe a favorite piece of jewelry. Encourage them to draw an enlargement of it on the board. Discuss with students the steps that might have been involved in creating this piece.

Portfolio Assessment

Sample items include:
• Definitions and sentences from Teaching the Lesson
• Lesson 3 Review answers

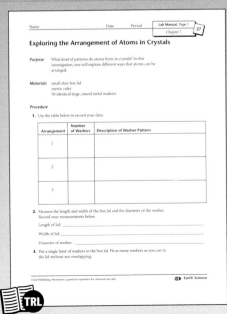

Lab Manual 27, pages 1–2

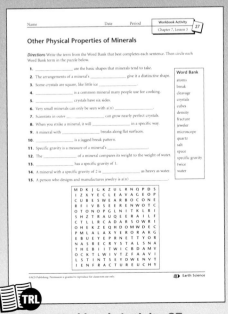

Workbook Activity 27

Minerals   Chapter 7   **167**

The Purpose portion of the student investigation begins with a question to draw students into the activity. Encourage students to read the investigation steps and formulate their own questions before beginning the investigation. This investigation will take approximately 45 minutes to complete. Students will use these process and thinking skills: collecting and organizing data, comparing, and using numbers.

Preparation

• Mineral samples should vary among students. Make sure samples will fit into the beakers without touching the container's bottom or sides. Also, the samples should be fairly small so that they don't exert excessive force on the scale and stretch the spring.

• In addition to labeling the envelopes, you might find it handy to label the specimens with permanent marker.

• Have plenty of paper towels on hand to dry off the specimens. Weighing the mineral samples when wet will cause inaccuracies.

• Students may use Lab Manual 28 to record their data and answer the questions.

Procedure

• Students may work individually or in cooperative groups. For group work, assign one student to gather equipment and another to clean up when finished. All students should take turns tying on samples with string, reading the scale, and holding the scale.

• Review the correct way to read a spring scale—at eye level. Have students practice reading the scale by gently tugging on the spring and reading the values. Remind students of the importance of both accuracy and precision.

• You might wish to run through the entire procedure once for the whole class. Write the weights on the board as you demonstrate Part A. Then work through the calculation for specific gravity outlined in Part B.

7-2 INVESTIGATION

Materials
◆ spring scale
◆ string
◆ 3 mineral samples in envelopes marked A, B, and C
◆ beaker of water

Finding Specific Gravity

Purpose

How could you determine the specific gravity of a mineral? In this investigation, you will find the specific gravity of unknown mineral samples.

Procedure

Part A: Collect Your Data

1. Copy the data table on a sheet of paper.

Property	Sample A	Sample B	Sample C
weight in air			
weight in water			
difference			
specific gravity			

2. Tie one end of the string to the scale. Tie the other end around a dry mineral sample.

3. Read the weight of the mineral. This is the mineral's weight in air. Record the weight in the data table, including the measurement unit.

4. Lower the sample into the beaker of water, as shown on the next page. Make sure the sample is completely underwater and is not touching the sides or bottom of the beaker. **Safety Alert: Wipe up any spills immediately.**

5. With the sample suspended in water, read its weight again. Record the weight of the sample in water. Then untie the sample and return it to its envelope.

6. Repeat steps 2 to 5 for the other two samples. Return the equipment and clean your work space.

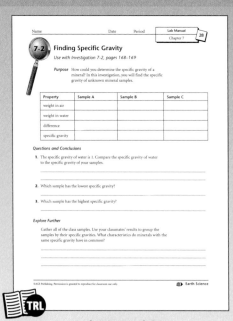

Lab Manual 28

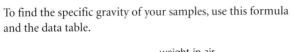

Part B: Calculate Your Results

To find the specific gravity of your samples, use this formula and the data table.

$$\text{specific gravity} = \frac{\text{weight in air}}{\text{weight in air} - \text{weight in water}}$$

1. Begin with sample A. Subtract its weight in water from its weight in air. The difference equals the weight of the water that the sample replaced. Record this difference in the data table.

2. Divide the weight of the mineral in air by the difference you just recorded. This number is the specific gravity of the sample. Record it in the data table. (Specific gravity has no measurement unit.)

3. Repeat your arithmetic for samples B and C.

Questions and Conclusions

1. The specific gravity of water is 1. Compare the specific gravity of water to the specific gravity of your samples.

2. Which sample has the lowest specific gravity?

3. Which sample has the highest specific gravity?

Explore Further

Gather all of the class samples. Use your classmates' results to group the samples by their specific gravities. What characteristics do minerals with the same specific gravity have in common?

- Explain to students that they need to be sure their samples are dry when they weigh them in air. Otherwise, their results will not be accurate.

- It is important that each student be able to determine specific gravity. For groups, insist that each student be responsible for determining the specific gravity of at least one sample. Other group members can watch and assist, if needed, as each student follows the calculation steps in Part B.

- Challenge students to devise a way to determine the specific gravity of a mineral that is soluble in water, such as halite (salt).

- Make sure students record the appropriate unit with each of their weight values. Specific gravity is unitless.

SAFETY ALERT

◆ Remind students to wipe up any spills immediately.

Results

Answers will vary, depending on the minerals used.

Questions and Conclusions Answers

1. The specific gravity of each sample is higher than the specific gravity of water.

2. Answers will depend on the minerals used.

3. Answers will depend on the minerals used.

Explore Further Answers

Answers will depend on the minerals used.

Assessment

Check that students accurately weigh and record their data. Verify that they can correctly use the mathematical formula to determine specific gravity. You might include the following items from this investigation in student portfolios:

- Data table
- Answers to Questions and Conclusions and Explore Further sections

Lesson at a Glance

Chapter 7 Lesson 4

Overview In this lesson, students learn how people use minerals in everyday life.

Objectives

- To relate the usefulness of minerals to their properties
- To identify minerals that are precious metals or gems

Student Pages 170–172

Teacher's Resource Library

Workbook Activity 28

Alternative Workbook Activity 28

Science Background

While there are more than 2,000 known minerals, only about a dozen make up most of the earth's rocks. These rock-forming minerals are called silicates and contain elements such as iron, sodium, magnesium, calcium, potassium, silicon, oxygen, and aluminum. Quartz, feldspar, olivine, pyroxene, amphibole, and mica are common silicate minerals.

1 Warm-Up Activity

Have students do a quick self-survey to determine how they use minerals in their daily lives. Guide students to recognize that metallic minerals, such as gold and silver, are used in jewelry, iron ores are used in rivets, metal zippers, and shoe eyelets, talc and mica are used in certain cosmetics, etc. Tell students that in this lesson they will be learning more about how people use minerals.

2 Teaching the Lesson

Tell students that when they finish reading they are to draw a picture showing some of the ways that people use minerals.

You might take this opportunity to discuss the need for recycling. Point out that when items, such as cans and bottles, are discarded instead of recycled, more quartz and bauxite must be extracted from the earth to make new cans and bottles.

Lesson 4   Common Uses of Minerals

Objectives

After reading this lesson, you should be able to

- relate the usefulness of minerals to their properties.
- identify minerals that are precious metals or gems.

Most diamonds are not gem quality. Instead of being used for jewelry, these diamonds are used in industry. Their hardness makes them ideal for tools used for drilling or cutting.

Minerals are all around you. Look at the objects shown below. All of them are made from minerals.

Minerals are important to people for many different reasons. Most minerals have been cut, crushed, melted, or chemically changed to do a specific job. Each mineral has a property that makes it valuable for the job it does. For example, diamond is so hard that it makes excellent drill tips.

Gold conducts electricity well and is often used in computer circuits and communications equipment. Copper also conducts electricity well and is cheaper than gold. Copper wire is used inside power cords for many household appliances. Some copper wire is braided into cable, as shown in the photo on page 152.

The lead in your pencil is not the mineral lead. It is the soft mineral graphite. When crushed, graphite can be used as a lubricant for metal locks. Talc is another soft mineral. It is crushed to make talcum powder, which some people use after a shower or bath.

Quartz is found in sand, which is melted to make glass for windows, bottles, and drinking glasses. Quartz vibrates at a precise, constant speed when electricity is passed through it. Clocks and watches contain tiny quartz crystals to keep time. The circuits in computers and televisions also contain quartz.

Silver · Bauxite · Halite · Quartz · Quartz · Lithium · Copper · Talc · Fluorite · Nickel · Platinum · Lead · Cadmium

The mineral bauxite contains aluminum, which is used to make soft-drink cans and cookware. Aluminum is a popular packaging material. It is light, does not rust, cools and heats fast, and is easy to shape.

The table below lists a few of the minerals used to build a house.

Minerals Used in Building Products		
Mineral	**How It Is Changed**	**Product**
talc	crushed	paint
iron	melted	nails
bauxite	melted	ladder
gypsum	crushed	wallboard
corundum	crushed	sandpaper
quartz	melted	glass

Besides practical uses, minerals are valued because they are rare or beautiful. Rare, gleaming metals, such as gold and silver, are called precious metals. People use them in jewelry, coins, and objects for ceremonies. People cut and polish certain minerals to make gems for jewelry and other decorations. Precious gems are made from minerals such as diamond, topaz, garnet, quartz, and tourmaline.

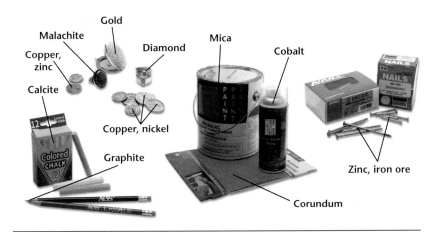

Gold
Malachite
Copper, zinc
Calcite
Diamond
Mica
Cobalt
Copper, nickel
Graphite
Zinc, iron ore
Corundum

CROSS-CURRICULAR CONNECTION

Social Studies

Have small groups of students investigate and report on minerals that traditionally have been used as pigments by American Indians. Choose American Indian peoples from different regions of North America so students can compare and contrast both the minerals and the ways they were used.

GLOBAL CONNECTION

Have students read about the discovery of the tomb of the Egyptian pharaoh Tutankhamen and the wealth of minerals that were found in it. Students might make and color sketches of his mask, throne, or jewelry. The minerals used in each of these items should be labeled.

TEACHER ALERT

Remind students that many rocks can be polished until they shine. This shiny surface does not indicate that a specimen is a pure mineral or that its natural luster is shiny.

Did You Know?

Have a volunteer read aloud the feature on page 171. If possible, display a sample of malachite. Explain to students that this mineral is used mainly as a decorative building material today. In the United States, malachite is found in Arizona. Other places in the world where malachite is found include Namibia, Mexico, Australia, and Russia.

IN THE COMMUNITY

Explain to students that not all minerals are beneficial. Until recently, lead was an ingredient of house paint, and asbestos was an important building material. Both are now known to be highly toxic. Have students find out whether these two minerals are a hazard in their community. Invite volunteers to present their findings to the class.

LEARNING STYLES

Logical/Mathematical

Write the word *karat* on the board and ask students what they think it means. Explain that it refers to the purity of gold. A 24-karat ring is 100 percent gold. A 14-karat (14k) ring is 14 parts gold and 10 parts other metals. Have students calculate the percent of gold in jewelry of the following popular karats: 8k, 9k, 10k, 14k, 18k, and 22k. *(33.3 percent, 37.5 percent, 41.7 percent, 58.5 percent, 75 percent, and 91.6 percent)*

Lesson 4 Review Answers

1. It is the hardest known mineral.
2. They conduct electricity well. **3.** quartz
4. Answers will vary. Sample answers:
diamond, ruby **5.** Answers will vary.
Sample answers: graphite (pencil lead),
iron (cars), quartz (glass), bauxite (soft-
drink cans), gypsum (wallboard)

Science in Your Life

Read together the Science in Your Life
feature on page 172. Ask students to share
their own experiences with recycling.
Encourage them to discuss the issue by
considering questions such as these:
What if no one recycled? Would you be
willing to pay more for a recycled
product? Will the world run out of
resources someday?

SCIENCE JOURNAL

Have students write
an editorial or
persuasive speech
on the topic of why we should make
an effort to conserve our worldwide
supply of minerals.

LEARNING STYLES

LEP/ESL

Write the word *recycle* on
the board and explain that it
means "to use something
again." Circle the prefix *re-* and
explain that it means "again." Divide
the class into small groups of English
language learners and English-
proficient students. Give each group
a dictionary. Ask the groups to find
three words in which *re-* means
"again." Invite the groups to present
their words to the class.

Portfolio Assessment

Sample items include:
• Drawings from Teaching the Lesson
• Lesson 4 Review answers

Write your answers to these questions on a sheet of paper.

1. Why is diamond used to make drill tips?

2. What property of gold and copper makes them useful in computer parts?

3. What mineral is used to make glass?

4. Name two minerals used to make gems.

5. List five minerals that you use. Name the products or objects in which they are found.

Recycling Aluminum

Aluminum comes from bauxite, a common mineral in the earth.
Aluminum has a variety of uses in manufacturing, transportation,
electronics, construction, and the food industry. Aluminum has
been recycled for as long as it has been produced, well over
100 years.

Most people are familiar with
recycling aluminum cans. In some
cities, curbside recycling programs
bring used aluminum cans to a
recycling center. The center sorts,
packages, and ships the cans to
a smelting plant. Here the cans
are shredded and have the paint
removed from them. Then they are
melted in hot furnaces and blended
with other molten, or melted,
metal. The molten metal is poured
into large molds, where it cools and
hardens. Steel rollers flatten the
metal into sheets that can be used
to make new aluminum cans.

Curbside recycling isn't the only way to recycle aluminum
cans. Some grocery stores have recycling machines that pay
people for depositing aluminum cans. Are there any recycling
machines near you? Does your community have curbside
recycling? Do you know where your local recycling center is?

Name _____ Date _____ Period _____ | Workbook Activity | **28**
Chapter 7, Lesson 4

Common Uses of Minerals: Terms Review

Directions Match each term with its definition. Write the letter of the correct
definition on the line.

_____ **1.** mineral
_____ **2.** luster
_____ **3.** streak
_____ **4.** hardness
_____ **5.** crystal
_____ **6.** cleavage
_____ **7.** fracture
_____ **8.** specific gravity

A color of the mark a mineral makes on a white tile
B ability to split along flat surfaces
C element or compound found in the earth
D ability of a mineral to resist scratches
E tendency to break with jagged edges
F how a mineral reflects light
G basic shape that minerals tend to take
H mineral's weight compared to the weight of water

Directions Read the story below. Find a mineral from the Word Bank that is used to
make each product. Write the mineral on the line.

Word Bank					
bauxite	copper	corundum	gypsum	iron	quartz	talc

Last weekend Paolo built a partition in his basement. First he set up his

stepladder (**9.** _____). Then he fastened studs to

the floor and ceiling with three-inch nails (**10.** _____).

He replaced a window (**11.** _____). A friend helped him fit

the wallboard (**12.** _____) in place. He plastered any gaps

and holes and smoothed them with sandpaper (**13.** _____).

He finished the job with two coats of white paint (**14.** _____).

He furnished the room and plugged in the power cord (**15.** _____)

on his new TV. He was ready to relax.

©AGS Publishing. Permission is granted to reproduce for classroom use only. 🌎 Earth Science

Workbook Activity 28

Chapter 7 SUMMARY

- A mineral is an element or a compound that occurs naturally, is a solid, is not alive or made of living things, has the same chemical makeup throughout, and has a definite arrangement of atoms.

- Common minerals include quartz, feldspar, mica, calcite, halite, and gypsum.

- Many minerals are found in rocks below the earth's surface. Some of these minerals are mined and purified for different uses.

- A mineral can be identified by its properties. These include color, luster, streak, hardness, crystal shape, break pattern, and specific gravity.

- The color of a mineral may vary because of impurities.

- Minerals have either a metallic or nonmetallic luster.

- A mineral's streak is tested by rubbing the mineral across a streak plate.

- Mohs' scale of hardness ranks minerals according to how well they resist being scratched.

- Most minerals form crystals. A crystal is the basic shape that a mineral tends to take.

- The shape of a crystal depends on the arrangement of its atoms.

- Cleavage is the ability of a mineral to easily split along flat surfaces.

- The tendency of some minerals to break unevenly is called fracture.

- Specific gravity is a measure of density. It compares the weight of a mineral to the weight of the same volume of water.

- Minerals are used to make many products. Some examples are jewelry, coins, electrical wire, glass, pencils, cake pans, and nails.

Science Words

cleavage, 165	fracture, 165	luster, 158	specific gravity, 165
crystal, 164	hardness, 159	mineral, 154	streak, 158

Chapter 7 Summary

Have volunteers read aloud each Summary item on page 173. Ask volunteers to explain the meaning of each item. Direct students' attention to the Science Words box on the bottom of page 173. Have them read and review each word and its definition.

Chapter 7 Review

Use the Chapter Review to prepare students for tests and to reteach content from the chapter.

Chapter 7 Mastery Test

The Teacher's Resource Library includes two parallel forms of the Chapter 7 Mastery Test. The difficulty level of the two forms is equivalent. You may wish to use one form as a pretest and the other form as a posttest.

Chapters 1–7 Midterm Mastery Test TRL

The Teacher's Resource Library includes the Midterm Mastery Test. This test is pictured on page 397 of this Teacher's Edition. The Midterm Mastery Test assesses the major learning objectives for Chapters 1–7.

Review Answers

Vocabulary Review

1. fracture 2. crystal 3. hardness
4. cleavage 5. mineral 6. streak 7. luster
8. specific gravity

Concept Review

9. C 10. B 11. D 12. B 13. A 14. D
15. cinnabar 16. galena

Critical Thinking

17. Minerals can be skimmed from the earth's surface in a strip mine or dug deep out of the ground by means of long shafts. 18. Weigh the sample in the air; then weigh it submerged in water. Subtract its weight in water from its weight in air. Divide the weight in air by the difference you calculated in the previous step. This number is the sample's specific gravity. 19. The samples are probably different varieties of the same mineral. 20. By testing the hardness and specific gravity of each mineral, you could determine which was quartz.

Word Bank
cleavage
crystal
fracture
hardness
luster
mineral
specific gravity
streak

Vocabulary Review

Choose the word or phrase from the Word Bank that best matches each phrase. Write the answer on your paper.

1. breaks with jagged edges
2. shape caused by a mineral's atomic arrangement
3. can be tested by scratching
4. breaks along flat surfaces
5. solid element or compound that is found in the earth
6. color of the mark left on a tile
7. glassy, pearly, or metallic
8. density compared to water

Concept Review

Choose the word or phrase that best completes each sentence. Write the letter of the answer on your paper.

9. Not all minerals are _____.
   - **A** solids
   - **B** found in the earth
   - **C** shiny
   - **D** formed naturally

10. Mineral A is harder than mineral B if _____.
    - **A** A weighs more than B
    - **B** A scratches B
    - **C** A leaves a bigger streak than B
    - **D** A is more dense than B

11. Gold and pyrite are different in _____.
    - **A** color
    - **B** luster
    - **C** feel
    - **D** streak

12. Two kinds of luster are _____.
    - **A** shiny and dull
    - **B** metallic and nonmetallic
    - **C** yellow and cube-shaped
    - **D** silver and gold

Name _____ Date _____ Period _____ | Mastery Test A, Page 1 — Chapter 7

Chapter 7 Mastery Test A

Part A Read each sentence. Write the letter of the correct answer on the line.

____ 1. Pencil lead is ___.
   A graphite   **B** lead   **C** quartz   **D** talc

____ 2. A diamond is unique because ___.
   A it is the most precious of minerals
   B no other mineral can scratch it
   C it can be cut and polished
   D it can be made into a cutting or drilling tool

____ 3. You can use ___ to tell gold from pyrite.
   A color   **B** luster   **C** streak   **D** break pattern

____ 4. Most minerals are found ___.
   A in running water on the earth's surface
   B in nuggets
   C mixed with other minerals in rocks
   D in the soil

____ 5. Strip mining involves ___.
   A removing long patches of soil
   B the use of huge smelting ovens
   C digging deep shafts into the earth
   D using chemicals to break apart the minerals

Part B Write the term from the Word Bank that best completes each sentence.

Word Bank
cleavage   crystal   hardness   Mohs'   streak
color   fracture   luster   specific gravity

6. Because the _____ of a mineral may vary, it is not the best way to identify minerals.
7. The color of the mark that a mineral leaves on white unglazed porcelain is called ___.
8. _____ is a measure of how well a mineral resists being scratched.

©AGS Publishing. Permission is granted to reproduce for classroom use only.   **Earth Science**

Name _____ Date _____ Period _____ | Mastery Test A, Page 2 — Chapter 7

Chapter 7 Mastery Test A, continued

9. The basic shape that a mineral tends to take is a _____.
10. _____ is the way a mineral picks up or reflects light.
11. Hardness is measured on _____ scale.
12. _____ is the tendency of minerals to break along flat planes or surfaces.
13. _____ is a comparison of a mineral's weight to the weight of the same volume of water.
14. The tendency of minerals to break unevenly, leaving jagged edges, is _____.

Part C Write a short answer to each question.

15. Explain what a mineral is.

16. Name three common minerals.

17. For any mineral, what are seven basic properties that can be measured or observed?

18. Calcite has a hardness of 3, and quartz has a hardness of 7. Which mineral can scratch the other one?

19. Copper has a specific gravity of 8.9. What does that mean?

20. Name three minerals and give a common use for each one.

©AGS Publishing. Permission is granted to reproduce for classroom use only.   **Earth Science**

Chapter 7 Mastery Test A

13. You test for streak by _____.
    A rubbing a mineral sample on a white tile
    B breaking a mineral sample
    C weighing a mineral sample in water
    D scratching a mineral with your fingernail

14. On Mohs' scale of hardness, diamond has the _____.
    A lowest hardness
    B brightest luster
    C darkest streak
    D highest number

Use the photos to answer questions 15 and 16.

15. Which mineral has fracture?

16. Which mineral has a cube-shaped crystal form?

Critical Thinking

Write the answer to each of the following questions.

17. Describe two ways minerals are mined.

18. Explain how you would find the specific gravity of an unknown mineral sample.

19. Two unknown mineral samples are different colors. Their other properties are the same. What does this tell you?

20. Two mineral samples are colorless and have a colorless streak. One sample is quartz. How would you identify which one it is?

Cinnabar

Galena

Test-Taking Tip When you have vocabulary words to learn, make flash cards. Write each word on the front of a card. Write its definition on the back. Use the flash cards in a game to test your vocabulary skills.

ALTERNATIVE ASSESSMENT

Alternative Assessment items correlate to the student Goals for Learning at the beginning of this chapter.

■ Draw two concentric circles on the board. Label the outer circle *Elements and Compounds* and the inner circle *Minerals*. Have students copy the diagram and fill it in with information about each category. Diagrams should reflect that, while minerals can be elements or compounds, not all elements and compounds are minerals. Compile students' ideas on the master diagram.

■ Have students research mining methods on the Internet or at the library. Ask them to choose one method to learn about and present to the class.

■ Have two groups of students each compile a list of familiar minerals. The groups should take turns playing "Go Fish" to guess the minerals on the other group's list. Keep track of successful guesses on the board.

■ Assign each student or small group one of the seven physical properties used in mineral identification. Ask each student or group to give a brief presentation about the importance of their property.

■ Obtain a variety of known mineral samples. Ask students to choose a sample, find out as many of its physical properties as they can, and list these on an index card. Display the samples with their cards. Allow time for students to compare the samples and their properties.

■ Collect mineral samples along with objects made from the minerals. Display them separately. Challenge students to match the minerals with the related objects. Invite students to contribute other mineral-object pairs for the display.

Chapter

Planning Guide

Rocks

	Student Pages	Vocabulary	Lesson Review
		Student Text Lesson	
Lesson 1 Rocks and Rock Types	178–180	✔	✔
Lesson 2 Igneous Rocks	181–184	✔	✔
Lesson 3 Sedimentary Rocks	185–191	✔	✔
Lesson 4 Metamorphic Rocks	192–193	✔	✔
Lesson 5 The Rock Cycle	194–198	✔	✔

Chapter Activities

Student Text
Science Center
Teacher's Resource Library
Community Connection 8: Rocks All
   Around

Assessment Options

Student Text
Chapter 8 Review

Teacher's Resource Library
Chapter 8 Mastery Tests A and B

	Student Text Features								Teaching Strategies						Learning Styles						Teacher's Resource Library				
Achievements in Science	Science at Work	Science in Your Life	Investigation	Science Myth	Note	Technology Note	Did You Know	Science Integration	Science Journal	Cross-Curricular Connection	Online Connection	Teacher Alert	Applications (Home, Career, Community, Global, Environment)	Auditory/Verbal	Body/Kinesthetic	Interpersonal/Group Learning	Logical/Mathematical	Visual/Spatial	LEP/ESL	Workbook Activities	Alternative Workbook Activities	Lab Manual	Resource File	Self-Study Guide
	180			179				179	179	179		179								29	29			✔
184					✔		183	183		183			182, 183		183			182		30	30	29, 30	15	✔
		189		190		✔	186		187	188	187		187, 188			188	187			31	31	31		✔
						✔				193		192	193	193						32	32			✔
196			197						195	195		194	195						195	33	33	32	16	✔

Pronunciation Key

a	hat	e	let	ī	ice	ô	order	ů	put	sh	she	a	in about
ā	age	ē	equal	o	hot	oi	oil	ü	rule	th	thin	e	in taken
ä	far	ėr	term	ō	open	ou	out	ch	child	ŦH	then	ə { i	in pencil
â	care	i	it	ȯ	saw	u	cup	ng	long	zh	measure	o	in lemon
												u	in circus

Alternative Workbook Activities

The Teacher's Resource Library (TRL) contains a set of lower-level worksheets called Alternative Workbook Activities. These worksheets cover the same content as the regular Workbook Activities but are written at a second-grade reading level.

Skill Track Software

Use the Skill Track Software for Earth Science for additional reinforcement of this chapter. The software program allows students using AGS textbooks to be assessed for mastery of each chapter and lesson of the textbook. Students access the software on an individual basis and are assessed with multiple-choice items.

Chapter 8:
Rocks
pages 176–201

Lessons

1. **Rocks and Rock Types**
   pages 178–180

2. **Igneous Rocks** pages 181–184

3. **Sedimentary Rocks**
   pages 185–191

   Investigation 8-1 pages 190–191

4. **Metamorphic Rocks**
   pages 192–193

5. **The Rock Cycle** pages 194–198

   Investigation 8-2 pages 197–198

Chapter 8 Summary page 199

Chapter 8 Review pages 200–201

Skill Track Software
   for Earth Science

Teacher's Resource Library **TRL**

Workbook Activities 29–33

Alternative Workbook Activities
29–33

Lab Manual 29–32

Community Connection 8

Resource File 15–16

Chapter 8 Self-Study Guide

Chapter 8 Mastery Tests A and B

(Answer Keys for the Teacher's
Resource Library begin on page 400
of the Teacher's Edition. The
Materials List for the Lab Manual
activities begins on page 415.)

Science Center

Display samples of various kinds of rocks
and have students analyze and describe
them. Ask small groups of students to
take turns grouping the rocks based on
similarities. Have the groups explain how
they decided to classify the rocks. As a
class, discuss how the rocks might have
formed. As students read the chapter,
they can adjust their classifications,
descriptions, and explanations about the
rocks to be more exact.

Community Connection 8

Name _____ Date _____ Period _____ Community Connection
                                                    Chapter 8   8

Rocks All Around

Rocks are all around you. People have used rocks for building, for tools and
weapons, and for art. How a rock is used depends on its properties. For
example, rocks that are easy to split into sheets, like slate, are useful for tiles.
Rocks that are strong and can be polished, like granite, are useful for
monuments.

Find examples of how rocks are used in your community. Try to find at least
one example of each of the three rock types. In the table below, name the rock,
tell how it is used, and describe it. Then tell why you think it was chosen for this
purpose.

Rock Type	Rock Name	Use	Description	Why Chosen
Igneous				
Sedimentary				
Metamorphic				

Chapter

8 Rocks

A large part of the earth is made of rock. The cliffs in the photo are made of a rock type called sedimentary rock. Rocks also form mountains, islands, valleys, and even the ocean floor. The rocks you see around you are thousands of years old. They haven't always looked the same. They haven't always stayed in the same place. Rocks change. In Chapter 8, you will learn how to classify, compare, and describe different types of rocks. You will also find out how one type of rock can change over time into another rock type.

Organize Your Thoughts

```
                Rock types and
  Igneous       the rock cycle       Metamorphic

Intrusive  Extrusive          Foliated   Nonfoliated

                 Sedimentary

         Clastic   Chemical   Organic
```

Goals for Learning

◆ To explain what a rock is

◆ To describe igneous, sedimentary, and metamorphic rocks

◆ To explain how each rock type is formed

◆ To compare and contrast different rocks within each rock type

◆ To describe the rock cycle and the forces involved in it

177

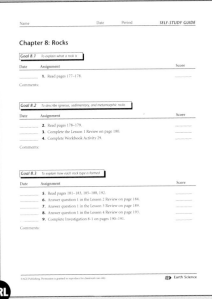

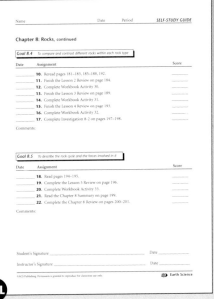

Chapter 8 Self-Study Guide

Introducing the Chapter

Have students look at the photo on page 176 and describe what they see. Encourage them to list exact details about the rocks they see. Ask students to predict how they think these rocks formed and how they are changing. Read the introductory paragraph together. Then ask students to read the Organize Your Thoughts chart and identify the three types of rocks.

Have students read the Goals for Learning. You may want to have them write questions based on the goals. As they read the chapter, they can read to find the answers.

Notes and Technology Notes

Ask volunteers to read the notes that appear in the margins throughout the chapter. Then discuss them with the class.

TEACHER'S RESOURCE

The AGS Teaching Strategies in Science Transparencies may be used with this chapter. The transparencies add an interactive dimension to expand and enhance the *Earth Science* program content.

CAREER INTEREST INVENTORY

The AGS Harrington-O'Shea Career Decision-Making System-Revised (CDM) may be used with this chapter. Students can use the CDM to explore their interests and identify careers. The CDM defines career areas that are indicated by students' responses on the inventory.

Lesson at a Glance

Chapter 8 Lesson 1

Overview In this lesson, students learn that rocks are composed of one or more minerals and that rocks are classified according to the way in which they form.

Objectives

- To explain what rocks are
- To explain why scientists study rocks
- To name three types of rocks

Student Pages 178–180

Teacher's Resource Library **TRL**

Workbook Activity 29

Alternative Workbook Activity 29

....

Vocabulary

igneous rock
metamorphic rock
rock
sedimentary rock

....

Science Background

Most rocks are made of a mixture of minerals, but a few rocks consist of just one mineral. For example, limestone is made of the mineral calcite. Some types of rocks always contain certain minerals, called essential minerals. For example, granite always contains quartz and feldspar. Accessory minerals are minerals that do not always appear in a particular rock. For example, mica and hornblende may appear in granite. Feldspar, in its various forms, makes up more than 50 percent of the earth's rocks.

◆1 Warm-Up Activity

Display a few common rocks, such as sandstone, granite, and marble, along with the minerals that are contained in each. (Most sandstones are primarily quartz. Marble is predominantly calcite.) Emphasize that rocks and minerals are not the same. Review the definition of *mineral* from Chapter 7, and tell students that they will learn what rocks are.

Objectives

After reading this lesson, you should be able to

- ◆ explain what rocks are.
- ◆ explain why scientists study rocks.
- ◆ name three types of rocks.

Rock

Natural, solid material made of one or more minerals

Igneous rock

Rock formed from melted minerals that have cooled and hardened

About 3,000 minerals occur in the earth. Most of them are not found in a pure form. They are mixed together in **rocks**. A rock is a solid, natural material made of one or more minerals. Only about 20 minerals make up 95 percent of the earth's rocks.

Geologists are interested in how rocks are formed and what minerals they contain. This information helps scientists and engineers locate valuable resources, such as oil and metals. Knowledge of rocks is necessary for undertaking construction projects and understanding the environment. Rocks also provide clues about the history of the earth and how the earth changes.

Geologists classify, or group, rocks into three main types, depending on how they form. Some rock forms when hot, melted minerals cool and harden. This rock is **igneous rock**. Igneous rock can form above or below the earth's surface.

Basalt is an example of igneous rock.

◆2 Teaching the Lesson

Have students rephrase the lesson objectives as questions. Allow time for them to write a sentence answering each question as they complete the lesson.

Invite students who collect rocks to share their collections. Encourage them to briefly point out physical characteristics, such as color and texture, and to tell where each rock was found.

Review the concept of mixtures from Chapter 6. Use trail mix to illustrate that rocks are mixtures of minerals. Each item in the mix represents a different mineral in a rock. Each mineral component of a rock keeps its properties even though it is combined with other minerals to form a mixture.

Another type of rock forms when bits of other rocks and the remains of living things are pressed and cemented together. The result is **sedimentary rock**. Sedimentary rock can form under a body of water or on the earth's surface.

Sandstone is an example of sedimentary rock.

Heat, pressure, and chemical reactions can change sedimentary or igneous rock into another type—**metamorphic rock**. Metamorphic rock always forms below the earth's surface.

The photos show examples of the three rock types. What features do you notice about each one? In this chapter, you will learn more about how each type of rock forms.

This metamorphic rock shows the squeezing effect of heat and pressure deep in the earth.

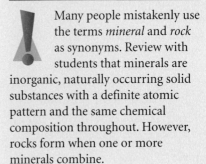

Lesson 1 Review Answers

1. a natural solid material made of one or more minerals 2. Rocks tell about the earth's history, help locate resources such as oil and coal, and explain changes in the environment. 3. igneous, sedimentary, and metamorphic 4. igneous 5. metamorphic

Science at Work

Ask volunteers to read the Science at Work feature about stonemasons on page 180. Invite students to imagine they are going to build a wall of stone. Have them list the steps they would need to follow. Discuss the skills and traits that would help them complete the project. Encourage students who may be interested in this kind of work to research the profession to learn more about it.

Portfolio Assessment

Sample items include:
• Sentences from Teaching the Lesson
• Lesson 1 Review answers

Write your answers to these questions on a sheet of paper.

1. What is a rock?

2. What information about the earth can rocks provide?

3. What are the three main types of rocks?

4. Which type of rock is formed from melted minerals?

5. Which type of rock is formed by intense heat, pressure, and chemical reactions?

▼◄▲▼◄▲▼◄▲▼◄▲▼◄▲▼◄▲▼◄▲▼◄▲▼◄▲▼◄▲▼◄▲▼◄▲▼◄▲▼

Science at Work

Stonemason

Stonemasons build things out of stone. They build stone walls along shorelines and in landscapes. They lay tiles and paving stones for floors and patios. They cut and polish stone slabs for kitchen countertops and fireplaces. They fix old buildings and carve cemetery statues. They work with either natural stone, such as marble, granite, and limestone, or artificial stone, such as concrete.

A stonemason begins a project by looking at or creating a plan drawing. In these drawings, stones may be numbered so they are correctly cut and placed. The stonemason then selects, splits, cuts, and shapes the stones. Stones can be set in different ways. For a wall, stones are first set in a shallow bed of mortar, then aligned and leveled. The wall is built by alternately placing stones and mortar.

Most stonemasons start out as apprentices. Apprentices observe and help experienced workers until the apprentices learn how to do the job alone. Vocational and technical schools also offer stonemason training.

Stonemasons need to be highly skilled at handwork. They need to be precise and creative in solving visual problems. Strength and physical fitness are important because of the tools, machines, and heavy materials involved. Stonemasons should be comfortable working at heights and in noisy environments.

Workbook Activity 29

Objectives

After reading this lesson, you should be able to

◆ explain how igneous rocks form.

◆ compare intrusive and extrusive igneous rocks.

◆ identify samples of igneous rocks.

How Igneous Rocks Form

Deep below the earth's surface, between 50 and 200 kilometers down, temperatures are about 1,400°C. These temperatures are high enough to melt minerals, forming hot liquid rock called **magma**.

Magma sometimes rises toward the surface of the earth through openings in the rock. As the magma rises, it cools and hardens, becoming igneous rock. Geologists classify igneous rocks into two types, based on where they form. Under the ground, magma hardens into rock slowly. On the earth's surface, magma hardens into rock quickly.

Intrusive Rocks

Igneous rock that forms underground is called **intrusive rock**. Look at the diagram. Find the pockets of magma that have cooled and hardened below the earth's surface.

Magma
Hot, liquid rock inside the earth

Intrusive rock
Igneous rock that forms underground from cooled magma

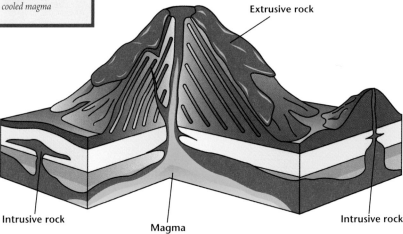

Extrusive rock

Intrusive rock

Magma

Intrusive rock

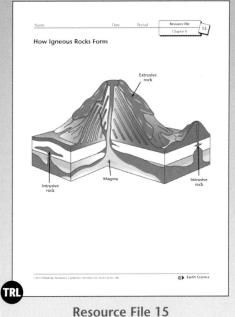

Chapter 8 Lesson 2

Overview In this lesson, students learn how igneous rocks form and how their texture shows where and how fast they formed.

Objectives

■ To explain how igneous rocks form

■ To compare intrusive and extrusive igneous rocks

■ To identify samples of igneous rocks

Student Pages 181–184

Teacher's Resource Library

Workbook Activity 30

Alternative Workbook Activity 30

Lab Manual 29–30

Resource File 15

Vocabulary

extrusive rock	magma
intrusive rock	texture
lava	

Science Background

Texture is the key to telling whether igneous rock was formed inside the earth or at its surface. Magma inside the earth cools slowly, allowing large mineral grains to form. Lava cools much faster, resulting in fine-grained igneous rock. Igneous rock containing both large and small mineral grains has a *porphyritic* texture. It has undergone two cooling periods: first, large grains form deep within the magma chamber; then, as the magma rises, a fine-grained matrix forms around the large crystals.

Basalt grains create the black sand beaches of Hawaii. Basalt is a volcanic igneous rock. Hot basalt lava shatters into small grains when it meets cold ocean water. The photo on this textbook cover, taken in 2002, shows lava from Kilauea Volcano in Hawaii falling into the ocean. The resulting basalt fragments wash up on the shore, adding black sand to the coastline.

1 Warm-Up Activity

Display four squares of black cloth having different textures, for example, cotton, velvet, wool, and polyester. Have students examine the squares and describe how they are different. (Students should note that each square has a very different feel, or texture.) Explain that they will learn about different textures of rocks.

2 Teaching the Lesson

Have students make a table with the headings *Intrusive Igneous Rocks* and *Extrusive Igneous Rocks*. As they read the lesson, have them list characteristics of each rock type under the appropriate heading.

Explain that magma rises toward the earth's surface because it is less dense than the surrounding rock.

When discussing texture, have a specimen of granite available for students to examine with a hand lens. Challenge them to find an adjective that describes the texture of granite. (Granite has *interlocking* mineral grains.) Then have students contrast the texture of granite with the texture of basalt.

If possible, bring in an obsidian arrowhead or show pictures of obsidian artifacts. Explain that obsidian's lack of crystals allows people to make very sharp implements from it. Point out that a coarse-grained rock, such as granite, could not be used to make sharp implements.

3 Reinforce and Extend

LEARNING STYLES

Visual/Spatial

Have students analyze the textures of granite and obsidian and create analogies describing them. For example, "The minerals in granite form a mosaic, like interlocking pieces of a jigsaw puzzle," or "Obsidian is smooth and shiny like a mirror."

Texture
Size of crystals in an igneous rock

Long ago, scientists did not think granite was an igneous rock. They thought all igneous rocks were like the fine-grained surface rocks formed from cooling lava. In the late 1700s, scientists correctly identified granite as igneous rock.

Many intrusive rocks have large crystals because magma below the surface cools slowly. The size of the mineral crystals in an igneous rock is called the rock's **texture**. Rocks with large crystals are said to have a coarse-grained texture. Therefore, most intrusive rocks have a coarse-grained texture.

One of the most common intrusive rocks is granite. The minerals in this coarse-grained rock are large enough for you to see. Find the feldspar, quartz, and mica that make up the granite in the photo. Most of the rock that forms the foundations of the continents is granite. Granite might be gray, pink, or red, depending on the kind of feldspar in it. Because granite is strong and can be highly polished, it is used for buildings and monuments.

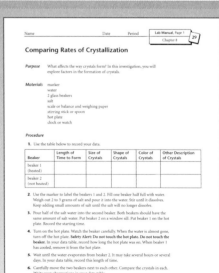

Feldspar —
Mica —
Quartz —

You can see the individual minerals that make up granite.

IN THE COMMUNITY

Suggest that students take a field trip to observe the different uses of granite in your community. (Museum facades, decorative fountains and monuments, older government buildings, and banks often have granite in their construction.) Encourage students to learn why granite is useful for each application.

Lab Manual 29, pages 1–2

Lava

Magma that comes out onto the earth's surface

Extrusive rock

Igneous rock that forms from cooled lava on the earth's surface

Did You Know?

Gases sometimes escape from the top layer of lava so quickly that the lava swells into a foam. The foam hardens into a rock that looks like a sponge. This rock is called pumice. It has so many holes that it floats in water. Powdered pumice is used in making abrasive soaps. Many toothpastes contain pumice.

Extrusive Rocks

Magma that reaches the earth's surface is called **lava**. When lava cools, it forms igneous rock called **extrusive rock**. Find the extrusive rock in the diagram on page 181.

Extrusive rocks have small crystals because lava cools too quickly for larger crystals to form. Most extrusive rocks, therefore, have a fine-grained texture. Andesite, pumice, and rhyolite are examples of fine-grained extrusive rock.

The most common extrusive rock is basalt. Most of the ocean floor is made of basalt. The Hawaiian Islands are made of basalt, resulting from volcanic eruptions. Much of the exposed rock of eastern Washington and Oregon is also basalt. It was formed during lava flows that spread away from large cracks in the ground.

Sometimes lava cools so quickly that no crystals have time to form. Such is the case with the extrusive rock obsidian. The lack of any crystals gives obsidian a glassy texture, as the photo shows. Obsidian forms in lava flows or from clots of lava thrown from a volcano. Like glass, obsidian can be chipped to make a very sharp edge. People have used obsidian to make knives, arrowheads, and ornaments.

Compare obsidian, above, with basalt, shown on page 178.

Did You Know?

Have a volunteer read aloud the Did You Know? feature on page 183. Compare sugar with cotton candy, which is sugar spun with air. Ask students to describe what happens when they bite into cotton candy. (*It seems to melt.*) Talk about how cotton candy and sugar are different. (*density, volume, mass, texture, appearance*) Have students explain how pumice and lava are like cotton candy and sugar. (*Pumice contains so much air that it is very light, even though it is made from a denser substance, lava.*)

SCIENCE INTEGRATION

 Physical Science

Allow students to float some large pieces of pumice in bowls of water. After they predict why the rocks float, explain that pumice has many open spaces where air is trapped inside. This makes it less dense than water, so it floats.

AT HOME

 Have students read the ingredient labels for toothpastes and abrasive soaps to verify that they contain bits of rock. Encourage students to plan an investigation to separate the abrasive rock bits from the toothpaste or soap mixture.

CROSS-CURRICULAR CONNECTION

 Language Arts

Explain that many rock words make more sense if you know their Latin meanings. List the following roots and prefixes and their meanings on the board.

ignis	fire
ex	out
in	in
trudere	thrust

Ask students to use these meanings to explain the words *igneous*, *intrusive*, and *extrusive*.

LEARNING STYLES

 Body/Kinesthetic

Give students samples of a variety of igneous rocks, including granite, peridotite, dunite, gabbro, andesite, and basalt. Have students observe the texture of each and use this property to classify the rocks as either extrusive or intrusive. (*Granite, peridotite, dunite, and gabbro are intrusive; andesite and basalt are extrusive.*)

Lesson 2 Review Answers

1. Igneous rocks form when hot, molten lava or magma cools and hardens.
2. Intrusive igneous rocks are coarse-grained because they form slowly deep within the earth. Extrusive igneous rocks are fine-grained rocks that form on the earth's surface. 3. Magma is hot, liquid rock inside the earth. Lava is magma that reaches the surface of the earth. 4. ocean floor, Hawaiian Islands, eastern Washington and Oregon 5. Granite is coarse-grained with crystals large enough to see. Basalt is fine-grained with small crystals. Obsidian is glassy and smooth with no crystals.

Achievements in Science

Ask volunteers to read aloud the Achievements in Science feature on page 184. Display a variety of field guides, including one on rocks or minerals. Demonstrate how to use a field guide to identify a bird, tree, or rock.

Explain that Georgius Agricola is the Latin name used by scientist Georg Bauer, who worked in the province of Saxony (today, part of Germany). He also wrote the first book on physical geology and is considered the founder of geology as a discipline. His field guide was a great advance in science because it classified rocks and minerals by physical properties. Previous works had listed them alphabetically or by their "mystical powers." Discuss with students why Agricola's method made identification easier. Then allow time for students to thumb through the display guides and note how they are organized.

Portfolio Assessment

Sample items include:
• Table from Teaching the Lesson
• Lesson 2 Review answers

Write your answers to these questions on a sheet of paper.

1. How do igneous rocks form?

2. What is the difference between an intrusive igneous rock and an extrusive igneous rock?

3. What is the difference between magma and lava?

4. Name one region where basalt is common.

5. Compare the texture of granite, basalt, and obsidian.

Achievements in Science

Field Guides for Rocks and Minerals

A field guide is a book used to identify natural objects. You may have seen a field guide for identifying things such as birds or trees. Geologists and rock collectors use field guides to identify rocks and minerals.

In 1546, German doctor Georgius Agricola wrote the first field guide for rocks and minerals. Agricola was a rock collector. He wrote the field guide as a way to organize all of the information he had gathered about rocks. Agricola classified rocks and minerals by their physical properties. These included color, crystal shape, hardness, and luster.

Since Agricola's time, thousands of mineral species have been discovered. More detailed systems for classifying rocks and minerals have been designed. Some systems still organize rocks and minerals by their physical properties. Other systems are based on chemical, genetic, or structural properties.

Modern field guides identify rocks and minerals using one or more of these classification systems.

Lab Manual 30, pages 1–2

Workbook Activity 30

How Sedimentary Rocks Form

What happens if you fill a jar with river water and let the jar sit for a while? Solid particles settle out on the bottom of the jar. These particles are **sediment**. They may include sand, soil, pebbles, and the remains of dead plants and animals. Sediment is the main ingredient of sedimentary rock.

How do bits of sand and soil get turned into rock? The diagram shows the most common way. Rivers carry sediment to a lake or ocean. The sediment settles to the bottom. As layers of sediment accumulate, the weight of the overlying sediment presses the bottom sediment together. In addition, the bottom sediment is cemented together by minerals, such as calcite, dissolved in the water. The result is sedimentary rock.

The formation of sedimentary rock does not require high temperatures or pressures. Although it commonly forms under a lake or ocean, sedimentary rock can also form on land.

Objectives

After reading this lesson, you should be able to

◆ explain how sedimentary rocks form.

◆ compare clastic, chemical, and organic sedimentary rocks.

◆ identify samples of sedimentary rocks.

Sediment

Solid material, such as sand, soil, pebbles, and organic matter, that is carried in air, water, or ice and settles out

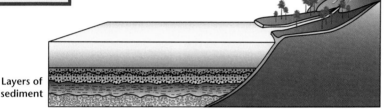

Layers of sediment

Lesson at a Glance

Chapter 8 Lesson 3

Overview This lesson explains how sedimentary rocks form and describes three types of sedimentary rocks: clastic, chemical, and organic.

Objectives

■ To explain how sedimentary rocks form

■ To compare clastic, chemical, and organic sedimentary rocks

■ To identify samples of sedimentary rocks

Student Pages 185–191

Teacher's Resource Library **TRL**

Workbook Activity 31

Alternative Workbook Activity 31

Lab Manual 31

Vocabulary

chemical rock	organic rock
clastic rock	sediment
conglomerate	

Science Background

Bedding, or the formation of rock in layers, is a record of the depositional history of sedimentary rock. The oldest bed in an undisturbed rock sequence is on the bottom; the youngest bed is at the top of the sequence. This concept is especially important to paleontologists in determining the relative age of two fossil specimens by comparing the layers in which they are found. (This topic will be covered in Chapter 14.) Ripple marks in sedimentary rock usually suggest that a rock was deposited in relatively shallow water. Mud cracks indicate periods of dryness during the depositional history of the rock. Cross-bedding indicates a shift in either water or wind direction. Sandstones that formed in arid regions are often cross-bedded.

Warm-Up Activity

Fill a quart jar about three-quarters full of water. Add 4 or 5 tablespoons of each of the following: white sand; dark, clay-rich soil; pea-sized gravel; and small rocks. Shake the jar vigorously and ask students to make a sketch that shows what the jar of water will look like in about 20 minutes. While most students will realize that the larger particles will reach the bottom first, some students may be surprised at the length of time the finer sediment remains suspended in the water.

Teaching the Lesson

As they read the lesson, have students make a concept map to compare and contrast sedimentary rocks. Their maps should include the terms *clastic rocks, sandstone, chemical rocks, limestone, organic rocks, coal, dead organisms, shale, chalk, conglomerate,* and *rock salt.*

Review the meaning of texture. Have students observe samples of sandstone, limestone, conglomerate, shale, and coal with hand lenses. Have students describe the texture of each sample. *(Sandstone and conglomerate are coarse-grained and feel gritty; limestone, shale, and coal are fine-grained and feel fairly smooth.)*

Allow students to examine a piece of coquina, which is a variety of limestone composed almost entirely of fossil shell fragments.

Reinforce and Extend

Did You Know?

Ask a volunteer to explain what a fossil is. Read aloud the Did You Know? feature on page 186. Invite volunteers to tell how they think fossils form in sedimentary rock. If possible, display examples of fossils embedded in rocks.

Clastic rock
Sedimentary rock made mainly from fragments of other rocks

Conglomerate
Clastic rock made of rounded pebbles cemented together

Did You Know?

Some sedimentary rocks carry parts of the past— fossils! A fossil is the preserved remains or imprint of a long-dead animal or plant. In Chapter 14, you will learn how fossils form in sediment.

Seventy-five percent of the rocks exposed at the earth's surface are sedimentary. These rocks are classified into three main types, based on the kinds of sediment that form them.

Clastic Rocks

Clastic rock is the most common type of sedimentary rock. Clastic rock forms from fragments of other rocks. Shale, for example, is made from fine particles of clay, mica, and other tiny grains that form as rocks break down on the earth's surface. These tiny particles form a muddy mixture of sediment on the bottom of a lake or ocean. Overlying layers squeeze out the water and air, forming shale. This process is similar to squeezing a handful of mud. As you force out the water and air, the mud becomes more compact and solid.

Compare the two clastic rocks in the photos below. Notice the size of the sediment in each sample. Sediment particles are clues to the environment in which the rock formed. For example, notice the rounded pebbles of the **conglomerate**. Rounded pebbles often form in rivers, where particles in the moving water break off sharp edges of rocks, making them round. The pebbles fall to the river bottom when the water slows down. So conglomerate might indicate the location of an ancient river.

The tiny particles that make up shale, however, tend to settle out of ocean water far from where a river would empty into an ocean. So shale suggests the location of an ancient ocean.

Conglomerate contains large, rounded pebbles.

Shale is made of fine grains of clay, mica, and other minerals.

Another kind of clastic rock is sandstone. As the name suggests, it is made of sand-sized grains that are mostly quartz. What do these rocks tell you about the environment in which they formed? You might have correctly guessed that sandstone formed from ancient beaches and sand dunes. This rock may also indicate an ancient delta—the land that builds up where a river empties into a body of water. A lot of sand from river water settles out to form a delta.

Chemical rock
Sedimentary rock that forms from chemicals dissolved in water

Chemical Rocks

A second type of sedimentary rock is **chemical rock**. It forms from chemicals dissolved in water. Some limestones are chemical rocks. Chemical and temperature changes in ocean water can cause particles of calcium carbonate to form. These particles accumulate on the ocean floor and become limestone. Other chemical rocks include rock salt and gypsum. These rocks form when seawater evaporates, leaving minerals behind.

The photo shows Mono Lake in California. This lake is unusual because it has no water outlet. As a result, the water has become very salty. As the lake water evaporates, fantastic shapes of rock salt remain.

Rock salt is a chemical sedimentary rock that is left behind when salt water evaporates.

Organic rock
Sedimentary rock that forms from the remains of living things

Organic Rocks

A third type of sedimentary rock is **organic rock**. It forms from the remains of living things. Some limestones form from the shells of sea animals. When shellfish, such as clams and mussels, die, their shells accumulate on the ocean floor. Layers of shells, which are made of calcite, are pressed and cemented together to form organic limestone. One type of organic limestone is chalk. This soft rock is made of the shells of microscopic organisms. The White Cliffs of Dover in England are made of chalk.

Coal is an organic rock that forms very slowly from layers of dead animals and plants. Coal is high in carbon and is mined and burned as a fuel source.

Technology Note

More than half of the electricity produced in the United States comes from burning coal. But how does a lump of coal turn on your lights and run your stove?

Once it is mined from the earth, coal is transported by trains and barges. Approximately 2.5 million metric tons of coal are delivered to power plants and factories in the United States every day.

When coal reaches a power plant, it is first washed. Then it is pulverized into a heavy powder. The coal powder is blown into a furnace, where it burns in the air. Water runs through tubes in the furnace. As the water boils, it produces steam. The steam passes through a turbine, which turns a generator. The generator produces electricity. This electricity is sent to your home.

Lesson 3 REVIEW

Write your answers to these questions on a sheet of paper.

1. How do sedimentary rocks form?

2. What are the three main types of sedimentary rocks?

3. How do the sizes of grains in shale, conglomerate, and sandstone compare to one another?

4. Give an example of a chemical rock.

5. What are organic rocks made of?

Science in Your Life

The Good and Bad of Coal

Coal is an organic sedimentary rock that forms from decaying plants and animals. Coal forms very slowly. In fact, it takes millions of years of heat and pressure to turn plant and animal remains into coal. The diagram below shows the stages of coal formation.

Coal is a source of energy. People mine and burn coal to create electricity and to run plants such as steel mills. The energy content of anthracite and bituminous coal is the highest. Some countries, such as Poland, use lignite for energy. In the United States, only Texas and North Dakota use lignite.

Sixty-four percent of the world's coal is used by China, the United States, India, Russia, and Germany. Most of the coal reserves in the world are found in Europe, Asia, Australia, and North America.

Using coal has some disadvantages. First, there is a limited amount of coal in the earth. It won't last forever. Second, coal must be mined by digging deep in the earth or by stripping off a shallow layer of earth. This harms the earth's surface and can be dangerous for miners. Third, burning coal increases air pollution. Find out about other sources of energy that are less harmful in Appendix B.

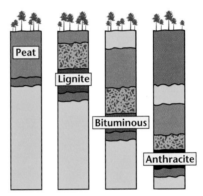

Peat
Lignite
Bituminous
Anthracite

---

1. Bits of rocks, minerals, and organic matter settle out of moving water, wind, or ice. These sediments then become compacted and cemented to form sedimentary rock. **2.** clastic, chemical, and organic **3.** Conglomerate contains the largest sizes of grains; sandstone has smaller grains; shale has the smallest grains. **4.** possible answers: rock salt, gypsum, and some limestones **5.** remains of living things

Science in Your Life

Ask volunteers to tell what they know about coal. Then have several other volunteers read aloud the Science in Your Life feature on page 189. Have students study the diagram and compare the depths of various stages of coal formation. Discuss the effect of this depth on the qualities of coal. (*Anthracite is the hardest and cleanest burning coal because it has been subjected to the greatest pressure.*) Have students work in pairs to list the advantages and disadvantages of using coal as a fuel. In a class discussion, encourage students to debate which alternative energy source in Appendix B should replace coal in the future.

Portfolio Assessment

Sample items include:
• Concept map from Teaching the Lesson
• Lesson 3 Review answers

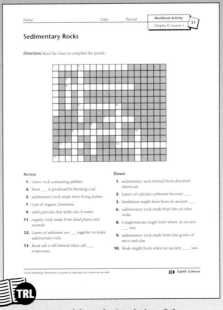

Workbook Activity 31

The Purpose portion of the student investigation begins with a question to draw students into the activity. Encourage students to read the investigation steps and formulate their own questions before beginning the investigation. This investigation will take approximately 40 minutes to complete. Students will use these process and thinking skills: experimenting, observing, measuring, communicating, and drawing conclusions.

Preparation

• Conical coffee filters can be substituted for filter paper.

• Have a large plastic bucket available for students to dispose of leftover liquids.

• Cover work areas with layers of newspaper to make cleanup easier. Have paper towels on hand to wipe up spills.

• Optional equipment to have available are hand lenses, useful for observing the white precipitate, and a stereoscopic microscope, which will allow students to see the rhombohedral shape of the calcite crystals.

• Students may use Lab Manual 31 to record their data and answer the questions.

Procedure

• Students may work individually or in groups. For group work, have one student gather equipment, but instruct all students to record results and clean up. Assign these tasks among group members: measuring and mixing the washing soda and water, measuring and mixing the calcium chloride and water, combining the two, and filtering the resulting solution and precipitate.

• Before students begin the activity, have them read through all the steps. Answer any questions and be sure they understand the procedure before having them proceed.

SAFETY ALERT

◆ Be sure all students wear aprons and safety glasses.

◆ Remind students *never* to taste any substances used in a science lab.

◆ Caution students to wipe up spills immediately.

8-1 INVESTIGATION

Materials

◆ safety glasses
◆ apron
◆ 2 test tubes in a stand
◆ teaspoon
◆ washing soda
◆ plastic stirrers
◆ calcium chloride
◆ 2 beakers
◆ filter paper
◆ funnel

Fold once.

Fold twice.

Open to make a cone.

Making Calcite

Purpose

What happens when you mix washing soda and calcium chloride? In this investigation, you will observe the formation of calcite.

Procedure

1. Copy the data table on a sheet of paper.

Material	Action	Observations
washing soda	mixed with water	
calcium chloride	mixed with water	
both mixtures	mixed together in beaker	
new substance	collected on filter paper	

2. Safety Alert: Put on the safety glasses and apron.

3. Fill one test tube with water. Slowly add 1 teaspoon of washing soda to the water. Stir to dissolve the washing soda. Use your data table to record what you see. **Safety Alert: Never taste any substance used in a science investigation. Wipe up any spills immediately.**

4. Fill the other test tube with water. Dissolve 1 teaspoon of calcium chloride in the water. Record your observations.

5. Pour the contents of both test tubes into one beaker.

6. Allow the beaker to stand for a few minutes. Observe the bottom of the beaker. Record your observations.

7. Fold the filter paper to fit inside the funnel as shown. Place the funnel over the empty beaker. Gently pour the contents of the first beaker through the filter and into the other beaker.

Name _____ Date _____ Period _____ | Lab Manual | 31
Chapter 8

8-1 Making Calcite

Use with Investigation 8-1, pages 190–191

Purpose What happens when you mix washing soda and calcium chloride? In this investigation, you will observe the formation of calcite.

Material	Action	Observations
washing soda	mixed with water	
calcium chloride	mixed with water	
both mixtures in beaker	mixed together	
new substance	collected on filter paper	

Questions and Conclusions

1. Describe the substance on the filter paper. _____

2. The solid that formed is calcite, or calcium carbonate ($CaCO_3$). Suggest where this solid came from in your investigation. (Washing soda is sodium carbonate, $NaCO_3$. Calcium chloride is $CaCl_2$.)

3. What type of sedimentary rock is formed in this investigation?

4. How is this investigation different from the formation of real rock?

Explore Further

Design and perform an investigation in which you model the formation of a clastic rock, a chemical rock, or an organic rock. Explain to classmates how your model is similar to and different from the formation of real rock.

©AGS Publishing. Permission is granted to reproduce for classroom use only.   ◆ Earth Science

Lab Manual 31

8. Look closely at the substance on the filter paper. Record your observations.

9. Clean your work space and wash the equipment.

Questions and Conclusions

1. Describe the substance on the filter paper.

2. The solid that formed is calcite, or calcium carbonate ($CaCO_3$). Suggest where this solid came from in your investigation. (Washing soda is sodium carbonate, Na_2CO_3. Calcium chloride is $CaCl_2$.)

3. What type of sedimentary rock is formed in this investigation?

4. How is this investigation different from the formation of real rock?

Explore Further

Design and perform an investigation in which you model the formation of a clastic rock, a chemical rock, or an organic rock. Explain to classmates how your model is similar to and different from the formation of real rock.

Results

During the chemical reaction, sodium ions and chlorine ions dissociate to form a salt solution, calcium ions bond with carbonate ions to form solid calcite, and carbon dioxide is given off as a gas, producing bubbles in the test tubes.

Questions and Conclusions Answers

1. Tiny white crystals (calcite) were observed on the filter.

2. The carbonate came from the washing soda; the calcium came from the calcium chloride.

3. chemical rock

4. The reaction was concentrated in a small area, and sedimentation of the crystals occurred quickly.

Explore Further Answers

Students' models should illustrate the process by which these types of rock are formed. However, students should recognize that factors such as time, pressure, temperature, and method of accumulation have been altered to make the model. Possible ideas include layering pebbles with a mixture of glue and water and letting it harden to model clastic (conglomerate) rock, doing the same with bits of shell to model organic rock, and allowing salt water to evaporate to model chemical rock.

Assessment

Check whether students follow procedures correctly and are able to identify the precipitate. Check that students use their observations to draw the correct conclusions. You might include the following items from this investigation in student portfolios:

• Data table

• Answers to Questions and Conclusions and Explore Further sections

Lesson at a Glance

Chapter 8 Lesson 4

Overview This lesson explains classes of metamorphic rocks and how they form.

Objectives

- To explain how metamorphic rocks form
- To identify samples of foliated and nonfoliated metamorphic rocks

Student Pages 192–193

Teacher's Resource Library **TRL**

Workbook Activity 32

Alternative Workbook Activity 32

Vocabulary

foliated rock
nonfoliated rock

 Warm-Up Activity

Display some metamorphic rocks and their parents rocks: marble and limestone, slate and shale, and gneiss and granite. Without identifying any samples, challenge students to pair them into before-and-after sets. Explain that this lesson shows students how rocks can change into other rocks.

2 **Teaching the Lesson**

After they have read the lesson, ask students to draw diagrams to illustrate the principal difference between foliated and nonfoliated metamorphic rocks. Below each diagram, they can write a summary sentence explaining the difference.

Have students brainstorm to make a list of ways that metamorphic rocks are like other rocks. (*Like igneous rocks, metamorphic rocks form under intense pressure and temperature within the earth. Like sedimentary rocks, they form from preexisting rocks.*)

As you teach this lesson, keep the samples from the Warm-Up Activity on hand for students to observe with hand lenses.

Lesson **4** **Metamorphic Rocks**

Objectives

After reading this lesson, you should be able to
- explain how metamorphic rocks form.
- identify samples of foliated and nonfoliated metamorphic rocks.

Foliated rock
Metamorphic rock in which minerals have been rearranged into visible bands

Nonfoliated rock
Metamorphic rock that does not show bands

How Metamorphic Rocks Form

Deep in the earth, heat and pressure from all sides can squeeze, bend, and twist rock. Hot fluids move through the rock. The heat, pressure, and liquids change the appearance and texture of the rock. The result is metamorphic rock. Metamorphic rocks can also form when liquids and gases escape from magma. The liquids and gases add new minerals to the surrounding rock. Geologists classify metamorphic rocks into two types.

Foliated Rocks

Foliated rocks form when heat and pressure have flattened the minerals into bands. Slate, schist, and gneiss are examples of foliated rocks. Slate forms from shale and has very thin bands. Slate contains a lot of mica, which has good cleavage. Therefore, slate splits easily along its bands into sheets of rock. This property makes slate a good material for tiles. Gneiss forms from granite and other rocks as mica and other minerals rearrange into bands. But gneiss does not have as much mica as slate and therefore does not split as well.

Slate splits into flat sheets.

Nonfoliated Rocks

Marble has no bands.

Rocks that are made largely of only one material, such as limestone and sandstone, result in metamorphic rocks without bands, called **nonfoliated rocks**. The crystals combine and interlock to form a harder rock. For example, marble is a nonfoliated rock formed from limestone. Pure marble is white. Small amounts of various minerals produce the colorful streaks and swirls in some marbles.

TEACHER ALERT

! Students may mistakenly think that metamorphic and igneous rocks form in the same way. However, metamorphic rocks do not form from melted rock, as igneous rocks do. Metamorphic rocks are subject to enough heat and pressure that their minerals recrystallize into larger or different minerals.

Lesson 4 **R E V I E W**

Write your answers to these questions on a sheet of paper.

1. How do metamorphic rocks form?

2. What is the difference between foliated and nonfoliated rocks?

3. From which rock type does slate form?

4. From which rock type does marble form?

5. Why is slate used to make tiles and gneiss is not?

Technology Note

Huge blocks or slabs of marble are often needed as building materials. Because of this, explosives are not used to mine marble. Explosives would shatter marble into pieces that are much too small.

Instead, special machines, called channeling machines, are used to mine marble. These machines cut holes in a "dotted line" across a marble rock. More "dotted lines" are cut until a large block shape is outlined. Then wedges are driven into the holes. The marble block is pried away from the surrounding marble and hauled to the surface.

Some marble blocks weigh as much as 2,000 tons. These blocks are later sawed into the desired sizes.

Rocks Chapter 8 **193**

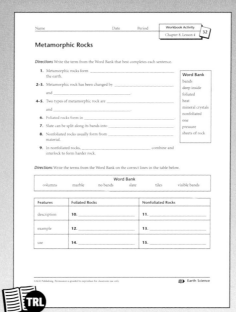

Workbook Activity 32

CROSS-CURRICULAR CONNECTION

Geography

Have students locate the Appalachian Mountains on a map. Then have them use encyclopedias to find out about the metamorphic provinces of this mountain range. *(Slate Belt in the Carolinas; regions in Vermont and Georgia where marble is mined)*

CAREER CONNECTION

Have a geologist talk to the class about the types of work geologists do, such as searching for natural resources and studying landforms. If possible, have the geologist bring in samples of rocks for students to analyze.

LEARNING STYLES

Auditory/Verbal

Have groups of three students review the formation of metamorphic, sedimentary, and igneous rocks by taking turns describing the processes to one another. Encourage listeners to check their textbook and give feedback.

Lesson 4 Review Answers

1. Preexisting rocks are transformed by heat, pressure, and hot fluids into metamorphic rocks. **2.** Foliated rocks contain minerals that have been rearranged into visible bands; nonfoliated rocks lack these bands. **3.** shale, a clastic sedimentary rock **4.** limestone, a chemical or organic sedimentary rock **5.** Slate contains a lot of mica, which causes it to split easily into thin sheets for tiles; gneiss has less mica and does not split well.

Portfolio Assessment

Sample items include:
• Diagrams from Teaching the Lesson
• Lesson 4 Review answers

Rocks Chapter 8 **193**

Lesson at a Glance

Chapter 8 Lesson 5

Overview In this lesson, students learn how one form of rock changes into other forms over time. These changes are called the rock cycle.

Objectives

- To describe how one type of rock can change into another type
- To explain the forces involved in the rock cycle

Student Pages 194–198

Teacher's Resource Library

Workbook Activity 33

Alternative Workbook Activity 33

Lab Manual 32

Resource File 16

Vocabulary

rock cycle

1 Warm-Up Activity

Ask students to list things that cause rocks to change. *(heat, pressure, hot liquid, water, wind, ice, etc.)* Display rocks of various sizes with a container of sand. Explain that sand forms as rocks are worn down into smaller and smaller bits. Tell students that in this lesson they will learn how rocks change from one form to another.

2 Teaching the Lesson

After reading the lesson, have students make a drawing to illustrate what they learned. Then ask them to use the drawing to explain the lesson to another person.

Before discussing the rock cycle, have students list other natural cycles. *(life cycles, the water cycle, the nitrogen cycle)* Guide students to see that a cycle repeats over and over.

You may wish to define some of the forces that contribute to the rock cycle. Weathering is the breaking down of rocks at or near the earth's surface. Erosion is the transport of this debris by water, wind, gravity, or ice. Students will learn more about these two processes in Chapter 12.

Objectives

After reading this lesson, you should be able to

- describe how one type of rock can change into another type.
- explain the forces involved in the rock cycle.

Rock cycle

Series of natural changes that cause one type of rock to become another type of rock

Rocks are always changing. Some melt deep in the earth, then harden. Some are built by layers of sediment. Others twist and bend because of underground heat and pressure. Each type of rock—igneous, sedimentary, and metamorphic—can also change into another type. The series of changes that cause one type of rock to become another type of rock is called the **rock cycle**. This cycle occurs over a long period of time.

Study the rock cycle diagram below. Each arrow is one possible pathway in the cycle. The label by each arrow tells you what force is causing the rock to change. There is no special starting place in the rock cycle. You can start with any type of rock and follow any pathway leading from it.

Follow the arrows as we travel along the cycle, starting with magma. As magma rises from deep in the earth, it cools and hardens into igneous rock. Volcanoes quickly deposit lava on the earth's surface as extrusive rock. Pressure eventually lifts intrusive rock to the surface as well.

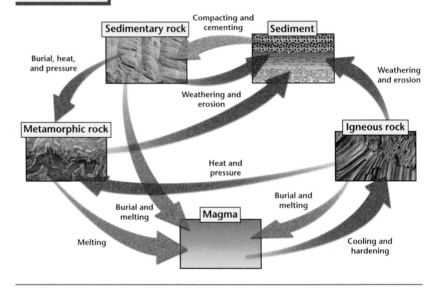

TEACHER ALERT

Because of the term *cycle*, students may mistakenly believe that the steps in the rock cycle always occur in a set order. The rock cycle may be better explained as a system of pathways, not a single path. Any of the three types of rock may become either of the other two types, depending on the forces in action.

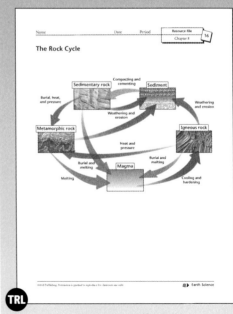

Resource File 16

Once on the earth's surface, all rock types begin to slowly break apart and move. When rocks break down into pebbles and then into fine grains like sand, they are easily carried away. This sediment often ends up in a large body of water. Many factors cause this breaking down and carrying away: wind, water, air, living things, ice, and gravity. You will learn more about this process when you study weathering and erosion in Chapter 12.

At the bottom of a lake or an ocean, sediment forms layers. Over time and under pressure, the layers compact and cement into sedimentary rock. Sometimes sedimentary rock is later brought to the earth's surface, where it begins to break down again.

Other times, sedimentary rock becomes buried deeper in the earth. There the rock is exposed to heat and pressure. These underground forces can bend and twist it into metamorphic rock. In the same way, intrusive rock can become metamorphic rock. Sometimes metamorphic rock is brought to the surface, where it begins to break down again.

In extreme underground heat, all three types of rock can melt. Most rocks melt at temperatures of 800°C or higher. Then they become magma deep in the earth, and the rock cycle continues.

Rocks do not always cycle from igneous to sedimentary to metamorphic. Each type of rock can change into the two other types. For example, how does igneous rock change into metamorphic? Follow the pathways on the diagram to find out. To become igneous rock, the other two types must first become magma.

Rocks change by forces inside the earth and by forces on the earth's surface. Look again at the diagram. Below the earth's surface, forces of heat and pressure cause rocks to bend or melt. Above ground, forces such as wind and water cause rocks to break down, move, and settle.

CROSS-CURRICULAR CONNECTION

Drama

Ask students to write a script for an imaginary tour of the rock cycle. They might pretend to be a guide taking students on a magic elevator deep inside the earth. At the surface, they could describe the formation of sedimentary rocks and igneous rocks, then follow them down to where they are transformed into metamorphic rocks.

LEARNING STYLES

LEP/ESL

Have students use their drawings from the Warm-Up Activity to be sure they understand how sedimentary, metamorphic, and igneous rocks form. Ask them to explain how each type of rock forms using the terms *cooling, heat, pressure, sediment, magma,* and *cementing.* You may wish to have students who are learning English work with a partner who is fluent. Partners can take turns explaining how rocks change because of the forces listed above.

AT HOME

Encourage students to search their homes and neighborhoods for examples of rocks of different types and in different stages of weathering (such as gravel and sand). They can create a chart listing each rock they found, where they found it, the type of rock it is, and how it is used.

SCIENCE JOURNAL

Ask students to imagine that they are a rock on a journey through the rock cycle. Have them write a brief account of their travels and the changes they undergo. The account may be as fanciful as they like, as long as it is consistent with the science facts of the lesson.

Lesson 5 Review Answers

1. Rocks break down, or weather, because of the forces of wind, water, living things, and gravity. The resulting sediment is carried, often by water, and deposited in layers, where it settles and eventually becomes cemented together. **2.** intense heat and pressure **3.** It must become hot enough to melt inside the earth. **4.** If buried deep enough, sedimentary rock may be altered by intense heat and pressure, forming metamorphic rock. **5.** Metamorphic rock might become hot enough to melt, becoming magma. When it cools, it would then be igneous rock.

Achievements in Science

Ask students how they could prove that rocks change over time. After listing their ideas on the board, have volunteers read aloud the Achievements in Science feature on page 196. Discuss the logic of Hutton's reasoning, based on his observations. Compare students' ideas and point out which ones are based on sound scientific reasoning.

Portfolio Assessment

Sample items include:
• Drawing from Teaching the Lesson
• Lesson 5 Review answers

Write your answers to these questions on a sheet of paper.

1. Name two ways that rocks on the earth's surface are changed.

2. Name two underground forces that change rocks.

3. What is required for a rock to become magma?

4. How might sedimentary rock become metamorphic rock?

5. How might metamorphic rock become igneous rock?

Achievements in Science

The Rock Cycle Theory

The idea of a rock cycle was first proposed in the 1700s. At that time, geology as a formal science did not exist. Most people believed the earth was only about 6,000 years old. Many thought that only major disasters such as earthquakes could change the earth's surface.

James Hutton was a Scottish physician and farmer. He loved to study science and ask questions. In particular, he wanted to find the origin of rocks and minerals.

By studying rocks in Scotland, Hutton noticed streaks of granite among sedimentary rock. He thought this showed that there was heat, even fire, deep in the earth. He also found vertical layers of rock topped with horizontal layers. He concluded that the lower layers had to be very old. They must have been tipped on their side before the new layers were added.

In 1785, Hutton published his theory of rocks in a book. He proposed that one rock type changes into another over time. These changes are caused by pressure and heat deep in the earth. He also stated that erosion, weathering, moving of sediment, and the uprising of rocks from beneath the earth's surface are all part of a cycle. Hutton believed that this cycle has been repeating for millions of years, not for thousands of years. Because of his contributions, James Hutton is called the father of geology.

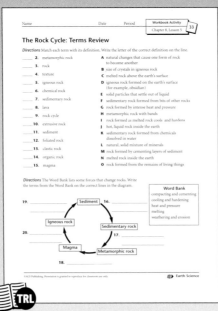

Workbook Activity 33

Identifying Rocks

Materials
- ◆ numbered rock samples
- ◆ hand lens

Purpose
How can you identify unknown rocks? In this investigation, you will observe properties of rocks and identify rock samples.

Procedure
1. Copy the data table on a sheet of paper.

Rock Number	Observations	Rock Name	Rock Type

2. Write the number of the first sample in the first column of your data table.

3. Use the hand lens to observe the sample. Is the sample foliated or nonfoliated? Is it fine-grained or coarse-grained? What is its color? Do you see any remains of past life? Do you see crystals? Pebbles? Layers? Write your observations in the second column of your data table. Be as detailed as you can.

4. Repeat steps 2 and 3 for each of the samples.

5. Use the table on page 198 to identify each rock sample. Record your findings in your data table.

6. Review the chapter to determine each sample's rock type: igneous, sedimentary, or metamorphic. Record your findings in the last column of your data table.

7. Clean your work space.

Investigation 8-2

The Purpose portion of the student investigation begins with a question to draw students into the activity. Encourage students to read the investigation steps and formulate their own questions before beginning the investigation. This investigation will take approximately 45 minutes to complete. Students will use these process and thinking skills: observing, classifying, comparing and contrasting, communicating, drawing conclusions, and collecting and organizing data.

Preparation

- Igneous samples include basalt, granite, obsidian, pumice, and rhyolite. Coal, conglomerate, limestone, sandstone, and shale are sedimentary; try to provide some samples containing fossils. Marble, gneiss, schist, and slate are metamorphic.

- Label the samples with a permanent marker. Provide a reference key to aid in identification.

- Create a kit for each student or group. Make sure each kit contains at least one type of each rock— metamorphic, sedimentary, and igneous.

- Provide one or two simple geology field guides to help students identify rocks. If possible, provide a stereoscopic microscope so that students can observe the fine-grained rock specimens.

- Students may use Lab Manual 32 to record their data and answer the questions.

Procedure

- Have students work individually or in pairs. Suggest that they use their textbook to help them identify the rock samples.

- Display labeled samples of some common minerals discussed in Chapter 7. Review the difference between a rock and a mineral.

Continued on page 198

Lab Manual 32

Continued from page 197

- Use these questions to help students differentiate the samples:

Would you expect to find fossils in metamorphic or igneous rocks? *(no; heat and pressure would destroy the organic remains.)*

Would you find pebbles in igneous rocks? *(no; pebbles are sediment; interlocking mineral grains form in igneous rocks.)*

Results

Most students should be able to classify rocks as igneous, metamorphic, or sedimentary. Identification of specific rock types may prove challenging.

Questions and Conclusions Answers

1. Answers will vary depending on the samples chosen. Rocks with distinctive textures, such as sandstone, pumice, and conglomerate, are generally easier to identify than fine-grained samples.

2. Rocks with similar textures and similar mineral compositions may be difficult to identify.

Explore Further Answers

Remind students to number their samples to keep them straight. Students' conclusions will vary. They might conclude that sedimentary rocks generally contain layers as well as organic matter such as fossils. Igneous rocks have a crystalline structure, although some may have crystals too small to see. Some metamorphic rocks have bands of minerals.

Assessment

Assess students' ability to note similarities and differences among the rock samples. They may be able to classify a sample as sedimentary, metamorphic, or igneous, even though they cannot identify the sample. You might include the following items from this investigation in student portfolios:

- Data table

- Answers to Questions and Conclusions and Explore Further sections

Name of Rock	Description
basalt	dark gray to black; crystals not visible; many small holes
coal	black; smudges fingers; no crystals
conglomerate	cemented pebbles
gneiss	bands of color that may or may not be bent; often visible crystals
granite	interlocking white, pink, gray, and dark crystals
limestone	may contain tiny shells or interlocking crystals; usually light colored
marble	often has swirling colors; large interlocking crystals
obsidian	dark; glassy; fractures with curved surface
pumice	lightweight and filled with holes; looks like a hardened sponge; light colored
rhyolite	pinkish tan; often contains larger visible crystals against a mass containing crystals too small to see
sandstone	cemented sand grains; color varies but often yellow-brown
schist	flaky, parallel layers; may sparkle
shale	color varies but usually dark; smells musty when moistened; fine grained; thin layers
slate	gray or gray-blue; harder than shale

Questions and Conclusions

1. Which samples were easiest to identify?

2. Which samples were hardest to identify?

Explore Further

Collect rock samples in a nearby park or along a shoreline. Repeat step 3 for each sample. What conclusions can you make from your observations?

- A rock is a solid, natural material made of minerals. The three types of rocks are igneous, sedimentary, and metamorphic.

- Information about rocks helps us understand the environment.

- Igneous rocks form from magma or lava that hardens.

- Intrusive igneous rocks form from magma underground and have a course-grained texture. Granite is an intrusive rock.

- Extrusive igneous rocks form from lava at the earth's surface and have a fine-grained or glassy texture. Basalt is an extrusive rock.

- Sedimentary rocks form from particles called sediment. The layered sediment gets pressed and cemented into rock.

- Clastic sedimentary rocks are made from fragments of other rocks. Shale and sandstone are clastic rocks.

- Chemical sedimentary rocks form from dissolved minerals. Gypsum and some limestones are chemical rocks.

- Organic sedimentary rocks form from the remains of plants and animals. Chalk, coal, and some limestones are organic rocks.

- Metamorphic rocks form from other rocks that are twisted and bent by heat and pressure.

- In foliated metamorphic rocks, minerals in the rocks have been rearranged into bands that can be seen. Slate is a foliated rock.

- Nonfoliated metamorphic rocks do not show banding. Marble is a nonfoliated rock.

- Rocks change from one type to another in the rock cycle. This cycle is driven by forces above and below the earth's surface.

Science Words

chemical rock, 187	intrusive rock, 181	nonfoliated rock, 192	sediment, 185
clastic rock, 186	lava, 183		sedimentary rock, 179
conglomerate, 186	magma, 181	organic rock, 188	
extrusive rock, 183	metamorphic rock, 179	rock, 178	texture, 182
foliated rock, 192		rock cycle, 194	
igneous rock, 178			

Chapter 8 Summary

Have volunteers read aloud each Summary item on page 199. Ask volunteers to explain the meaning of each item. Direct students' attention to the Science Words box on the bottom of page 199. Have them read and review each word and its definition.

Chapter 8 Review

Use the Chapter Review to prepare students for tests and to reteach content from the chapter.

Chapter 8 Mastery Test

The Teacher's Resource Library includes two parallel forms of the Chapter 8 Mastery Test. The difficulty level of the two forms is equivalent. You may wish to use one form as a pretest and the other form as a posttest.

Review Answers

Vocabulary Review

1. lava 2. sediment 3. rock cycle 4. magma
5. metamorphic rock 6. sedimentary rock
7. igneous rock 8. texture 9. extrusive
rock 10. conglomerate

Concept Review

11. B 12. A 13. B 14. D 15. D
16. sedimentary 17. sedimentary
18. igneous 19. sedimentary
20. metamorphic 21. sedimentary
22. igneous 23. sedimentary

TEACHER ALERT

In the Chapter Review, the Vocabulary Review activity includes a sample of the chapter's vocabulary terms. The activity will help determine students' understanding of key vocabulary terms and concepts presented in the chapter. Other vocabulary terms used in the chapter are listed below:

chemical rock   nonfoliated rock
clastic rock   organic rock
foliated rock   rock
intrusive rock

Word Bank

conglomerate
extrusive rock
igneous rock
lava
magma
metamorphic rock
rock cycle
sediment
sedimentary rock
texture

Vocabulary Review

Choose the word or phrase from the Word Bank that best completes each sentence. Write the answer on your paper.

1. Hot, liquid rock on the earth's surface is called _____.

2. Fragments of rocks, minerals, and remains of living things are _____.

3. Rocks change from one type to another in the _____.

4. Hot, liquid rock beneath the earth's surface is _____.

5. _____ forms from rocks that have been changed by heat, pressure, and hot fluids.

6. Layers of sediment that are pressed together and cemented can form _____.

7. Liquid rock that cools on or below the surface forms _____.

8. Some igneous rocks have a coarse-grained _____.

9. _____ forms when lava cools on the earth's surface.

10. Rock made of pebbles cemented together is _____.

Concept Review

Choose the word or phrase that best completes each sentence. Write the letter of the answer on your paper.

11. A rock is a mixture of _____.
   A animals   **B** minerals   **C** plants   **D** bands

12. The two kinds of igneous rocks can be identified by _____.
   A texture   **B** color   **C** bands   **D** weight

13. An igneous rock that formed from magma cooling slowly would have _____.
   A a fine grain   **C** no crystals
   B large crystals   **D** no grain

Chapter 8 Mastery Test A

Mastery Test A, Page 1
Chapter 8

Chapter 8 Mastery Test A

Part A Read each sentence. Write the letter of the correct answer on the line.

___ **1.** Rocks that form within the earth from cooling magma are called ___.
   A chemical sedimentary rocks   **C** intrusive igneous rocks
   B foliated metamorphic rocks   **D** clastic rocks

___ **2.** An example of an organic sedimentary rock is ___.
   A basalt   **B** coal   **C** slate   **D** conglomerate

___ **3.** You can see bands in a(n) ___ rock.
   A foliated metamorphic   **C** chemical sedimentary
   B intrusive igneous   **D** extrusive igneous

___ **4.** Igneous rocks are classified according to ___.
   A their types of bands   **C** whether they contain sediment
   B their color   **D** whether they form above or below the earth's surface

___ **5.** Rocks are solid mixtures of ___.
   A magma   **B** minerals   **C** conglomerate   **D** sediment

Part B Match each term with its meaning. Write the letter of the correct answer on the line.

___ **6.** magma   **A** melted, cooled, and hardened rock
___ **7.** igneous rock   **B** rock formed by heat or pressure
___ **8.** coal   **C** rock and organic bits pressed together and cemented
___ **9.** sandstone   **D** igneous rock that forms underground
___ **10.** rock salt   **E** igneous rock that forms on the earth's surface
___ **11.** metamorphic rock   **F** hot, liquid rock inside the earth
___ **12.** sedimentary rock   **G** solid material that settles
___ **13.** intrusive rock   **H** example of clastic rock
___ **14.** extrusive rock   **I** example of chemical rock
___ **15.** sediment   **J** example of organic rock

Earth Science

Mastery Test A, Page 2
Chapter 8

Chapter 8 Mastery Test A, *continued*

Part C Write the term from the Word Bank that best completes each sentence.

Word Bank

| clastic | intrusive | nonfoliated | rock cycle |
| extrusive | magma | organic | |

16. Granite is an example of _____ igneous rock.

17. Lava is _____ that comes out onto the earth's surface.

18. Obsidian is an example of _____ igneous rock.

19. The _____ describes how a rock may be changed from igneous to sedimentary to metamorphic.

20. The three types of sedimentary rock are clastic, chemical, and _____.

21. Shale and conglomerate are examples of _____ sedimentary rock.

22. Metamorphic rocks are classified as foliated and _____.

Part D Write a short answer for each question.

23. What is a rock?

24. How are metamorphic and igneous rocks alike and different?

25. What is the rock cycle?

Earth Science

Chapter 8 Mastery Test A

14. The three main types of rocks are _____.
  A clastic, extrusive, and intrusive
  B sedimentary, organic, and foliated
  C quartz, feldspar, and mica
  D metamorphic, igneous, and sedimentary

15. Limestone is mostly the mineral _____.
  A mica   **B** talc   **C** quartz   **D** calcite

Copy the list below on your paper. Decide whether each rock or kind of rock is igneous, sedimentary, or metamorphic. Write the answer next to each item.

16. clastic   **19.** organic   **22.** basalt

17. chemical   **20.** nonfoliated   **23.** coal

18. granite   **21.** sandstone

Critical Thinking

Write the answer to each of the following questions.

24. A handful of sand contains bits of igneous rock. How did the igneous rock get there? How might the sand become sedimentary rock? To answer these questions, make a rock cycle diagram using the following words: magma, igneous rock, breaking into fragments, cooling, sediment, and pressing and cementing.

25. The wall of a canyon is layered and seems to be made of sand cemented together. In one part of the wall, you see a pattern like the one shown. What rock type is it? How was the rock formed? Where did it form and why?

Test-Taking Tip When studying for a test, write your own test questions with a partner. Then answer each other's questions. Check your answers.

Review Answers
Critical Thinking

24. The diagram should show a part of the rock cycle. The steps in the diagram, in order, should be: magma cooling to form igneous rock; igneous rock breaking down into fragments to form sediment; and sediment being pressed and cemented to form sedimentary rock.
25. Sedimentary rock (sandstone); it formed as layers of sand were compacted and cemented together. Sedimentary rock forms on the earth's surface or at the bottom of a lake or ocean. The fossil shell indicates that the rock formed in an ancient ocean or lake bed.

ALTERNATIVE ASSESSMENT

Alternative Assessment items correlate to the student Goals for Learning at the beginning of this chapter.

- Provide students with a rock sample and a mineral sample and have them explain why the two are different.

- Give students an example of each type of rock: igneous, sedimentary, and metamorphic. Have them tell which is which and explain how they knew.

- Write the terms *Igneous, Sedimentary,* and *Metamorphic* on the board as column headings. Under each heading, ask students to write the steps that occur in the formation of that type of rock.

- Provide rock samples or pictures of two different sedimentary rocks. Have students tell how they are alike and different. Repeat the process with pairs of igneous rocks and pairs of metamorphic rocks.

- Distribute copies of the rock cycle diagram (see Resource File 16) with all labels removed except for *Igneous rock, Sedimentary rock,* and *Metamorphic rock.* Have students add labels indicating the forces that occur as one type of rock changes into another.

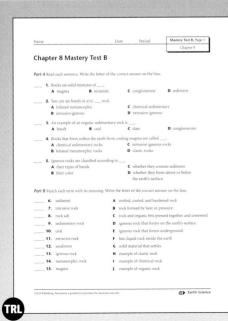

Chapter 8 Mastery Test B

Chapter

Planning Guide

The Earth's Atmosphere

| | | Student Text Lesson | |
	Student Pages	Vocabulary	Lesson Review
Lesson 1 Gases in the Atmosphere	204–207	✔	✔
Lesson 2 Layers of the Atmosphere	208–210	✔	✔
Lesson 3 Clouds	211–215	✔	✔
Lesson 4 Precipitation	216–220	✔	✔
Lesson 5 Wind Patterns	221–224	✔	✔

Chapter Activities

Student Text
Science Center
Teacher's Resource Library
Community Connection 9: Observing
    Weather

Assessment Options

Student Text
Chapter 9 Review

Teacher's Resource Library
Chapter 9 Mastery Tests A and B

Achievements in Science	Science at Work	Science in Your Life	Investigation	Science Myth	Note	Technology Note	Did You Know	Science Integration	Science Journal	Cross-Curricular Connection	Online Connection	Teacher Alert	Applications (Home, Career, Community, Global, Environment)	Auditory/Verbal	Body/Kinesthetic	Interpersonal/Group Learning	Logical/Mathematical	Visual/Spatial	LEP/ESL	Workbook Activities	Alternative Workbook Activities	Lab Manual	Resource File	Self-Study Guide
		207			✔		204	205, 206	206	207				206						34	34	33	17	✔
210							209			209	209	209	209	209						35	35		18	✔
	214		215							213	213		212			212		213		36	36	34, 35	19	✔
218			219	217	✔				217	217			217, 218				217		217	37	37	36		
						✔			223	224			223	223	223					38	38		20	✔

Pronunciation Key

a	hat	e	let	ī	ice	ô	order	ù	put	sh she
ā	age	ē	equal	o	hot	oi	oil	ü	rule	th thin
ä	far	ėr	term	ō	open	ou	out	ch	child	℔H then
â	care	i	it	ȯ	saw	u	cup	ng	long	zh measure

ə { a in about, e in taken, i in pencil, o in lemon, u in circus }

Skill Track Software

Use the Skill Track Software for Earth Science for additional reinforcement of this chapter. The software program allows students using AGS textbooks to be assessed for mastery of each chapter and lesson of the textbook. Students access the software on an individual basis and are assessed with multiple-choice items.

Chapter 9:
The Earth's Atmosphere
pages 202–227

Lessons

1. **Gases in the Atmosphere**
   pages 204–207

2. **Layers of the Atmosphere**
   pages 208–210

3. **Clouds** pages 211–215

Investigation 9-1 page 215

4. **Precipitation** pages 216–220

Investigation 9-2 pages 219–220

5. **Wind Patterns** pages 221–224

Chapter 9 Summary page 225

Chapter 9 Review pages 226–227

Skill Track Software
  for Earth Science

Teacher's Resource Library **TRL**

Workbook Activities 34–38

Alternative Workbook Activities
34–38

Lab Manual 33–36

Community Connection 9

Resource File 17–20

Chapter 9 Self-Study Guide

Chapter 9 Mastery Tests A and B

(Answer Keys for the Teacher's
Resource Library begin on page 400
of the Teacher's Edition. The
Materials List for the Lab Manual
activities begins on page 415.)

Science Center

Have students prepare a display entitled
"Things That Depend on Air." They can
cut out pictures from magazines and
mount them on poster board. Below each
picture, students should write a sentence
explaining how the object in the picture
depends on air. For example, they might
mount a picture of a hot-air balloon and
write a sentence stating that air is heated
by a burner to make the balloon rise into
the air. Or they might show a picture of a
person and write a sentence stating that
people need oxygen in the air to breathe.

Community Connection 9

9 The Earth's Atmosphere

The earth's atmosphere is around us all the time. The air we breathe is part of the atmosphere. The clouds in the sky are part of the atmosphere. Rainbows remind us that the atmosphere contains moisture. When sunlight passes through water droplets in the air, the different colors that make up the light separate. We see this separation of light as a rainbow. In Chapter 9, you will learn about the gases and layers that make up our atmosphere. You will also learn about clouds, precipitation, and wind patterns.

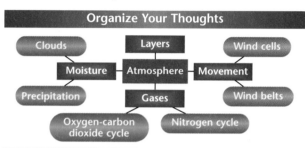

Organize Your Thoughts

Clouds — Layers — Wind cells

Moisture — Atmosphere — Movement

Precipitation — Gases — Wind belts

Oxygen-carbon dioxide cycle — Nitrogen cycle

Goals for Learning

◆ To explain what the earth's atmosphere is

◆ To explain how gases in the air cycle through the environment

◆ To describe the structure of the atmosphere

◆ To classify clouds

◆ To explain how precipitation forms

◆ To describe the earth's wind patterns

203

Introducing the Chapter

Have students look at the photograph on page 202. A double rainbow arches across the sky. Ask students if they have seen a double rainbow like this. Ask volunteers to tell when, why, and where they think rainbows occur. Then read together the introductory paragraph on page 203. Rainbows result when raindrops in the air act like a prism, breaking sunlight into rays of color. As students examine the picture, they should be able to easily distinguish land and air, or the atmosphere. Write the word *atmosphere* on the board. Ask pairs of students to write as many facts as they can think of about the atmosphere. After about 10 minutes, have the pairs read aloud their list of facts. Write each fact on a large sheet of poster board and display the poster board in the classroom. As students study Chapter 9, ask them to put a check mark next to each fact that is verified by what they learn. Also ask them to cross out any statements that they discover are incorrect.

Notes and Technology Notes

Ask volunteers to read the notes that appear in the margins throughout the chapter. Then discuss them with the class.

TEACHER'S RESOURCE

The AGS Teaching Strategies in Science Transparencies may be used with this chapter. The transparencies add an interactive dimension to expand and enhance the *Earth Science* program content.

CAREER INTEREST INVENTORY

The AGS Harrington-O'Shea Career Decision-Making System-Revised (CDM) may be used with this chapter. Students can use the CDM to explore their interests and identify careers. The CDM defines career areas that are indicated by students' responses on the inventory.

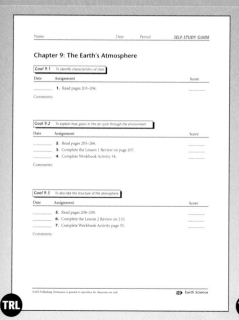

Chapter 9 Self-Study Guide

Lesson at a Glance

Chapter 9 Lesson 1

Overview This lesson introduces students to the atmosphere. They learn what gases make up the atmosphere and how some of these gases cycle in the environment.

Objectives

■ To identify the gases in the atmosphere
■ To describe the oxygen-carbon dioxide cycle
■ To describe the nitrogen cycle

Student Pages 204–207

Teacher's Resource Library **TRL**

Workbook Activity 34

Alternative Workbook Activity 34

Lab Manual 33

Resource File 17

Vocabulary

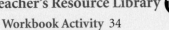

atmosphere

Science Background

Bacterial action produces 90 percent of nitrogen compounds. Soil bacteria that change nitrogen into usable forms often grow in association with legumes, such as peas, clover, and soybeans. The bacteria that take up nitrogen live in enlarged nodules on the roots of legumes. Lightning produces about 10 percent of nitrogen compounds. As lightning passes through air, the energy breaks apart molecules of nitrogen, oxygen, and other gases. The individual atoms of oxygen and nitrogen recombine to form nitrogen compounds. These compounds are washed into the ground by rain.

Carbon dioxide is exhaled by people and animals. However, it also enters the atmosphere as a product of decomposition and when fossil fuels, such as coal, natural gas, and oil, are burned.

1 Warm-Up Activity

Before class, cut two apple wedges. Wrap one tightly in plastic wrap and allow the other to brown, uncovered. Show students the apple wedges. Ask them to speculate why one piece of apple has

---

Objectives

After reading this lesson, you should be able to

◆ identify the gases in the atmosphere.
◆ describe the oxygen-carbon dioxide cycle.
◆ describe the nitrogen cycle.

Atmosphere

Layer of gases that surrounds the earth

 Did You Know?

The composition of the atmosphere has changed over time and will continue to change. Scientists can study actual samples of ancient air. The samples come from air bubbles trapped for millions of years in ice and hardened tree sap.

What basic things do you need in order to live? At the top of the list is the air you breathe. When you breathe in (inhale), you take in gases that your body needs to work. When you breathe out (exhale), you release gases that are needed by other living things.

The layer of gases that surrounds the earth is called the **atmosphere**. Most people simply refer to the atmosphere as the air. Although some other planets have atmospheres, ours is the only one known to support life.

The earth's atmosphere contains many different gases. Some of these gases are elements. Others are compounds. From the circle graph, you can see that oxygen and nitrogen make up most of the earth's atmosphere. What other gases are in the air you breathe?

Oxygen and nitrogen are needed by all living things. Plants and animals take these gases from the atmosphere, use them, and then return them to the atmosphere. Oxygen and nitrogen go through these natural cycles over and over.

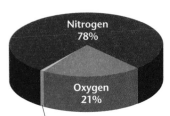

Nitrogen 78%

Oxygen 21%

Argon, carbon dioxide, water vapor, neon, helium, krypton, xenon, methane, hydrogen, ozone 1%

---

changed color and the other has not. *(One was exposed to air.)* Unwrap the protected piece of apple. After a few minutes, it too should begin to darken. Explain to students that one of the gases in air causes this change to occur. Tell students it is the same gas they need to breathe. Ask them if they can name the gas. *(oxygen)* Explain that they will be learning about the gases surrounding the earth.

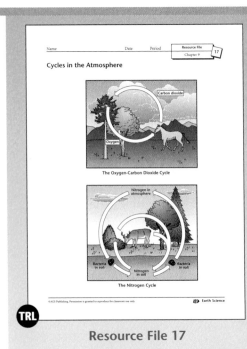

Name ___ Date ___ Period ___ Resource File 17 Chapter 9

Cycles in the Atmosphere

Carbon dioxide

Oxygen

The Oxygen-Carbon Dioxide Cycle

Nitrogen in atmosphere

Bacteria in soil

Nitrogen in soil

Bacteria in soil

The Nitrogen Cycle

Earth Science

TRL

Resource File 17

Plants make their own food: sugar. They use sunlight to change carbon dioxide and water into sugar and oxygen. This process is called photosynthesis.

The Oxygen-Carbon Dioxide Cycle

The diagram below shows how oxygen and carbon dioxide circulate between living things and the atmosphere. When animals and people breathe in air, their bodies use the oxygen to change the food they eat into energy. When they breathe out, they release carbon dioxide into the air. Plants take in this carbon dioxide. They use carbon dioxide, water, and the sun's energy to make sugar and oxygen. Plants use or store the sugar, but release the oxygen into the air. Animals and people take in this oxygen, and the cycle continues.

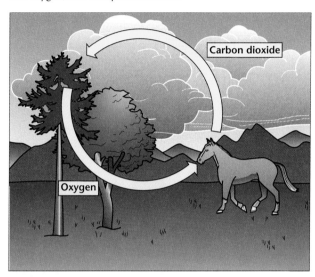

Carbon dioxide

Oxygen

The Earth's Atmosphere   Chapter 9   **205**

SCIENCE INTEGRATION

Physical Science

Point out that the atmosphere contains elements, such as helium, and compounds, such as carbon dioxide. Encourage students to recall that an element has only one kind of atom. A compound is formed when atoms of two or more elements join together. Have them name several examples of each. Then have them identify each atmospheric gas named on page 204 as an element or a compound. *(Carbon dioxide, water vapor, and methane are compounds. Nitrogen, oxygen, argon, neon, helium, krypton, xenon, and hydrogen are elements. Ozone is a form of oxygen.)*

 Teaching the Lesson

Have students locate the lesson's subheads and write one or two questions about what they might learn in each. For example, "The Oxygen-Carbon Dioxide Cycle" might suggest the question, What is a cycle? As they read, students should write the answers to their questions.

Draw students' attention to the circle graph on page 204. Ask students to name the two gases that make up most of the earth's atmosphere. Then show them a helium-filled balloon. Ask students what will happen to the balloon if you let it go. *(It will float upward.)* Explain that light gases, such as helium and hydrogen, drift upward and away from the earth. That is why there is very little of those two gases in the earth's atmosphere.

Have pairs of students create a simple flowchart of the oxygen-carbon dioxide cycle. Have each pair make eight strips of paper with these labels: *people and animals, carbon dioxide, plants, oxygen, plants take in carbon dioxide, people and animals take in oxygen, plants give off oxygen, people and animals give off carbon dioxide.* Ask students to glue the first four strips in a circle on a sheet of paper in the sequence given. Then have them draw arrows from one strip to the next, in the correct direction, and label these arrows with the four remaining strips.

As you discuss the nitrogen cycle, point out to students that when a plant or an animal dies, it is decomposed, or broken down, by organisms, forming simple nitrogen compounds and nitrogen gas. The nitrogen compounds go into the soil where plants can use them, and the nitrogen gas goes back into the atmosphere.

 Reinforce and Extend

Did You Know?

Have a volunteer read aloud the Did You Know? feature on page 204. Explain that some scientists believe the earth's earliest atmosphere was made of helium, hydrogen, ammonia, and methane, a combination of gases that would not have supported life as we know it.

Auditory/Verbal

Ask students to verbally compare and contrast the roles of plants and animals in the oxygen-carbon dioxide cycle and in the nitrogen cycle. (*In both cycles, plants and animals take in substances produced by other organisms and release substances that are used by other organisms. In the nitrogen cycle, bacteria converts nitrogen to usable forms.*)

SCIENCE INTEGRATION

Biology

Tell students that compost piles return nitrogen compounds to the soil—compounds that plants need. Have interested students find out how to build a compost pile. They can share this information with the class.

SCIENCE JOURNAL

Ask students to think about how the composition of the atmosphere might change if huge forests were cut down and not replanted. Ask students to write about how these changes in the atmosphere might affect other life on the earth.

The Nitrogen Cycle

Nitrogen also cycles through the environment, as shown below. All living things need nitrogen. Most living things cannot use nitrogen gas directly from the air. However, bacteria in the soil can use this form of nitrogen. These organisms change nitrogen gas into chemical compounds that plants use. Animals take in nitrogen when they feed on plants or on plant-eating animals. Nitrogen is returned to the soil in animal waste. Nitrogen is also returned to the soil when plants and animals die. Bacteria in the soil break down these wastes, releasing nitrogen into the air and into the soil. The return of nitrogen gas to the atmosphere allows the cycle to continue.

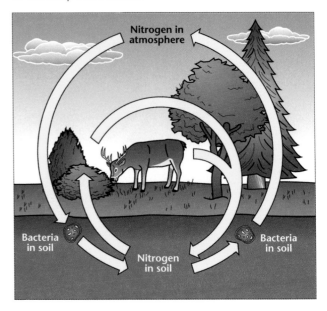

Lesson 1   R E V I E W

Write your answers to these questions on a sheet of paper.

1. What are the two main gases in the atmosphere?

2. Describe the path oxygen and carbon dioxide take through the environment.

3. What is the source of oxygen in the oxygen-carbon dioxide cycle?

4. What living things in soil are needed to change nitrogen into a form plants can use?

5. How is nitrogen released back into the atmosphere?

Science in Your Life

Ozone: Protector and Pollutant

Ozone makes up a tiny but important part of the atmosphere. Ozone is a form of oxygen. A thin layer of ozone high in the atmosphere absorbs ultraviolet radiation from the sun. This prevents most of the radiation from reaching the earth. This radiation can cause sunburn and skin cancer.

People have damaged this protective ozone layer. For example, certain gases from spray cans and refrigeration equipment drift high into the atmosphere and break down ozone. Laws now limit the use of such gases.

Scientists have been monitoring a hole that has appeared in the ozone layer over Antarctica. In 2000, this hole reached a size of 17.6 million square kilometers. But in 2002, the Antarctic ozone hole decreased to 9.6 million square kilometers. It also split into two separate holes.

Ozone holes in the atmosphere are harmful. But too much ozone at the earth's surface is also harmful. Ozone is one of the ingredients of smog. This hazy mixture of gases damages people's lungs and worsens heart disease. How does ozone collect at ground level? It is made by people. Factories make and use ozone for cleaning flour, oil, fabrics, and water. Car exhaust also releases ozone.

The Earth's Atmosphere   Chapter 9   **207**

Surveying Air Quality

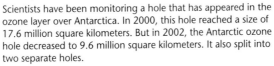

Lab Manual 33, pages 1–2

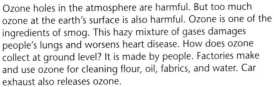

Gases in the Atmosphere

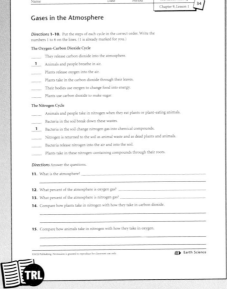

Workbook Activity 34

Lesson 1 Review Answers

1. nitrogen and oxygen **2.** Plants give off oxygen. Animals and people take in the oxygen and release carbon dioxide, which plants take in to make sugar and oxygen. **3.** plants **4.** bacteria **5.** Bacteria in the soil break down animal wastes and dead plants and animals, releasing nitrogen into the air.

Science in Your Life

Ask for volunteers to take turns reading aloud the Science in Your Life feature on page 207. Explain that the difference between ozone and regular oxygen is that an ozone molecule consists of three oxygen atoms (O_3), while a regular oxygen molecule consists of only two (O_2). Point out that too much ozone causes burning eyes and breathing problems. Some cities issue ozone alerts on days when ozone in the air reaches a certain level.

CROSS-CURRICULAR CONNECTION

Health

Discuss with students the health dangers of air polluted with ozone and other gases. If you live in an area that issues smog or ozone alerts, talk about how and when these are issued. Note the times of year or weather conditions when the air may be most unhealthful in your area. Review health problems that can result from air pollution, such as asthma, bronchitis, and heart disease. Have students describe measures that individuals should take to protect themselves during periods of heavy smog.

Portfolio Assessment

Sample items include:
• Questions and answers and flowchart from Teaching the Lesson
• Lesson 1 Review answers

The Earth's Atmosphere   Chapter 9   **207**

Objectives

After reading this lesson, you should be able to

◆ identify the four layers of the atmosphere.

◆ name one characteristic of each layer.

Troposphere

Bottom layer of the atmosphere, extending from ground level up to about 16 kilometers above the earth

Imagine four glass balls, one inside the other. Now picture the earth at the very center of the glass balls. You've just imagined a model of the earth and its atmosphere. The atmosphere consists of four layers. Refer to the diagram below as you read about each one.

You live in the **troposphere**, the bottom layer of the atmosphere. The troposphere extends from the earth's surface upward to about 16 kilometers. Air particles are packed more tightly in this layer than in other layers because of the weight of the air above. Therefore, even though the troposphere is the smallest of the four layers, it contains 75 percent of the air particles in the entire atmosphere.

Air gets colder and thinner, or less dense, as you go higher in the troposphere. That's why mountain climbers often need extra clothing and oxygen tanks when they climb. The troposphere is characterized by up-and-down as well as side-to-side air movements, or air currents. Most of the clouds you see in the sky are in the troposphere.

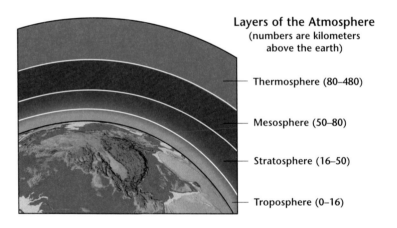

Layers of the Atmosphere
(numbers are kilometers above the earth)

- Thermosphere (80–480)
- Mesosphere (50–80)
- Stratosphere (16–50)
- Troposphere (0–16)

---

they read, students should write a few facts about each that will help them remember what and where each layer is.

Explain to students that the earth's atmosphere acts much like a protective blanket. While it allows heat and light from the sun to reach the earth, part of it shields the earth's surface from dangerous radiation from the sun. Explain that without the ozone layer in the atmosphere, the radiation from the sun would destroy most living things on the earth.

Point out to students that radio signals carry farther at night because, when the sun sets, the strength of the lower ionosphere is diminished, allowing reflection to occur from the upper ionosphere.

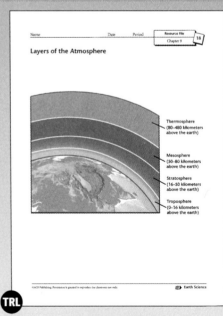

Stratosphere

Second layer of the atmosphere; includes the ozone layer

Mesosphere

Third layer of the atmosphere; the coldest layer

Thermosphere

Outermost layer of the atmosphere; includes most of the ionosphere

Ionosphere

Layer of the atmosphere containing ions, or electrically charged particles

Did You Know?

Clouds and weather activity occur in the troposphere. Airplanes, especially jets, usually fly in the stratosphere. Satellites orbit well above the ionosphere.

The **stratosphere** is above the troposphere. It extends from about 16 to 50 kilometers above the earth's surface. The stratosphere is clear and dry. Temperature increases with increasing height in the stratosphere. The ozone layer is in the lower half of the stratosphere. The ozone layer is important because it absorbs harmful radiation from the sun.

Above the stratosphere is the **mesosphere**. Here, temperature decreases with increasing height. The mesosphere is the coldest layer of the atmosphere. It is located from about 50 to 80 kilometers above the earth's surface.

The outermost layer is called the **thermosphere**. The air is the thinnest here. Temperature increases with height. It can reach 2,000°C because nitrogen and oxygen atoms absorb the sun's energy. This energy strips electrons from these atoms, making them electrically charged particles, or ions. Most of these ions are found between 60 and 300 kilometers above the earth. Therefore, this section of the atmosphere is called the **ionosphere**.

If you have ever wondered how you are able to pick up a radio station hundreds of kilometers away, the answer is the ionosphere. AM radio waves bounce off the ions in the ionosphere and travel back to the earth. As the diagram shows, this reflection of waves can carry radio messages great distances. This is especially true at night, when the sun's energy does not cause interference.

Ionosphere

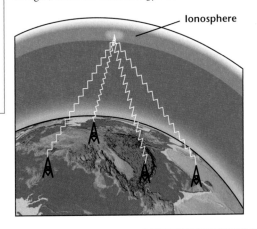

IN THE ENVIRONMENT

Ask students to research the types of clothing and other equipment mountain climbers use. Ask students to explain why these things are needed.

Did You Know?

Have a volunteer read aloud the Did You Know? feature on page 209. You might share other facts about different layers of the atmosphere. For example, heat caused by friction when an asteroid enters the mesosphere causes the asteroid to burn up. Remind students that this creates a brief streak of light known as a meteor or "shooting star."

 3 **Reinforce and Extend**

TEACHER ALERT

 Students might think that the top layer of the atmosphere ends abruptly. Explain that space flights have shown that the atmosphere actually extends out as much as 60,000 kilometers before fading away.

LEARNING STYLES

Body/Kinesthetic

Use a bicycle pump to pump air into a bicycle tire. Then allow students to feel the cold draft as you let air out of the tire. Explain that as the squeezed air in the tire is released, it spreads out and cools. Explain that when warm air rises through the lowest level of the atmosphere, it spreads out and cools, too. Tell students that is why it is colder on the tops of mountains.

CROSS-CURRICULAR CONNECTION

 Math

Remind students that as you go higher in the troposphere, it gets colder. Then explain that it gets colder at a steady rate, about 6°C per 1,000 meters. Ask students to calculate how much colder the temperature would be at the top of a mountain compared to sea level (0 meters) if the mountain was 2,000 meters high (*12°C colder*), 4,000 meters high (*24°C colder*), and 5,000 meters high (*30° colder*). Finally, ask students to calculate the temperature at the top of a mountain (elevation 4,500 meters) if they started out at sea level with a temperature of 27°C. (*0°C*)

Lesson 2 Review Answers

1. The troposphere extends from the earth's surface to about 16 kilometers above it; air particles are packed most tightly in this layer; it contains 75 percent of the air particles in the entire atmosphere; most weather activity occurs in this layer. The stratosphere extends from 16 to 50 kilometers above the earth's surface; it is clear and dry; the ozone layer is in the lower half. The mesosphere extends from about 50 to 80 kilometers above the earth; it is the coldest layer. The thermosphere extends from about 80 to 480 kilometers above the earth; the air is thinnest here; the temperature in this layer increases with altitude, reaching 2,000°C; most of the ionosphere is in the thermosphere. **2.** troposphere **3.** near the bottom of the stratosphere **4.** In the ionosphere, the sun's energy strips electrons from atoms, making them ions. **5.** AM radio waves bounce off the ions in the ionosphere and travel back to the earth.

Achievements in Science

Ask students to take turns reading aloud the feature on page 210. Point out to students that today gas balloons are used for a number of scientific purposes. Meteorologists and other scientists use them to carry instruments that record atmospheric conditions, including air pressure, humidity, and temperature.

Portfolio Assessment

Sample items include:
• Names and facts about atmosphere layers from Teaching the Lesson
• Lesson 2 Review answers

Lesson 2   R E V I E W

Write your answers to these questions on a sheet of paper.

1. Describe the four layers of the atmosphere.

2. Which layer of the atmosphere do you breathe?

3. Where is the ozone layer?

4. Why is part of the atmosphere called the ionosphere?

5. Explain how the ionosphere is used to transmit radio waves.

Achievements in Science

Balloon Pilots

Aeronauts, or balloon pilots, have been challenging the atmosphere for hundreds of years. In 1783, the first hot-air balloon to fly with passengers was built by the Montgolfier brothers in France. The passengers included a duck, a rooster, and a sheep. Following the historic 8-minute flight, all three landed safely.

To launch their cloth-and-paper balloon, the brothers placed it over a fire. They thought the balloon flew because it was filled with smoke. They didn't understand that the key to flight was hot air. Hot air is less dense than cool air. Because hot air in a balloon is lighter than the air outside it, the balloon rises.

Since then, aeronauts have also piloted gas balloons. These are balloons filled with a light gas such as hydrogen. The record holders for the highest gas-balloon flight are two United States Navy officers. In 1961, they reached the middle of the stratosphere, more than 34 kilometers above the earth.

Layers of the Atmosphere

Directions 1-8. Look at the diagram of the atmosphere. Then write the names of the numbered layers in the first column of the table below. Complete the table by writing a short description of each layer.

Name of Layer	Description
1.	5.
2.	6.
3.	7.
4.	8.

Directions Answer the questions.

9. Why does the troposphere contain 75 percent of the air particles in the atmosphere?

10. Why do mountain climbers often need oxygen tanks when they climb?

11. Where is the ozone layer? Why is it important?

12. In which layer of the atmosphere is the air thinnest?

13. In which layer of the atmosphere is weather activity?

14. Where are ions found in the atmosphere? How are ions formed?

15. Why are radio messages transmitted better at night?

Workbook Activity 35

Objectives

After reading this lesson, you should be able to

◆ explain how clouds form.

◆ identify three kinds of clouds.

Evaporate

Change from a liquid to a gas

Water vapor

Water in the form of a gas

Condense

Change from a gas to a liquid

Have you ever seen your breath on a cold day? You are seeing a cloud. It forms the same way as a cloud in the sky.

How Clouds Form

Much of the earth's surface is covered with water. The sun's heat causes some of this liquid water to **evaporate**, or change into a gas. This gas, called **water vapor**, becomes part of the air. When this air is heated, it becomes less dense than the surrounding air. Therefore, the heated air rises, taking the water vapor with it. As the air continues to rise, it cools. Then the water vapor **condenses**, or changes back to liquid water. The droplets of water are so tiny that they stay afloat in the air. Billions of tiny droplets form a cloud, as shown in the left diagram.

The diagram at the right shows that clouds also form when air containing water vapor is forced up a mountainside. As the air rises, it cools. The water vapor condenses into tiny droplets of water to form clouds. The tops of some mountains are often hidden in clouds.

So how is a cloud like the breath you can see? Air in your lungs contains water vapor. When you breathe out, the vapor meets the cold air outside and condenses into tiny droplets—a cloud.

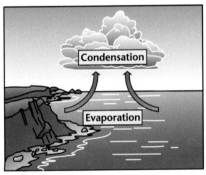 

The Earth's Atmosphere Chapter 9 **211**

Resource File 19

Lesson at a Glance

Chapter 9 Lesson 3

Overview In this lesson, students learn that clouds form by the process of condensation. Students also learn how to identify different kinds of clouds and the weather associated with them.

Objectives

■ To explain how clouds form

■ To identify three kinds of clouds

Student Pages 211–215

Teacher's Resource Library TRL

Workbook Activity 36

Alternative Workbook Activity 36

Lab Manual 34–35

Resource File 19

Vocabulary

altitude	evaporate
cirrus cloud	fog
condense	stratus cloud
cumulus cloud	water vapor

Science Background

When water vapor rises and cools, it does not automatically condense to form clouds. Tiny particles of dust, smoke, and salt in the air, called condensation nuclei, are needed for condensation to occur. The cloud droplets that form around these nuclei are much smaller than the tiniest raindrops. The average size of a cloud droplet is 20 microns. (One micron is one thousandth of a millimeter.)

1 Warm-Up Activity

Hold a cold plate over a bowl of hot water. Ask students to look closely at what forms on the bottom of the plate. Students should be able to detect water droplets. Tell them that in this lesson they will learn how clouds form in a similar way.

2 Teaching the Lesson

Have students write the lesson title and objectives on a sheet of paper. As they read the lesson, they can write one or two sentences that meet each objective.

Continued on page 212

The Earth's Atmosphere Chapter 9 **211**

Continued from page 211

Emphasize that evaporation and condensation are opposite processes. Evaporation is the change from a liquid to a gas, while condensation is the change from a gas to a liquid.

Use the two diagrams on page 211 to discuss how clouds form. Ask volunteers to explain in their own words the two ways clouds can form.

Ask students to explain why windows inside a car fog up when people are riding in the car on a cold day. Students should realize that the warm, moist air people exhale is cooled and the water vapor condenses on the inside of the window.

Ask students if they have ever been inside a cloud or above a cloud in an airplane. Ask them to describe the experience.

3 Reinforce and Extend

LEARNING STYLES

Interpersonal/ Group Learning

Give small groups of students an empty metal can. Have them fill the can with a mixture of ice and water. Tell them to be sure the outside of the can is dry. (Provide paper towels to dry the cans.) Then ask students to observe the outside of the can for several minutes. Students should observe that the outside of the can is soon covered with water drops. Explain that the water drops on the outside of the can came from moisture in the air and that this is similar to how clouds form.

AT HOME

Ask students to make observations around their homes for several days and keep a record of examples of evaporation and condensation. They might notice that water has evaporated from a birdbath, for example, or a boiling pot. They might notice that condensation has occurred on bathroom mirrors or on eyeglasses.

Altitude

Height above the earth's surface

Stratus cloud

Low, flat cloud that forms in layers

Fog

Stratus cloud that forms near the ground

Types of Clouds

Clouds are grouped according to their shape and **altitude**, or height above the earth's surface. There are three basic types of clouds.

Stratus clouds are low, flat clouds that form in layers. Their altitude is less than 2,000 meters. These clouds are wider than they are high, often covering the entire sky like a blanket. Often, you can see only their gray bottoms because they block out much of the sunlight. Stratus clouds often bring rain.

A stratus cloud near the ground is **fog**. How does this kind of cloud form? Without sunlight, the ground cools quickly at night. The cold ground cools the air directly above it. If the water vapor in this air condenses, a cloud forms. Fog usually develops in the early morning after a clear, calm, cold night. Fog settles in low areas. Sometimes fog forms over warm bodies of water.

Stratus clouds are flat and low in the sky.

Name _____ Date _____ Period _____ Lab Manual, Page 1 • Chapter 9 • 34

Comparing Evaporation Times

Purpose How long does it take water to evaporate? In this investigation, you will compare how different conditions affect evaporation.

Materials 4 identical shallow dishes
100-milliliter graduated cylinder
water
sticky notes
tablespoon
salt
stirring stick or spoon
electric fan
lamp with 100-watt bulb (optional)

Procedure

1. Use the table below to record your data.

Dish	Observations	Evaporation Time
dish 1		
dish 2		
dish 3		
dish 4		

2. Use the graduated cylinder to measure and pour 100 milliliters of water into each dish. Use sticky notes to label the dishes 1 to 4.

3. Set dish 1 in a safe, protected spot. It should be away from heat, direct sunlight, and wind.

4. Add 2 tablespoons of salt to dish 2 and stir to dissolve it. Place it near the first dish.

5. Set dish 3 in another safe spot. It should be away from heat and direct sunlight. Plug in the fan and turn it on. Set it so that it blows across the water in the dish.

6. Set dish 4 near a heat source, either on a working radiator or in direct sunlight. If these heat sources aren't convenient, use the lamp, placing the light bulb near the surface of the water. Turn on the lamp.

7. Note the day and time you started the investigation.

8. Observe all four dishes as the water evaporates. It may take several hours, or it may take several days. Write your observations in your data table. Record the length of time it took for the water in each dish to evaporate completely.

©AGS Publishing. Permission is granted to reproduce for classroom use only.   Earth Science

Lab Manual 34, pages 1–2

Cumulus cloud

Puffy, white cloud occurring at medium altitudes

Cirrus cloud

High, wispy cloud made of ice crystals

Cumulus clouds are puffy, white clouds at altitudes from 2,000 to 7,000 meters. They look like piles of cotton balls. You can usually see their sides and tops shining brilliant white in sunlight. Their shaded bottoms are flat and may look gray. Cumulus clouds are often seen in fair weather.

When you think of clouds, you probably picture white, puffy cumulus clouds like these.

Cirrus clouds look like thin, wispy streaks high in the sky. Their altitude ranges from 7,000 to 13,000 meters. They are made of ice crystals instead of water droplets because the air at that altitude is below freezing. Cirrus clouds often accompany fair weather, but they may mean rain or snow is on the way.

Thin, wispy cirrus clouds are made of ice crystals.

The Earth's Atmosphere   Chapter 9   **213**

LEARNING STYLES

Visual/Spatial

Suggest that students use instant cameras to take photographs of different types of clouds. Students can then print the type of cloud on the back of each photograph and use the photographs to test one another on cloud type identification.

CROSS-CURRICULAR CONNECTION

Language Arts

Obtain a copy of the poem "Fog" by Carl Sandburg, which begins "The fog comes on little cat feet. . ." Ask students whether this is an appropriate description of fog or not. Then have students write a poem or short story in which fog plays a part.

ONLINE CONNECTION

Students can find links to information about and photographs of clouds and precipitation at www.geol.vt.edu/vesr/meteo/vesrMcloud.html.

Lesson 3 Review Answers

1. a mass of water droplets in the air
2. (1) The sun's heat causes some of the water on the earth's surface to evaporate, and it becomes part of the air. When the air is heated, it rises and takes water vapor with it. It cools as it rises, and the water vapor turns back into liquid. These are tiny droplets that stay afloat as a cloud. (2) When air is forced up a mountain, it cools. The water vapor in this air condenses to form clouds. **3.** At night the ground and the air above it cool quickly. If the water vapor in this air condenses, fog forms. **4.** Cumulus clouds are puffy and white, at altitudes from 2,000 to 7,000 meters. Cirrus clouds are thin and wispy, at altitudes from 7,000 to 13,000 meters. **5.** Stratus clouds are low, flat clouds in layers at altitudes less than 2,000 meters.

Science at Work

Have students take turns reading aloud the Science at Work feature on page 214. Have interested students find out how local government or environmental agencies collect air samples and test them for air pollution. They might also research local air pollution laws or local training programs for environmental science technicians.

Portfolio Assessment

Sample items include:
- Objectives and sentences from Teaching the Lesson
- Lesson 3 Review answers

Write your answers to these questions on a sheet of paper.

1. What is a cloud?

2. Describe two ways that clouds form.

3. Explain how fog forms.

4. Compare cumulus and cirrus clouds.

5. Name and describe the type of cloud that may indicate rain.

▼◄▲▼◄▲▼◄▲▼◄▲▼◄▲▼◄▲▼◄▲▼◄▲▼◄▲▼◄▲▼

Science at Work

Environmental Science Technician

Environmental science technicians perform tests to identify and measure pollution in air, water, or soil. They collect samples to test. They look for ways to reduce or prevent pollution. Environmental science technicians also manage and control hazardous wastes. They make sure pollution laws are carefully followed.

Environmental science technicians use science and mathematics to solve problems. They use laboratory equipment to perform tests or analyze samples. They often use computers. They keep detailed reports and interpret data.

Some environmental science technicians have a bachelor's degree in chemistry, biology, or environmental science. Others have two years of specialized training or an associate degree in a field of applied science. Successful environmental science technicians are organized, enjoy detailed tasks, and can interpret and communicate scientific results. They are often very concerned about protecting the environment.

Workbook Activity 36

Lab Manual 35

9-1 INVESTIGATION

Observing Clouds

Purpose
Can you identify cloud types? In this investigation, you will observe and classify clouds over several days.

Procedure

1. Copy the data table on your paper.

Date	Time	Weather Conditions	Cloud Observations

2. Find a location where you can observe a large portion of the sky. You should use this place for all of your observations.

3. In your data table, record the date, the time, and your observations about the weather conditions.

4. In the last column of your table, record your observations about the clouds. Include a sketch of the clouds you observe. Label the sketch with its cloud type.

5. Make observations on four or more days. Follow steps 3 and 4 each day.

Questions and Conclusions

1. Which types of clouds were most common?

2. What relationship did you find between cloud type and weather?

Explore Further
Make cloud observations in the morning and evening for several days. Is there a relationship between cloud type and time of day?

Questions and Conclusions Answers

1. Answers should match student data. Cloud identifications should be fairly consistent across the class.

2. Answers will vary, depending on what types of clouds were observed and whether they varied from day to day. In general, cumulus clouds are related to fair weather, stratus clouds are related to rainy weather, and cirrus clouds are related to fair weather followed by rain or snow.

Explore Further Answers

Answer will vary. Students might notice a correlation between cloud type and time

of day. You might point out that the sun warms the earth in varying degrees over the course of a day.

Assessment

Student data tables should agree with one another. Check the tables to see that students correctly identified cloud types and accurately recorded weather conditions. Check answers to the questions to be sure that they are supported by observations. You might include the following items from this investigation in student portfolios:

• Data table

• Answers to Questions and Conclusions and Explore Further sections

Investigation 9-1

The Purpose portion of the student investigation begins with a question to draw students into the activity. Encourage students to read the investigation steps and formulate their own questions before beginning the investigation. This investigation will take approximately 45 minutes to complete. Students will use these process and thinking skills: observing, classifying, inferring, comparing and contrasting, and making generalizations.

Preparation

• Select an outdoor spot where students can have a good view of the sky.

• You might want to choose a spot that can also be observed from inside so that, in case of rain, students could observe rain-bearing clouds.

• Students may use Lab Manual 35 to record their data and answer the questions.

Procedure

• This investigation is best done by students working individually.

• If students are having difficulty identifying cloud types, refer them to the photos on pages 212–213.

• Point out to students that sometimes more than one type of cloud is present at the same time. Students should record all types of clouds that they observe.

• You might want to check students' data tables on the first day to be sure they are identifying cloud types correctly.

• Suggest that students make a note of the direction in which clouds are moving.

• Encourage students to bring along extra paper so that they can sketch the clouds they see. The act of sketching can lead them to observe greater detail.

Results

After several days of observing clouds, students should begin to see a relationship between cloud type and weather. For example, cumulus clouds are usually associated with fair weather; stratus clouds are usually associated with rain; cirrus clouds are usually associated with fair weather but may indicate that rain or snow is in the forecast.

Continued at left

Lesson at a Glance

Chapter 9 Lesson 4

Overview In this lesson, students learn how precipitation forms. They learn about different kinds of precipitation and the conditions necessary for forming each kind.

Objectives

- To describe how precipitation forms
- To describe four kinds of precipitation

Student Pages 216–220

Teacher's Resource Library

Workbook Activity 37

Alternative Workbook Activity 37

Lab Manual 36

Vocabulary

precipitation

Science Background

Much of the earth's precipitation begins as ice crystals or frozen water in the form of hail, ice pellets, snow, or sleet. As these particles fall and enter warmer air, the smaller particles melt before they reach the ground and fall as rain.

1 Warm-Up Activity

Using tongs, hold a beaker over the spout of a boiling tea kettle. Keep the beaker over the steam until water droplets collect on the outside. Then move the beaker away from the steam. Have students observe what happens to the water droplets. *(They should notice that droplets will collect on and fall from the bottom of the beaker.)* Explain that in this lesson students will learn how rain forms.

2 Teaching the Lesson

Write the two lesson objectives on the board. Have students copy the objectives on a sheet of paper, using them as headings. When students finish reading the lesson, they should use the space under the headings to describe the formation of precipitation and the different kinds of precipitation.

Objectives

After reading this lesson, you should be able to
- describe how precipitation forms.
- describe four kinds of precipitation.

Precipitation

Moisture that falls to the earth from the atmosphere

The movement of water between the atmosphere and the earth's surface is known as the water cycle. This is described fully in Chapter 11.

The droplets of most clouds are small enough to stay in the air, suspended by air currents. But if the droplets grow large enough, they fall to the earth. Any moisture that falls from the atmosphere to the earth's surface is called **precipitation**. There are several kinds of precipitation.

Near the equator, between 30°N and 30°S latitudes, the sunlight is most direct. Here, temperatures within most stratus clouds are above freezing. These clouds are made entirely of water droplets. The droplets collide and combine to form larger drops. When the drops become large enough, they fall as rain.

Clouds in the middle and high latitudes usually form in air that is below freezing. Then water vapor turns directly to ice crystals. In a cloud, ice crystals combine until they are heavy enough to fall. If the air temperature beneath the cloud is above freezing, the ice crystals melt and fall as rain. If the air temperature is below freezing, the crystals fall as snow. If rain falls through a layer of cold air and freezes into ice particles, sleet, or freezing rain, results. If the temperature near the ground is between 3°C and 0°C, rain will not freeze until it hits an object. The result is an ice storm. You can see the effects of an ice storm in the photo.

The weight of sleet can break tree branches.

Explain to students that liquid precipitation can be classified as mist, drizzle, or rain. The classification is based on the size of the droplets. Mist has the smallest droplets, and rain has the largest droplets.

Ask students to think of ways that rain, sleet, snow, and hail can be harmful to people and the environment. They might suggest auto accidents, crop damage, downed power lines, heart attacks caused by snow shoveling, etc.

Encourage students to use an almanac to find out where and when the most rain or snow has fallen in one day or one year. They might also want to find and report to the class other precipitation records, such as the largest hailstone ever found.

TEACHER ALERT

After watching weather reports, students may think that the amount of precipitation that is officially recorded for a given area is the amount of rain that every location in that area actually received. Point out that precipitation can vary widely within a fairly small area. For example, in the summer of 1996, the southern part of one Wisconsin county received more than 28 centimeters (11 inches) of rain, while the official reporting station, 32 kilometers to the north, reported less than 10 centimeters (4 inches).

Hailstones form in tall cumulus clouds that produce storms. The temperature is below freezing at the top of the clouds. Strong winds toss the ice crystals up and down many times through the clouds. Each time, a layer of water freezes around the crystal, forming a hailstone. Hailstones are usually the size of a pea, but can be bigger than a baseball.

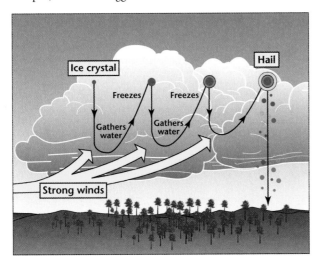

Science Myth

Some people may think that raindrops are shaped like teardrops.

Fact: Small raindrops (less than 2 millimeters in diameter) are spherical, or round. Larger raindrops are shaped more like hamburger buns. The largest raindrops (about 4.5 millimeters in diameter) are shaped like hot-air balloons.

LEARNING STYLES

 Logical/Mathematical

Stress that different geographical regions experience different amounts of precipitation. Have students make a bar graph showing how precipitation varies during the year for San Francisco, California, and Atlantic City, New Jersey.

Precipitation (centimeters)		
Month	San Francisco	Atlantic City
January	11.2	8.9
February	8.1	7.9
March	7.9	9.1
April	3.6	9.1
May	0.5	8.4
June	0.3	6.6
July	0	9.7
August	0.3	10.4
September	0.5	7.4
October	3.0	7.1
November	7.4	9.1
December	7.9	8.4

IN THE COMMUNITY

 Have students bring in a variety of local newspapers to see what kinds of weather information they provide. Do they include a brief daily forecast or a more comprehensive, extended forecast? Do they give both local and national weather information? Discuss and compare the information each paper provides.

CROSS-CURRICULAR CONNECTION

 Art

Have students choose an art form, such as water color, photography, or collage, to depict a form of precipitation.

Science Myth

Ask one student to read aloud the myth portion and one the fact portion of the feature on page 217. Suggest that students make a chart illustrating the shapes of various sizes of raindrops.

SCIENCE JOURNAL

 Have students write a description of what they like or do not like about a particular kind of precipitation.

LEARNING STYLES

 LEP/ESL

Ask volunteers to draw diagrams on the board showing how rain, snow, sleet, and hail form.

GLOBAL CONNECTION

GLOBAL CONNECTION

Have students use a precipitation map in an atlas to find the average annual amount of precipitation for your area. Then ask them to find the annual precipitation amounts for other places throughout the world. Discuss how different amounts of precipitation affect the way people live.

Lesson 4 Review Answers

1. Water droplets in clouds combine into bigger droplets until they become heavy enough to fall. **2.** rain, snow, sleet, hail **3.** The sunlight is most direct there, so temperatures within most stratus clouds are above freezing. These clouds are made entirely of water droplets and not ice crystals. **4.** Snow forms when the air temperature is below freezing beneath a cloud made of ice crystals. Sleet forms when rain falls through a layer of cold air and freezes into ice particles. **5.** Strong winds cause ice crystals to move up and down inside a thunderstorm cloud. Layers of water gather and freeze around the crystals, developing hailstones.

Achievements in Science

Have students take turns reading aloud the feature on page 218. Explain that cloud seeding is controversial. Some scientists think that artificially increasing rain in one area takes away rain from another area. Some states have laws limiting or banning cloud seeding. Encourage students to research techniques for cloud seeding and current views on its safety and effectiveness.

Portfolio Assessment

Sample items include:
- Objectives and descriptions from Teaching the Lesson
- Lesson 4 Review answers

Write your answers to these questions on a sheet of paper.

1. How does precipitation form?

2. What are four kinds of precipitation?

3. Why doesn't it snow near the equator?

4. What is the difference between sleet and snow?

5. How does hail form?

Achievements in Science

Cloud Seeding

Cloud seeding is the science of forcing clouds to release precipitation. Cloud seeding began in the 1940s. It is often used to increase the amount of rain or snow. It helps farmers grow crops. Cloud seeding also can help scatter fog and prevent or decrease hail.

There are two types of cloud seeding: cold cloud seeding and warm cloud seeding. In cold cloud seeding, an ice-forming material, such as silver iodide, is dropped from airplanes into clouds. This increases the production of snowflakes within the clouds. It can also make clouds larger and longer lasting. Warm cloud seeding is used when clouds have temperatures above freezing. A material, such as salt, is dropped into these clouds. This increases the condensation of water droplets within clouds.

During cold months, cloud seeding works less than 30 percent of the time. However, during warm months, the success rate for cloud seeding is nearly 100 percent.

218 *Chapter 9   The Earth's Atmosphere*

| Name | Date | Period | Workbook Activity |
| | | | Chapter 9, Lesson 4 37 |

Precipitation

Directions 1-8. Complete the table using answers from both Answer Banks. Write the letter of the correct answer in each numbered space in the table.

Kind of Precipitation	What It Is	How It Forms
rain	1.	5.
hail	2.	6.
sleet	3.	7.
snow	4.	8.

Answer Bank for "What It Is" Column
A freezing rain
B ice crystals
C droplets of water
D balls of ice

Answer Bank for "How It Forms" Column

E Raindrops fall through a layer of cold air and freeze into ice particles. The ice particles may form as the raindrops hit a surface or before they hit the ground.

F Water droplets or ice crystals collide in clouds and combine. Then they fall through above-freezing air.

G Ice crystals in clouds in middle and high latitudes combine until they are heavy enough to fall. They fall through below-freezing air.

H Strong winds toss ice crystals up and down in tall cumulus clouds. The clouds are below freezing at the top, but above freezing near the bottom. Layers of water freeze around the ice crystals before they fall.

Directions Write a short answer for each question.

9. What is precipitation? _____

10. Where above the earth are most stratus clouds made of water droplets? _____

11. Where above the earth are most clouds made of ice crystals? _____

12. Describe what happens in an ice storm. _____

13. How are sleet and snow alike? _____

14. How are sleet and snow different? _____

15. What determines whether precipitation falls as a liquid or a solid? _____

©AGS Publishing. Permission is granted to reproduce for classroom use only.

Earth Science

Workbook Activity 37

9-2 INVESTIGATION

Materials

◆ newspaper
◆ books
◆ plastic binder (or other flat, plastic surface)
◆ spray mister containing water
◆ magnifying glass
◆ paper towels

Making a Model of Rain

Purpose

How does a raindrop form? In this investigation, you will make a model of water droplets and observe how they combine.

Procedure

1. Copy the data table on your paper.

Spray Number	Description of Mist on Surface	Number of Running Droplets
1		
2		
3		
4		
5		

2. Cover your work surface with newspaper. Use the books to prop open the binder cover as shown in the figure on page 220. The plastic surface should make a slope.

3. Adjust the mister nozzle to produce a fine mist. Hold the mister about 30 centimeters from the plastic surface. Then gently spray the surface just once with the mister. **Safety Alert: Wipe up any spills immediately.**

4. Using a magnifying glass, look closely at the mist on the surface. Notice the different sizes of water droplets. In your data table, describe the mist. Count any water droplets running down the slope. Record this in your data table.

5. Repeat steps 3 and 4 at least four more times.

6. Use the paper towels to dry all wet surfaces. Clean your work area and return the equipment.

The Earth's Atmosphere Chapter 9 **219**

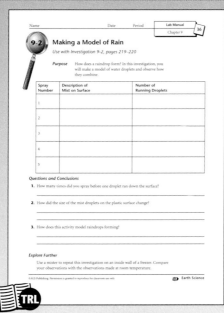

Lab Manual 36

Investigation 9-2

The Purpose portion of the student investigation begins with a question to draw students into the activity. Encourage students to read the investigation steps and formulate their own questions before beginning the investigation. This investigation will take approximately 40 minutes to complete. Students will use these process and thinking skills: making models, observing, and collecting and interpreting data.

Preparation

* If dark plastic binders or trays are not available, you might want to cover sheets of cardboard with dark plastic trash bags.
* Before class, you might want to set up a sample work station like the one shown on page 220. Students could refer to this when setting up their own work stations.
* Students may use Lab Manual 36 to record their data and answer the questions.

Procedure

* Students may work individually or in groups. For group work, assign one student to gather equipment. All students should get a chance to spray the sloped surface. Group members should cooperatively record results and clean up when finished.
* You might want to demonstrate the spraying technique once for the class.
* You might want to check each setup before students proceed with misting. Be sure the plastic surface is propped securely at an angle. Be sure the books supporting the surface are not positioned so they will get wet. Have students cover them with newspaper if necessary.
* Be sure that students have adjusted their sprayer for a fine mist.
* Before students start to spray, have them measure off the appropriate distance from sprayer to surface— approximately 30 centimeters.
* Remind students to observe the droplets after every spray.

SAFETY ALERT

◆ Caution students to wipe up any spills immediately.

The Earth's Atmosphere Chapter 9 **219**

Results

As students spray more and more water onto the surface, some droplets will land close enough to others to join together. When enough droplets have joined together, the resulting droplets will be heavy enough to run down the sloping surface.

Questions and Conclusions Answers

1. Depending on the equipment, a droplet will usually run after the first or second spray.

2. Small droplets combined to form larger ones. Even larger droplets formed, causing several small streams to run down the slope.

3. Tiny water droplets joined to form larger droplets, until they became heavy enough to fall. This models the way water droplets combine in clouds until they are heavy enough to fall to the earth as rain.

Explore Further Answers

The mist usually freezes right away on the freezer surface. Therefore, drops do not form or form very slowly.

Assessment

Students' results will vary somewhat according to the individual sprayers. Results will also depend on how close students held the sprayer to the surface and how hard they sprayed. However, their tables should still reflect the growing size of droplets and the growing number of running droplets. Verify that students understand how this investigation models the formation of rain. You might include the following items from this investigation in student portfolios:

• Data table

• Answers to Questions and Conclusions and Explore Further sections

Questions and Conclusions

1. How many times did you spray before one droplet ran down the surface?

2. How did the size of the mist droplets on the plastic surface change?

3. How does this activity model raindrops forming?

Explore Further

Use a mister to repeat this investigation on an inside wall of a freezer. Compare your observations with the observations made at room temperature.

Objectives

After reading this lesson, you should be able to

◆ explain what causes air to move.

◆ recognize how air moves in wind cells.

◆ identify three wind belts.

Wind cell

Continuous cycle of rising warm air and falling cold air

When you see a flag waving or leaves blowing, you know that moving air is moving these objects. But what do you think starts the air moving?

Wind Cells

The earth's atmosphere is constantly in motion. Moving air is known as wind. The motion of air is caused by unequal heating of the earth's surface by the sun. When the sun's energy heats air, the air expands because the air particles are moving farther apart. This makes the warmed air lighter, or less dense, than the cold air around it. The lighter air begins to rise. Then cold air moves in to take the place of the rising air. The new air is then warmed. This cycle of air flow is called a **wind cell**. As the diagram shows, a wind cell is a continuous cycle of rising warm air and falling cold air.

On the earth, some of the warmest air is near the equator. Warm air near the equator rises. It moves toward the North Pole and the South Pole. As the air gets closer to the poles, it becomes colder. The cold air falls back to the earth and moves back toward the equator. As this air warms up, the cycle repeats.

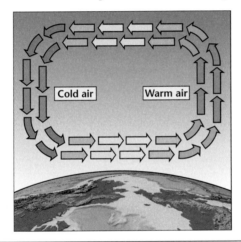

Cold air   Warm air

The Earth's Atmosphere *Chapter 9* **221**

Lesson at a Glance

Chapter 9 Lesson 5

Overview In this lesson, students will learn how differences in heating of the earth's surface cause the air to move, creating wind cells. Students will also learn how the earth's rotation causes global wind patterns.

Objectives

■ To explain what causes air to move

■ To recognize how air moves in wind cells

■ To identify three wind belts

Student Pages 221–224

Teacher's Resource Library

Workbook Activity 38

Alternative Workbook Activity 38

Resource File 20

....

Vocabulary

polar easterly	wind belt
prevailing westerly	wind cell
trade wind	

....

Science Background

As the sun shines on the earth, the sun heats up some parts of the land and water more than others. Air above these hot spots is warmed, becomes lighter, and begins to rise. Elsewhere, cool air sinks because it is heavier. The global circulation of air moves warm air from the equator to the poles and cold air in the opposite direction. Because the earth is spinning, winds bend to the right north of the equator and to the left south of the equator. This is called the Coriolis effect, and its strength increases with latitude.

Trade winds—strong, reliable winds that blow just north and south of the equator—were highly prized by crews of wind-powered trading ships. However, near the equator, the trade winds meet, pushing against each other and causing a region of light, sluggish winds. Crews dreaded being caught in this region, where they sometimes became stranded. Students might be interested to know that this area is called the doldrums, just as a person who feels sluggish or lacking in energy is said to be in the doldrums.

Warm-Up Activity

Tape a short piece of string to the closed end of each of two small paper bags. Attach the bags to opposite ends of a meterstick by taping the string to the stick. Tie a loop of string around the middle of the meterstick and hang it from a stand. Be sure the meterstick is balanced so the bags hang at the same height. Place a small lighted candle below one of the bags, far enough away so that the bag does not catch fire. Ask students to observe what happens when the air in the bag is heated. *(The bag begins to rise.)* Point out that the other bag contains cooler air. Ask what happens to the other bag. *(It begins to sink.)* Tell students that this is similar to how air on the earth moves when it is heated unevenly.

Teaching the Lesson

As they read each section of this lesson, have students find topic sentences that state important ideas. Students can also create their own topic sentences from the ideas presented. Ask them to read their sentences aloud.

Demonstrate how the earth's rotation causes winds to curve. Make a small hole in a hollow rubber ball and fill it with water. Tie a matchstick to a piece of thread and push the matchstick through the hole so that the ball is suspended from the thread. Hang the ball from a ruler in a fish tank. The water in the tank should just cover the top of the ball. Start the ball spinning smoothly. Then add a drop or two of food coloring at the "north pole" of the ball. Students should be able to see that the food coloring is deflected more and more to one side, just as winds blowing from a pole to the equator are deflected.

Global Winds

| **Wind belt** |
| Pattern of wind movement around the earth |

The rotation of the earth breaks large wind cells into smaller cells. These smaller wind cells are shown by black circular arrows in the diagram below. These wind cells make up the wind patterns of the earth. For example, at about 30°N and 30°S latitudes, some of the air headed for the poles falls back to the earth. As this mass of air hits the surface, it divides into two masses. One half of the air returns to the equator. The other half moves toward the North or South Pole. Look at the diagram to see where other wind cells occur.

Winds move around the earth in patterns called **wind belts**. On different parts of the earth, the belts move in different directions. Wind belts are shown by the wide arrows in the diagram.

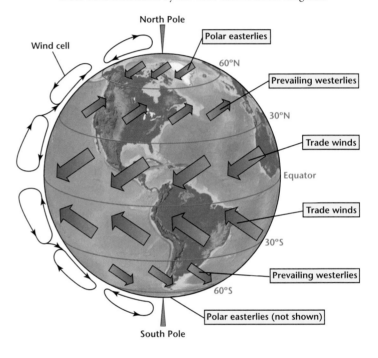

222   *Chapter 9   The Earth's Atmosphere*

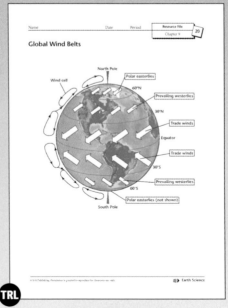

Resource File 20

Trade wind

Strong, reliable wind just north or south of the equator; blows from the east

Prevailing westerly

Wind generally between 30°N and 60°N latitudes (or 30°S and 60°S); blows from the west

Polar easterly

Wind near a pole; blows from the east

The equator is an area of rising air. Winds blowing along the surface are very light. Without enough wind, ships sailing in this area can become stranded.

The two wind belts just north and south of the equator are known as **trade winds**. Find these wind belts on the diagram. These winds blow from the northeast in the Northern Hemisphere and from the southeast in the Southern Hemisphere. Trade winds are strong and reliable. They have been called trade winds since the days when trading ships were powered by wind alone. The captains of those sailing ships sought out the steady trade winds to help them on their way. Hawaii lies within this wind belt.

Most of the United States and southern Canada are affected by the northern belt of the **prevailing westerlies**. Find the two prevailing westerly belts on the diagram. These winds generally occur between 30°N and 60°N latitudes and between 30°S and 60°S latitudes. They usually blow from west to east, the opposite direction of trade winds. Prevailing westerlies are not as predictable as the winds in other belts. The next time you watch a weather forecast, notice that weather moves across these wind belts from west to east. The weather comes from the west because it is carried by prevailing westerlies.

Wind belts also blow from the poles toward warmer latitudes. Winds in these belts are called **polar easterlies**. They move from east to west, like trade winds. Polar easterlies bring cold, stormy weather. Most of Alaska lies within this wind belt.

LEARNING STYLES

Body/Kinesthetic

Place a container filled with dry ice on a tripod or elevate it over a desk. Allow students to put their hands under the container to feel the wind. Point out that the cold air around the container is heavier and it moves downward. When it does so, it replaces the warmer air.

LEARNING STYLES

Interpersonal/ Group Learning

Most of the United States and southern Canada are influenced by the northern prevailing westerly belt. Weather in this belt usually moves from west to east. Have groups of students research how consistent this pattern is where they live. For example, if they live in New York, do they often experience the weather that Cleveland, Ohio, had a day or two ago? Have students share their research methods and findings.

SCIENCE JOURNAL

Ask students to write about how they think global wind patterns might be different if the earth did not rotate.

CAREER CONNECTION

Students may think that meteorologists are weather forecasters who work for newspapers and television stations. Explain that meteorologists do many jobs and work for a variety of government agencies and private businesses. Some meteorologists forecast short-term weather by studying maps and weather conditions. But others forecast long-term weather conditions, such as wind belt patterns or seasonal hurricane activity. Still others research and analyze technology used to measure or predict weather.

Lesson 5 Review Answers

1. unequal heating of the earth's surface by the sun 2. a continuous cycle of rising warm air and falling cold air 3. near the equator 4. Trade winds are found just north and south of the equator; they blow from the northeast in the Northern Hemisphere and from the southeast in the Southern Hemisphere. 5. Most of the United States and southern Canada are in a prevailing westerly wind belt, which carries weather from west to east.

CROSS-CURRICULAR CONNECTION

History

Ask volunteers to read the Technology Note on page 224. After discussing the use of wind power on land, explain that ancient Egyptians learned to harness wind to sail boats in about 3000 B.C. Around 1450, shipbuilders in Mediterranean areas began building full-rigged sailing ships. These ships enabled the great European explorers of the 15th and 16th centuries to sail all over the world. Have students find out more about full-rigged ships, also known as square riggers. Have them make illustrations of the sails, masts, and ropes that made up the rig of these ships.

Portfolio Assessment

Sample items include:
• Topic sentences from Teaching the Lesson
• Lesson 5 Review answers

Write your answers to these questions on a sheet of paper.

1. What causes air to move?

2. What is a wind cell?

3. Where is the earth's warmest air?

4. Where are trade winds found? From what direction do they blow?

5. Does the weather in the United States and southern Canada usually move to the east or to the west? Why?

Technology Note

Wind has been a source of power for centuries. As early as the 1100s, people in Europe used windmills to pump water and grind grain. Many windmills used broad sails to catch the wind.

The first windmill that powered an electric generator was built in 1890 in Denmark. These electricity-making windmills were improved and became popular. However, by the 1940s, coal-burning steam plants could produce electricity faster and cheaper.

In 1931, the first large-scale wind turbine was built in what is now Russia. A wind turbine is usually driven by two or three blades, much like an airplane propeller. The blades are mounted on a tall structure. Today, wind turbines are used to generate electricity for cities and farms. Often, many turbines operate together on a wind farm.

A wind farm may have several hundred wind turbines. The location of the wind farm is important. There must be a steady and strong wind. For this reason, most wind farms are near mountain passes and coastal hills. In 1984, the electricity produced by U.S. wind farms was more than 150 million kilowatt-hours. This seems like a lot. But it is much less than 1 percent of the total U.S. electricity produced. To learn more about sources of energy, see Appendix B.

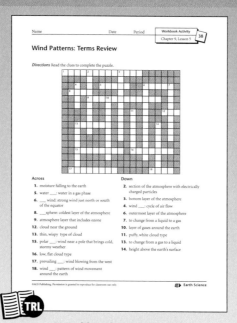

Workbook Activity 38

- The atmosphere is the layer of gases that surrounds the earth.

- The earth's atmosphere consists mostly of the elements nitrogen and oxygen.

- Oxygen and nitrogen move between the atmosphere and living things through the oxygen-carbon dioxide cycle and the nitrogen cycle.

- The four layers of the atmosphere are the troposphere, stratosphere, mesosphere, and thermosphere.

- The ozone layer is in the stratosphere.

- The ionosphere is located in the upper mesosphere and lower thermosphere. It contains ions, which are positively charged particles.

- Clouds are masses of water droplets or ice crystals in the atmosphere.

- Clouds form in the atmosphere when water evaporates into the air and then cools and condenses.

- Three main types of clouds are stratus, cumulus, and cirrus. Fog is a stratus cloud near the ground.

- Precipitation is moisture that falls to the earth from the atmosphere. It may fall as rain, snow, sleet, or hail.

- The sun's unequal heating of the earth's surface causes wind.

- Continuous cycles of rising warm air and falling cold air occur in the atmosphere and are known as wind cells.

- Trade winds, prevailing westerlies, and polar easterlies make up the earth's major wind belts.

- Prevailing westerlies carry weather from west to east.

Science Words

altitude, 212	fog, 212	prevailing westerly, 223	troposphere, 208
atmosphere, 204	ionosphere, 209		water vapor, 211
cirrus cloud, 213	mesosphere, 209	stratosphere, 209	wind belt, 222
condense, 211	polar easterly, 223	stratus cloud, 212	wind cell, 221
cumulus cloud, 213	precipitation, 216	thermosphere, 209	
evaporate, 211		trade wind, 223	

The Earth's Atmosphere Chapter 9 **225**

Chapter 1 Summary

Have volunteers read aloud each Summary item on page 225. Ask volunteers to explain the meaning of each item. Direct students' attention to the Science Words box on the bottom of page 225. Have them read and review each word and its definition.

Chapter 9 Review

Use the Chapter Review to prepare students for tests and to reteach content from the chapter.

Chapter 9 Mastery Test

The Teacher's Resource Library includes two parallel forms of the Chapter 9 Mastery Test. The difficulty level of the two forms is equivalent. You may wish to use one form as a pretest and the other form as a posttest.

Review Answers
Vocabulary Review

1. trade winds 2. altitude 3. precipitation 4. condenses 5. evaporates 6. water vapor 7. polar easterlies 8. wind belt 9. stratus clouds 10. cirrus clouds

Concept Review

11. A thermosphere B mesosphere C stratosphere D troposphere 12. A 13. D 14. B 15. C 16. C 17. D 18. A

TEACHER ALERT

In the Chapter Review, the Vocabulary Review activity includes a sample of the chapter's vocabulary terms. The activity will help determine students' understanding of key vocabulary terms and concepts presented in the chapter. Other vocabulary terms used in the chapter are listed below:

atmosphere
cumulus cloud
fog
ionosphere
mesosphere
prevailing westerly
stratosphere
thermosphere
troposphere
wind cell

Word Bank
altitude
cirrus clouds
condenses
evaporates
polar easterlies
precipitation
stratus clouds
trade winds
water vapor
wind belt

Vocabulary Review

Choose the word or phrase from the Word Bank that best matches each phrase. Write the answer on your paper.

1. steady winds north and south of the equator
2. height above the earth's surface
3. water that falls from the atmosphere
4. what water vapor does to become cloud droplets
5. what liquid water does to become water vapor
6. gas form of water
7. winds near the poles that blow from the east
8. pattern of wind movement around the earth
9. low, flat, gray clouds
10. high, wispy clouds

Concept Review

11. Refer to the diagram. Name each lettered layer of the atmosphere. Write your answers on your paper.

Choose the word or phrase that best completes each sentence. Write the letter of the answer of your paper.

12. The gases of the atmosphere that move in cycles as living things use them are _____.
    A oxygen, carbon dioxide, and nitrogen
    B methane, hydrogen, and helium
    C argon, neon, and ozone
    D nitrogen, xenon, and oxygen

13. The _____ reflects radio signals.
    A troposphere   C mesosphere
    B stratosphere   D ionosphere

Name _____ Date _____ Period _____ | Mastery Test A, Page 1 / Chapter 9

Chapter 9 Mastery Test A

Part A Match each term with its description. Write the letter of the correct description on the line.

_____ 1. ionosphere
_____ 2. stratosphere
_____ 3. ozone layer
_____ 4. troposphere
_____ 5. condense
_____ 6. evaporate
_____ 7. stratus clouds
_____ 8. cirrus clouds
_____ 9. cumulus clouds
_____ 10. trade winds

A clouds that often bring rain
B puffy, white, fair-weather clouds
C to change from a liquid to a gas
D strong, reliable wind belts
E layer with most tightly packed air particles
F clear, dry atmosphere layer
G wispy streaks high in the sky
H layer with electrically charged particles
I to change from a gas to a liquid
J layer that absorbs harmful radiation

Part B Read each sentence. Write the letter of the correct answer on the line.

_____ 11. The ozone layer is in the lower half of the ___.
    A troposphere   B stratosphere   C mesosphere   D thermosphere

_____ 12. When the sun's energy strips electrons from atoms in the atmosphere, it creates ___.
    A wind   B sleet   C ions   D hail

_____ 13. Clouds often form over mountains because ___.
    A air goes down the mountain and collects moisture
    B air is trapped and can't move
    C air rises and heats up
    D air is forced upward and cools

_____ 14. Hailstones form in ___.
    A tall cumulus clouds   C fog
    B thin cirrus clouds   D low stratus clouds

_____ 15. The cause of wind is ___.
    A the revolution and rotation of the earth
    B moving air in the atmosphere
    C warm temperatures near the equator
    D the sun's unequal heating of the earth's surface

Earth Science

Name _____ Date _____ Period _____ | Mastery Test A, Page 2 / Chapter 9

Chapter 9 Mastery Test A, continued

Part C Write a short answer for each question.

16. What is the earth's atmosphere?

17. Explain how oxygen, carbon dioxide, and nitrogen gases cycle through the environment.

18. Name the three types of clouds and describe them by shape and altitude.

19. How does precipitation form?

20. Name and describe the three main wind belts.

Earth Science

Chapter 9 Mastery Test A

14. The _____ is important because it absorbs most of the harmful ultraviolet radiation from the sun.
   A troposphere   **C** mesosphere
   B ozone layer   **D** ionosphere

15. Fluffy, white clouds are called _____.
   A cirrus clouds   **C** cumulus clouds
   B stratus clouds   **D** rain clouds

16. Rain forms when _____.
   A cumulus clouds are present
   B radio waves reflect from a layer of the atmosphere
   C water collects as heavy droplets in clouds
   D sunlight hits the earth at an indirect angle

17. A continuous cycle of rising warm air and falling cold air is called _____.
   A water vapor   **C** the nitrogen cycle
   B a thunderstorm   **D** a wind cell

18. The prevailing westerlies are _____.
   A winds coming from the west
   B the wind belts nearest the equator
   C trade winds
   D winds blowing to the west

Critical Thinking

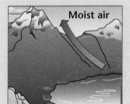

Moist air

Write the answer to each of the following questions.

19. When a rain forest is destroyed, how does this affect the composition of the atmosphere?

20. Moist air is pushed up a mountainside, as shown. How might the weather on the right side of the mountain be different from that on the left side?

Test-Taking Tip Do not wait until the night before a test to study. Plan your study time so that you can get a good night's sleep before a test.

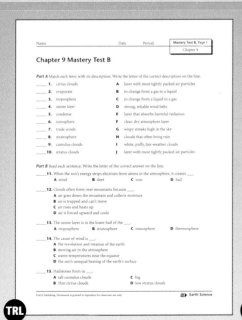

Chapter 9 Mastery Test B

Review Answers
Critical Thinking

19. Plants take in carbon dioxide and release oxygen. A decrease in plant life results in more carbon dioxide and less oxygen in the air. **20.** The right side of the mountain may experience rain as the wind pushes the clouds higher, causing vapor to condense. The left side of the mountain may remain dry, since the water in the clouds already fell to the ground on the journey up the mountain.

ALTERNATIVE ASSESSMENT

Alternative Assessment items correlate to the student Goals for Learning at the beginning of this chapter.

- Ask students to write a simple definition of the earth's atmosphere. They can include an illustration if they wish.

- Ask students to draw simple diagrams with labels of the oxygen-carbon dioxide cycle and the nitrogen cycle.

- Ask students to make and label a simple model that illustrates the four layers of the atmosphere. Then ask them to write a sentence describing each of the layers.

- Have students make a chart that summarizes the characteristics of the three cloud types. Make sure they include cloud shape and altitude. Ask them to illustrate each type of cloud.

- Ask volunteers to explain how each type of precipitation forms and summarize their responses in a four-column chart on the board. Then use this chart to help students compare and contrast snow, rain, sleet, and hail.

- Use a large globe to show the earth's major wind belts. Place a thin strip of masking tape around the globe at the equator and the 30° and 60° latitudes. Ask volunteers to point out and name a belt and its direction. Allow time for students to choose a location on the globe and identify the wind belt affecting it.

Planning Guide

Weather and Climate

		Student Text Lesson	
	Student Pages	Vocabulary	Lesson Review
Lesson 1 Weather Conditions and Measurements	230–237	✔	✔
Lesson 2 Weather Patterns and Predictions	238–243	✔	✔
Lesson 3 Storms	244–246	✔	✔
Lesson 4 World Climates	247–250	✔	✔

Chapter Activities

Student Text
Science Center
Teacher's Resource Library
Community Connection 10: The
  Climate Where You Live

Assessment Options

Student Text
Chapter 10 Review

Teacher's Resource Library
Chapter 10 Mastery Tests A and B

Achievements in Science	Science at Work	Science in Your Life	Investigation	Science Myth	Note	Technology Note	Did You Know	Science Integration	Science Journal	Cross-Curricular Connection	Online Connection	Teacher Alert	Applications (Home, Career, Community, Global, Environment)	Auditory/Verbal	Body/Kinesthetic	Interpersonal/Group Learning	Logical/Mathematical	Visual/Spatial	LEP/ESL	Workbook Activities	Alternative Workbook Activities	Lab Manual	Resource File	Self-Study Guide
	235	236					234	234	232	232, 233		232	233		234		232			39	39	37, 38	21	✔
241		242					238	240		240	240		239						240	40	40	39, 40	22, 23	✔
				244		✔			246	245	246		246	245						41	41			✔
			250		✔			248		249	249	248	248			249		249		42	42			✔

Student Text Features | **Teaching Strategies** | **Learning Styles** | **Teacher's Resource Library**

Pronunciation Key

a	hat	e	let	ī	ice	ô	order	ù put
ā	age	ē	equal	o	hot	oi	oil	ü rule
ä	far	ėr	term	ō	open	ou	out	ch child
â	care	i	it	ȯ	saw	u	cup	ng long

sh she
th thin
ᵺ then
zh measure

ə { a in about / e in taken / i in pencil / o in lemon / u in circus }

Alternative Workbook Activities

The Teacher's Resource Library (TRL) contains a set of lower-level worksheets called Alternative Workbook Activities. These worksheets cover the same content as the regular Workbook Activities but are written at a second-grade reading level.

Skill Track Software

Use the Skill Track Software for Earth Science for additional reinforcement of this chapter. The software program allows students using AGS textbooks to be assessed for mastery of each chapter and lesson of the textbook. Students access the software on an individual basis and are assessed with multiple-choice items.

Chapter 10:
Weather and Climate
pages 228–253

Lessons

1. **Weather Conditions and Measurements** pages 230–237

   Investigation 10-1 pages 236–237

2. **Weather Patterns and Predictions** pages 238–243

   Investigation 10-2 pages 242–243

3. **Storms** pages 244–246

4. **World Climates** pages 247–250

Chapter 10 Summary page 251

Chapter 10 Review pages 252–253

Skill Track Software for Earth Science

Teacher's Resource Library TRL

Workbook Activities 39–42

Alternative Workbook Activities 39–42

Lab Manual 37–40

Community Connection 10

Resource File 21–23

Chapter 10 Self-Study Guide

Chapter 10 Mastery Tests A and B

(Answer Keys for the Teacher's Resource Library begin on page 400 of the Teacher's Edition. The Materials List for the Lab Manual activities begins on page 415.)

Science Center

Display a large world map on a bulletin board. Have students cut out photographs from old magazines showing a variety of climates around the world. Discuss the climate shown in each picture and ask the student who cut it out to connect the picture to the appropriate place on the map with yarn or string and tacks. As students learn about the different climate zones of the earth, have them add labels to the pictures.

Name _____ Date _____ Period _____ Community Connection 10
Chapter 10

The Climate Where You Live

Look at the world map on page 247 in your textbook. Find the climate zone where you live. Then read the descriptions of the regions in that climate zone on the chart on page 249. Determine your climate region. Write your climate zone and climate region on the lines below. Then complete the table by writing a description of the typical weather you experience in your region each season.

Climate zone: _____

Climate region: _____

Season	Weather
winter	
spring	
summer	
fall	

Use this information and your own observations to answer the following questions.

1. Describe the weather you've had this past week. Include the precipitation, temperature, humidity, wind, and sky conditions.

2. Is this weather typical for your climate region at this time of year? Why or why not?

Chapter

10 Weather and Climate

eather takes many different forms. One form of severe weather begins as a tropical storm over an ocean. As the storm gains energy, it becomes a spinning hurricane. This satellite photo shows what a hurricane looks like from space. Can you see the eye of the hurricane at its center? The swirling white masses around the eye are clouds. In Chapter 10, you will learn about different weather conditions and how they are measured. You also will explore weather patterns and climate zones.

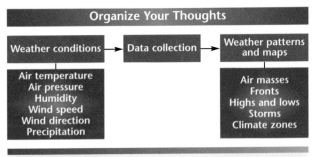

Organize Your Thoughts

Weather conditions → **Data collection** → **Weather patterns and maps**

Weather conditions:
Air temperature
Air pressure
Humidity
Wind speed
Wind direction
Precipitation

Weather patterns and maps:
Air masses
Fronts
Highs and lows
Storms
Climate zones

Goals for Learning

◆ To describe weather conditions
◆ To identify instruments that measure weather conditions
◆ To explain how fronts, highs, and lows affect weather
◆ To read a weather map
◆ To describe various kinds of storms
◆ To describe the earth's major climates

229

Introducing the Chapter

Ask students if they know what is shown in the photo on page 228. Read together the introductory paragraph on page 229. Invite students to tell what they know about hurricanes. Tell them that the photo shows Hurricane Fran approaching the coast of North Carolina in 1996. When this storm hit land, it caused great property damage and flooding. Wind speeds reached 200 kilometers per hour (125 miles per hour). One region received 27 centimeters (almost 11 inches) of rain in 3 hours. For an explanation and list of hurricane names, visit www.fema.gov/kids/hunames.

Besides hurricanes, ask students to name other types of weather. Have small groups of students write a short story about a weather condition. They can describe the weather and activities they might be doing, for example. Ask them to incorporate safety precautions. When they are finished, ask a member of each group to read the group's story to the class. Discuss the weather facts each group presented and write these on a master list. Display the list. As students study the chapter, they can review and revise information on the list and modify their stories to reflect new information.

Notes and Technology Notes

Ask volunteers to read the notes that appear in the margins throughout the chapter. Then discuss them with the class.

TEACHER'S RESOURCE

The AGS Teaching Strategies in Science Transparencies may be used with this chapter. The transparencies add an interactive dimension to expand and enhance the *Earth Science* program content.

CAREER INTEREST INVENTORY

The AGS Harrington-O'Shea Career Decision-Making System-Revised (CDM) may be used with this chapter. Students can use the CDM to explore their interests and identify careers. The CDM defines career areas that are indicated by students' responses on the inventory.

TRL

| Name | Date | Period | SELF-STUDY GUIDE |

Chapter 10: Weather and Climate

Goal 10.1 To describe weather conditions

| Date | Assignment | Score |

1. Read pages 229–234.

Comments:

Goal 10.2 To identify instruments that measure weather conditions

| Date | Assignment | Score |

2. Review pages 230–234.
3. Complete the the Lesson 1 Review on page 235.
4. Complete Workbook Activity 39.
5. Complete Investigation 10-1 on pages 236–237.

Comments:

Goal 10.3 To explain how fronts, highs, and lows affect weather

| Date | Assignment | Score |

6. Read pages 238–240.
7. Complete the Lesson 2 Review on page 241.
8. Complete Workbook Activity 40.

Comments:

©AGS Publishing. Permission is granted to reproduce for classroom use only.   Earth Science

---

TRL

| Name | Date | Period | SELF-STUDY GUIDE |

Chapter 10: Weather and Climate, continued

Goal 10.4 To read a weather map

| Date | Assignment | Score |

9. Reread the bottom of page 240.
10. Complete Investigation 10-2 on pages 242–243.

Comments:

Goal 10.5 To describe various kinds of storms

| Date | Assignment | Score |

11. Read pages 244–245.
12. Complete the Lesson 3 Review on page 246.
13. Complete Workbook Activity 41.

Comments:

Goal 10.6 To describe the earth's major climates

| Date | Assignment | Score |

14. Read pages 247–249.
15. Complete the Lesson 4 Review on page 250.
16. Complete Workbook Activity 42.
17. Read the Chapter 10 Summary on page 251.
18. Complete the Chapter 10 Review on pages 252–253.

Comments:

Student's Signature _____ Date _____
Instructor's Signature _____ Date _____

©AGS Publishing. Permission is granted to reproduce for classroom use only.   Earth Science

Chapter 10 Self-Study Guide

230   Chapter 10   Weather and Climate

Lesson at a Glance

Chapter 10 Lesson 1

Overview In this lesson, students learn about air temperature, air pressure, humidity, wind speed and direction, and precipitation. They also learn how these conditions are measured.

Objectives

- To explain what weather is
- To describe how temperature is measured
- To define air pressure and humidity
- To tell how wind speed, wind direction, and precipitation are measured

Student Pages 230–237

Teacher's Resource Library **TRL**

Workbook Activity 39

Alternative Workbook Activity 39

Lab Manual 37–38

Resource File 21

Vocabulary

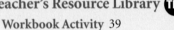

air pressure	rain gauge
anemometer	relative humidity
barometer	weather
humidity	wind vane
psychrometer	

Science Background

The scientific study of weather began in Italy in the 17th century when instruments were developed to measure changes in the temperature, pressure, and moisture content of the air. Around 1600, Galileo made the first thermometer. In 1644, Evangelista Torricelli made the first practical barometer.

1 Warm-Up Activity

Ask students how they knew what would be appropriate to wear outdoors today. Discuss why people need to know the temperature and other weather conditions from day to day. *(to dress appropriately, plan suitable activities, decide whether travel is safe, etc.)* Tell students this lesson describes weather conditions and the instruments used to measure them.

Objectives

After reading this lesson, you should be able to

- explain what weather is.
- describe how temperature is measured.
- define air pressure and humidity.
- tell how wind speed, wind direction, and precipitation are measured.

Weather

State of the atmosphere at a given time and place

Look out the window. Is it a cloudy day? Is it windy? *Cloudy* and *windy* refer to conditions of the atmosphere. **Weather** is the state of the atmosphere at a given time and place.

The weather is always changing because conditions in the atmosphere are always changing. A meteorologist measures these conditions, looks for patterns, and uses this information to predict the weather.

Air Temperature

One of the first weather conditions you hear on a weather report is the temperature of the air. Air temperature is measured with a thermometer. Most thermometers are made of a thin tube filled with colored alcohol. Heat causes a liquid to expand, or take up more space. So when the air gets warmer, the liquid in the thermometer expands and moves up the tube. If the air gets cooler, the liquid contracts, or takes up less space. Then the liquid moves down the tube.

The unit of measure for temperature is the degree (°). Two scales for measuring temperature are shown in the diagram. People in the United States usually use the Fahrenheit scale. People in most other countries use the Celsius scale. All scientists use the Celsius scale. Compare the common temperatures shown on both scales.

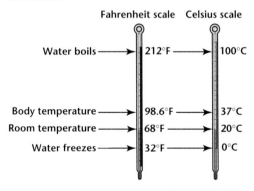

	Fahrenheit scale	Celsius scale
Water boils	212°F	100°C
Body temperature	98.6°F	37°C
Room temperature	68°F	20°C
Water freezes	32°F	0°C

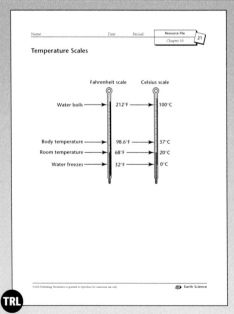

TRL

Resource File 21

Air Pressure

Think about what happens when you blow air into a balloon. The balloon gets bigger because the air particles push against the inside wall of the balloon. The push, or force, of air against an area is called **air pressure**.

Air in the atmosphere exerts pressure, too. The air above you and around you constantly pushes against your body. You don't feel this pressure because air in your body pushes out with the same amount of force. But what happens if air pressure suddenly changes? For example, while riding upward in an elevator, you may have felt your ears "pop." Your ears pop because they are adjusting to a drop in air pressure. As you move higher in the atmosphere, there is less air present to push on you, so air pressure drops.

Air pressure is measured with an instrument called a **barometer**. Two kinds of barometers are shown here. In a mercury barometer, air pushes down on a dish of mercury, forcing the mercury to rise in a tube. In an aneroid barometer, air pushes on a short metal can. A pointer connected to the can shows the amount of air pressure. Aneroid barometers are lightweight and portable.

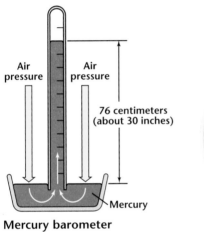

Air pressure | Air pressure

76 centimeters (about 30 inches)

Mercury

Mercury barometer

Aneroid barometer

As they read the lesson, have students create a table of weather instruments and the weather condition each measures. In a third column, they can describe how the instrument works.

If possible, set up a wind sock outside. Demonstrate to students how to use a compass and the wind sock to record wind direction. (Wind rushes into the large end, causing the smaller end to extend out behind. The larger end, therefore, points into the direction from which the wind is coming.)

Make available thermometers that show both Fahrenheit and Celsius scales. Review the proper reading of a thermometer. Ask pairs of students to read and record the temperature of the room, of a beaker of ice water, and of a beaker of hot (but not boiling) water. They should record each temperature in both degrees Fahrenheit and degrees Celsius.

Ask students to listen to a weather forecast for two days in a row and record the air pressure. Discuss any change and how the weather conditions changed along with the air pressure.

PRONUNCIATION GUIDE

Use this list to help students pronounce difficult words in this lesson. Refer to the pronunciation key on the Chapter Planning Guide for the sounds of these symbols.

barometer (bə rom´ ə tər)

psychrometer (sī krom´ ə tər)

anemometer (an´ ə mom´ ə tər)

Humidity
Amount of water vapor in the air

Relative humidity
Amount of water vapor in the air compared to the maximum amount of water vapor the air can hold

Psychrometer
Instrument used to measure relative humidity

Different scales are used to measure air pressure. Most weather reports give the air pressure in inches. Air pressure usually ranges from 29 to 31 inches (74 to 79 centimeters), which is the height of mercury in a mercury barometer.

A change in air pressure indicates a change in weather. A rise in air pressure usually means drier weather is on the way. A drop in air pressure often means precipitation is coming.

Humidity

Have you ever described a hot day as sticky or muggy? Such days are uncomfortable because of high **humidity**. Humidity is the amount of water vapor in the air. When the air contains a lot of water vapor, the humidity is high. The maximum amount of water vapor that the air can hold, or its capacity, depends on the air temperature. Warmer air can hold more water vapor than colder air can.

The amount of water vapor in the air compared to its capacity is called **relative humidity**. It is calculated as a percent. A relative humidity of 50 percent means that the air contains half, or 50 percent, of its water vapor capacity. When the air is completely filled with water vapor and cannot hold more, the relative humidity is 100 percent.

A **psychrometer** is an instrument used to measure relative humidity. It is actually made up of two thermometers. The bulb of one thermometer is covered with a damp cloth. As water evaporates from the cloth, it cools. The temperature of this thermometer is lower than the temperature of the dry thermometer. The lower the humidity, the faster the water evaporates and the lower the temperature drops. The relative humidity is then found by comparing the temperatures of the two thermometers to a special chart.

Wind Speed and Direction

Anemometer

Instrument used to measure wind speed

Wind vane

Instrument used to find wind direction

The speed of the wind is an important weather condition. It helps meteorologists predict how fast an approaching storm will arrive. Wind speed is measured with an **anemometer**. An anemometer has three or four arms, with a cup attached to the end of each arm. These cups catch the wind and cause the arms to rotate. When the wind speed increases, the arms rotate faster. This spinning rate may be indicated on a dial or digital display.

The photo shows a simple anemometer with three arms. It also shows another important weather instrument: a **wind vane**.

A wind vane shows the direction from which the wind is blowing. It is often shaped like an arrow. Wind hits the larger back section of the vane. The vane turns so that it points into the wind.

Wind is named by the direction from which it comes. A wind that moves from north to south is called a north wind. A north wind causes a wind vane to point north.

A quick glance at this anemometer and wind vane will tell you both wind speed and direction.

CAREER CONNECTION

Invite a meteorologist to speak to your class. He or she might tell students about the many kinds of work that meteorologists do in addition to giving weather forecasts on the news.

GLOBAL CONNECTION

Wind vanes are among the earliest known weather instruments. Have students work in small groups to research wind vanes from different cultures. Encourage them to find or draw pictures of unusual examples. They can make wind vanes of their own based on the pictures they find. Let them demonstrate their wind vanes outside. Then display the wind vanes in the classroom.

CROSS-CURRICULAR CONNECTION

Art

Have students design and make a wind vane with an artistic shape. Ask them to explain how the design works to show wind direction.

Did You Know?

Have a volunteer read aloud the Did You Know? feature on page 234. Remind students that trade winds are the strong, reliable winds that blow just north and south of the equator. In the Northern Hemisphere, the trade winds blow from northeast to southwest. The Hawaiian Islands lie in the path of these trade winds. Besides producing rainfall on Mount Waialeale and other mountains, the trade winds help moderate Hawaii's warm climate.

PRONUNCIATION GUIDE

Use the pronunciation below to help students pronounce *Mount Waialeale*. Refer to the pronunciation key on the Chapter Planning Guide for the sounds of these symbols.

Mount Waialeale   (mount wī ə lā ə´ lā)

LEARNING STYLES

Body/Kinesthetic

Have students build a rain gauge using simple materials such as a centimeter ruler, clear packing tape, and a tall, narrow jar. Suggest that they observe the rain gauge after rainfalls and record their observations.

SCIENCE INTEGRATION

Physical Science

Review the terms *solid*, *liquid*, and *gas* with students. Ask them to draw pictures showing the differences in the amount of space around molecules of water in ice, liquid water, and water vapor. Relate these differences to differences in the heat energy contained in the water and to temperature. (*As temperature rises, the molecules take on more heat energy and move farther apart, changing the state of water from sleet or snow to rain or from rain to water vapor. As temperatures drop, the molecules lose heat energy and move closer together, changing water vapor to rain or rain to sleet or snow.*)

Rain gauge
Instrument used to measure the amount of rainfall

Did You Know?

The wettest place on the earth is Mount Waialeale. This soggy mountain is on the island of Kauai in Hawaii. It receives about 12 meters of rain a year. This rain comes from trade winds carrying rain clouds up the side of the mountain.

Precipitation

Chapter 9 described four kinds of precipitation: rain, snow, sleet, and hail. If any precipitation falls, a weather report usually tells you how much. A **rain gauge** measures the amount of rainfall. As you can see, a rain gauge is a container that collects rain. A scale along the side shows the amount in centimeters or inches. Snow depth is usually measured simply by inserting a meterstick in a flat area of snow. Hail can be measured in two ways: by its depth on the ground and by the diameter of the hailstones.

Rain gauges come in different shapes and sizes. To accurately measure rainfall, rain gauges should be placed in open areas.

Write your answers to these questions on a sheet of paper.

1. What is weather?

2. How does a thermometer work?

3. What does a change in air pressure tell you about the weather?

4. Why does air pressure drop as you go higher in the atmosphere?

5. What weather condition does each of these instruments measure: barometer, thermometer, rain gauge, anemometer, psychrometer?

▼◄▲▼◄▲▼◄▲▼◄▲▼◄▲▼◄▲▼◄▲▼◄▲▼◄▲▼◄▲▼◄▲▼◄▲▼◄▲▼◄▲▼

Science at Work

Atmospheric Scientist

A scientist who studies the atmosphere is called an atmospheric scientist. These specialists study the atmosphere's properties and patterns. They also study how weather affects the environment and how people affect the atmosphere.

Atmospheric scientists collect air samples and gather data from weather satellites, Doppler radar, and weather balloons. They use this information to create computer models of the atmosphere and to design experiments.

Atmospheric scientists predict long-term weather changes. They research the effect of pollution on clouds. They study how processes in the ocean and on the sun change weather. They design better instruments and give advice to government and industry leaders.

Atmospheric scientists must have at least a bachelor's degree in meteorology, atmospheric science, or a related science field. A graduate degree is often helpful.

People who want to work in this field should have strong computer and mathematics skills. A good atmospheric scientist is creative, patient, organized, and stays up-to-date on research methods.

Weather and Climate   Chapter 10   **235**

Lesson 1 Review Answers

1. the state of the atmosphere at a given time and place **2.** The narrow tube of a thermometer contains alcohol, which expands when the temperature rises, causing the fluid to rise in the tube, and contracts when the temperature falls, causing the fluid to fall in the tube. **3.** A change in air pressure means the weather will change. A rise usually means drier weather, and a drop often means precipitation is coming. **4.** There is less air to press on objects at higher altitudes, so the air pressure drops. **5.** air pressure, air temperature, amount of precipitation, wind speed, relative humidity

Science at Work

Ask volunteers to read the Science at Work feature about atmospheric scientists on page 235. Review the term *meteorology* from Chapter 1. (*It is the scientific study of the atmosphere, especially as it relates to weather and weather forecasting.*) Invite interested students to research this career further. They might learn how computer models are generated; how weather balloons, Doppler radar, and weather satellites are used; and what long-term weather changes atmospheric scientists are observing.

Portfolio Assessment

Sample items include:
• Table of weather instruments from Teaching the Lesson
• Lesson 1 Review answers

The Purpose portion of the student investigation begins with a question to draw students into the activity. Encourage students to read the investigation steps and formulate their own questions before beginning the investigation. This investigation will take approximately 45 minutes to complete. Students will use these process and thinking skills: making models, observing, measuring, recording data, predicting, recognizing cause and effect, and making generalizations.

Preparation

• You might use hard plastic containers or metal cans in place of the glass jars. A large coffee can will produce more dramatic movement of the straw. Be sure the balloons are large enough to fit over the top of whatever containers you use.

• Have extra balloons on hand. Some are likely to tear in making the barometers.

• Before class, set up a sample barometer using the materials students will be using.

• Make both masking tape and glue available for attaching the straw to the balloon.

• Students may use Lab Manual 38 to record their data and answer the questions.

Procedure

• Students may work independently or with a partner to complete the investigation. Be sure each pair has an assigned space for their barometer that will not be in direct sunlight.

• Check to be sure stretched balloons make an airtight seal with the jar.

• Check all setups to see that the straw is positioned at the zero mark on the index card.

SAFETY ALERT

◆ Caution students to be careful when stretching the balloon. Balloons can snap and cause injuries.

INVESTIGATION

10-1

Materials

◆ large, round balloon
◆ scissors
◆ glass baby-food jar
◆ rubber band
◆ drinking straw
◆ glue
◆ marking pen
◆ index card
◆ centimeter ruler
◆ masking tape

Measuring Air Pressure

Purpose

Does the air pressure change in your classroom? In this investigation, you will construct a barometer and collect weather data.

Procedure

1. Copy the data table on your paper.

Date and Time	Barometer Reading	Weather Observations

2. Cut off the neck of a balloon. Stretch the balloon tightly over the top of a jar. Hold the balloon in place with a rubber band. **Safety Alert: Use care when stretching the balloon. It can snap and cause injury.**

3. Cut one end of a drinking straw so that it forms a point. Glue the other end of the straw to the center of the balloon cover, as shown in the figure.

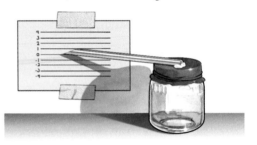

---

4. With a pen, mark a scale on the unlined side of an index card, as shown. Make the lines 0.5 centimeter apart. Number them from −4 to 4.

5. Place your barometer near a wall. Tape the index card to the wall so that the straw on the barometer points to the zero line. Make sure the barometer is not in direct sunlight.

6. When the glue has dried, observe the position of the straw. In your data table, record the number indicated by the straw. Also record the date, time, and outside weather conditions.

7. Repeat step 6 at least once each day for the next four days.

Questions and Conclusions

1. What does an upward movement of the straw indicate about air pressure?

2. What does a downward movement of the straw indicate about air pressure?

3. How did air pressure change during the five days of observations?

4. Use your readings to make a prediction about upcoming weather. Explain your prediction.

Explore Further

Find out how accurate your predictions were. Use a local newspaper to compare your data with weather reports for the same days.

Results

If the air pressure in the room increases, the room air will push down on the balloon surface, causing the end of the pointer to move up. If the air pressure decreases, the pointer will move down. Rising air pressure often indicates fair weather. Falling air pressure often indicates bad weather.

Questions and Conclusions Answers

1. Air pressure increased.

2. Air pressure decreased.

3. Answers will vary according to local weather. However, student data should be consistent across the class.

4. Answers will vary according to local weather. Predictions should reflect the understanding that rising air pressure suggests drier weather is coming, decreasing pressure suggests wetter weather is coming, and no change in pressure indicates a stable, or unchanging, pattern in current weather.

Explore Further Answers

Encourage students to compare their prediction with those from both a newspaper and a televised weather report. They can then compare all of the predictions with the weather that actually occurs.

Assessment

Check that students are correctly reading their barometers. Use their answers to the questions to verify that they recognize how barometric readings relate to changes in the weather. You might include the following items from this investigation in student portfolios:

• Data table

• Answers to Questions and Conclusions and Explore Further sections

Lesson at a Glance

Chapter 10 Lesson 2

Overview In this lesson, students learn how weather data are gathered and used to predict weather as well as how to interpret weather maps.

Objectives

- To describe ways that weather data are collected
- To explain how fronts, highs, and lows affect weather
- To read the information on a weather map

Student Pages 238–243

Teacher's Resource Library (TRL)

Workbook Activity 40

Alternative Workbook Activity 40

Lab Manual 39–40

Resource File 22–23

Vocabulary

air mass	isobar
cold front	low
front	warm front
high	

Science Background

In a warm front, a warm air mass glides up over a cool air mass. In a cold front, a cold air mass pushes into a warm air mass. In some cases, two air masses stay in the same area for days. The boundary, therefore, does not move and is called a stationary boundary. Cold fronts move faster than warm fronts. This means that sometimes a cold front catches up with a warm front. The warm air mass, wedged between two cold air masses, is squeezed so that it rises above the cold air masses. This is called an occluded front.

1 Warm-Up Activity

Place a short piece of plastic tubing into the opening of a balloon and secure it with a rubber band. Remove all air from the balloon. Have a volunteer hold the plastic tubing. Blow up a second balloon and pinch the neck closed while stretching the balloon's opening around the free end of the tubing. Ask students to observe what happens to the balloons. Hold the blown-up balloon securely in

Objectives

After reading this lesson, you should be able to

- describe ways that weather data are collected.
- explain how fronts, highs, and lows affect weather.
- read the information on a weather map.

? Did You Know?

In 1869, more than 1,900 ships sank in the Great Lakes during storms. The U.S. government reacted to this huge loss by setting up a weather service for the nation. The service was called the Army Signal Service. Its job was to predict the weather and post weather warnings.

Collecting Weather Data

To predict the weather, meteorologists need data from many places. At about 10,000 weather stations worldwide, measurements are taken at the exact same time several times a day. In the United States, the National Weather Service (NWS) collects these data for meteorologists to use.

Weather information is collected in many ways. Weather stations are collections of instruments that measure temperature, air pressure, humidity, cloud cover and type, precipitation, and wind speed and direction. Measurements are recorded automatically or taken by weather observers and transmitted to NWS centers.

Weather balloons more than a meter in diameter carry instruments high into the atmosphere. Weather satellites in orbit around the earth provide views of cloud patterns. Radar sends out radio waves that bounce off rain or snow. The returning waves make an image that shows where precipitation is occurring, as shown in the photo.

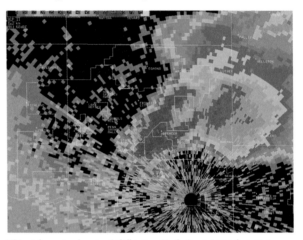

This radar map shows rainfall amounts during a tornado system. Notice the colored legend: red is heavy rain, lavender and gray are light rain, and black is no rain.

place on the tubing but allow the air to escape from it. (Air leaves the inflated balloon and flows into the other balloon.) Explain that air always flows from regions of high pressure toward regions of low pressure. Tell students that, on a very large scale, movements such as this cause weather changes.

Did You Know?

Ask students how they think weather forecasts are helpful to the crews on ships and planes. Then have them read the Did You Know? feature on page 238. Have interested students read more about the history of a government weather service. Ask them to report on their findings.

Air Masses and Fronts

Air mass

Large section of the atmosphere with the same temperature and humidity throughout

Front

Moving boundary line between two air masses

Warm front

Boundary ahead of a warm air mass that is pushing out and riding over a cold air mass

Cold front

Boundary ahead of a cold air mass that is pushing out and wedging under a warm air mass

Weather data from a large area of the earth show meteorologists where **air masses** are located. An air mass is a huge body of the lower atmosphere that has similar temperature and humidity throughout. An air mass can be warm or cold. It can have a lot of water vapor or very little. Air masses are so large that two or three of them can cover the United States. As air masses move, they bring their weather to new places.

A **front** is a moving boundary line between two air masses. Look at the diagrams below as you read about two types of fronts.

A **warm front** occurs where a warm air mass glides up and over a cooler air mass. As the warm air rises, it cools and water vapor condenses. Typically, high cirrus clouds appear. Low stratus clouds follow. The barometer falls continuously, and a period of steady precipitation begins. When the front passes, skies clear and the barometer rises. The temperature rises as warm air replaces the cooler air.

A **cold front** occurs where a cold air mass pushes out and wedges under a warmer air mass. The warm air mass rises quickly. If the warm air mass has a lot of water vapor, towering storm clouds form quickly. Heavy precipitation follows, but only for a short period of time. Several hours after the front passes, the weather becomes clear and cool.

Warm front

Cold front

Weather and Climate   Chapter 10   **239**

2 ▸ Teaching the Lesson

Ask students to make a chart with columns labeled *Cause* and *Effect.* As they read the lesson, have them find examples of cause-and-effect relationships to record in their charts. Remind students that a cause can have a series of effects, and the same effect can be produced by different causes. For example, a warm front causes cirrus clouds to form, then stratus clouds, then steady precipitation.

Review types of clouds with students. Display photos of cloud types, pointing out cirrus clouds and stratus clouds.

Fill a large jar half full of cold water. Fill a small jar to the rim with hot water and a few drops of red food coloring. With a rubber band, secure a piece of aluminum foil over the top of the small jar. Lower the small jar into the large jar. Use a pencil to poke a small hole in the foil and have students observe what happens. *(The warm, colored water rises.)* Point out that cold air and warm air act in this way—warm air will rise above cold air.

Cover a regional wall map with a sheet of acetate. Draw symbols for highs, lows, and fronts and review them with the class. Point to different areas and have students explain what weather conditions they would expect in each one.

3 ▸ Reinforce and Extend

IN THE COMMUNITY

Have a small group of students research your area's weather stations to find out how and where data are gathered.

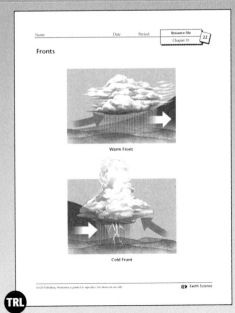

Fronts

Warm Front

Cold Front

Resource File 22

Weather and Climate   Chapter 10   **239**

Biology

Have students choose an animal and do research to find out how it is affected by weather. Questions they might answer include these: What does the animal do when the weather is cold and snowy? How is the animal affected by very hot, dry weather? How does the animal protect itself from storms and rain? Let students share their findings in oral reports to the class.

CROSS-CURRICULAR CONNECTION

Geography

With students study the patterns of weather in various regions of the country. Then study a topographic map of the country. Explain how various features, such as mountains, deserts, and plains, affect the type of weather that an area is most likely to have at any given time of the year.

LEARNING STYLES

LEP/ESL

Tape a televised weather forecast. Have students watch it and listen for the weather terms they are learning. Pause the tape when they have questions or need explanations. After students have seen and understood the whole forecast, replay it. Pause the tape from time to time and have students explain what the forecaster's map shows, using the terms *warm front, cold front, high, low,* and *isobar.*

High
Cold area of high air pressure

Low
Warm area of low air pressure

Isobar
Line on a weather map connecting areas of equal air pressure

Highs and Lows

Cold air is more dense than warm air. Therefore, cold air exerts more pressure on the earth's surface than does warm air. A cold air mass, then, is usually an area of high pressure, or a **high**. Highs often have fair weather. Look at the map below. You can see that air moves outward from a high in a clockwise rotation. However, air moves into an area of low pressure, or a **low**. The air coming into a low is warm and rotates counterclockwise. Lows often have clouds and precipitation. On a map, lines called **isobars** connect areas of equal pressure. Isobars form a circular pattern around highs and lows.

In most of the United States and Canada, weather moves from west to east. Therefore, a high passing through Oklahoma may soon pass through Arkansas. The high will likely bring similar weather to both places.

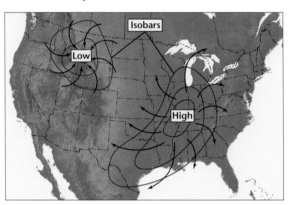

Weather Maps

As you can see, meteorologists must consider a lot of data to develop a weather forecast. They organize these data on weather maps, like the one above and the one on page 243. Weather maps generally include information about precipitation, cloud cover, air masses, highs, lows, and fronts. Weather maps may also include isobars, temperatures, wind speeds, and wind directions. As you learned in Chapter 1, to read these maps, you first need to understand their symbols.

ONLINE CONNECTION

The Central Iowa Power Cooperative (CIPCO) sponsors a site called WeatherEye, which provides lesson ideas and experiments on weather:

http://weathereye.kgan.com/cadet/index.html

AskERIC Education Information, a site funded by the U.S. Department of Education, contains lesson plans and activities about meteorology:

http://askeric.org/cgi-bin/lessons.cgi/Science/Meteorology

Write your answers to these questions on a sheet of paper.

1. Describe four ways weather data are collected.

2. How is a cold front different from a warm front?

3. What is the difference between a high and a low?

4. What are isobars?

5. Name three kinds of information found on a weather map.

Achievements in Science

Doppler Radar

The ability to predict weather events has improved greatly in the last century. Even as recently as 15 years ago, meteorologists could provide only a 2-day forecast. Today, improved technology helps them provide a mostly accurate 4-day forecast.

One of the tools that meteorologists use is a Doppler radar system. This type of radar uses a high-powered antenna that rotates and sends out radio waves. Some of these waves bounce off raindrops or snowflakes in the air and return to the antenna. A computer detects and measures how these waves have changed. It also measures the time it took for the waves to return. From this information, the computer calculates the distance and direction of the precipitation. Wind speed and direction also can be calculated.

This information is used to create a Doppler map. The map shows the locations and amounts of precipitation. You have probably seen a Doppler map on television weather reports. Meteorologists are trained to use these maps and other resources to understand and predict weather.

Weather and Climate   Chapter 10   **241**

Lesson 2 Review Answers

1. from weather stations, weather balloons, weather satellites, and radar 2. A cold front is a cold air mass pushing into and under a warm air mass. A warm front is a warm air mass gliding up and over a cold air mass. Both fronts are boundaries of air masses and both often produce precipitation. Precipitation at a cold front is usually more severe and shorter-lasting than at a warm front. 3. A high is a cold area of high pressure that results in fair weather and causes air to move outward in a clockwise rotation. A low is an area of low pressure, with warm air moving inward counterclockwise. Lows often have clouds and precipitation. 4. lines used on a weather map to connect areas of equal pressure 5. Answers will vary. Possible responses: air pressure, cloud cover, fronts, air masses, highs, lows, isobars, precipitation, cloud conditions, wind speed, wind direction, temperature

Achievements in Science

Invite volunteers to tell what they think radar is. (*Radar stands for radio detecting and ranging. It consists of a radio transmitter for sending out radio waves and a receiver for detecting those that are reflected. Waves reflect off an object, such as a plane, and return to the receiver, allowing scientists to pinpoint the object's exact location, direction, and speed.*) Have volunteers read the feature on page 241. If possible, display a picture of a Doppler map. Students can compare it to other weather maps.

Portfolio Assessment

Sample items include:
• Chart from Teaching the Lesson
• Lesson 2 Review answers

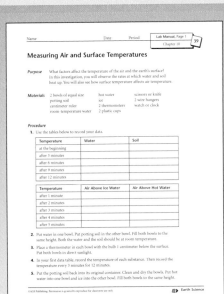

Lab Manual 39, pages 1–2

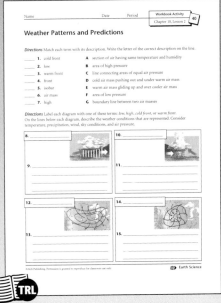

Workbook Activity 40

Investigation 10-2

The Purpose portion of the student investigation begins with a question to draw students into the activity. Encourage students to read the investigation steps and formulate their own questions before beginning the investigation. This investigation will take approximately 30 minutes to complete. Students will use these process and thinking skills: making models, interpreting maps, predicting, and recognizing cause and effect.

Preparation

• Students may use the map on Resource File 23 to record their data and Lab Manual 40 to answer the questions.

Procedure

• Have students work individually to complete this activity.

• Before students begin the activity, review warm and cold fronts. Discuss the meanings of the weather symbols in the legend. Reinforce the idea that, for map symbols to be useful, they must be explained on the map itself. Referring to the weather map, review the cardinal directions (north, south, east, west) and intermediate directions (northwest, northeast, southeast, southwest).

• As students begin, have them first copy the legend of weather symbols onto their own maps. Then instruct them to copy all of the symbols from the weather map on page 243 onto their maps.

• Remind students what they learned in Chapter 9: In general, the weather pattern in the central region of North America moves west to east with the prevailing westerlies.

INVESTIGATION

10-2

Materials
◆ map without weather symbols

Using a Weather Map

Purpose

How can you show weather conditions on a map? In this investigation, you will make and interpret a weather map.

Procedure

1. On your map, copy the weather information from the weather map on page 243. Copy the legend of symbols, too.

2. Show that it is raining across southern Florida.

3. Show that snow is falling in Minnesota and Ontario behind the cold front.

4. Show that a warm front is occurring across Alabama, Georgia, and South Carolina and heading toward Florida.

5. Show that it is now cloudy in Honolulu, Hawaii, and partly cloudy in Juneau, Alaska.

Questions and Conclusions

1. Which cities have clear skies?

2. Which kind of front is heading toward Dallas and Chicago? What kind of weather will these cities have after the front passes them?

3. From your map, predict what will happen to temperatures in Florida tomorrow. Explain your answer.

4. Suggest two more symbols that could be added to your map. Explain the symbols. How do they make the map more useful?

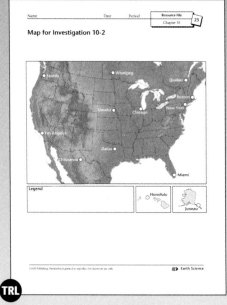

Resource File 23

Lab Manual 40

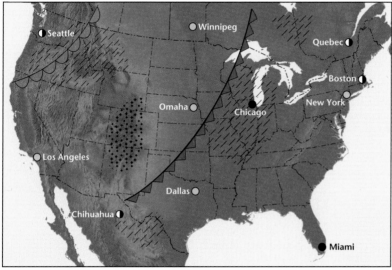

Seattle Winnipeg Quebec Boston New York Omaha Chicago Los Angeles Dallas Chihuahua Miami

 Rain ○ Clear   Cold front   Honolulu
 Snow ◑ Partly cloudy ● Cloudy Warm front Juneau

Explore Further

Compare local weather maps for two days in a row. How accurate was the first day's forecast? Did the fronts move as expected? Are there any new fronts? From which direction did they arrive?

Results

Student maps should show the weather symbols shown on the map on page 243 as well as the correct symbols for rain over southern Florida, snow behind (west of) a cold front in Minnesota and southern Ontario, and a warm front heading across Alabama, Georgia, and South Carolina toward Florida. In addition, Honolulu should be marked by a filled-in circle and Juneau should be marked by a half-filled circle.

Questions and Conclusions Answers

1. Los Angeles, Omaha, Winnipeg, Dallas, and New York

2. cold front; a short period of heavy showers followed by clear, cool weather

3. The temperatures will rise because a warm front will be coming through.

4. Answers will vary. Possible answers include symbols for wind speed, wind direction, air pressure, and temperature. Added symbols provide more weather information that can help in planning outdoor activities, making clothing and travel decisions, and preparing for adverse weather.

Explore Further Answers

Answers will vary depending on predictions and the local weather. Verify that students' answers reflect an understanding of weather symbols and concepts and an ability to read a weather map. Students might note that weather predictions can give a good idea of upcoming weather, but may not always be accurate. New fronts will most probably come from the west.

Assessment

Check students' maps to be sure that they followed directions and used the correct weather symbols. Verify that their answers reflect an understanding of the map symbols and how weather moves. You might include the following items from this investigation in students' portfolios:

• Weather map

• Questions and Conclusions and Explore Further answers

Lesson at a Glance

Chapter 10 Lesson 3

Overview In this lesson, students learn how thunderstorms, tornadoes, and hurricanes form and the distinguishing features of each kind of storm.

Objectives

■ To explain how lightning and thunder form

■ To describe a tornado

■ To explain how a hurricane develops

Student Pages 244–246

Teacher's Resource Library **TRL**

Workbook Activity 41

Alternative Workbook Activity 41

....

Vocabulary

hurricane   tornado

....

Science Background

Every day some 40,000 thunderstorms occur around the earth. The majority of them occur near the equator. Thunderclouds can tower more than 16 kilometers into the air. The building up of such a cloud requires very strong updrafts. These updrafts usually occur along cold fronts or above areas greatly heated by sunlight.

A tornado starts within a thundercloud when a column of rising air is set spinning by high winds blowing through the cloud's top. As air is sucked into the swirling column, it spins faster and faster. Finally, a spinning funnel descends from the cloud's base, forming the tornado.

Hurricanes are also called typhoons and tropical cyclones in other parts of the world.

 1 Warm-Up Activity

Tape a sheet of polyethylene to a table. Place a lump of clay in the center of an aluminum pie plate. Touching only the clay, rub the pie plate vigorously on the plastic sheet. After a few minutes, the dish should have a strong electric charge. Darken the room and hold a pair of metal scissors about 2–3 centimeters

---

Objectives

After reading this lesson, you should be able to

◆ explain how lightning and thunder form.

◆ describe a tornado.

◆ explain how a hurricane develops.

Science Myth

Some people may think that heat lightning is the result of high temperatures.

Fact: Heat lightning has nothing to do with heat. It is simply lightning from thunderstorms far away. Heat lightning is usually seen close to the horizon. This explains why it appears orange or red. When you look at the horizon, you are looking through the troposphere. The particles in the troposphere scatter the light you see.

Storms are violent kinds of weather. They are caused by rapid changes in the movement of air masses. Storms usually include precipitation and high winds.

Thunderstorms

Perhaps the most familiar kind of storm is the thunderstorm. This kind of storm occurs when warm air is forced upward by a cold front. Large, dark, cumulus clouds form. Such clouds are also called thunderheads. These clouds produce heavy rain and sometimes hail. They also produce lightning and thunder.

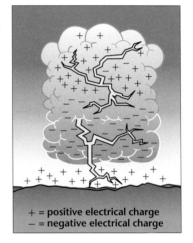

+ = positive electrical charge
− = negative electrical charge

The diagram shows how lightning forms. Within a thunderhead, air moves up and down. This motion causes electrical charges to build. An electric current passes between the negative and positive charges. This current is lightning. A streak of lightning may be only a few centimeters wide, but it heats that part of the air intensely. The heated air expands so quickly that it produces a sound wave we call thunder. You see the lightning before you hear the thunder because light travels faster than sound.

---

from the pan. Students should see the sparks created as the static electricity discharges from the pan to the scissors. Explain that rubbing the pan over the sheet is similar to the air particles rubbing together inside a thundercloud, producing lightning.

Science Myth

Have a volunteer read aloud the first sentence of the Science Myth feature on page 244. Invite those who have heard of heat lightning to predict what causes it. Review the meaning of troposphere. Have a second volunteer read the fact portion. Discuss why light is scattered by the troposphere, causing lightning on the horizon to appear red or orange. (Explain the characteristics of wave motion and the visible spectrum of light.)

Tornadoes

Tornado

Powerful wind storm with a whirling, funnel-shaped cloud and extremely low pressure

Hurricane

Severe tropical storm with high winds that revolve around an eye

A **tornado** is a small but powerful wind storm with a whirling, funnel-shaped cloud. Tornadoes sometimes form in thunderstorms when warm, humid air rushes up to meet cool, dry air. Tornadoes have very low air pressure and can rotate at speeds up to 450 kilometers per hour. When they touch the ground, they can uproot trees, toss cars, and destroy houses. Tornadoes last for a very short time.

Tornadoes usually form in open, level areas like the prairies of the central and southern United States. In these areas, there are few mountains or forests to break the high winds.

Tornadoes usually occur in April, May, and June.

Hurricanes

A **hurricane** is a large tropical storm that often covers thousands of square kilometers. Winds spiral toward the center of the storm, with speeds up to 320 kilometers per hour. At the center of a hurricane is an area of calm air called the eye. In the satellite photo on page 228, notice how the clouds spiral around the eye of a hurricane.

All hurricanes form over the ocean near the equator. They collect warm, moist air and begin to spin. They grow stronger over the warm tropical water. As hurricanes approach land, their wind pushes the water of the ocean against the shore, and flooding occurs. Hurricanes may drop tremendous amounts of rain as they move inland, causing further damage. Hurricanes lose their force as they continue to move over land because they are no longer fed by the heat and moisture of tropical seas. Friction with the land also slows the winds of the storm.

Weather and Climate   Chapter 10   **245**

---

2 Teaching the Lesson

Have students write the lesson objectives, spacing them about a third of a page apart on a sheet of paper. As they read the lesson, students can write sentences that meet each objective.

Explain that thunderstorms are very active electrically. The top of a thunderhead has a positive charge, and its base is part negative and part positive. The ground is positively charged, and its charge becomes stronger as the cloud's charge increases. When these differences grow large enough, electricity is discharged as lightning. Lightning moves from cloud to cloud or from cloud to ground.

Discuss with students why tornadoes might be considered more dangerous than hurricanes. *(Meteorologists can track hurricanes over the ocean for days. They can usually give plenty of warning so that people can evacuate areas in the path of the storm. Tornadoes, however, usually develop very quickly, and people often have little warning.)*

On a map, point out the location of what is known as Tornado Alley—northern Texas, Oklahoma, Kansas, and Nebraska. Discuss with students the regions most likely to be affected by hurricanes. Remind them that hurricanes form over oceans near the equator. In the United States, they most often affect the Gulf coast, Florida, the southeast Atlantic coast, and Hawaii.

3 Reinforce and Extend

LEARNING STYLES

Auditory/Verbal

Pretend to be a reporter "on location" during a storm. Begin your broadcast by describing what is happening with the weather and what people are doing to prepare. When students recognize what kind of storm you are reporting on, have them write this on a slip of paper. Check the accuracy of students' predictions. Then have a volunteer repeat the process, reporting details for another kind of storm.

CROSS-CURRICULAR CONNECTION

History

Ask students to learn about Benjamin Franklin's famous experiment with lightning. They can report on his invention, the lightning rod. Ask them to make a labeled diagram to show how it works to protect buildings.

AT HOME

Have students find out what safety practices should be followed at home during watches and warnings for severe thunderstorms, tornadoes, and hurricanes. (The Federal Emergency Management Agency's Web site www.fema.gov/kids gives disaster preparedness information designed for students.) Have students make a list of safety practices they would follow in their homes. Suggest that they share the list with family members.

SCIENCE JOURNAL

Have students write about their experiences during a major weather event, such as a thunderstorm, hurricane, tornado, blizzard, flood, or heat wave.

ONLINE CONNECTION

Both NASA and NOAA provide vast quantities of information about clouds, weather, and storms at the following sites:

http://asd-www.larc.nasa.gov/SCOOL/

http://www.nssl.noaa.gov/edu

Lesson 3 Review Answers

1. A cold front forces up warm air, forming thunderheads. **2.** an electric current passing between negative and positive charges **3.** a powerful wind storm with a whirling, funnel-shaped cloud and very low pressure **4.** The warm, moist air over equatorial ocean water collects and begins to spin. **5.** Land causes a hurricane to lose its force because it removes the storm from the heat and moisture of the ocean and causes friction, which slows the storm winds.

Portfolio Assessment

Sample items include:
• Objective sentences from Teaching the Lesson
• Lesson 3 Review answers

Write your answers to these questions on a sheet of paper.

1. How does a thunderstorm form?

2. What is lightning?

3. What is a tornado?

4. Under what conditions does a hurricane form?

5. What causes a hurricane to lose its force?

Technology Note

Weather satellites allow meteorologists to see weather patterns that can't be observed from the ground. There are two basic types of weather satellites. One type, the polar-orbiting satellite, circles the earth. The first weather satellite sent into space was a polar-orbiting satellite. It was launched in 1960. It circled the earth every 2 hours at about 1,000 kilometers above the earth's surface. It has since been replaced by more complex polar-orbiting satellites.

The other type of weather satellite is the geostationary satellite. It stays in a fixed position about 36,000 kilometers above the equator. The most well-known satellites of this type are the geosynchronous operational environmental satellites (GOES). The first one was launched in 1975. Several more have been launched since. These satellites take pictures of the earth's atmosphere and measure weather conditions in space. They even help with search and rescue operations.

The National Weather Service uses GOES images to monitor severe storms and hurricanes. GOES technology also allows local meteorologists to take pictures of small areas of weather.

Name _____ Date _____ Period _____ Workbook Activity 41 — Chapter 10, Lesson 3

Storms

Directions: Write the word from the Word Bank that best completes each sentence. Then find and circle each word in the puzzle below.

1. A whirling, funnel-shaped cloud formed in a thunderstorm is a(n) _____

2. Large, dark clouds that produce heavy rain are _____

3. A(n) _____ occurs when warm air is forced up by a cold front.

4. _____ forms in clouds when electrical current passes between negative and positive charges.

5. When lightning occurs, _____ is the sound made by the suddenly expanding, heated air.

6. Tornadoes are likely to occur over flat areas such as _____

7. A(n) _____ is the largest kind of storm.

8. You see lightning _____ you hear thunder.

9. Air pressure in a tornado is very _____

10. When a hurricane moves inland, it drops a lot of _____

11. A force that slows hurricanes on land is _____

12. As it moves over land, a hurricane loses force because it has no source of heat and _____

13. The calm area at the center of a hurricane is called the _____

14. _____ are caused by rapid changes in the movement of air masses.

15. Hurricanes form in the tropics near the _____

Word Bank
before
equator
eye
friction
hurricane
lightning
low
moisture
prairies
rain
storms
thunder
thunderheads
thunderstorm
tornado

```
A B S E I R I A R P Q W T I
C E V Z Y D B P U T Y E H N
T N B S T E E C K B O G U D
H A F R B L F U D P C N N T
U K R A I N O W A E J I D A
N Y I O T C R Y T S H N E R
D E C A U K E Q L V U T R P
E U T R T H U N D E R H S N
R V I Y O V W R J U R G T W
H K O S R P O S A O I I O B
E S N L N T Q M B W C L R E
A T B O A E C R Y D A P M O
D C D U D N J O T J N C V C
S W Q M O I S T U R E K A W
N E O V D R E S K R A U Y S
```

Earth Science

Workbook Activity 41

Objectives

After reading this lesson, you should be able to

◆ compare and contrast the three world climate zones.

◆ identify factors that affect climate.

Climate

Average weather of a region over a long period of time

What kind of weather do people have on the other side of the world? It may be similar to yours. Scientists have identified global patterns in weather.

Climate Zones

Like weather, **climate** describes conditions of the atmosphere. Weather is the state of the atmosphere at a given time and place. Climate is the average weather of a region over a long period of time. A region's climate depends on two kinds of measurements:

◆ The average temperature pattern during a year
◆ The average amount of precipitation in a year

The climates of the world are divided into three major groups, called climate zones. Find each zone on the map. Refer to this map as you learn more about these zones.

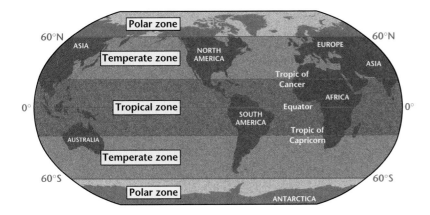

Chapter 10 Lesson 4

Overview This lesson explains climate zones and regions and the factors that influence climate.

Objectives

■ To compare and contrast the three world climate zones

■ To identify factors that affect climate

Student Pages 247–250

Teacher's Resource Library

Workbook Activity 42

Alternative Workbook Activity 42

Vocabulary

climate

1 Warm-Up Activity

In a darkened room, shine one flashlight on the ceiling at a 90° angle. Shine an identical flashlight on the ceiling at approximately a 45° angle. Ask students to compare the brightness and concentration of the two spots of light. Explain that the angle at which sunlight hits a region of the earth is the major cause of the region's climate. Point out that students will be learning about this and other factors that determine climate.

2 Teaching the Lesson

As they read about each climate zone, students can make a drawing to show the environment they would expect to find there. After reading, have students use their drawings to explain the differences between climate zones.

Shine a flashlight on a globe so that light falls directly on the equator. Have students observe and describe the angle of light reaching the temperate and polar zones. Reinforce the concept that direct light produces more heat.

Review the descriptions of the three climate zones. Ask students to identify the climate zone in which they live. Then read aloud the descriptions of the climate regions within that zone. Ask students to identify their climate region.

Continued on page 248

Continued from page 247

Write these dates on the board: *January 1, April 1, July 1, October 1.* Have groups of students write a description of the type of clothing they would probably wear on each date. After groups share their descriptions, assign each group an area in a different climate zone. Have the groups decide how the clothing worn in that area would differ from the clothing they described earlier.

 3 Reinforce and Extend

SCIENCE INTEGRATION

 Biology

Explain that plants and animals living in various regions are adapted for the climate. Ask students to use encyclopedias or books about plants and animals to find out how living things survive in different climates. They can write a report or draw pictures to explain the information they find.

IN THE ENVIRONMENT

 Have several interested students explore the effects of El Niño on climate. (Next to the seasons, El Niño is the biggest factor affecting human activity. A warming of Pacific waters, it affects ocean currents, the distribution of heat in the ocean, and circulation and rainfall patterns in the tropical atmosphere. Secondary effects include droughts in some regions (Africa, Indonesia, Australia, Brazil) and floods in others (California, South America). Droughts, in turn, often lead to fires that destroy vast tracts of tropical forest and may require the evacuation of many people.) Ask students to explain some of these effects to the class, using pictures if possible.

The mild climates in areas near large bodies of water are called marine climates. The more extreme climates in areas far from water are called continental climates.

Polar climates are marked by generally cold temperatures. There is little precipitation in these climates, and it is usually in the form of snow. The temperatures are so low that very little snow melts. Polar climates generally extend from the poles to about 60° latitude. They also exist at very high elevations on mountains.

Temperate climates generally extend from 60°N latitude to the tropic of Cancer and from 60°S latitude to the tropic of Capricorn. These climates feature the greatest changes in weather. There are four different weather seasons in these climates, where winters are cold and summers are warm.

Tropical climates occur near the equator between the tropic of Capricorn and the tropic of Cancer. These climates are marked by the highest average temperatures on the earth. Tropical climates are also the most humid regions. There is little variation in the kind of weather from one month to the next.

Each of the three major climate zones is further divided into climate regions. The table on page 249 provides some information about these regions.

Factors That Affect Climate

Why is one climate different from another? The main factor is the angle at which sunlight hits the earth. Because the earth is a sphere, sunlight hits the tropics more directly than areas toward the poles. The more direct sunlight provides warmer temperatures.

Climate is also affected by how high a place is above sea level. The temperatures in a mountain region are cooler than the temperatures in a nearby valley. In general, higher places tend to be cooler. This is why you can find snow-capped mountains near the equator.

The nearness of large bodies of water also affects climate. In general, areas that are close to an ocean or a large lake get more precipitation than areas farther from water. Water heats up and cools off more slowly than land. As a result, areas near large bodies of water have more mild temperatures than areas far from water.

TEACHER ALERT

 A fourth factor in determining climate is the shape of land in a region. For example, in many mountainous regions of North America, air masses move eastward up a slope. As they rise, they cool and release rain or snow. By the time the air masses start down the other side, they have lost most of their moisture. Therefore, the west side of the mountain receives more precipitation; the climate on the east side is drier.

Polar Climates

Ice cap climate

Temperatures below freezing	Precipitation less than 25 centimeters per year	No visible plant life

Tundra climate

Temperatures slightly higher than ice cap	Precipitation less than 25 centimeters per year	Mosses and small shrubs

Subarctic climate

Short summer, cold winter	Precipitation 25–30 centimeters per year	Small pines, spruce, and fir

Temperate Climates

Marine west coast climate

Temperatures generally above freezing	Precipitation 50–76 centimeters per year	Thick evergreen forests

Deserts and steppes

Warm to hot summer, cold winter	Precipitation less than 25 centimeters per year	Cactus in deserts, grasses in steppes

Mediterranean climate

Warm summer, mild and wet winter	Precipitation 25 centimeters per year	Scattered trees, low shrubs

Humid subtropical climate

Warm and humid summer, mild winter	Precipitation 76–165 centimeters per year	Heavy plant growth and forests

Humid continental climate

Warm and humid summer, cold winter	Precipitation 76 centimeters per year	Hardwood and softwood forests, grass prairies

Tropical Climates

Tropical rain forest

Always hot and humid	Precipitation 254 centimeters per year	Very thick forests and plant growth

Tropical desert

Dry and relatively hot	Precipitation less than 25 centimeters per year	Almost no plant life

Savannah

Humid and warm summer, dry and cool winter	Precipitation 76–152 centimeters per year	Scattered trees and shrubs, tall grasses

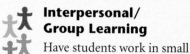

Lesson 4 Review Answers

1. near the earth's poles 2. near the earth's equator 3. the temperate zone 4. Higher places tend to be cooler. 5. Areas near water have more precipitation and milder temperatures than those far from water.

Science in Your Life

Ask students to describe the average spring, summer, fall, and winter day for your region. Have them locate 60°N latitude, the tropic of Cancer, 60°S latitude, and the tropic of Capricorn on a globe or world map. Have them identify the three climate zones and their boundaries. Have volunteers read aloud the feature on page 250. Students can identify their climate zone and locate it on the globe or world map.

Discuss the severe storms your region has experienced in recent years. Invite students to describe what they did to prepare for a storm or how they stayed safe until it passed. If possible, display a disaster preparedness kit. The Red Cross may be able to loan one or provide you with a list of items such a kit should contain for your area.

Portfolio Assessment

Sample items include:
• Drawings from Teaching the Lesson
• Lesson 4 Review answers

Lesson 4 R E V I E W

Write your answers to these questions on a sheet of paper.

1. Where do polar climates occur?

2. Where do tropical climates occur?

3. Which climate zone has warm summers and cold winters?

4. How does height above sea level affect climate?

5. What effect does a large body of water have on climate?

Science in Your Life

Your Climate Zone

Now that you have learned about climate zones, identify the zone you live in. How would you describe the climate in your zone? If you have friends or family who live in other climate zones, compare your zone with theirs. Do you think you'd rather live in their climate zone?

What kinds of severe weather occur in your climate zone? How would you know if severe weather was predicted for your area? Local newspapers provide important weather information. They may also show radar and satellite images of weather patterns that could affect your area. Radio stations regularly broadcast weather reports.

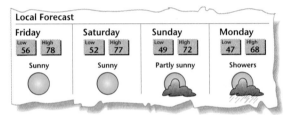

Local Forecast			
Friday	**Saturday**	**Sunday**	**Monday**
Low 56 / High 78	Low 52 / High 77	Low 49 / High 72	Low 47 / High 68
Sunny	Sunny	Partly sunny	Showers

Are you prepared for severe weather? In your class or at home, discuss what you should do in a weather emergency. How can you prepare now for severe weather?

The Federal Emergency Management Agency recommends that you have a disaster supply kit ready in case of a weather emergency. The kit should include water, a first-aid kit, a flashlight, a radio, a few basic tools, extra clothes, canned food, and a can opener.

Name		Date	Period	Workbook Activity 42
				Chapter 10, Lesson 4

World Climates: Terms Review

Directions Write the answer to the question in each box.

What are the three major climate zones from coldest (1) to warmest (3)?	What are three factors that affect climate?
1. _____	4. _____
2. _____	5. _____
3. _____	6. _____

Directions Match each term with its definition. Write the letter of the correct definition on the line.

_____ 7. relative humidity   A state of the atmosphere at a given time and place

_____ 8. hurricane   B amount of water vapor in air compared to the maximum amount of water vapor air can hold

_____ 9. tornado   C section of air with the same temperature and humidity

_____ 10. front   D line on a weather map connecting areas of equal pressure

_____ 11. isobar   E tropical storm with high winds revolving around an eye

_____ 12. high   F powerful wind storm with whirling, funnel-shaped cloud and very low pressure

_____ 13. climate

_____ 14. air pressure   G cold area of high air pressure

_____ 15. weather   H warm area of low air pressure

_____ 16. low   I moving boundary line between two air masses

_____ 17. air mass   J force of air against a unit of area

   K average weather pattern of a region over a long time

Directions Write the weather condition that each instrument measures.

18. anemometer _____

19. psychrometer _____

20. barometer _____

AGS Publishing. Permission is granted to reproduce for classroom use only.   ● Earth Science

Workbook Activity 42

Chapter 10 SUMMARY

- Weather is the state of the atmosphere at a given time and place.

- To study weather, meteorologists gather information about air temperature, air pressure, humidity, wind speed, wind direction, type of precipitation, and amount of precipitation.

- A barometer measures air pressure. A psychrometer measures relative humidity. An anemometer measures wind speed. A wind vane shows wind direction.

- Weather data are collected by using weather balloons, weather satellites, and radar.

- An air mass is a large body of air near the earth's surface. It has the same temperature and humidity throughout.

- Fronts are the moving boundaries of air masses.

- At a warm front, warm air glides up and over cooler air. Steady precipitation often results.

- At a cold front, cold air pushes under warmer air. A short storm often results.

- Data about fronts, air masses, highs, and lows are recorded on weather maps and used to predict weather.

- Storms are severe weather conditions and include thunderstorms, tornadoes, and hurricanes.

- Climate is the average weather of a region over a long period of time.

- The major world climates are divided into three zones: polar, temperate, and tropical.

- Climate is affected by the angle of sunlight, height above sea level, and nearness of large bodies of water.

Science Words

air mass, 239	front, 239	psychrometer, 232	weather, 230
air pressure, 231	high, 240	rain gauge, 234	wind vane, 233
anemometer, 233	humidity, 232	relative	
barometer, 231	hurricane, 245	humidity, 232	
climate, 247	isobar, 240	tornado, 245	
cold front, 239	low, 240	warm front, 239	

Chapter 10 Summary

Have volunteers read aloud each Summary item on page 251. Ask volunteers to explain the meaning of each item. Direct students' attention to the Science Words box on the bottom of page 251. Have them read and review each word and its definition.

Chapter 10 Review

Use the Chapter Review to prepare students for tests and to reteach content from the chapter.

Chapter 10 Mastery Test

The Teacher's Resource Library includes two parallel forms of the Chapter 10 Mastery Test. The difficulty level of the two forms is equivalent. You may wish to use one form as a pretest and the other form as a posttest.

Review Answers
Vocabulary Review

1. hurricane 2. barometer 3. weather
4. air mass 5. tornado 6. anemometer
7. psychrometer 8. climate 9. isobar
10. humidity

Concept Review

11. B 12. A 13. D 14. C 15. B 16. A
17. C 18. D

TEACHER ALERT

In the Chapter Review, the Vocabulary Review activity includes a sample of the chapter's vocabulary terms. The activity will help determine students' understanding of key vocabulary terms and concepts presented in the chapter. Other vocabulary terms used in the chapter are listed below:

air pressure	rain gauge
cold front	relative humidity
front	warm front
high	wind vane
low	

Word Bank
air mass
anemometer
barometer
climate
humidity
hurricane
isobar
psychrometer
tornado
weather

Vocabulary Review

Choose the word or phrase from the Word Bank that best matches each phrase. Write the answer on your paper.

1. tropical storm that forms over an ocean

2. instrument for measuring air pressure

3. state of the atmosphere at a given time and place

4. large section of the atmosphere having the same humidity and temperature throughout

5. storm with a dangerous funnel cloud

6. instrument for measuring wind speed

7. instrument for measuring relative humidity

8. average weather over a long period of time

9. line on a weather map connecting areas of equal air pressure

10. amount of water vapor in the air

Concept Review

Choose the word or phrase that best completes each sentence. Write the letter of the answer on your paper.

11. In an area of low pressure, the _____.
    A air is moving out   C air rotates clockwise
    B temperature is warm   D skies are sunny

12. The force of the atmosphere against the earth's surface is _____.
    A air pressure   C wind
    B air temperature D precipitation

13. A wind vane shows _____.
    A altitude   C air pressure
    B wind speed D wind direction

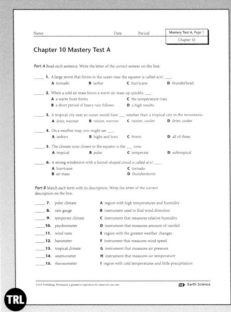
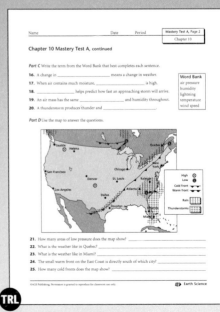

Chapter 10 Mastery Test A

14. Lightning is best described as _____.
  A positive electrical charges
  B a moving thunderhead
  C electric current
  D high pressure

15. A moving boundary between two air masses is called a(n) _____.
  A eye **B** front **C** isobar **D** storm

16. A hurricane forms over a(n) _____.
  A ocean **C** forest
  B prairie **D** mountain

17. The _____ climate zone has warm summers and cold winters.
  A polar **B** tropical **C** temperate **D** tundra

18. A warm front often brings _____.
  A storm clouds **C** heavy rain
  B cool weather **D** steady rain

Critical Thinking

Write the answer to each of the following questions.

19. Two cities are located in the temperate climate zone. One city is located on the coast at sea level. The other city is located in the mountains, high above sea level. How would you expect the climates of the two cities to be the same and different? Explain your answer.

20. If a high pushes out a low in your area today, what weather changes would you expect?

Test-Taking Tip To prepare for a test, study in short sessions rather than in one long session. During the week before the test, spend time each evening reviewing your notes.

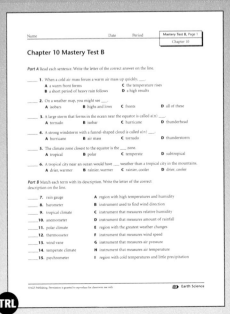

Chapter 10 Mastery Test B

Review Answers
Critical Thinking

19. Both cities would have four seasons, including a cold winter and a warm summer. The city near the ocean would get more precipitation and have more moderate high and low temperatures; the city in the mountains would receive less precipitation and have more extreme cold temperatures in winter. **20.** increase in barometric pressure, cooling temperatures, ending of precipitation, clearing skies, and change of wind direction

ALTERNATIVE ASSESSMENT

Alternative Assessment items correlate to the student Goals for Learning at the beginning of this chapter.

■ Ask students to describe the weather conditions outside today as a meteorologist would. Provide pictures of different weather conditions and repeat the activity.

■ Display pictures of instruments that measure weather conditions. Write the terms *thermometer, barometer, psychrometer, anemometer, wind vane,* and *rain gauge* on index cards. Have students label the instruments appropriately. Read aloud the function of each instrument and have students identify the matching picture and name.

■ Ask students to draw two diagrams showing a warm front and a cold front.

■ Display a large regional map on which you have drawn weather symbols. Have students explain what each symbol means and the weather associated with it.

■ Give students a chart with these column headings: *Thunderstorm, Tornado, Hurricane.* Have them write three facts about each of these storms.

■ Make a globe available. Ask students to point out the regions of the earth that experience a polar climate, a temperate climate, and a tropical climate. Have them describe the weather conditions found in each kind of climate.

Planning Guide
The Earth's Water

		Student Pages	Vocabulary	Lesson Review
Lesson 1	The Water Cycle	256–258	✔	✔
Lesson 2	Sources of Fresh Water	259–266	✔	✔
Lesson 3	Oceans	267–274	✔	✔

Chapter Activities

Student Text
Science Center
Teacher's Resource Library
Community Connection 11: Local Water
   Resources

Assessment Options

Student Text
Chapter 11 Review

Teacher's Resource Library
Chapter 11 Mastery Tests A and B

Achievements in Science	Science at Work	Science in Your Life	Investigation	Science Myth	Note	Technology Note	Did You Know	Science Integration	Science Journal	Cross-Curricular Connection	Online Connection	Teacher Alert	Applications (Home, Career, Community, Global, Environment)	Auditory/Verbal	Body/Kinesthetic	Interpersonal/Group Learning	Logical/Mathematical	Visual/Spatial	LEP/ESL	Workbook Activities	Alternative Workbook Activities	Lab Manual	Resource File	Self-Study Guide
		258			✔		257	257	257	258									257	43	43	41	24	✔
	264		265			✔	262		262			262	261, 262, 263	261		261	263			44	44	42	25	✔
272			273	271	✔		267	270	271	269	271	270	271		270			269		45	45	43, 44	26	✔

Pronunciation Key

a	hat	e	let	ī	ice	ô	order
ā	age	ē	equal	o	hot	oi	oil
ä	far	ėr	term	ō	open	ou	out
â	care	i	it	ȯ	saw	u	cup

ù	put	sh	she
ü	rule	th	thin
ch	child	ᵀH	then
ng	long	zh	measure

ə { a in about, e in taken, i in pencil, o in lemon, u in circus }

Alternative Workbook Activities

The Teacher's Resource Library (TRL) contains a set of lower-level worksheets called Alternative Workbook Activities. These worksheets cover the same content as the regular Workbook Activities but are written at a second-grade reading level.

Skill Track Software

Use the Skill Track Software for Earth Science for additional reinforcement of this chapter. The software program allows students using AGS textbooks to be assessed for mastery of each chapter and lesson of the textbook. Students access the software on an individual basis and are assessed with multiple-choice items.

Chapter 11:
The Earth's Water
pages 254–277

Lessons

1. **The Water Cycle** pages 256–258

2. **Sources of Fresh Water**
   pages 259–266

Investigation 11-1 pages 265–266

3. **Oceans** pages 267–274

Investigation 11-2 pages 273–274

Chapter 11 Summary page 275

Chapter 11 Review pages 276–277

Skill Track Software
for Earth Science

Teacher's Resource Library

Workbook Activities 43–45

Alternative Workbook Activities
43–45

Lab Manual 41–44

Community Connection 11

Resource File 24–26

Chapter 11 Self-Study Guide

Chapter 11 Mastery Tests A and B

(Answer Keys for the Teacher's
Resource Library begin on page 400
of the Teacher's Edition. The
Materials List for the Lab Manual
activities begins on page 415.)

Science Center

Have students cut out magazine or
newspaper pictures that show examples
of the earth's water. As each picture is
placed on a display, have students write
on an index card a description of what is
shown in the picture. For example, they
should indicate if the picture shows an
ocean, a lake, a river, clouds, and so on.
They should also indicate whether the
water is fresh water or salt water. Ask
students to group the pictures to form a
model of the water cycle, using large
cutout arrows.

Community Connection 11

11 The Earth's Water

E arth is called the water planet for a good reason. More than 70 percent of the earth's surface is covered with water. Water is also in the atmosphere and under the ground. All of this water is continuously moving. For example, ocean water evaporates into the air. Clouds gather and carry this moisture. Eventually, water droplets in clouds fall back to the earth. In Chapter 11, you will learn how water moves and changes. You will also learn about different bodies of water, such as rivers, lakes, and oceans.

Organize Your Thoughts

```
              Water cycle
         ┌──────────┴──────────┐
     Locations              Processes
    Atmosphere             Evaporation
    Groundwater            Condensation
  Rivers and lakes         Precipitation
      Oceans                  Runoff
```

Goals for Learning

◆ To explain the water cycle

◆ To compare fresh water and salt water

◆ To explain the water table

◆ To describe the sources and movement of fresh water

◆ To describe ocean water, waves, currents, and the ocean floor

255

Introducing the Chapter

Have a volunteer read the introductory paragraph on page 255. Review with students the Organize Your Thoughts chart. Tell them that in this chapter they will learn about the locations of the earth's water and the processes that move water from one location to another.

Have students work in small groups. Ask each group to draw three columns on a sheet of paper and label them *I Definitely Know*, *I Think I Know*, and *I Would Like to Know*. Write the three lesson titles on the board. Ask students to think about the three topics and write as many statements as possible in each column. After about 10 minutes, ask the groups to read aloud the statements they recorded. As each group reads its statements, write them in a master list. Display the list in the classroom. As students progress through the chapter, have them put check marks next to statements that are verified and cross out or revise statements that are incorrect.

Notes and Technology Notes

Ask volunteers to read the notes that appear in the margins throughout the chapter. Then discuss them with the class.

TEACHER'S RESOURCE

The AGS Teaching Strategies in Science Transparencies may be used with this chapter. The transparencies add an interactive dimension to expand and enhance the *Earth Science* program content.

CAREER INTEREST INVENTORY

The AGS Harrington-O'Shea Career Decision-Making System-Revised (CDM) may be used with this chapter. Students can use the CDM to explore their interests and identify careers. The CDM defines career areas that are indicated by students' responses on the inventory.

Chapter 11: The Earth's Water

Goal 11.1 To explain the water cycle

Date	Assignment	Score
	1. Read pages 255–257.	
	2. Complete the Lesson 1 Review on page 258.	
	3. Complete Workbook Activity 43.	

Comments:

Goal 11.2 To compare fresh water and salt water

Date	Assignment	Score
	4. Review page 257.	

Comments:

Goal 11.3 To explain the water table

Date	Assignment	Score
	5. Read page 259.	

Comments:

Chapter 11: The Earth's Water, continued

Goal 11.4 To describe the sources and movement of fresh water

Date	Assignment	Score
	6. Read pages 259–263.	
	7. Complete the Lesson 2 Review on page 264.	
	8. Complete Workbook Activity 44.	
	9. Complete Investigation 11-1 on pages 265–266.	

Comments:

Goal 11.5 To describe ocean water, waves, currents, and the ocean floor

Date	Assignment	Score
	10. Read pages 267–271.	
	11. Complete the Lesson 3 Review on page 272.	
	12. Complete Workbook Activity 45.	
	13. Complete Investigation 11-2 on pages 273–274.	
	14. Read the Chapter 11 Summary on page 275.	
	15. Complete the Chapter 11 Review on pages 276–277.	

Comments:

Student's Signature _____ Date _____

Instructor's Signature _____ Date _____

Chapter 11 Self-Study Guide

Lesson at a Glance

Chapter 11 Lesson 1

Overview In this lesson, students learn how water cycles from the earth's surface to the atmosphere and back. They also compare fresh water and salt water.

Objectives

- To describe the movement of water through the water cycle
- To identify how water runs off land
- To compare fresh water and salt water

Student Pages 256–258

Teacher's Resource Library **TRL**

Workbook Activity 43

Alternative Workbook Activity 43

Lab Manual 41

Resource File 24

....

Vocabulary

groundwater   **water cycle**
runoff

....

Science Background

Most of the rain and snow that falls on land comes from water that evaporates from the oceans. The moist air above the oceans cools over the land, forming clouds. Precipitation falls from these clouds, filling ponds, lakes, and rivers. Water from the rivers eventually reaches the oceans, where the cycle repeats. Some areas near the Great Lakes receive rain or snow that comes from water that evaporated from these lakes. People who live in these areas are familiar with *lake-effect snow,* produced when moist air over a lake is blown toward land during winter months.

 1 Warm-Up Activity

Use 100 milliliters of colored water to represent the earth's water. Label five jars *Oceans, Glaciers, Groundwater, Lakes and Rivers,* and *Atmosphere.* Tell students that 1 milliliter represents 1 percent of the earth's water supply. With an eyedropper, put 3 drops into the *Groundwater* jar, 2 drops into the *Lakes and Rivers* jar, and 1

Objectives

After reading this lesson, you should be able to

- describe the movement of water through the water cycle.
- identify how water runs off land.
- compare fresh water and salt water.

Water is everywhere. Almost all of the earth's water is in the oceans. But it is also in rivers and lakes, under the ground, in the air, and even in your own body.

Earth's water is in continuous motion. It moves from the atmosphere to the earth's surface and back to the atmosphere. This movement of water is called the **water cycle**. Study the diagram below and notice the different forms that water takes as it goes through a complete cycle.

The water cycle is powered by the sun. Heat from the sun evaporates surface water, and the water vapor rises into the atmosphere. The rising water vapor cools and condenses into clouds. Water droplets or ice crystals in the clouds grow larger, then fall to the earth as precipitation.

Water cycle

Movement of water between the atmosphere and the earth's surface

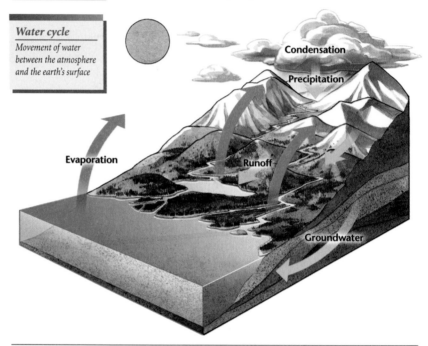

drop into the *Atmosphere* jar. Pour 2 milliliters of water into the *Glaciers* jar. Pour the rest (97 milliliters) of the water into the *Oceans* jar. Ask students from which of these sources we get most of our drinking water. (*groundwater, lakes and rivers*) Ask why the most abundant water source is not suitable for drinking. (*Ocean water is too salty.*)

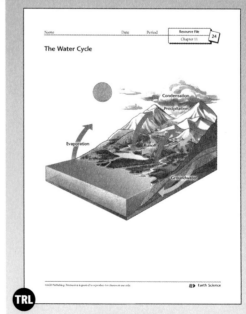

Resource File 24

Groundwater
Water that sinks into the ground

Runoff
Water that runs over the earth's surface and flows into streams

As water travels through the water cycle, it carries dissolved gases and minerals. For example, lake and ocean water contains dissolved oxygen gas. That is what fish "breathe" through their gills.

Did You Know?

The Dead Sea is a saltwater lake in the Middle East. It is almost nine times saltier than any ocean. Nothing lives in the Dead Sea except bacteria.

What happens after precipitation falls? Some of it sinks into the ground and becomes **groundwater**. This water collects in the spaces between rocks and moves slowly underground. Precipitation that does not sink into the ground is called surface water. Some surface water evaporates. But most of it becomes **runoff**—surface water that flows over the land and into streams and rivers.

Why doesn't all precipitation sink into the ground? There are three main reasons.

1. The ground may be saturated, or completely soaked, and unable to hold any more water. It is like pouring water on a sponge. Eventually, the sponge fills and water runs off it.

2. On a slope, the water may run off too quickly to sink in.

3. The ground may not have enough vegetation to stop the water from flowing elsewhere. Plants and their roots soak up water.

Eventually, surface water evaporates or rivers carry it to the oceans. If you have ever tasted ocean water, you know it is much too salty to drink. Salt water also cannot be used for farms and industry. Salt water kills most land plants and ruins machinery. In Lesson 3, you will learn more about the properties of salt water.

Like the water on land, ocean water evaporates and moves back into the atmosphere. Dissolved salts are left behind, however. So the water that condenses in the atmosphere and falls onto the land contains no salt. It is fresh water.

*The Earth's Water   Chapter 11   **257***

---

2 Teaching the Lesson

Ask students to make a chart with two columns, one labeled *Cause* and the other *Effect*. As they read the lesson, ask them to find examples of cause-and-effect relationships. Give students a cause, such as *heat from the sun*. Tell them to keep in mind that different causes can produce the same effect, and that the same cause can lead to different effects.

Place a dry sponge on one end of a cookie sheet. Elevate that end of the cookie sheet with two or three books. Explain that the sponge represents the ground. Pour water, a little at a time, onto the sponge. Ask students to predict what will happen when the sponge is full of water. *(The water will run off the sponge and down the cookie sheet.)* Ask what source of water you modeled. *(runoff)*

Allow students to guide you as you draw a diagram of the water cycle on the board. Start with some waves for ocean water. Ask: How does ocean water move into the atmosphere? *(Heat from the sun causes it to evaporate.)* How does water get from the atmosphere onto the earth's surface? *(Water vapor condenses, forms clouds, and falls as precipitation.)* Where does the water go when it reaches the earth's surface? *(Some soaks in to become groundwater, some evaporates, and some becomes runoff.)* Stress that some precipitation falls back into the ocean.

3 Reinforce and Extend

LEARNING STYLES

LEP/ESL
Fill a wide-mouth jar halfway with warm water. Cover it with plastic wrap, secured with a rubber band. Tell students that this jar is a model of the water cycle. Set the jar in a warm, sunny place. Allow the jar to sit for a day or two. Students should observe that water condenses on the plastic wrap. Explain that this water evaporated from the "ocean" into the "atmosphere." When enough water vapor condenses on the plastic wrap as "clouds," it will drip as "precipitation." Stress that the amount of water in the water cycle does not change; it just moves from place to place.

Did You Know?

Have a volunteer read aloud the Did You Know? feature on page 257. Explain that, unlike most lakes, the Dead Sea has no outlet, so its water can't escape via a river or moving groundwater. Instead, the water that falls or drains into the Dead Sea escapes only by evaporating in the hot sun, leaving behind more and more salt. The Dead Sea's shores are covered with white salt crystals.

SCIENCE JOURNAL

Ask students to imagine that they are a drop of water. Have them write a short story of their journey through the water cycle.

SCIENCE INTEGRATION

Biology
Have students set up covered terrariums so that they can observe the water cycle.

*The Earth's Water   Chapter 11   **257***

Lesson 1 Review Answers

1. Ocean water moves to the atmosphere by evaporation, and water vapor in the atmosphere condenses and falls to the earth's surface as precipitation. **2.** Groundwater is precipitation that sinks into the ground. Surface water is precipitation that does not sink into the ground. **3.** Runoff is surface water that runs over the land and flows into streams instead of sinking into the ground or evaporating. **4.** Sometimes the ground is saturated and can hold no more water; water on a slope may run off before it can sink in; the ground may not have plant roots that soak up and hold the water. **5.** Salt water is too salty to drink or to use in farming or industry. Fresh water does not contain salt and is used for drinking, watering plants, and operating machinery.

Science in Your Life

Before reading the feature, have students write estimates of how much water is used for a shower, a load of laundry, and a load of dishes. Then have volunteers read aloud the feature on page 258. Discuss ways to save water for several of the tasks. For example, instead of washing a half load of dishes or laundry, wait until there is a full load. Help students recognize that a 10-minute shower uses more water than a bath does. Have students make a water budget as described. Discuss their budget decisions.

Cross-Curricular Connection

Mathematics

Have students refer to the chart of water uses on page 258. Ask them to estimate how much water one person uses on an average day. Then have them calculate how much water is used per day by the entire class, by the school's student body, and by the community.

Portfolio Assessment

Sample items include:
- Cause-and-effect chart from Teaching the Lesson
- Lesson 1 Review answers

Lesson 1 REVIEW

Write your answers to these questions on a sheet of paper.

1. How does water move between the atmosphere, the land, and bodies of water?

2. What is the difference between groundwater and surface water?

3. What is runoff?

4. Why doesn't all precipitation soak into the ground?

5. How are salt water and fresh water different?

Science in Your Life

Your Water Budget

How much water do you use? Probably more than you think. The table lists the average amount of water used for different tasks. Estimate how much water you have used so far today. Think about ways to cut down on the water you use. Then make a water budget by planning the amount of water you will "spend" each week.

Water Uses

Task	Average Amount Used
drinking water	2 liters per person per day
flushing a toilet	11 to 19 liters per flush
taking a shower	19 liters per minute
taking a bath	133 to 152 liters per bath
running a dishwasher	38 to 57 liters per load
doing laundry	72 to 171 liters per load
washing hands	1 liter
brushing teeth	4 liters
washing a car	76 to 114 liters
watering a lawn	912 liters per half hour

Where does used water go? If your home is connected to a sewer system, the water you use drains into a sewer. Sewer pipes carry this water to a treatment plant, where it is cleaned and filtered.

258 *Chapter 11 The Earth's Water*

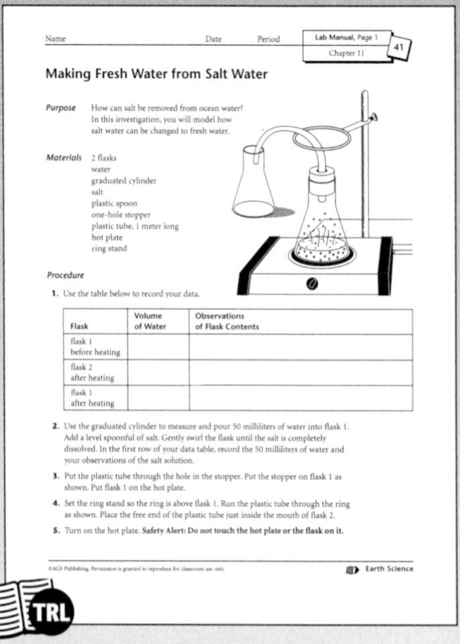
Name Date Period | Lab Manual, Page 1 | Chapter 11 | 41

Making Fresh Water from Salt Water

Purpose How can salt be removed from ocean water? In this investigation, you will model how salt water can be changed to fresh water.

Materials 2 flasks, water, graduated cylinder, salt, plastic spoon, one-hole stopper, plastic tube, 1 meter long, hot plate, ring stand

Procedure

1. Use the table below to record your data.

Flask	Volume of Water	Observations of Flask Contents
flask 1 before heating		
flask 2 after heating		
flask 1 after heating		

2. Use the graduated cylinder to measure and pour 50 milliliters of water into flask 1. Add a level spoonful of salt. Gently swirl the flask until the salt is completely dissolved. In the first row of your data table, record the 50 milliliters of water and your observations of the salt solution.
3. Put the plastic tube through the hole in the stopper. Put the stopper on flask 1 as shown. Put flask 1 on the hot plate.
4. Set the ring stand so the ring is above flask 1. Run the plastic tube through the ring as shown. Place the free end of the plastic tube just inside the mouth of flask 2.
5. Turn on the hot plate. **Safety Alert: Do not touch the hot plate or the flask on it.**

©AGS Publishing. Permission is granted to reproduce for classroom use only. Earth Science

TRL Lab Manual 41, pages 1–2

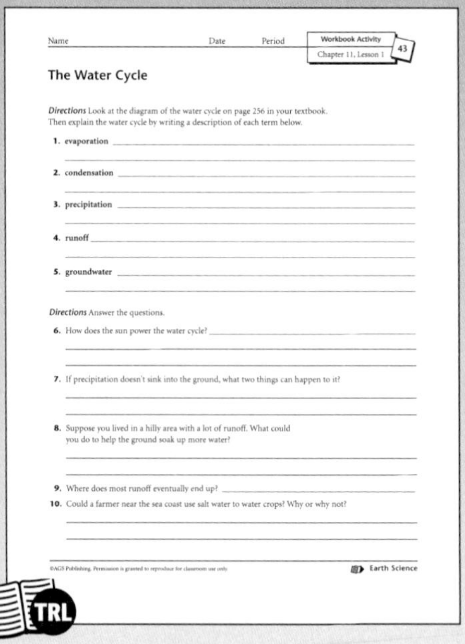
Name Date Period | Workbook Activity | Chapter 11, Lesson 1 | 43

The Water Cycle

Directions Look at the diagram of the water cycle on page 256 in your textbook. Then explain the water cycle by writing a description of each term below.

1. **evaporation** ______
2. **condensation** ______
3. **precipitation** ______
4. **runoff** ______
5. **groundwater** ______

Directions Answer the questions.

6. How does the sun power the water cycle? ______
7. If precipitation doesn't sink into the ground, what two things can happen to it?
8. Suppose you lived in a hilly area with a lot of runoff. What could you do to help the ground soak up more water?
9. Where does most runoff eventually end up? ______
10. Could a farmer near the sea coast use salt water to water crops? Why or why not?

©AGS Publishing. Permission is granted to reproduce for classroom use only. Earth Science

TRL Workbook Activity 43

Objectives

After reading this lesson, you should be able to

◆ explain how groundwater moves and forms the water table.

◆ describe springs, geysers, and caves.

◆ describe how runoff creates rivers, drainage basins, and lakes.

◆ identify three purposes of reservoirs.

Porous

Containing many spaces through which air and water can move

Water table

Top of the groundwater layer

Fresh water is an important resource. Think of the many ways you use it every day, such as for drinking, washing, and cooking. Farms and industry, however, use 90 percent of the fresh water consumed in the United States. Fresh water can be found in many places, both above and below the ground.

Groundwater

Groundwater starts as precipitation or runoff that soaks into the earth. The water can sink into the ground because most soil is **porous**, or has spaces between its particles. Loose soil, such as sandy soil or soil with a lot of decayed plant material, is very porous. The rocks beneath the soil may also be porous. Water trickles around broken rock pieces and through cracks.

The diagram shows what happens as water continues downward. Eventually, water comes to a solid rock layer through which it cannot move. Groundwater collects on top of the rock layer, filling the spaces above it. The top of this wet earth layer is the **water table**. Find the water table in the diagram. If you drill a well down past the water table, water flows into the well and can be pumped to the surface. About half the drinking water in the United States comes from groundwater.

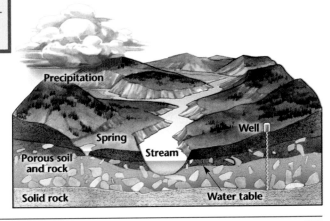

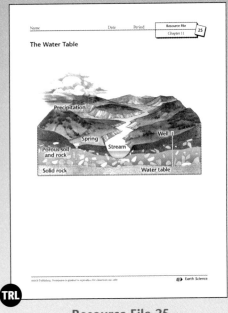

Resource File 25

Chapter 11 Lesson 2

Overview In this lesson, students learn how groundwater moves, creating the water table, springs, geysers, caves, and sinkholes. Students also explore these sources of fresh water: rivers, drainage basins, lakes, and reservoirs.

Objectives

■ To explain how groundwater moves and forms the water table

■ To describe springs, geysers, and caves

■ To describe how runoff creates rivers, drainage basins, and lakes

■ To identify three purposes of reservoirs

Student Pages 259–266

Teacher's Resource Library

Workbook Activity 44

Alternative Workbook Activity 44

Lab Manual 42

Resource File 25

Vocabulary

divide	sinkhole
drainage basin	spring
geyser	tributary
porous	water table
reservoir	

Science Background

A river system consists of a main valley and all its tributaries. Because of gravity, streams and rivers always flow downhill. A river's gradient describes how much the water drops vertically over a given distance. Sometimes the gradient is very small. For example, over much of its course, the Amazon River has a fall of only 0.3 centimeters per kilometer. Most streams and rivers have much higher gradients, ranging from several centimeters to more than a meter per kilometer.

1 Warm-Up Activity

Display a large regional map. Have students identify rivers, lakes, oceans, and other bodies of water. Ask them to tell which are sources of fresh water.

2 Teaching the Lesson

This lesson contains a large number of vocabulary words. As students come to each vocabulary word in the text, have them define the term in their own words.

Discuss places where students have seen wells. Students living in rural areas who get their water from a well may be able to explain how deep their well is and how it works.

Point out to students that geysers erupt only periodically because time is needed for water to gather in the pockets below the geyser and boil.

Students may be familiar with ponds in your area. Explain that ponds are smaller than most lakes. The areas of most ponds are only a few acres to less than an acre. Plants often grow in a pond because it is shallow enough for sunlight to reach the bottom.

Explain that some reservoirs are hydroelectric power plants. These plants generate electricity by using water power to turn devices called turbines. Make a model of a turbine using a cylindrical oatmeal box and cover. In the cover and bottom, cut two holes large enough to fit a dowel rod. Then cut six evenly spaced square flaps in a band around the middle of the cylinder so that the attached side of each flap runs the long way down the box. Bend the flaps open. Put the dowel through the holes. Holding the ends of the dowel, turn the box on its side and position it in a sink so that a stream of running water strikes the flaps. The turbine will spin. Explain to students that this demonstrates how water can be used to power a generator.

Spring
Place where groundwater flows naturally out of the ground

Geyser
Place where hot groundwater and steam blast into the air

Sinkhole
Funnel-shaped depression that results when the roof of a cave collapses

Springs, Geysers, and Caves

The water under the ground is moving. Notice in the diagram on page 259 what happens when the water table reaches the surface on a hillside. Groundwater flows out of the ground as a natural **spring**.

Certain springs, called **geysers**, shoot water and steam into the air. Geysers occur where groundwater lies close to hot rock or magma. Pockets of groundwater are heated and turned to steam. The steam rises, pushing the hot water above it. The steam and water erupt as a geyser. Geysers occur in Wyoming, New Zealand, and Iceland. The eruptions of some geysers are predictable. Castle Geyser, below left, erupts twice a day.

Moving groundwater creates some other unusual features. For example, groundwater seeping through cracks in limestone may dissolve the rock and form caves. Some caves are barely large enough to crawl through. Others are immense.

The photo below right shows what happens when the roof of a cave collapses. A funnel-shaped **sinkhole** forms. Sinkholes may fill with groundwater and rain to become ponds.

Castle Geyser in Yellowstone National Park, Wyoming, blasts water for 20 minutes, then steam for another 30 minutes.

In 1981, this sinkhole formed in one day. The city of Winter Park, Florida, made it into a lake.

Rivers and Drainage Basins

Tributary

River that joins another river of equal or greater size

Drainage basin

Land area that is drained by a river and its tributaries

Divide

Ridge that separates drainage basins

Much of the fresh water above ground flows as rivers. Rivers begin as runoff that moves over the land, carving small paths in the ground. These paths get wider and deeper as water continues to flow through them. The paths become streams. They always flow downhill because of gravity. The streams join and become rivers. These rivers then join and form even larger rivers. Rivers that join other rivers are called **tributaries**. Notice the rivers on the map below. You can see how water and sediment in the most distant tributaries end up in the main river.

The land area in which runoff drains into a river and its tributaries is a **drainage basin**. The map shows five drainage basins. The Mississippi-Missouri River basin covers about 40 percent of the United States. Notice how rain that falls in Montana can eventually reach the Gulf of Mexico. Ridges that separate drainage basins are called **divides**. One divide runs along the Rocky Mountains. Rivers east of this divide flow into the Gulf of Mexico. Rivers west of this divide flow into the Pacific Ocean. What other divide is shown?

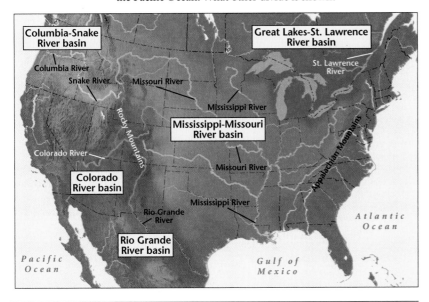

The Earth's Water *Chapter 11* **261**

LEARNING STYLES

 Auditory/Verbal

Read aloud to students passages describing caves from books such as *Tom Sawyer* and *Treasure Island*. Ask students to compare the descriptions. Invite students who have visited caves to share their experiences with their classmates.

LEARNING STYLES

 Interpersonal/ Group Learning

Provide small groups of students with different regional maps, perhaps from an old road atlas. Have students place a sheet of acetate over their map and use a fine-tip marker to trace the tributaries and rivers shown on the map. Students should label the drawing with the name of the region. Display each group's tracing on an overhead projector. Discuss the treelike pattern formed by the joining rivers.

IN THE COMMUNITY

 Have students describe the kinds of lawns and gardens in their community and the water that is used to care for them. For example, if they live in a suburban community with many lawns, how many months of the year do they need to be watered? From what fresh water source does this water come? Does the community limit the amount of water that can be used for lawns? Have students discuss alternatives to grass lawns that need large quantities of water for maintenance.

Rivers are important sources of fresh water. They provide much of the water that people use every day. Yet rivers make up a tiny percent of the earth's water. The diagram shows that only 3 percent of the earth's water is fresh water. Only 1 percent of all fresh water is not frozen or underground. Of this available fresh water, less than 1 percent is in rivers.

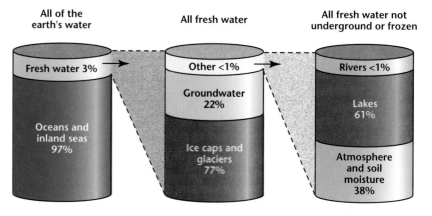

Lakes

Surface water does not always flow along a path. Some of it collects in depressions, or low areas. Water eventually fills the depressions, forming lakes. Even though some of the water evaporates, lakes continue to be fed by precipitation, runoff, springs, and rivers. Many lakes also lose water through outflowing streams or moving groundwater.

Lakes are many different sizes. For example, some lakes in Wisconsin are only a few meters deep. You can hear people talking from the opposite shore. The Great Lakes, on the other hand, are so wide that you cannot see across them. Lake Superior is the largest freshwater lake in the world. Its deepest point is about 400 meters. Many of the lakes in the northern United States and Canada formed when huge sheets of moving ice gouged out depressions. You will learn more about this process in Chapter 12.

Technology Note

Electricity is produced by generators at power plants. Most power plants burn coal or another fuel to run the generators. But hydroelectric power plants or dams use water power. About 10 percent of U.S. electricity comes from hydroelectric dams. Canada, the United States, and Brazil are the top hydroelectric power producers in the world.

Reservoirs

Many cities store large supplies of fresh water in artificial lakes called **reservoirs**. Reservoirs are made by constructing dams along rivers. As you can see in the photo below, water backs up behind the dam, turning part of the river into a lake. Reservoirs serve several purposes, as described below.

Reservoirs store water for home use, farming, and industry. This water can be piped to dry areas. Much of southern California's water, for example, comes through a canal from Lake Havasu. This lake is actually a reservoir behind Parker Dam on the Colorado River between California and Arizona.

Reservoirs control flooding. During periods of heavy rain and runoff, a reservoir may fill up. This water can be released slowly and safely downstream through gates in the dam.

Reservoirs produce electricity. In a hydroelectric dam, the water moves through generators near the bottom of the dam. The rushing water turns the blades of a turbine, which spins a magnet. When the magnet spins through loops of wire, electricity is produced.

This California reservoir was built because of unreliable rains and occasional floods. Besides supplying water, it produces electricity.

Lesson 2 Review Answers

1. the top of a groundwater layer 2. A sinkhole forms when the roof of a cave collapses. 3. The runoff flows as a stream into a tributary. This tributary joins with other tributaries, which eventually flow into a main river. This river carries the water to the ocean. 4. Lakes lose water through evaporation, outflowing streams, or moving groundwater. They gain water from precipitation, runoff, springs, and rivers. 5. They store water for later use, help control flooding, and produce electricity.

Science at Work

Have volunteers take turns reading aloud the feature on page 264. Point out that people have been harnessing water for power since ancient Roman times. Water power became especially important during the Industrial Revolution. Have interested students find out more about ways water power has been used through history and present one method in a diagram.

Portfolio Assessment

Sample items include:
• Definitions from Teaching the Lesson
• Lesson 2 Review answers

Write your answers to these questions on a sheet of paper.

1. What is a water table?

2. How does a sinkhole form?

3. How can runoff on a mountain end up in an ocean 2,000 kilometers away?

4. How do lakes gain and lose water?

5. How are reservoirs useful?

▼◄▲▼◄▲▼◄▲▼◄▲▼◄▲▼◄▲▼◄▲▼◄▲▼◄▲▼◄▲▼◄▲▼◄▲▼◄▲▼

Science at Work

Hydroelectric Power Plant Operator

Hydroelectric power plant operators manage an entire plant and supervise many people. They control the water flow in the dam and the machinery that generates electricity. This includes gates, valves, turbines, and generators.

Plant operators adjust the plant's power output to meet changing electricity demands. They check water, voltage, and electricity flows. Plant operators maintain and repair equipment. They prepare reports about equipment or performance.

Hydroelectric power plant operators must have at least a high-school diploma. College-level courses in mechanical or technical fields are helpful. Computer, math, and science skills are important. A good plant operator has mechanical ability, is responsible, and understands equipment and safety procedures.

Plant operators must be willing to work under tiring conditions. Their job requires constant attention. They may spend hours sitting or standing at control stations. They also may maintain buildings, grounds, and access roads.

Name	Date	Period	Workbook Activity
			44
			Chapter 11, Lesson 2

Sources of Fresh Water

Directions Match each term with its description. Write the letter of the correct description on the line.

_____ **1.** divide   **A** forms when the roof of a cave collapses

_____ **2.** drainage basin   **B** top of the groundwater layer

_____ **3.** geyser   **C** river that joins another river

_____ **4.** porous   **D** made by constructing a dam across a river

_____ **5.** reservoir   **E** hot groundwater and steam shooting into the air

_____ **6.** sinkhole   **F** land area drained by a river and its tributaries

_____ **7.** spring   **G** having many spaces for water and air to flow

_____ **8.** tributary   **H** separates two drainage basins

_____ **9.** water table   **I** groundwater flowing naturally out of the ground

Directions Write an answer to each question.

10. What is the water table? _____

11. How does a sinkhole form? _____

12. Name three bodies of fresh water that are above the ground.

13. What percent of the earth's water is fresh water? _____

14. How do lakes gain and lose water? _____

15. What are three purposes of reservoirs? _____

AGS Publishing. Permission is granted to reproduce for classroom use only.   Earth Science

Workbook Activity 44

INVESTIGATION

Exploring Evaporation

Purpose

How does heat affect evaporation? In this investigation, you will discover factors that cause evaporation.

Procedure

1. Copy the data table on your paper.

Time	Uncovered Dish	Covered Dish	Uncovered Dish with Lamp
start			
time of evaporation			

2. Place the petri dishes on a tabletop. Use the dropper to place one drop of water in the center of each dish.

3. Place a cover over one of the dishes.

4. Move one of the uncovered dishes at least 50 centimeters away from the other two. Position the lamp directly over this dish, as shown.

Materials

- 3 plastic petri dishes
- plastic eye dropper
- small container of water
- petri dish cover
- lamp with at least a 60-watt bulb
- clock or stopwatch
- paper towels

The Earth's Water   Chapter 11   **265**

Investigation 11-1

The Purpose portion of the student investigation begins with a question to draw students into the activity. Encourage students to read the investigation steps and formulate their own questions before beginning the investigation. This investigation will take approximately 30 minutes to complete. Students will use these process and thinking skills: making models, observing, making comparisons, and collecting and interpreting data.

Preparation

- Prepare a small cup of water for each student or group.
- Students may use Lab Manual 42 to record their data and answer the questions.

Procedure

- Students can work individually or in small groups. For group work, assign one student to gather equipment. All group members should observe, record results, and clean up when finished.
- Make sure students measure each drop precisely and center it in the dish. Drops should not spread or separate into smaller drops.

SAFETY ALERT

- ◆ Make sure students do not touch the lamp or bulb after it is turned on.
- ◆ Caution students to wipe up any spills immediately.

Continued on page 266

Name _____ Date _____ Period _____   Lab Manual Chapter 11   42

11-1 Exploring Evaporation
Use with Investigation 11-1, pages 265–266

Purpose How does heat affect evaporation? In this investigation, you will discover factors that cause evaporation.

Time	Uncovered Dish	Covered Dish	Uncovered Dish with Lamp
start			
time of evaporation			

Questions and Conclusions

1. Which drop of water took the longest time to evaporate? _____
2. Which drop took the shortest time to evaporate? _____
3. What conclusions can you make about the factors that affect evaporation? _____

4. What predictions can you make about the evaporation rate on a hot, sunny day and on a cool, cloudy day? _____

Explore Further

Design an experiment to find out how wind affects evaporation. How could you model wind blowing over a petri dish? How could you vary the amount of wind modeled?

©AGS Publishing. Permission is granted to reproduce for classroom use only.   📖 Earth Science

Lab Manual 42

Continued from page 265

Results

Students should find that applying heat to water makes it evaporate more quickly. Water in a closed container will evaporate more slowly than water in an open container.

Questions and Conclusions Answers

1. The drop in the covered dish took the longest time to evaporate.

2. The drop under the lamp took the shortest time to evaporate.

3. Students should conclude that heat and air circulation speed evaporation.

4. Students should predict that water evaporates more quickly on a hot, sunny day than on a cool, cloudy day.

Explore Further Answers

Students might suggest using an electric or manual fan to create air circulation over a petri dish. They could vary the amount of wind modeled by changing the speed of the fan or its distance from the dish.

Assessment

Check data tables to be sure that students observed that the heated water evaporated most quickly, followed by the open dish of water. You might include the following items from this investigation in student portfolios:

• Data table

• Answers to Questions and Conclusions and Explore Further sections

5. Turn on the lamp. If you have a clock, record the time. If you have a stopwatch, start the watch. **Safety Alert: The lamp will become very hot. Do not touch the bulb or the lamp.**

6. Observe the three dishes every 2 minutes. Record the time when each drop evaporates.

7. Clean your work area and return the equipment.

Questions and Conclusions

1. Which drop of water took the longest time to evaporate?

2. Which drop took the shortest time to evaporate?

3. What conclusions can you make about the factors that affect evaporation?

4. What predictions can you make about the evaporation rate on a hot, sunny day and on a cool, cloudy day?

Explore Further

Design an experiment to find out how wind affects evaporation. How could you model wind blowing over a petri dish? How could you vary the amount of wind modeled?

Objectives

After reading this lesson, you should be able to

◆ identify two properties of ocean water.

◆ explain what causes ocean waves and currents.

◆ describe several features of the ocean floor.

◆ identify three major groups of ocean life.

Properties of Ocean Water

The water in the oceans is salt water. The circle graph shows why. Notice that 96.5 percent of ocean water is pure water. But 3.5 percent is dissolved salt. That amount of salt makes a mouthful of ocean water saltier than a mouthful of potato chips. Most of the salt is sodium chloride—common table salt. This salt comes from rocks in the ocean floor. Salt also washes into oceans from rivers.

Salt 3.5%

Water 96.5%

Not all parts of oceans are equally salty. The saltiness, or **salinity**, of ocean water varies. In warm, dry climates, ocean water evaporates quickly. Since salt doesn't evaporate, the salt that remains makes the salinity greater than average. In some oceans, the salinity is less than average. This happens in rainy climates or where rivers and melting ice add fresh water to oceans.

Salinity

Saltiness of water

Did You Know?

On average, 1 cubic meter of ocean water contains about 35 kilograms of salt.

Ocean water is warmest at the surface where the sun heats it. Near the equator, the surface temperature can reach 30°C. Near the poles, the ocean surface is frozen. The diagram shows average ocean temperatures in a tropical or temperate zone. Notice how the water temperature decreases with depth.

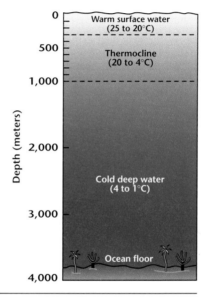

Depth (meters)

0 — Warm surface water (25 to 20°C)

500 — Thermocline (20 to 4°C)

1,000

2,000

Cold deep water (4 to 1°C)

3,000

Ocean floor

4,000

Lesson at a Glance

Chapter 11 Lesson 3

Overview In this lesson, students learn about the oceans. They explore properties of ocean water, its movement, the topography of the ocean floor, and kinds of organisms found in oceans.

Objectives

- To identify two properties of ocean water
- To explain what causes ocean waves and currents
- To describe several features of the ocean floor
- To identify three major groups of ocean life

Student Pages 267–274

Teacher's Resource Library **TRL**

Workbook Activity 45

Alternative Workbook Activity 45

Lab Manual 43–44

Resource File 26

Vocabulary

benthos	plankton
continental shelf	salinity
continental slope	seamount
current	thermocline
mid-ocean ridge	trench
nekton	wave

Science Background

Trenches are the deepest places on the earth, and the Mariana Trench is the deepest of all. With a depth of 11,033 meters, this underwater canyon is deeper than the highest mountain is high. Mount Everest is only 8, 800 meters high. The Mariana Trench in the western portion of the Pacific Ocean is almost 2,000 meters deeper than the second deepest ocean trench. The Puerto Rico Trench in the Atlantic Ocean is 9,219 meters deep.

Did You Know?

Have a volunteer read aloud the Did You Know? feature on page 267. Explain that salt dissolved in water increases the water's density. A lightweight object that would normally sink in fresh water, such as an egg, can float in the more dense salt water. Not all parts of the ocean are equally salty. The saltiest ocean is the Atlantic. But the saltiest water in the world is found in the Dead Sea.

Warm-Up Activity

Half fill a large, clear glass baking dish with water and set it on a table. In the dish, place several small objects that will float in the water (such as corks). Create waves by moving a piece of plastic or wood a short distance back and forth in one end of the dish. Have students observe the formation of waves in the water and the movement of the corks. Tell students that, in this lesson, they will learn about ocean waves and ocean currents. While waves do not move water or objects in water, currents do. This is why the floating corks bobbed up and down but did not move forward with the waves.

Teaching the Lesson

As they read, students can write a few sentences in response to each lesson objective. Students should meet each objective before moving to the next.

Use food coloring and water to make some colored ice cubes. Place a colored ice cube in a clear glass jar filled with warm water. Ask students to observe what happens as the ice cube melts. Students should notice that the colored water sinks to the bottom of the glass. Point out that cold water is more dense than warm water, so it sinks to the bottom. This is why the coldest water in the ocean is at the bottom.

Allow small groups of students to construct a wave-maker. Have them fill a small jar two-thirds full of water. Add a few drops of blue food coloring to each jar. Then have students fill the rest of the jar with mineral oil, allowing as little air space at the top as possible. Have them tightly secure the lid. Then tell them to hold the jar sideways and gently tip it back and forth to create waves. Ask students to observe the positions of the crests and troughs of the waves.

Point out that some whales, which are classified as nekton, eat plankton in quantities of four tons a day.

Thermocline

Ocean layer between about 300 and 1,000 meters below the surface, where the temperature drops sharply

Wave

Up-and-down motion of water caused by energy moving through the water

Along the edges of oceans are smaller bodies of salt water. They are called gulfs, seas, or bays. The Gulf of Alaska is part of the Pacific Ocean. The Mediterranean Sea is part of the Atlantic Ocean. The word *sea* can also be used in a general sense to mean "ocean."

The temperature is fairly constant near the surface because winds and waves keep the water well-mixed. However, in the **thermocline**, between 300 and 1,000 meters below the surface, the temperature drops sharply. Below the thermocline, the temperature decreases slowly. The bottoms of oceans are near freezing.

Ocean Waves

When you think of oceans, you probably picture **waves**. A wave is the regular up-and-down motion of water caused by energy traveling through the water. A wave gets its energy from wind. When the wind blows, it pushes up the water to start small waves. The waves become larger as the wind blows longer and harder. Most ocean waves are less than 3 meters high. However, storms can produce waves as high as 30 meters—the height of a 10-story building. No matter what the size, all waves have the parts shown below.

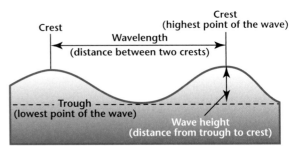

Have you ever seen a leaf bob up and down on passing waves? The waves move forward, but the leaf does not. Although it looks like waves constantly push water forward, the water generally stays in the same place. Only the waves move forward.

As a wave approaches shallow water and a shore, the wave rubs against the ocean floor. Friction slows the bottom of the wave, but the crest keeps moving at the same speed. Therefore, the crest moves ahead of the rest of the wave. The wave tilts forward and tumbles over, or breaks. After a wave breaks on a shore, the water can actually move quite a distance. It may be hurled against rocks or pushed up the slope of a beach.

Ocean Currents

Current

Large stream of water flowing in oceans, in rivers, and in some large lakes

Although waves do not move water, **currents** do. Ocean currents are large streams of water flowing in oceans. Winds cause currents near the ocean surface. Therefore, currents tend to follow the major wind belts. On the map below, trade winds and prevailing westerlies are shown as wide arrows. Major ocean currents are shown as thin arrows. Compare the trade winds with the currents near the equator. Both move westward.

Currents carry warm water from the equator toward the poles and bring cold water back toward the equator. In so doing, currents affect climates on land by warming or cooling the coasts of continents. Both wind and land absorb heat from warm ocean currents.

The Gulf Stream and the North Atlantic Drift are currents that have a warming effect. Find these currents on the map. The Gulf Stream carries warm water from the tropics up along the east coast of North America. The North Atlantic Drift carries this warm water across the Atlantic. It gives western Europe mild summers and winters.

Now locate the California Current on the map. This current carries cold water from high latitudes. It has an "air-conditioned" effect along the west coast of the United States and Mexico.

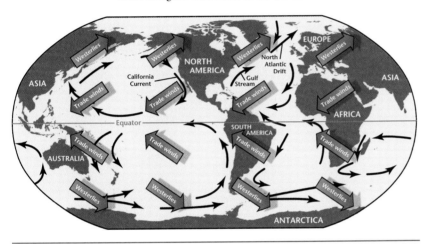

LEARNING STYLES

Visual/Spatial

Demonstrate how wind causes currents. Fill a large, clear glass baking dish with water. Sprinkle sawdust or pencil shavings on the water. Position an electric fan to blow gently across the water. Have students observe the motion of the pencil shavings in the water. Remind students that ocean currents reflect the pattern of global winds.

CROSS-CURRICULAR CONNECTION

Physical Education

Ask if students have participated in an ocean sport such as sailing, surfing, or scuba diving. Point out that lessons are necessary for all of these sports and that scuba divers must also earn a certification to go on dives. Have groups of students find out more about each sport, such as the training and equipment required and safety measures used.

Continental shelf
Part of a continent that extends from a shoreline out into an ocean
Continental slope
Steep slope between the continental shelf and the deep ocean floor
Mid-ocean ridge
Mountain chain on the ocean floor
Seamount
Underwater mountain that is usually a volcano
Trench
Deep valley on the ocean floor

The Ocean Floor

Until the late 1800s, the ocean floor was a great mystery. Today oceanographers use complex technology to measure distances and take pictures underwater. They also travel to the ocean floor. The main features of the ocean floor are listed below and shown in the diagram.

◆ A **continental shelf** is the part of a continent that extends underwater. A continental shelf slopes gently. The average water depth is 130 meters. The average width is 75 kilometers.

◆ A **continental slope** dips sharply from a continental shelf to the deeper ocean floor.

◆ Plains are wide, flat areas where sediment constantly settles. About half of the ocean floor consists of plains. Their average depth is about 4,000 meters.

◆ A **mid-ocean ridge** is an underwater mountain chain. Such a chain may extend for thousands of kilometers along the ocean floor.

◆ A **seamount** is an underwater mountain. Many of these are active or extinct volcanoes. A seamount that rises above sea level forms an island.

◆ A **trench** is a long, deep valley. Trenches are the deepest places on the earth. Some are 10 kilometers deep.

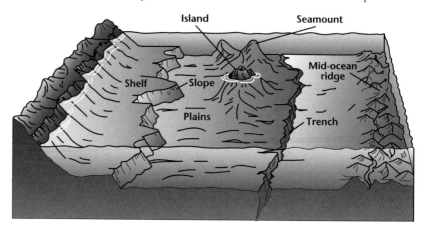

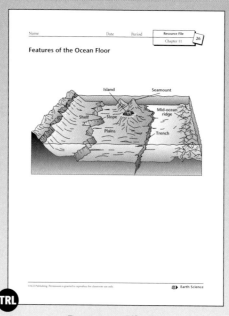

Resource File 26

Ocean Life

Ocean environments support a rich variety of living things. Scientists divide these forms of life into three groups, based on how and where they live. Look at the cross section of ocean life below. Which group provides most of the seafood people eat?

Plankton are one form of life in oceans. This group includes tiny plants and animals that float at or near the ocean surface. Plankton are a source of food for larger animals.

Animals that swim freely are classified as **nekton**. This group includes the widest variety of sea creatures, from the tiniest fish to the largest whale.

Organisms that live on the ocean floor are called **benthos**. They do not swim. Some, such as corals, remain in one place their whole lives. Others, such as snails and crabs, crawl along the ocean floor.

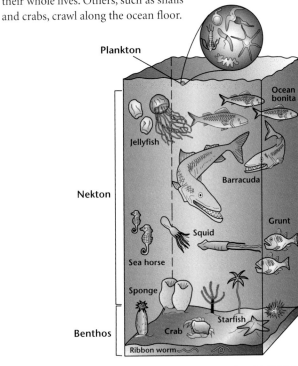

Plankton

Jellyfish

Ocean bonita

Barracuda

Nekton

Squid

Grunt

Sea horse

Sponge

Starfish

Benthos

Crab

Ribbon worm

Lesson 3 Review Answers

1. rocks on the ocean floor and rivers
2. The temperature of the surface stays fairly constant but drops sharply in the thermocline. Below the thermocline it decreases slowly. The bottoms of oceans are near freezing. 3. wind 4. Currents carry warm water from the equator toward the poles and bring cold water back toward the equator. This warms or cools the coasts of continents. 5. Answers will vary. Possible responses: continental shelves, continental slopes, mid-ocean ridges, trenches, seamounts, plains, islands, and volcanoes

Achievements in Science

Have students take turns reading aloud the feature on page 272. Encourage them to find a copy of *Silent Spring* and read some excerpts. Have them share passages they think are interesting with the class.

Portfolio Assessment

Sample items include:
- Lesson objective sentences from Teaching the Lesson
- Lesson 3 Review answers

Write your answers to these questions on a sheet of paper.

1. What are two sources of salt in ocean water?

2. Describe how water temperature changes with ocean depth.

3. What causes most ocean waves and currents?

4. How do currents affect climate?

5. What are several features of the ocean floor?

Achievements in Science

Protecting the Environment

Today most people know the importance of clean water, land, and air. However, protecting the environment has not always been a popular concern. Before 1960, there were few laws about what people could dump in rivers, on land, or into the air. Thousands of people died from smog, or polluted air, given off by factories in London and in U.S. cities. The Cuyahoga River in Cleveland often caught on fire because of the oil floating in it. Many fish in Lake Erie died because of pollution.

By 1960 the public began to understand how chemicals and other wastes could affect their health and the environment. Rachel Carson was a biologist who helped promote this awareness. In 1962 she wrote a book that warned about the dangers of pest-killing chemicals, or pesticides, on the environment. Her book, *Silent Spring*, had a strong impact on its readers. In fact it led to the banning of DDT and other pesticides.

In 1970 the U.S. Environmental Protection Agency was created to protect people and the environment. Now federal and state laws exist to preserve and improve the quality of our water, land, and air.

Name ____ Date ____ Period ____   Lab Manual, Page 1
Chapter 11   **43**

Modeling How Ocean Water Gets Salty

Purpose Why is ocean water salty? In this investigation, you will model one way that salt gets into ocean water.

Materials 2 clear plastic cups
marker
graduated cylinder
water
rocks
plastic wrap
2 plastic spoons
2 petri dishes

Procedure

1. Use the table below to record your data.

Water Sample	Color of Water	Other Observations	Observations after Evaporation
1			
2			

2. Use the marker to number the cups and petri dishes 1 and 2. Set aside the petri dishes. Use the graduated cylinder to measure and pour 250 milliliters of water into each cup.

3. Put several rocks in cup 2.

4. Cover both cups with plastic wrap. Put them next to each other in direct sunlight. Let the cups sit for 24 hours.

©AGS Publishing. Permission is granted to reproduce for classroom use only.   **Earth Science**

Lab Manual 43, pages 1–2

Name ____ Date ____ Period ____   Workbook Activity
Chapter 11, Lesson 3   **45**

Oceans: Terms Review

Directions Write the term from the Word Bank that best completes each sentence.

Word Bank				
benthos	divide	nekton	salinity	trench
continental shelf	drainage basin	porous	seamount	tributary
continental slope	geysers	reservoir	sinkhole	water cycle
currents	mid-ocean ridge	runoff	thermocline	water table

1. Precipitation that sinks into the ground becomes _____

2. Precipitation that does not sink into the ground or evaporate becomes _____

3. Water moving between the atmosphere and the earth's surface is the _____

4. A river that joins another river is a _____

5. When the roof of a cave collapses, a _____ forms.

6. The top of the groundwater layer is the _____

7. Water can sink into the ground because the soil is _____

8. The land area in which runoff drains into a large river is a _____

9. An artificial lake made by building a dam is a _____

10. A ridge that separates drainage basins is a _____

11. The saltiness of water is _____

12. A deep valley in the ocean floor is a _____

13. A mountain chain on the ocean floor is a _____

14. The temperature drops sharply in the _____

15. The part of a continent that extends underwater is the _____

16. A _____ dips from a continental shelf down to the ocean floor.

17. An underwater mountain that is often a volcano is a _____

18. Ocean life includes plankton, _____, and _____

19. Winds cause up-and-down waves as well as flowing ocean streams called _____

20. Groundwater flows out of springs and blasts out of _____

©AGS Publishing. Permission is granted to reproduce for classroom use only.   **Earth Science**

Workbook Activity 45

Measuring the Effect of Salt Water on Floating

Purpose

Will an object float higher in salt water or fresh water? In this investigation, you will observe the effect of salt water on floating.

Procedure

Materials

- 2 small, clear plastic soft-drink bottles
- tablespoon
- table salt
- fine-tip waterproof marker
- masking tape
- drinking straw
- centimeter ruler
- modeling clay

1. Copy the data table on your paper.

Trial	Fresh Water	Salt Water
1		
2		

2. Fill the two soft-drink bottles about three-quarters full of water. Add 6 tablespoons of salt to one bottle. Carefully swirl the contents to dissolve the salt. **Safety Alert: Never taste any substances used in a science investigation. Wipe up any spills immediately.**

3. Label the saltwater bottle *S* and the freshwater bottle *F*.

4. Make a float meter. Put a 6-centimeter strip of tape along one end of a drinking straw. Mark off 0.5-centimeter lengths along the tape. Push a pea-size ball of clay onto that end of the straw.

5. Drop the float meter into the fresh water. Count how many markings on the tape stay above water. Record your observations.

The Earth's Water   *Chapter 11*   **273**

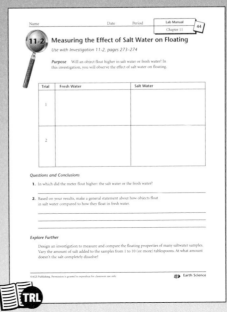

Lab Manual 44

The Purpose portion of the student investigation begins with a question to draw students into the activity. Encourage students to read the investigation steps and formulate their own questions before beginning the investigation. This investigation will take approximately 45 minutes to complete. Students will use these process and thinking skills: making models, observing, measuring, describing, comparing, and making generalizations.

Preparation

- Be sure the markers you use for this investigation are waterproof.
- Plastic straws will work better than paper straws.
- Students may use Lab Manual 44 to record their data and answer the questions.

Procedure

- This investigation may be done individually or in pairs.
- Be sure students swirl the salt and water enough to completely dissolve the salt.
- When students are marking off the distances on the tape, caution them not to press so hard that they split the straw.
- In step 5, if a float meter sinks to the bottom of the bottle, there is too much clay on the end of the straw. If it tilts to one side, there is too little clay.
- Explain to students that the salt water used in this investigation is several times saltier than ocean water. Ocean water has a salinity of about 35 grams per liter (less than 2 teaspoons of salt per cup of water).

SAFETY ALERT

- Caution students to wipe up any spills immediately.
- Remind students that substances in a science investigation are not clean and may be harmful. That is why students should never taste anything used in an investigation.

Continued on page 274

The Earth's Water   *Chapter 11*   **273**

Continued from page 273

Results

Students should observe that the float meter floats higher in salt water than in fresh water.

Questions and Conclusions Answers

1. salt water

2. Answers will vary. Possible response: Objects float higher in salt water than they do in fresh water. This is because salt water is more dense than fresh water.

Explore Further Answers

Answers will vary. Students may suggest using a series of soft-drink bottles, each with a different amount of salt in it. They may suggest a numbered scale on the float meter to make the comparisons easier.

Assessment

Check students' data tables to see that they observed the correct results. Verify that their general statement for question 2 is a logical response to their data. You might include the following items from this investigation in student portfolios:

• Data table
• Answers to Questions and Conclusions and Explore Further sections

6. Drop the float meter into the salt water. Count the markings above water. Record your observations.

7. Repeat steps 5 and 6 for trial 2.

Questions and Conclusions

1. In which did the meter float higher: the salt water or the fresh water?

2. Based on your results, make a general statement about how objects float in salt water compared to how they float in fresh water.

Explore Further

Design an investigation to measure and compare the floating properties of many saltwater samples. Vary the amount of salt added to the samples from 1 to 10 (or more) tablespoons. At what amount doesn't the salt completely dissolve?

- Water moves between the land, the atmosphere, and bodies of water in the water cycle.

- The earth's water includes salt water, which is too salty to drink, and fresh water, which does not contain salt. Most of the earth's water is salt water.

- Water under the earth's surface is called groundwater.

- Springs, geysers, and caves are evidence of moving groundwater.

- Groundwater moves downward in the ground and collects to form a soaked layer, the top of which is called the water table.

- Rivers and their tributaries drain runoff from large areas of land called drainage basins.

- Lakes form when water collects in a depression on land.

- Reservoirs are lakes made when people dam a river. Reservoirs store water, control flooding, and produce electricity.

- Ocean water is salt water because it contains dissolved salt.

- The temperature of ocean water decreases with depth.

- A wave is the up-and-down motion of water caused by energy from the wind.

- Currents move ocean water. Currents are caused by winds and follow the same general pattern as global winds.

- Features of the ocean floor include continental shelves and slopes, mid-ocean ridges, trenches, seamounts, and plains.

- Ocean life includes floating plankton, free-swimming nekton, and ocean floor-dwelling benthos.

Science Words

benthos, 271	drainage basin, 261	porous, 259	thermocline, 268
continental shelf, 270	geyser, 260	reservoir, 263	trench, 270
continental slope, 270	groundwater, 257	runoff, 257	tributary, 261
current, 269	mid-ocean ridge, 270	salinity, 267	water cycle, 256
divide, 261	nekton, 271	seamount, 270	water table, 259
	plankton, 271	sinkhole, 260	wave, 268
		spring, 260	

Chapter 11 Summary

Have volunteers read aloud each Summary item on page 275. Ask volunteers to explain the meaning of each item. Direct students' attention to the Science Words box on the bottom of page 275. Have them read and review each word and its definition.

Chapter 11 Review

Use the Chapter Review to prepare students for tests and to reteach content from the chapter.

Chapter 11 Mastery Test

The Teacher's Resource Library includes two parallel forms of the Chapter 11 Mastery Test. The difficulty level of the two forms is equivalent. You may wish to use one form as a pretest and the other form as a posttest.

Review Answers
Vocabulary Review

1. tributary 2. drainage basin 3. water table 4. geyser 5. trench 6. mid-ocean ridge 7. salinity 8. continental shelf

Concept Review

9. A 10. D 11. D 12. B 13. B 14. C 15. C 16. A 17. B

TEACHER ALERT

In the Chapter Review, the Vocabulary Review activity includes a sample of the chapter's vocabulary terms. The activity will help determine students' understanding of key vocabulary terms and concepts presented in the chapter. Other vocabulary terms used in the chapter are listed below:

benthos	reservoir
continental slope	runoff
current	seamount
divide	sinkhole
groundwater	spring
nekton	thermocline
plankton	water cycle
porous	wave

Word Bank

continental shelf
drainage basin
geyser
mid-ocean ridge
salinity
trench
tributary
water table

Vocabulary Review

Choose the word or phrase from the Word Bank that best completes each sentence. Write the answer on your paper.

1. A river that flows into another river is a _____.

2. The land area in which runoff flows into a river and its tributaries is a _____.

3. Underground water forms a soaked layer, the top of which is the _____.

4. Heated groundwater blasts out of the ground at a _____.

5. A deep valley on the ocean floor is called a _____.

6. A mountain chain on the ocean floor is called a _____.

7. Water with more salt has greater _____ than water with less salt.

8. A _____ extends from a shoreline out into an ocean.

Concept Review

Choose the word or phrase that best completes each sentence. Write the letter of the answer on your paper.

9. In the water cycle, water moves from oceans to the atmosphere by _____.
   A evaporation   C precipitation
   B condensation   D runoff

10. The water cycle is powered by _____.
   A oceans and rivers   C the water table
   B precipitation   D the sun's heat

11. Precipitation that doesn't evaporate or sink into the ground _____.
   A is not part of the water cycle
   B becomes groundwater
   C flows out of the ground as a spring
   D flows into streams as runoff

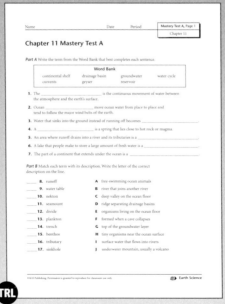

Chapter 11 Mastery Test A

12. As ocean water deepens, its temperature _____.
   A gets warmer   **C** stays the same
   B gets colder   **D** varies

13. Artificial lakes that supply fresh water, control flooding, and produce electricity are called _____.
   A water tables   **C** drainage basins
   B reservoirs   **D** tributaries

14. The top of a wave is the _____.
   A trough   **B** wave height   **C** crest   **D** seamount

15. Ocean currents are caused by _____.
   A waves   **B** tides   **C** winds   **D** runoff

16. A fish swimming in an ocean is classified as _____.
   A nekton   **B** benthos   **C** plankton   **D** salinity

17. Moisture that sinks into the ground is called _____.
   A plankton   **C** surface water
   B groundwater   **D** a reservoir

Critical Thinking

Write the answer to each of the following questions.

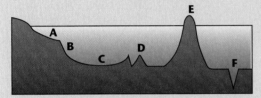

18. Refer to the diagram. Name each lettered feature of the ocean floor.

19. After a dry summer, water no longer comes up through a well. What has happened?

20. One way to make salt water fit to drink is to heat it and collect the water vapor. How is this like the water cycle?

 **Test-Taking Tip** Before writing out an answer on a test, read the question twice to make sure you understand what it is asking.

Review Answers
Critical Thinking

18. A continental shelf **B** continental slope **C** plain **D** mid-ocean ridge **E** seamount or island **F** trench **19.** The increased water use, along with the lack of rain, has lowered the water table below the depth of the well. **20.** In the water cycle, water evaporates, condenses, and returns to the earth as precipitation. When salt water evaporates, the salt is left behind and the water vapor condenses as fresh water.

ALTERNATIVE ASSESSMENT

Alternative Assessment items correlate to the student Goals for Learning at the beginning of this chapter.

- Have students form a circle. Ask one student to describe a part of the water cycle. Have the student to his or her left describe what would happen to the water next. (Where multiple answers would be correct, several students in a row could give one answer each.) Continue around the circle until everyone has had a turn. Make sure the complete path of the water cycle has been described at least once.

- Have students take turns telling what fresh water can be used for. After each statement, have another student tell whether salt water can be used for the same purpose.

- Have students construct a diagram with labels describing groundwater and the water table.

- Give students a regional map. Ask them to identify a main river in your area. Then ask them to identify its tributaries. Finally, ask students to tell the name of the larger river, lake, or ocean into which the main river empties.

- Divide the class into two groups. Ask one group to make a labeled drawing of a wave. Ask the other group to make a labeled drawing of the ocean floor. Have the first group explain to the second group what a wave is, what causes waves, and how waves are similar to and different from currents. Then have the second group explain the features of the ocean floor and the properties of ocean water.

Chapter 11 Mastery Test B

Chapter

12

Planning Guide

Weathering and Erosion

	Student Pages	Vocabulary	Lesson Review
Lesson 1 Weathering	280–285	✔	✔
Lesson 2 Erosion Caused by Water	286–293	✔	✔
Lesson 3 Erosion Caused by Glaciers	294–299	✔	✔
Lesson 4 Erosion Caused by Wind and Gravity	300–302		✔

Column group header: **Student Text Lesson**

Chapter Activities

Student Text
Science Center
Teacher's Resource Library
Community Connection 12: The Results
of Weathering and Erosion

Assessment Options

Student Text
Chapter 12 Review
Teacher's Resource Library
Chapter 12 Mastery Tests A and B

Student Text Features								Teaching Strategies						Learning Styles						Teacher's Resource Library				
Achievements in Science	Science at Work	Science in Your Life	Investigation	Science Myth	Note	Technology Note	Did You Know	Science Integration	Science Journal	Cross-Curricular Connection	Online Connection	Teacher Alert	Applications (Home, Career, Community, Global, Environment)	Auditory/Verbal	Body/Kinesthetic	Interpersonal/Group Learning	Logical/Mathematical	Visual/Spatial	LEP/ESL	Workbook Activities	Alternative Workbook Activities	Lab Manual	Resource File	Self-Study Guide
			284			✔		282		282		282	282						282	46	46	45	27	✔
		291	292		✔		287		287	288			289, 290	289	289	290	288	287		47	47	46, 47	28	✔
299					✔		296			297	296		297, 298		298					48	48			✔
	302			300	✔		300	301	301	301		301								49	49	48		✔

Pronunciation Key

a hat	e let	ī ice	ô order	u̇ put	sh she	⎧ a in about
ā age	ē equal	o hot	oi oil	ü rule	th thin	⎪ e in taken
ä far	ėr term	ō open	ou out	ch child	ᵺ then	ə ⎨ i in pencil
â care	i it	ȯ saw	u cup	ng long	zh measure	⎪ o in lemon
						⎩ u in circus

Alternative Workbook Activities

The Teacher's Resource Library (TRL) contains a set of lower-level worksheets called Alternative Workbook Activities. These worksheets cover the same content as the regular Workbook Activities but are written at a second-grade reading level.

Skill Track Software

Use the Skill Track Software for Earth Science for additional reinforcement of this chapter. The software program allows students using AGS textbooks to be assessed for mastery of each chapter and lesson of the textbook. Students access the software on an individual basis and are assessed with multiple-choice items.

Chapter at a Glance

Chapter 12:
Weathering and Erosion
pages 278–305

Lessons

1. **Weathering** pages 280–285

Investigation 12-1 pages 284–285

2. **Erosion Caused by Water**
pages 286–293

Investigation 12-2 pages 292–293

3. **Erosion Caused by Glaciers**
pages 294–299

4. **Erosion Caused by Wind and
Gravity** pages 300–302

Chapter 12 Summary page 303

Chapter 12 Review pages 304–305

**Skill Track Software
for Earth Science**

Teacher's Resource Library **TRL**

Workbook Activities 46–49

Alternative Workbook Activities
46–49

Lab Manual 45–48

Community Connection 12

Resource File 27–28

Chapter 12 Self-Study Guide

Chapter 12 Mastery Tests A and B

(Answer Keys for the Teacher's
Resource Library begin on page 400
of the Teacher's Edition. The
Materials List for the Lab Manual
activities begins on page 415.)

Science Center

Have students photograph, as a class or individually, evidence of changes to rock formations, buildings, monuments, or other local objects made of rock. Have them sort the photos into four piles— changes caused by water, changes caused by wind, changes caused by ice, and changes caused by gravity. Divide a display board into four sections and label each section with one of these agents of change. Have students place the photos from the Introducing the Chapter activity into the most likely category. As they master the information in each lesson, have students check and change, if necessary, the placement of the photos. Alternatively, they may find photos in old magazines such as *National Geographic* for their displays.

| Name | Date | Period | Community Connection |
| | | | Chapter 12 |

The Results of Weathering and Erosion

You may not realize it, but the results of weathering and erosion are all around you. Do research to locate and describe as many of the following landforms in your area as possible. If there are not any nearby, find out about the landforms closest to where you live. Then complete the chart.

Landform	Name	Location	Description
cave			
stream/river			
valley/canyon			
floodplain			
delta/alluvial fan			
sand dune			
beach			
glacier			
moraine			
glacial lake			

©AGS Publishing. Permission is granted to reproduce for classroom use only. ● Earth Science

TRL

12 Weathering and Erosion

Materials on the earth's surface are constantly changing. Rocks and soil break down and move. Sometimes we notice these changes. But most of the time, they happen very gradually. At one time, the tree in the photo was barely noticeable as it sprouted. What did the rock look like then? What happened to the rock as the tree grew? How did the rock crack? In Chapter 12, you will learn about the processes of weathering and erosion. You also will learn about some landforms caused by erosion.

Organize Your Thoughts

```
        Mechanical ── Weathering ── Chemical

        Water ── Erosion ── Gravity

              Glaciers    Wind
```

Goals for Learning

◆ To explain weathering and soil formation
◆ To describe how a river and its valley age
◆ To describe how water, glaciers, wind, and gravity cause erosion
◆ To give examples of several eroded landforms
◆ To describe how deposited landforms develop

279

Introducing the Chapter

Take students on a short field trip in your area to observe rock outcrops, sidewalks, buildings made of stone, park statues, etc. Encourage students to suggest how these features may have changed since they were built, if humanmade, or since they were formed, if natural. Students should be able to see some signs of weathering—tarnish, rust, bits of rock debris, sediment (clay, sand, pebbles), or rough, smooth, cracked, or pitted surfaces. Have them write down any changes they see and a brief sentence describing what they think might have caused the change. Explain to students that they will learn in this chapter how rocks change due to water, wind, ice, and gravity. Take along a camera and allow students to photograph the changes they observe. They can use the photos for the chapter's Science Center activity.

Notes and Technology Notes

Ask volunteers to read the notes that appear in the margins throughout the chapter. Then discuss them with the class.

TEACHER'S RESOURCE

The AGS Teaching Strategies in Science Transparencies may be used with this chapter. The transparencies add an interactive dimension to expand and enhance the *Earth Science* program content.

CAREER INTEREST INVENTORY

The AGS Harrington-O'Shea Career Decision-Making System-Revised (CDM) may be used with this chapter. Students can use the CDM to explore their interests and identify careers. The CDM defines career areas that are indicated by students' responses on the inventory.

TRL   TRL

Chapter 12 Self-Study Guide

Lesson at a Glance

Chapter 12 Lesson 1

Overview In this lesson, students learn that rocks constantly change due to physical and chemical processes at or very near the earth's surface. Students also find out that soil forms as a result of these changes.

Objectives
- To define weathering
- To give examples of mechanical and chemical weathering
- To identify different soil layers

Student Pages 280–285

Teacher's Resource Library **TRL**

Workbook Activity 46

Alternative Workbook Activity 46

Lab Manual 45

Resource File 27

....

Vocabulary

chemical weathering
mechanical weathering
oxidation
soil
subsoil
topsoil
weathering

....

Science Background

Weathering processes break rocks into smaller pieces. Physical weathering does not change the composition of rocks; chemical weathering does. Many factors affect the rates at which rocks weather. Climate, for example, can aid or deter weathering. Warm, moist climates tend to increase the rate at which a rock weathers. Rocks in cold polar regions, on the other hand, are very resistant to weathering processes. The composition of a rock also affects the rate at which it weathers. Rocks made of feldspar, biotite (mica), and amphibole weather more readily than rocks made of the minerals quartz and muscovite (mica). Topography also affects weathering rates. Hilly, vegetated areas experience more chemical weathering. Arid regions with angular rock formations experience more mechanical weathering.

Objectives

After reading this lesson, you should be able to
- ◆ define weathering.
- ◆ give examples of mechanical and chemical weathering.
- ◆ identify different soil layers.

Weathering
Breaking down of rocks on the earth's surface

Mechanical weathering
Breaking apart of rocks without changing their mineral composition

The earth is constantly changing. Even a hard material like rock changes. Over the years, these carved and polished grave markers have broken down, tilted, and become discolored.

The breaking down of rocks on the earth's surface is known as **weathering**. Weathering occurs when rocks are exposed to air, water, or living things. All these factors help to break rocks apart.

How have these rocks weathered?

Mechanical Weathering

In **mechanical weathering**, rocks break into smaller pieces, but their chemical makeup stays the same. The photo on page 278 shows one way that rocks break. This tree started growing in soil that collected in a small crack of the rock. As the tree grew, its roots pushed against the rock and split it. You might see this kind of mechanical weathering in a sidewalk near a tree. The growing roots often lift and crumble the sidewalk.

Mechanical weathering also occurs as water freezes in the cracks of rocks. When water freezes, it expands. As the freezing water expands, it pushes the rock apart, as shown in the diagram. The ice may melt, and the water may refreeze. Each time the water freezes, the cracks get bigger. Finally, the rock breaks apart.

Soil, a mixture of air, water, organic matter, and bits of rocks and minerals, is a product of weathering. Soils are often described by their texture, which is dictated by the size of the particles present. The four designations are clay, silt, sand, and loam. Clay soils contain particles that are less than 0.0004 millimeters in diameter. Silty soils contain particles that are larger than those of clay soils. However, both hold much water and drain poorly, and plant roots have a difficult time penetrating these soils. Therefore, they make poor soil for growing crops. Sandy soil is composed mostly of grains of sand, which are much larger than grains of silt or clay, and sandy soil drains readily. Soils, however, usually contain mixtures of clay, silt, and sand. The mixture is known as loam. Soils may be called sandy loam, silty clay loam, and so on, indicating which particle size is predominant.

Chemical Weathering

Chemical weathering
Breaking apart of rocks caused by a change in their chemical makeup

Oxidation
Process in which minerals combine with oxygen to form new substances

In **chemical weathering**, changes occur in the chemical makeup of rocks. New minerals might be added to or taken away from the rock. The minerals might be changed into new substances.

For example, in a process called **oxidation**, oxygen from the air or water combines with the iron in rocks. As a result, a new, softer substance called iron oxide, or rust, forms. Iron oxide stains rocks various shades of yellow, orange, red, or brown. How is the rocky bluff below like the rusty, old can?

A rusting can slowly crumbles.

"Rusting" rock also slowly breaks apart.

Chemical weathering also occurs when water changes minerals in the rocks. For example, the mineral feldspar is part of many rocks. Water changes feldspar to clay and washes it away. Without the feldspar to hold the other minerals together, the rock falls apart.

The limestone cave shown on the next page is the result of chemical weathering. Rain and groundwater combine with carbon dioxide in the air to form carbonic acid. This is the same acid found in carbonated soft drinks. As carbonic acid trickles through the ground, it dissolves calcite—the main mineral in limestone. As more and more limestone is dissolved, small holes become huge caves.

 1 Warm-Up Activity

Show students a piece of sandstone and a saucer of sand. Ask them what the two samples have in common. Students should recognize that both are made of sand-sized grains. Ask them whether either sample can be changed into the other. Students may say that the sand grains can become compacted and cemented together to form sandstone. They may also say that the sandstone can break down to form sediment (the sand). Both pathways are part of the rock cycle, described in Lesson 5 of Chapter 8. You might want to review the rock cycle diagram on page 194, pointing out the processes of weathering and erosion.

2 Teaching the Lesson

This lesson contains a number of new science terms. Before students begin reading the lesson, have them read the definition of each word. Then, as they read the lesson, ask them to define each term in their own words.

Show students some pieces of sandstone, which crumbles easily. Allow them to rub two of the pieces together over a sheet of notebook paper. Have students observe the sediment on the paper. Stress that mechanical weathering breaks rocks into smaller pieces but does not change the composition of the rock.

Students might be interested to learn that oxidation produced the sea-green color of the Statue of Liberty on Liberty Island off the coast of New Jersey. This copper monument once had the color of a new penny. The copper reacted with oxygen in the air to form the greenish copper oxide.

Dig up a small quantity of topsoil. Place a spoonful of the topsoil on a white paper plate. Have students observe the topsoil with a hand lens or a stereoscopic microscope. Have them list physical characteristics of the soil—its color, texture, and whether it appears to contain sand or any organic components.

TEACHER ALERT

Make sure students don't confuse the process of weathering with the term weather. Weather is the condition of the earth's atmosphere at a given time and place, while weathering is the breaking down of rocks on the earth's surface.

LEARNING STYLES

LEP/ESL

Use the illustration of the rock cycle on page 194 to discuss how weathering changes rocks. Reiterate that mechanical weathering changes only the size of rocks, while chemical weathering changes the composition of rocks.

CROSS-CURRICULAR CONNECTION

Literature

Have interested students read John W. Powell's *The Exploration of the Colorado River and Its Canyons,* which includes descriptions of the Grand Canyon, one of the most awesome examples of weathering and erosion.

SCIENCE INTEGRATION

Biology

Have students find out about the role of living things in soil formation. (*Microbes decompose dead plants and animals; worms and insects break down organic matter in the soil and leave burrows for air and water to seep in.*)

AT HOME

Ask students to examine the topsoil in their neighborhood. Have them collect and bring in a cup of soil from their yard or other nearby area. Then have them write a soil profile. This description should include soil color, composition, texture, particle size, and presence of organic matter. Have students compare the samples and profiles. Then have the class design an experiment to find out how well each soil sample grows a particular plant or crop.

Soil

Mixture of tiny pieces of weathered rock and the remains of plants and animals

Topsoil

Top layer of soil, rich with oxygen and decayed organic matter

Subsoil

Layer of soil directly below the topsoil

Carlsbad Caverns are limestone caves in New Mexico.

How Soil Forms

When rock has weathered for a long time, **soil** may develop. Soil is a mixture of tiny pieces of weathered rock and the remains of plants and animals. The makeup of soil depends on the types of rock particles and remains that are found in it.

As soil develops, it forms layers. Fully developed soil has three layers. Look at the diagram as you read about soil layers.

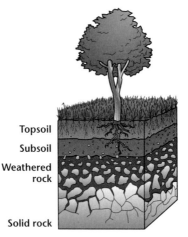

Topsoil
Subsoil
Weathered rock
Solid rock

Most soil you see is **topsoil**. This layer has the greatest amount of oxygen and decayed organic matter. The organic matter helps the soil hold moisture.

Directly below the topsoil is the **subsoil**. It contains minerals that were washed down from the topsoil. Many of these minerals are forms of iron oxide. They give the subsoil a yellowish or reddish color. Plant roots grow into the subsoil to get minerals and water.

The next layer contains chunks of partially weathered rock. Near the bottom of this layer, rock fragments sit directly on solid rock.

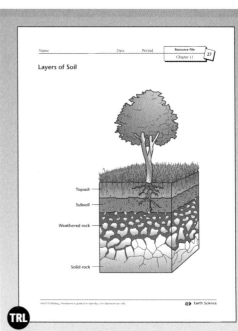

Lesson 1 R E V I E W

Write your answers to these questions on a sheet of paper.

1. What factors in the environment cause weathering?

2. Name two causes of mechanical weathering.

3. Explain how a limestone cave forms.

4. What layer of soil contains the most decayed material?

5. What lies below the three layers of soil?

Technology Note

Many people study and explore caves. Maps help people find their way in unfamiliar caves without getting lost.

Early cave maps were sketched from memory and were not accurate. Today more precise cave maps are made with compasses and measuring tapes. Some maps are made with computers and electronic tools called laser range finders. Maps made with these devices accurately lay out cave features.

Computer programs allow mapmakers to gather data from cave surveys and create three-dimensional cave models. These on-screen models can be rotated to view any angle of the cave. While exploring a cave, people can use a global positioning system device to look at these computer models. These models can be used to find different cave routes and entrances.

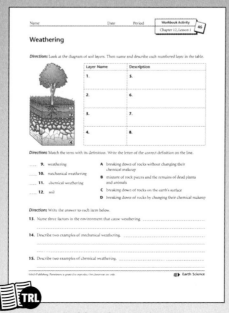

Workbook Activity 46

1. air, water, and living things 2. A plant may grow in a small crack of a rock; as the plant grows, its roots split the rock. Water may freeze in the cracks of rocks. As the freezing water expands, it pushes the rock apart. After the water melts and refreezes several times, the rock breaks apart. 3. Rain and groundwater combine with carbon dioxide in the air. The resulting carbonic acid dissolves calcite in limestone, eventually changing small holes into huge caves. 4. topsoil
5. solid rock

Portfolio Assessment

Sample items include:
• Definitions from Teaching the Lesson
• Lesson 1 Review answers

The Purpose portion of the student investigation begins with a question to draw students into the activity. Encourage students to read the investigation steps and formulate their own questions before beginning the investigation. This investigation will take approximately 30 minutes to complete. Students will use these process and thinking skills: experimenting, observing, measuring, communicating, drawing conclusions, and inferring.

Preparation

• Limestone chips can be purchased from a local nursery or a large retail store with a garden department. Some students might be able to bring in limestone chips from home flower beds.

• If you choose to use chalk, use white classroom chalk rather than colored chalk.

• White distilled vinegar works best for this activity.

• Keep paper towels handy to wipe up spills.

• Covering the work areas with several layers of newspaper will facilitate cleaning up after this investigation.

• Students may use Lab Manual 45 to record their data and answer the questions.

Procedure

• Students can work individually or in pairs.

• Review the properties of the mineral calcite from Chapter 7. Point out that calcite is calcium carbonate. It can be white or tan in color, effervesces in dilute hydrochloric acid, and has a hardness of about 3. Remind students that limestone is basically made of one mineral, calcite.

• Relate this activity to the formation of limestone caves.

• After the investigation, ask students to hypothesize if and how shaking the cup with the rocks and acid would affect weathering. Students should deduce that shaking the container would increase the rate of weathering.

12-1 INVESTIGATION

Observing Chemical Weathering

Purpose

What will happen when limestone is exposed to acid? In this investigation, you will model and observe chemical weathering.

Procedure

1. Copy the data table on your paper.

Limestone	Observations
before weathering	
after weathering	

2. Use the hand lens to look at the surfaces of the limestone chips. In the data table, describe their appearance.

3. Safety Alert: Put on your safety glasses.

4. Place the chips in the cup. Pour enough vinegar into the cup to cover the chips. Let the chips sit overnight. **Safety Alert: Never taste any substances used in a science investigation. Wipe up any spills immediately.**

5. Pour the vinegar and limestone chips through a strainer over a sink. Run water over the chips to rinse off the vinegar.

6. Place the limestone chips on paper towels. Use the hand lens to look at the limestone surfaces. In the data table, describe any changes you see.

Materials

◆ hand lens
◆ safety glasses
◆ 5 limestone chips or pieces of chalk
◆ clear plastic, 12-ounce cup
◆ 1 cup of vinegar
◆ strainer
◆ water
◆ paper towels

Lab Manual 45

Questions and Conclusions

1. How did the surfaces of the limestone change?

2. Vinegar is an acid. What did the vinegar do to change the appearance of the limestone?

Explore Further

Design a similar experiment that varies the soaking time or uses other rocks. For example, you might soak one set of limestone chips for a day, another set for two days, another for three days, and so on. How would each set compare? What would you predict about the mass of each set before and after soaking? Another idea is to repeat the experiment using chips of sandstone, granite, and marble. Which rocks are most resistant to this kind of chemical weathering?

Results

When the acid in vinegar mixes with the limestone or chalk, a chemical reaction takes place. The calcite (in the limestone or chalk) reacts with the acid to form calcium ions, carbon dioxide, and water. The release of carbon dioxide is indicated by the bubbling that occurs when the acid is poured over the rock chips.

Questions and Conclusions Answers

1. The chips became pitted and the edges became more rounded.

2. The vinegar dissolved some of the limestone.

Explore Further Answers

If limestone chips are left in vinegar for longer periods of time, the reaction will continue. After a few weeks in vinegar, limestone chips would be very smooth and extremely pitted. Students should predict that the mass would decrease after soaking. They should find that granite and sandstone are most resistant to this kind of chemical weathering. Marble, because it is predominantly calcite, will react slightly with the vinegar.

Assessment

Be sure that students accurately record their observations. Verify that their answers to the questions indicate an understanding of the reaction they observed. You might include the following items from this investigation in student portfolios:

• Data table

• Answers to Questions and Conclusions and Explore Further sections

Lesson at a Glance

Chapter 12 Lesson 2

Overview In this lesson, students learn how moving water changes the shape of the land. Water sculpts the earth's landscape by eroding weathered materials and depositing them elsewhere.

Objectives

- To explain how rivers erode the land
- To describe how river valleys form and age
- To explain deposition and delta formation
- To identify shoreline features caused by waves

Student Pages 286–293

Teacher's Resource Library

Workbook Activity 47

Alternative Workbook Activity 47

Lab Manual 46–47

Resource File 28

Vocabulary

alluvial fan	floodplain
delta	meander
deposition	mouth
erosion	oxbow lake

 1 Warm-Up Activity

Make a model beach, using sand, water, and a shallow paint tray with an incline. Build the sand up at the high end to represent the beach. Ask students to recall any experiences they have had with waves at a beach. Allow them to hypothesize how waves affect beach areas. Push the water to simulate waves moving up over the sand area. Demonstrate that a beach is always changing as waves bring sand toward the shore and remove it in one quick pass.

 Teaching the Lesson

As students read each section of this lesson, have them summarize the information in a sentence or two.

After students have read page 286, have a volunteer compare and contrast weathering and erosion. The student should note that both processes change the earth's rocks. They differ in that weathering is the physical and chemical breakdown of rocks; erosion is the transport of the products of weathering.

If possible, visit a nearby river to observe it eroding its bed. Have students attempt to classify the river as young, mature, or old. A topographic map showing the river and surrounding area may help them determine the stage of the river. Such maps are available from a regional branch of the U.S. Geological Survey.

Objectives

After reading this lesson, you should be able to

- explain how rivers erode the land.
- describe how river valleys form and age.
- explain deposition and delta formation.
- identify shoreline features caused by waves.

Erosion

Wearing away and moving of weathered rock and soil

After rock has been loosened by weathering, it is worn away and moved to another place. The wearing away and moving of weathered rock and soil is called **erosion**. The main agents, or causes, of erosion are rivers, waves, glaciers, wind, and gravity.

River Erosion

Water running downhill is a powerful force. In fact, rivers and their tributaries change more of the landscape than any other agent of erosion. After rain falls to the earth, the water flows downhill. The water pushes soil and rock fragments as it moves. These solid particles are sediment. The water and sediment flow into small gullies, which lead to rivers.

As water flows in a river, it erodes the banks and riverbed, which is the bottom of the river. Compare the eroding power of a river to a hose. The force of water from the hose can easily dig up soil and move it across a lawn. A jet of water may even chip away at a sidewalk. Similarly, river water erodes the land. Sand and stones in the river scrape against the banks and riverbed, causing more erosion. The boulders in the photo below have been worn smooth by fast-moving water and sediment.

Water and sediment act like sandpaper on these rocks in the Madison River in Wyoming.

The Life of a River Valley

As you run your finger through sand, your finger carves out a little valley. As a river erodes the land, it also carves out a valley. Some valleys are narrow with steep walls. These are called canyons. Other valleys are wide and shallow. The shape of the valley largely depends on how old it is. Rivers and their valleys go through three stages: youth, maturity, and old age. Study the diagrams below as you read about the life of a river.

A young river is narrow and fast. Its swift waters rapidly cut down through rock, carving out a V-shaped valley. The river covers all or most of the valley floor. The fast waters have a lot of energy and can push rocks along the river's path. Rapids and waterfalls are common. The Yellowstone River and Niagara River are examples of young rivers.

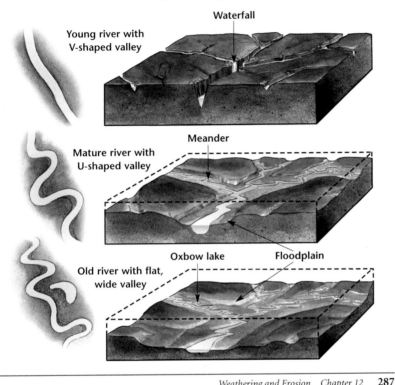

Young river with V-shaped valley

Waterfall

Mature river with U-shaped valley

Meander

Old river with flat, wide valley

Oxbow lake   Floodplain

Resource File 28

Did You Know?

Ask a volunteer to read aloud the Did You Know? feature on page 287. Point out that the falls were originally about 11 kilometers downriver. Draw a diagram, or have a student do so, to make the information clear. Explain that, in the 1950s, two water-diversion projects helped reduce this erosion. A hydroelectric power plant was built on the Canadian side of the river. This project significantly reduced the river's flow rate. On the American side, a project was carried out to spread the river's flow more evenly over the crest of the waterfall. Now the erosion rate at Niagara Falls is about 3.6 centimeters per year.

LEARNING STYLES

Visual/Spatial

Ask students to draw sketches illustrating a young river, a mature river, and an old river. Have them base their drawings on the information and diagrams in the text and on photographs of rivers that they locate. Have students label and display their illustrations.

SCIENCE JOURNAL

Have students write a description of what they would see and experience if they rafted down first a young river and then an old river.

Meander

Looping curve in a river

Floodplain

Low, flat area that a river covers when it overflows its banks

Oxbow lake

C-shaped body of water formed when a meander is cut off from the rest of the river

The exact cause of meanders is not known. Objects or landforms may block the path of a river. The earth's rotation or a change in river stage may also cause a river to twist and turn.

As erosion continues, a river becomes mature. At this stage, the boulders and rocky ledges that cause rapids and waterfalls have been eroded away. The slope, or angle, of the river is less steep, so the river does not flow as fast. It can move pebbles, sand, and mud, but not large rocks. The valley of a mature river is much wider than the river itself. The Ohio River and Missouri River are mature rivers.

All rivers have curves. Mature rivers usually have more of them. Compare the rivers in the diagram on page 287. The water flows faster and pushes harder against the outside of each curve and erodes that bank faster. Water slows down on the inside of each curve, allowing sediment to settle and build up. This process creates large, looping bends called **meanders**.

As a mature river's meanders grow, its **floodplain** also grows. A floodplain is the low, flat area that a river covers when it overflows its banks. Floodwaters leave behind rich soil and nutrients on floodplains.

The valleys of old rivers are broad and flat. By this time, the river has eroded its way down to near sea level. Old rivers tend to have enlarged meanders and more of them. As a meander continues to grow, it forms almost a complete circle. During a flood, the river may break through its banks and flow straighter. The meander is cut off and becomes a C-shaped **oxbow lake**. The Mississippi River, shown in the radar image, is an old river.

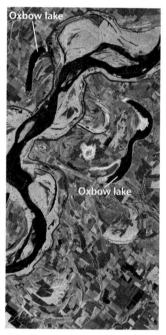

This image, taken from a space shuttle, shows oxbow lakes along the Mississippi River.

River Deposits

Sediment carried by the agents of erosion is eventually dropped in a process called **deposition**. For example, when a river slows down, it may drop, or deposit, its sediment. Heavy particles, such as stones, drop out first. As the river slows down further, lighter sediment, such as sand and clay, drops out.

A river slows down considerably as it empties into a lake or an ocean. The place where a river flows into a larger body of water is called the **mouth** of the river. Sediment settles out at the river's mouth. Eventually, the sediment builds up above the water level and forms a fan-shaped area of land called a **delta**. As the diagram below shows, a river usually branches off as it winds through the delta and empties. A delta provides rich farmland. Much of Egypt's farmland, for example, is located on the fertile Nile River delta.

An **alluvial fan** is similar to a delta. It forms at the base of a mountain where a mountain stream meets level land.

Deposition

Dropping of eroded sediment

Mouth

Place where a river flows into a larger body of water

Delta

Fan-shaped area of land formed when sediment is deposited where a river empties into a lake or an ocean

Alluvial fan

Fan-shaped area of land deposited where a mountain stream moves onto flat land

LEARNING STYLES

Body/Kinesthetic

Students can model three types of loads carried by rivers. Have students put a tablespoon of sugar or salt, some clay-rich soil, and a few small pebbles in a jar of hot tap water. Instruct students to shake the jar. The pebbles will settle, like boulders dragged along the bottom of a river—called the bed load; the clay will remain suspended—the suspended load; and some of the sugar/salt will dissolve—the dissolved load.

CAREER CONNECTION

Explain that civil engineers are involved in construction projects dealing with water resources, such as dams, canals, and bridges. Some civil engineers are experts in soil and rocks. This knowledge is essential for many building projects. Have interested students find out about college or university civil engineering programs.

LEARNING STYLES

Auditory/Verbal

Encourage interested students to write a script describing the various types of water erosion. Have them use the script to create an audiotape and play it for the class.

Interpersonal/ Group Learning

Have groups of students make a list of ways that water changes the land in your area. Lists might include rainwater running off an empty dirt lot, rain washing away loose soil or mulch from a flower bed, a local river or stream eroding and depositing sediment, waves lapping up on a beach, rivers flooding, or water freezing and thawing in cracks in the pavement.

IN THE ENVIRONMENT

Encourage students to adopt a vacant lot or other area that is subject to erosion. They might plant grass, flowers, and even tree seedlings to help beautify the area and reduce erosion from moving water. If this is not practical, suggest that students draw up a plan of how they would approach such a task. You may wish to do this activity after completing Investigation 12-2.

Wave Erosion

Waves in an ocean or a large lake change the shoreline through erosion and deposition. As waves pound the shoreline, they hurl not only water but also bits of rock and sand against the coast. These materials chip away at the rocky shore. Waves also force water into cracks in rocks along the shoreline. With each wave, the water presses against the sides of the cracks. The cracks get bigger, and pieces of rock split off.

This type of erosion formed the cliffs, towers, and other rocky shapes shown in the photo below. During storms, waves reach higher on cliffs and carve steep sides. Arches form when waves erode through a cliff. If the top of an arch collapses, a tower of rock called a sea stack is left standing.

How has wave erosion shaped this shoreline in Australia?

Wave Deposits

Beaches are areas where waves have deposited sand, pebbles, or shells. Some of this beach material is sediment from nearby eroded rocks. Other beach material is sediment carried to the lake or ocean by rivers. Currents near the shore carry sediment to different parts of the shoreline. As waves break on shore, the sediment is pushed onto the beach.

Currents along the shore can change the shape of a beach. One result is a spit, or curved finger of sand, sticking out into the water. Waves and currents can also carry sand away from the beach and deposit a long, underwater sandbar offshore.

Write your answers to these questions on a sheet of paper.

1. What is erosion?

2. How does a young river differ from an old river?

3. Explain how a meander becomes an oxbow lake.

4. How does a delta differ from an alluvial fan?

5. From where does the sand on a beach come?

Science in Your Life

Erosion Caused by People

People's actions sometimes cause too much erosion. This can be harmful to the environment and to people. One way that people increase erosion is by using off-road vehicles (ORVs) such as dirt bikes, dune buggies, and all-terrain vehicles. Their overuse has damaged land and threatened the survival of plants and animals.

The photo below illustrates this problem. This hillside used to be covered with grass. The roots of grass and other plants hold soil in place and catch water runoff. Animals use the plants and the areas around them as habitats. Many of the plants are food for animals.

Within weeks, ORVs dug up the vegetation and created ruts. When it rained, the rainwater followed these ruts and formed deep gullies. The exposed soil now erodes quickly from the hill. Areas have been set aside for ORVs, but some people go into closed areas.

Are there areas around your home where people are causing erosion? Go for a walk and take your own survey. Look for evidence of erosion from human activity. Can you think of ways to prevent this erosion?

Weathering and Erosion   Chapter 12   **291**

Lab Manual 46, pages 1–2

Workbook Activity 47

Lesson 2 Review Answers

1. the wearing away and moving of weathered rock and soil. **2.** A young river is narrow and fast, can move boulders, and occupies most of its V-shaped valley. It may contain rocky ledges, waterfalls, and rapids. An old river slowly moves across a flat, wide valley that has eroded to near sea level. It meanders across a floodplain, can move only small sediment, and may have created oxbow lakes over time. Its valley is much wider than the river itself. **3.** As a meander continues to grow, it forms a more pronounced loop, almost a circle. During a flood, the river may break through its banks and flow straighter, cutting off the meander and forming an oxbow lake. **4.** A delta is formed by sediment building up at the mouth of a river. An alluvial fan forms similarly, but at the base of a mountain where a mountain stream meets flat land. **5.** Sand comes from eroded rocks along the shore and from rivers that flow over rocks as they make their way to the lake or ocean.

Science in Your Life

Have volunteers take turns reading aloud the feature on page 291. Have students make a list of examples of erosion caused by humans. Examples might include construction and development, poor farming practices, misuse of beaches, and cutting down forests. Discuss these examples and ask students to suggest ways to prevent this erosion. Suggestions might include creating laws that prevent specific practices and educating people about the importance and methods of prevention.

Portfolio Assessment

Sample items include:
• Section summaries from Teaching the Lesson
• Lesson 2 Review answers

Weathering and Erosion   Chapter 12   **291**

The Purpose portion of the student investigation begins with a question to draw students into the activity. Encourage students to read the investigation steps and formulate their own questions before beginning the investigation. This investigation will take approximately 45 minutes to complete. Students will use these process and thinking skills: observing, comparing and contrasting, making and using models, collecting and organizing data, communicating, and drawing conclusions.

Preparation

• Oblong cake pans propped up with small blocks of wood can be substituted for the paint trays.

• If time is a limiting factor, begin to grow the grass a week or so before you introduce students to this activity. Alternatively, you can use small pieces of sod.

• Make sure the sprinkling cans have small holes. Too much water flowing from the can will erode most of the soil in the pan without the grass.

• Students may use Lab Manual 47 to record their data and answer the questions.

Procedure

• This investigation may be done individually or in groups. For groups, assign one student to gather equipment. Suggest how group members can cooperatively delegate the planting and watering tasks. All students should record results and clean up when finished.

• Check student setups to ensure that the soil is packed firmly but not so densely that erosion will not occur.

• Before they begin sprinkling the hillsides, have students determine how they will measure the amount of soil eroded in both trays. While there is no need to determine an exact amount, students should be prepared to contrast the amounts of eroded soil to make valid conclusions.

• Make sure students realize that in any valid scientific investigation, only one factor is varied and tested at a time. The variable in this investigation is the effect

12-2 INVESTIGATION

Comparing Erosion

Materials
◆ newspaper
◆ 2 paint trays
◆ soil
◆ grass seeds
◆ sprinkling can
◆ water

Purpose
Do the trees, shrubs, and plants growing on a hillside help prevent erosion? In this investigation, you will find out if vegetation affects erosion.

Procedure

1. Cover your work surface with newspaper. Spread a layer of soil in each paint tray to a depth of about 5 centimeters. Cover only the part of the tray that gently slopes downward. This will model a hillside. Wet or pack the soil a little if necessary so that it stays on the hillside.

2. Plant a handful of grass seeds evenly in the soil of one tray. Wash your hands and clean your work space. Place the trays side by side on clean newspaper.

3. Gently water the seeds every day for about a week, until the grass grows a few centimeters. **Safety Alert: Wipe up any spills immediately.**

4. Copy the data table on your paper.

Trial	Bare Soil	Soil with Grass
1		
2		
3		
4		
5		

5. Sprinkle water over each tray for 5 seconds. Sprinkle toward the top of the tray so that the water can run down the hill. In the data table, record your observations about how the water runs down each hill and how much erosion occurs.

6. Repeat the 5-second sprinkling four more times. Record your observations after each sprinkling.

Questions and Conclusions

1. What differences in water flow did you observe between the two hillsides?

2. What differences in erosion did you observe between the two hillsides?

3. What differences did you observe about the color of the water at the bottom of the two trays?

4. How can you use the results of this experiment to prevent unwanted erosion in areas near your home?

Explore Further

Do certain kinds of vegetation reduce erosion better than others? Redesign the experiment to find out.

Weathering and Erosion   Chapter 12   **293**

SAFETY ALERT

◆ Caution students to wipe up any spills immediately.

---

of vegetation on soil erosion. The amount of water, the length of time that it flows from the can, and the height from which it is sprinkled must be the same for both trays.

Results

Students will discover that the effects of vegetation on soil erosion are twofold: the blades of grass act as baffles to reduce the force with which the water hits the soil, and the roots of the grass anchor the soil.

Questions and Conclusions Answers

1. The hillside with the grass held more of the water than the bare hillside, so less of the water ran all the way down the hill. The water also flowed more slowly down the grassy hillside.

2. More erosion occurred on the bare hillside than on the grassy hillside.

3. The water at the bottom of the hillside without grass was darker because it contained more soil.

4. Students might suggest planting vegetation on slopes or even on flat land to prevent erosion by water.

Explore Further Answers

Ideas will vary, but students might suggest testing the effects of dense ground cover compared to spotty vegetation, or grass compared to other plant species. Before students attempt to carry out the new experiment, have them write a hypothesis and a detailed procedure. Once you have checked the procedures, allow students to test their hypotheses.

Assessment

Be sure that students have accurately and fully recorded their observations. Check that they have a method of comparing the amount of erosion between the two models. Be sure that students have used their observations to arrive at the correct generalization that planting vegetation lessens the effects of erosion. You might include the following items from this investigation in student portfolios:

- Data table
- Answers to Questions and Conclusions and Explore Further sections

Chapter 12 Lesson 3

Overview In this lesson, students learn about another kind of water erosion—erosion by frozen bodies of water called glaciers. Students will compare and contrast alpine and continental glaciers and how they change the earth's surface.

Objectives

- To define two types of glaciers
- To explain how glaciers erode the land
- To describe features caused by glaciers

Student Pages 294–299

Teacher's Resource Library **TRL**

Workbook Activity 48

Alternative Workbook Activity 48

Vocabulary

cirque	horn
glacier	moraine

Science Background

Glaciers are masses of ice in motion. There are two kinds of glaciers: alpine glaciers and continental glaciers. Today, glaciers cover parts of the earth with a combined volume of 25 million cubic kilometers of ice. During some periods of the earth's history, called ice ages, alpine and continental glaciers were much more extensive than they are today. There were at least four ice ages in North America during the past 2 million years, at which time over 70 million cubic kilometers of ice covered the earth. The cause of ice ages is most commonly thought to be slight variations in the earth's orbit around the sun.

Objectives

After reading this lesson, you should be able to

- ◆ define two types of glaciers.
- ◆ explain how glaciers erode the land.
- ◆ describe features caused by glaciers.

Glacier

Thick mass of ice that covers a large area

Two conditions are needed for glaciers to form: year-round cold temperatures and heavy snowfall. Siberia in northern Russia has constant cold weather. But because it receives little snowfall, no glaciers form there.

In cold climates, water falls as snow. This snow can build up into thick layers. If the snow does not melt, increasing pressure causes the snow below to form solid ice. Year after year, more ice builds up. Eventually, a **glacier** may form. A glacier is a thick mass of ice that covers a large area. Glaciers may be as small as a football field or hundreds of kilometers long.

Glaciers form only where average temperatures stay below freezing. So they are found only in mountain regions and near the poles. Glaciers in mountain regions are called alpine glaciers. They move slowly downhill. Notice how the alpine glacier in the photo below extends down the valley. Glaciers that cover broad areas of land near the poles are called continental glaciers. Continental glaciers cover most of Antarctica and Greenland.

The Muldrow Glacier in Alaska flows down the north side of Mount McKinley. It is a popular climbing route.

Cirque

Bowl-like basin in a mountain that is carved out by an alpine glacier

Horn

Jagged, pyramid-shaped peak formed by the intersection of three or more cirques

Gravity causes glaciers to move. As glaciers move, they pick up loose sediment. Because of their great size, glaciers move huge boulders and soil. These materials freeze onto the bottom and sides of the glacier. They act like grinding and cutting tools as the glacier continues to move. The photo below shows how large rocks in the bottom of a glacier cut long grooves in the surface rock. Small rocks in a glacier act like sandpaper, smoothing and shaping the land beneath.

This limestone cliff on Kelleys Island in Lake Erie was carved by a glacier.

A horn forms where several cirques come together.

Alpine Glaciers

Alpine glaciers begin in the upper reaches of mountain valleys. As they begin to move, these glaciers carve out bowl-shaped basins called **cirques**. Several cirques around the top of the mountain may form a pyramid-shaped peak called a **horn**. The Matterhorn in Switzerland, shown in the photo on the left, is one of the most famous horns.

*Weathering and Erosion   Chapter 12   **295***

Warm-Up Activity

To demonstrate how glaciers erode the land, prepare a model of a glacier ahead of time. Fill an empty cardboard juice carton three-fourths full of water. Add about 5 tablespoons of sand and some pea gravel to the water. Fasten the top securely so that it can be laid on its side without leaking. Lay the carton on its side in a freezer. Allow the water to freeze. Peel off the cardboard. To demonstrate how glaciers act as agents of erosion, push the "glacier," sediment side down, along a bed of dry sand in a large baking pan. Allow students to inspect the scars left by the gravel. Ask them what will happen when the glacier melts. (*The gravel embedded in the bottom will stay behind.*) Explain to students that they will learn about glacial erosion and deposition in this lesson. Freeze the glacier for use in Teaching the Lesson.

Teaching the Lesson

On the board, write a brief outline with the following major heads: *Glaciers, Erosion by Glaciers, Deposition by Glaciers.* As students read this lesson, have them complete the outline on a sheet of paper. They should include details about the two types of glaciers and how each changes the earth's surface.

Use a globe to point out locations around the world where glaciers might be found. Continental glaciers cover much of Greenland and Antarctica. Alpine glaciers form in mountainous regions and can be found in the Rocky Mountains and Alaska in the United States, high in the Andes in South America, in parts of northern Canada, in the Himalayas, and in the Alps.

Use the "glacier" and pan of sand from the Warm-Up Activity to demonstrate how glacial grooves are used to indicate the direction of glacier movement. Without students watching, drag the glacier along the model landscape to erode the area. Show students the eroded sand and have them deduce the glacier's direction.

Place the glacier in the pan of sand. Allow it to melt and deposit its load to model a moraine.

Moraine

Ridge of sediment deposited by a glacier

Did You Know?

The majestic fjords of Norway and Alaska are U-shaped glacial valleys that are partly filled by ocean water.

The largest alpine glaciers are in northern Canada, Alaska, the Andes in South America, and the Himalayas in Asia.

Before it was covered with a glacier, a mountain valley may have been shaped by a river. The valley would have had a typical V shape. As the glacier moves down the mountain, it gouges out the valley like a giant ice cream scoop. As a result, the V-shaped valley becomes a U-shaped valley.

The glacier continues to move down the mountain until it reaches temperatures warm enough to melt. As the ice melts, it deposits sediment. The sediment forms ridges called **moraines**. Moraines are the "footprints," or evidence, of a glacier, telling us it was here. In the photo, notice the U-shaped valley, glacial lake, and moraines. Trace the glacier's path with your finger.

Some glaciers move into a body of water before they melt. When a piece of a glacier breaks off in the water, it becomes an iceberg.

This Montana scene shows where a glacier slid down a mountain valley and melted. Trees now grow on the moraines around the lake.

Continental Glaciers

Ice shelves are continental glaciers that extend over water. Antarctica is surrounded by many ice shelves. Ice caps are small, dome-shaped continental glaciers. Part of Iceland is covered by an ice cap.

Continental glaciers are up to 4 kilometers thick. Because of their tremendous size and weight, these glaciers transform the surface of the land. They change the courses of rivers and create lakes great and small. Continental glaciers can even move boulders the size of houses hundreds of kilometers.

About 10 percent of the earth is currently covered by glaciers. Most of these glaciers are the continental glaciers that cover Antarctica and Greenland. These two large land areas are often shown in white on maps and globes.

Continental glaciers covered parts of North America and Europe long ago. How do we know? Like alpine glaciers, continental glaciers mark their boundaries by leaving behind moraines. The map shows the location of major moraines surrounding the Great Lakes. These moraines are left from the last ice age, when much of the Northern Hemisphere was covered by continental glaciers. This ice age started more than a million years ago and ended about 10,000 years ago.

Moraines

CROSS-CURRICULAR CONNECTION

Geography

Scientists estimate that if the Antarctic ice sheet were to melt completely, sea level would rise 60 to 70 meters. Have students use a regional or country map to make a list of major coastal cities and other areas that would be affected by this rise in sea level.

GLOBAL CONNECTION

The continental glacier, or ice cap, on Greenland covers 1,833,909 square kilometers, 85 percent of the island. The ice cap is an average of 1.6 kilometers thick. Parts are as much as 3 kilometers thick. The most active glacier on the island is located at Ilulissat. It moves 25 to 30 meters per day. Greenland has been growing warmer since the early 1900s, and therefore the ice cap is shrinking. Greenland has 55,000 people, who live on the southwestern coast. Have students find more facts about and pictures of Greenland on the Internet or in the library and write an itinerary for a visit to this Arctic nation.

LEARNING STYLES

Body/Kinesthetic

Have small groups of students create and perform skits illustrating lesson concepts about glaciers. Each skit could center on either continental or alpine glaciers and should incorporate location, movement, erosion, deposition, and any other information students wish to include.

IN THE COMMUNITY

If your area was glaciated in the past, take students on a field trip to observe the erosion and deposition that resulted from these masses of ice in motion. Obtain topographic maps of your area before you go and have students compare what they see with how these features are represented on the map.

At the end of this ice age, the glaciers began to melt. Huge blocks of ice broke off from the glaciers. As shown below, these blocks became partly buried in sediment. When an ice block melted, it left a hole in the ground. The hole filled with water. Many of the small lakes in Wisconsin and Minnesota formed this way.

Large lakes formed from these continental glaciers, too. Some glaciers carved wide, deep basins. As they melted, the glaciers filled the basins with water. Moraines dammed parts of the lakes. This process created the Great Lakes, the Finger Lakes in New York, and Lake Winnipeg in Canada.

1. An ice block breaks off a glacier.

2. The ice block gets partly buried in sediment.

3. The ice block melts to form a lake.

Lesson 3 REVIEW

Write your answers to these questions on a sheet of paper.

1. Describe the two kinds of glaciers.

2. How does a glacier erode the land as the glacier moves?

3. How does a horn form?

4. How does a moraine form?

5. Describe how the Great Lakes formed.

Achievements in Science

Artificial Glaciers

A new process is being developed to capture and hold water needed for crops. This process creates artificial glaciers. Some scientists think artificial glaciers may someday help many water-starved villages around the world.

Chewang Norphel, an engineer from Ladakh, India, has experimented with artificial glaciers. Norphel wanted to solve the water shortage in Ladakh. This farming village is located high in the Himalayas. It gets very little rain.

In the 1990s, Norphel helped Ladakh build five artificial glaciers. The new glaciers increased the village's water supply and improved farming.

Creating the glaciers was simple. Before winter set in, water from an existing stream was piped to valley areas. Then this water was forced to flow downhill. Along the way, stone walls were built to stop the water flow and form pools. As temperatures fell, the pools froze. The process of flowing, pooling, and freezing was repeated for many weeks. The pools became thick sheets of ice—artificial glaciers.

It cost only $2,000 to build Ladakh's glaciers. Because of the success of Norphel's experiment, interest in artificial glaciers is growing. A major project to create glaciers in Pakistan has already begun.

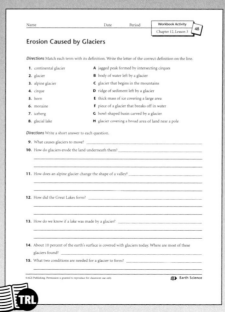

Workbook Activity 48

Lesson 3 Review Answers

1. Alpine glaciers form in mountain valleys. Continental glaciers are much bigger and cover large areas of land. **2.** The mass of moving ice and the scraping action of the rocks embedded near the bottom of the glacier cause erosion of the land as the glacier moves and drops soil and rocks. **3.** A horn forms when several cirques around the top of a mountain form a pyramid-shaped peak. **4.** A moraine forms when glacier ice melts and deposits sediment, forming ridges. **5.** Continental glaciers carved wide, deep basins. When they melted, the water filled the basins, forming the Great Lakes.

Achievements in Science

Have students take turns reading aloud the feature on page 299. Ask them to describe the kinds of areas in which artificial glaciers could be used. Point out that the areas would have to have lakes or streams and would have to get very cold in winter. Therefore, desert areas in warm climates could not be helped by this technology.

Portfolio Assessment

Sample items include:
• Outline from Teaching the Lesson
• Lesson 3 Review answers

Lesson at a Glance

Chapter 12 Lesson 4

Overview In this lesson, students find out how wind and gravity act as agents of erosion. They learn how sand dunes form and how gravity moves loosened soil and rock.

Objectives

- To describe how wind erodes land
- To explain how sand dunes form
- To identify examples of erosion by gravity

Student Pages 300–302

Teacher's Resource Library 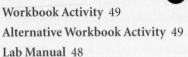 **TRL**

Workbook Activity 49

Alternative Workbook Activity 49

Lab Manual 48

Science Background

As an agent of erosion and deposition, wind is most effective in arid and semiarid regions of the world. Scant precipitation and vegetation in these regions allow the wind to pick up, transport, and deposit vast amounts of fine sediment (sand and silt).

Gravity is an agent of erosion and deposition all over the earth, causing water, ice, soil, sediment, and rocks to move down riverbeds, valleys, mountains, and hillsides.

▶ 1 Warm-Up Activity

Use a blow dryer, sand, a shallow cardboard box, and a small pebble to model how sand dunes form. Put safety goggles on and instruct students to do the same. Put the pebble toward one end of the box. Add the sand to the other end of the box. With the dryer on low, blow the sand toward the pebble and watch the dune form. Change the direction of the "wind" and have students observe how changing wind direction alters the shape of the dune.

Objectives

After reading this lesson, you should be able to

- describe how wind erodes land.
- explain how sand dunes form.
- identify examples of erosion by gravity.

 Did You Know?

Some sand dunes in the Sahara, a desert in Africa, grow to be hundreds of meters tall.

Science Myth

Many people think of deserts as hot, sandy places.

Fact: Deserts are harsh environments with little rainfall and extreme temperatures. Parts of frozen Antarctica are considered deserts.

Wind Erosion and Deposits

Wind is another cause of erosion. Like water, wind picks up and carries materials from one place to another. Wind also erodes by blowing sand against rock. This action is similar to a sandblaster used to clean buildings discolored by pollution. If you have ever been stung in the face by windblown sand, you know wind can be an effective agent of erosion. Much rock in desert areas is pitted with tiny holes from windblown sand.

You are probably familiar with wind deposits called sand dunes. These are mounds formed as the wind blows sand from one place to another. Sand dunes are most common in deserts, but they also occur around beaches.

Wind may bounce sand along the ground until it hits an obstacle, such as a small rock. A small sand pile forms behind the rock. The pile blocks other sand grains, and a larger mound forms. The mound continues to grow, forming a sand dune. The dune moves as wind blows sand up the gentle slope and deposits it on the steeper back slope, as shown below.

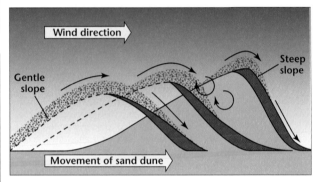

Did You Know?

Have a volunteer read aloud the Did You Know? feature on page 300. Point out that the Sahara is the world's largest desert, covering about 9 million square kilometers. Have students find the desert on a world map. Explain that this desert consists of rock and gravel plateaus and plains as well as huge shifting areas of sand called ergs. Encourage interested students to find photos of the Sahara online or in the library.

Science Myth

Have one volunteer read the myth portion and one the fact portion of the feature on page 300. Explain that some scientists define a desert as an area that receives less than 25 centimeters of precipitation per year.

Landslides can occur because of earthquakes, floods, and volcanic eruptions. These events loosen soil and rock. Human activities, such as cutting down trees or overdeveloping areas, can increase the likelihood of landslides.

The Role of Gravity in Erosion

Gravity plays a part in all erosion. For example, rivers and alpine glaciers flow because of gravity. Gravity can move only material that has been loosened in some way. One way rock and soil are loosened is by freezing and thawing. Another way this happens is by heavy rains. A great deal of water can make soil smooth and slippery. Soil in this condition flows easily. When material on a hillside is loosened, gravity can cause rapid erosion. Mudflows and landslides are examples of this.

The photo below shows how gravity can make erosion happen rapidly. This hillside was loosened until it gave way to gravity's downward pull. In this case, the result was a landslide that damaged a Colorado road. Have you ever seen a sign that reads Caution: Falling Rock? Then you know about another result of erosion by gravity.

Gravity works slowly, too. You may have noticed old telephone poles or grave markers that tilt downhill. Loose soil and rocks move slowly downhill, tilting objects along the way.

This road in the Rocky Mountains crosses an area of landslide activity.

Weathering and Erosion Chapter 12 **301**

Teacher Alert

 Point out that gravity erodes certain types of landscapes more than others. It affects mountainous and hilly areas more than flat areas.

Science Journal

 Ask students to recall a specific example of a formation discussed in this chapter that they have seen. Ask them to remember what impressed them about this formation. Then have them write a description of it. They might choose a canyon, delta, sand dune, cave, river, waterfall, shoreline or beach, glacier, glacial valley, or glacial lake. If they haven't seen any of these, they might choose to describe an example of weathering or erosion caused by gravity.

2 Teaching the Lesson

As they read the lesson, have students make concept maps that illustrate how wind and gravity change the land.

Explain that, unlike a river, wind can only carry sediment that is sand-sized or smaller. Like a river, though, the wind has a bed load and a suspended load. The bed load of wind is sand, which seldom travels more than a meter above the ground; the wind's suspended load is made of fine, clay-sized particles that travel higher and farther.

Have students revisit their results from Investigation 12-2. Ask them to hypothesize why vegetation on beach dunes should never be disturbed. *(Students should reason that, like the grass in the investigation, dune vegetation holds the sand in place to prevent erosion.)*

3 Reinforce and Extend

CROSS-CURRICULAR CONNECTION

 Social Studies
In the Dust Bowl of the 1930s, much of the topsoil eroded from the American Great Plains. Have interested students research this event, its causes, and ways to avoid such drastic erosion.

SCIENCE INTEGRATION

 Physical Science
Newton's second law of motion states that the force needed to accelerate an object is proportional to its mass, meaning that it takes less force to lift small objects than large objects. Therefore, it takes less wind force to blow fine particles of soil than large grains of sand. These fine particles also blow farther, sometimes forming loamy deposits called loess instead of dunes. Loess deposits create very fertile topsoils.

Lesson 4 Review Answers

1. by blowing particles against rocks and by transporting particles to other places **2.** A sand dune forms when wind causes sand to pile up behind an obstacle. As the sand accumulates, it blocks more sand and eventually a large dune is formed. **3.** in deserts and around beaches **4.** Possible answers include mudflows, landslides, falling rocks, and tilted objects. **5.** by freezing and thawing and by heavy rains

Science at Work

Have students take turns reading the paragraphs in the feature on page 302. Lead them in a discussion about flooding in your area: recent floods, their causes, and the resulting damage. If possible, invite a floodplain manager or civil engineer to class to discuss flood prevention.

Portfolio Assessment

Sample items include:
- Concept map from Teaching the Lesson
- Lesson 4 Review answers

Write your answers to these questions on a sheet of paper.

1. What are two ways that wind erodes the land?

2. How does a sand dune form?

3. Where do sand dunes form?

4. Give examples of erosion caused by gravity.

5. How are rocks and soil loosened?

▼◄▲▼◄▲▼◄▲▼◄▲▼◄▲▼◄▲▼◄▲▼◄▲▼◄▲▼◄▲▼◄▲▼◄▲▼◄▲▼

Science at Work

Floodplain Manager

Flooding can cause great loss, damage, and danger to people and the environment. Rebuilding after a flood is costly. Floodplain managers help prevent floods and reduce flood damage. They also protect water and soil resources.

Floodplain managers inspect systems that hold storm water. Floodplain managers make sure that builders follow rules for excavating, or digging, at construction sites. They also meet with government officials and city planners.

Many floodplain managers have a bachelor's degree in civil engineering. Some local governments offer floodplain management training programs. These training programs focus on storm water runoff, erosion control, and rules to prevent water pollution.

Floodplain managers should have a strong math and science background. They should be able to understand blueprints and maps. Computer and communication skills are also important. A good floodplain manager cares about the environment and safety.

302 *Chapter 12 Weathering and Erosion*

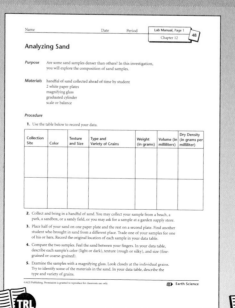

Lab Manual 48, pages 1–2

Workbook Activity 49

Chapter 12 SUMMARY

- All rock exposed at the surface begins to break apart.

- Mechanical weathering is the process of breaking up rocks without changing their mineral makeup.

- Chemical weathering is the process of breaking up rocks by changing the minerals in them.

- Soil is a mixture of weathered rock and the remains of plants and animals.

- Fully developed soil includes a topsoil, a subsoil, and a layer of partially weathered rock.

- The process by which weathered rock bits and soil are moved is called erosion.

- Erosion is caused by water, glaciers, wind, and gravity.

- As a river erodes the land, it carves out a valley. Rivers and valleys change with time.

- A river deposits sediment where it flows into a lake or an ocean, forming a delta.

- Waves wear away the shoreline in some places and build it up in others.

- Glaciers are moving masses of ice. Alpine glaciers move down mountains. Continental glaciers cover broad areas of land.

- Glaciers form U-shaped valleys and scrape the land.

- Glaciers leave ridges of sediment called moraines. Glaciers have formed many lakes.

- Wind causes erosion by carrying sediment and by blowing it against rock.

- Sand dunes form as sand collects into a huge mound.

- Gravity moves rock and soil downhill. This process can occur quickly or slowly.

Science Words

alluvial fan, 289	erosion, 286	mechanical weathering, 280	oxidation, 281
chemical weathering, 281	floodplain, 288	moraine, 296	soil, 282
cirque, 295	glacier, 294	mouth, 289	subsoil, 282
delta, 289	horn, 295	oxbow lake, 288	topsoil, 282
deposition, 289	meander, 288		weathering, 280

Chapter 12 Summary

Have volunteers read aloud each Summary item on page 303. Ask volunteers to explain the meaning of each item. Direct students' attention to the Science Words box on the bottom of page 303. Have them read and review each word and its definition.

Chapter 12 Review

Use the Chapter Review to prepare students for tests and to reteach content from the chapter.

Chapter 12 Mastery Test

The Teacher's Resource Library includes two parallel forms of the Chapter 12 Mastery Test. The difficulty level of the two forms is equivalent. You may wish to use one form as a pretest and the other form as a posttest.

Review Answers
Vocabulary Review

1. erosion 2. delta 3. weathering
4. meander 5. horn 6. soil 7. alpine
8. moraine 9. oxbow lake 10. cirque

Concept Review

11. B 12. D 13. A 14. C 15. C 16. D

TEACHER ALERT

In the Chapter Review, the Vocabulary Review activity includes a sample of the chapter's vocabulary terms. The activity will help determine students' understanding of key vocabulary terms and concepts presented in the chapter. Other vocabulary terms used in the chapter are listed below:

alluvial fan
chemical weathering
deposition
floodplain
glacier
mechanical weathering
mouth
oxidation
subsoil
topsoil

Chapter 12 R E V I E W

Vocabulary Review

Choose the word or phrase from the Word Bank that best completes each sentence. Write the answer on your paper.

Word Bank
alpine
cirque
delta
erosion
horn
meander
moraine
oxbow lake
soil
weathering

1. The process of moving weathered rock and soil is _____.

2. Sediment settles out where a river empties into an ocean, forming a(n) _____.

3. The breaking down of rocks on the earth's surface is _____.

4. A large, looping curve in a river is a(n) _____.

5. Several cirques can intersect to form a jagged _____.

6. A mixture of bits of weathered rock and decayed material is _____.

7. Glaciers that form in mountain valleys are _____ glaciers.

8. Rock and sediment that drop from a glacier form a ridge called a(n) _____.

9. A C-shaped body of water formed when a meander is cut off is a(n) _____.

10. A bowl-shaped basin carved out of a mountain by an alpine glacier is a(n) _____.

Concept Review

Choose the word or phrase that best completes each sentence. Write the letter of the answer on your paper.

11. Two characteristics of a young river are a _____.
   A U-shaped valley and slow-moving water
   B V-shaped valley and fast-moving water
   C wide valley and many meanders
   D shallow valley and oxbow lakes

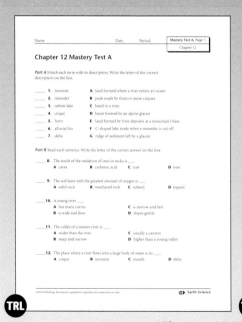

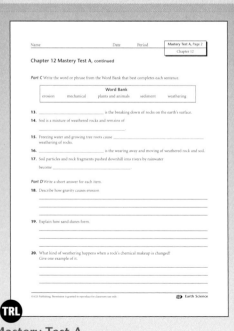

Chapter 12 Mastery Test A

12. During oxidation, oxygen combines with iron to form iron oxide, or _____.
    A clay   B carbonic acid   C feldspar   D rust

13. The land covered by an overflowing river is the river's _____.
    A floodplain   C delta
    B water table   D topsoil

14. Water freezing in the cracks of rocks is an example of _____.
    A deposition   C mechanical weathering
    B chemical weathering D erosion

15. The main process that forms a beach is _____.
    A weathering   C deposition
    B erosion   D oxidation

16. An alluvial fan forms at the base of a mountain and is similar to a _____.
    A sand dune   B cirque   C glacier   D delta

Critical Thinking

Write the answer to each of the following questions.

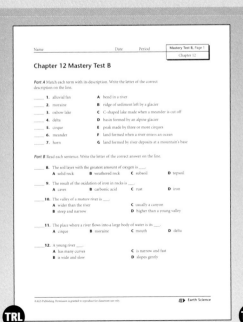

17. Name each lettered layer shown in the diagram.

18. Why would a farmer plow across a hillside instead of plowing straight down the slope?

19. Once a rock breaks into pieces, weathering occurs faster. Explain why.

20. Sand dunes near a beach are being blown toward a neighborhood. Residents want to keep the dunes, but they don't want the blowing sand. What can they do?

Test-Taking Tip When studying for a test, use the titles and subtitles within a chapter to help you recall information.

Review Answers
Critical Thinking

17. A topsoil B subsoil C weathered rock D solid rock 18. Plowed tracks across a hillside would be level, helping prevent soil erosion when water runs down the slope. Plowed tracks down a hillside would be sloped like the hill, increasing soil erosion by water and gravity. 19. As a rock breaks into smaller pieces, more of it is exposed to air, water, and living things, factors that promote more weathering. 20. Students might suggest that barricades be built around the dunes to prevent their blowing into the neighborhood. A better solution would be to grow plants on the dunes, as vegetation would anchor the sand and keep it from being blown away.

ALTERNATIVE ASSESSMENT

Alternative Assessment items correlate to the student Goals for Learning at the beginning of this chapter.

- Have students use the boldfaced terms in Lesson 1 to write a paragraph explaining how physical and chemical weathering of sandstone might eventually produce a sandy soil.

- Instruct students to draw a diagram showing how a river and its valley change with time.

- Divide the class into four groups. Assign each group one agent of erosion: water, ice, wind, and gravity. Have the groups design and carry out for the class a simple activity that shows how their agent causes loosened rock and soil to wear away and move.

- Have each student draw a different type of eroded landform: river valleys and floodplains, shorelines, cliffs, sea stacks, glacial valleys and grooves, cirques, horns, pitted sand-blown rock, or landslides. Then make a class collage, grouping the landforms by their agent of erosion.

- Ask students to prepare a chart that lists deposited landforms and their causes. The chart should list deltas, alluvial fans, beaches, sandbars, moraines, and sand dunes.

Chapter 12 Mastery Test B

Planning Guide

Forces in the Earth

		Student Pages	Vocabulary	Lesson Review
Lesson 1	Movement of the Earth's Crust	308–312	✔	✔
Lesson 2	Volcanoes	313–316	✔	✔
Lesson 3	Mountains	317–321	✔	✔
Lesson 4	Earthquakes	322–328	✔	✔

Chapter Activities

Student Text
Science Center
Teacher's Resource Library
Community Connection 13: Mountain
 Making

Assessment Options

Student Text
Chapter 13 Review

Teacher's Resource Library
Chapter 13 Mastery Tests A and B

	Student Text Features								Teaching Strategies						Learning Styles						Teacher's Resource Library				
Achievements in Science	Science at Work	Science in Your Life	Investigation	Science Myth	Note	Technology Note	Did You Know	Science Integration	Science Journal	Cross-Curricular Connection	Online Connection	Teacher Alert	Applications (Home, Career, Community, Global, Environment)	Auditory/Verbal	Body/Kinesthetic	Interpersonal/Group Learning	Logical/Mathematical	Visual/Spatial	LEP/ESL	Workbook Activities	Alternative Workbook Activities	Lab Manual	Resource File	Self-Study Guide
312					✔		311	310	309	310	310	310	309, 311		309		309	311	311	50	50	49	29, 30	✔
		316			✔		314			315	314	314	314, 315			315				51	51			✔
			320	318	✔				318	318					318					52	52	50		✔
	326	327					323	325		324	325		324, 325	324						53	53	51, 52		✔

Pronunciation Key

a	hat	e	let	ī	ice	ô	order	ù	put	sh	she	ə	a in about
ā	age	ē	equal	o	hot	oi	oil	ü	rule	th	thin		e in taken
ä	far	ėr	term	ō	open	ou	out	ch	child	ᵮH	then		i in pencil
â	care	i	it	ȯ	saw	u	cup	ng	long	zh	measure		o in lemon
													u in circus

Alternative Workbook Activities

The Teacher's Resource Library (TRL) contains a set of lower-level worksheets called Alternative Workbook Activities. These worksheets cover the same content as the regular Workbook Activities but are written at a second-grade reading level.

Skill Track Software

Use the Skill Track Software for Earth Science for additional reinforcement of this chapter. The software program allows students using AGS textbooks to be assessed for mastery of each chapter and lesson of the textbook. Students access the software on an individual basis and are assessed with multiple-choice items.

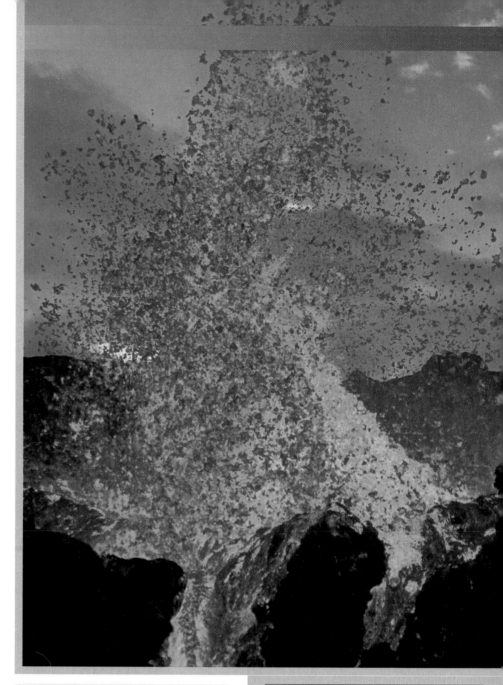

Chapter at a Glance

Chapter 13:
Forces in the Earth
pages 306–331

Lessons

1. **Movement of the Earth's Crust** pages 308–312

2. **Volcanoes** pages 313–316

3. **Mountains** pages 317–321

   Investigation 13-1 pages 320–321

4. **Earthquakes** pages 322–328

   Investigation 13-2 pages 327–328

Chapter 13 Summary page 329

Chapter 13 Review pages 330–331

Skill Track Software
for Earth Science

Teacher's Resource Library **TRL**

Workbook Activities 50–53

Alternative Workbook Activities
50–53

Lab Manual 49–52

Community Connection 13

Resource File 29–30

Chapter 13 Self-Study Guide

Chapter 13 Mastery Tests A and B

(Answer Keys for the Teacher's
Resource Library begin on page 400
of the Teacher's Edition. The
Materials List for the Lab Manual
activities begins on page 415.)

Science Center

Display a large world map. Make
available resources that provide
information on occurrences of
earthquakes and volcanic eruptions.
Magazines (for example, *Earth* magazine)
and newspapers are good sources of
current activity; encyclopedias and earth
science books are good sources of historic
activity. For each earthquake or eruption
they learn about, have students write the
location, date, and other important data
on an index card. They can mark its
location on the map with a pushpin, then
use yarn to connect the pushpin and the
information card.

PRONUNCIATION GUIDE

Use the pronunciation shown
below to help students pronounce
Piton de la Fournaise. Refer to the
pronunciation key on the Chapter
Planning Guide for the sounds of
the symbols.

Piton de la Fournaise
(pē ȯn´ di lä fôr nāz´)

Name _____ Date _____ Period _____ **Community Connection** 13
Chapter 13

Mountain Making

Mountains may form in several ways. They may build up from volcanic
eruptions. They may be created by folds in the earth's crust when two plates
collide. They may be raised by movement along faults. Look at a map and find
the mountain or mountain range closest to your home. Use the map scale to
measure how far away it is. Research its history to find out how it formed.
Record this information below.

Name of mountain or range: _____

Distance from home: _____

How it formed: _____

_____

Draw a picture of the mountain or mountain range in the box. Then tell how its
appearance gives clues to how it formed.

What it looks like:

Clues to how it formed: _____

_____

PACS Publishing. Permission is granted to reproduce for classroom use only. **Earth Science**

TRL

13 Forces in the Earth

Red hot lava bursts forth as the Piton de la Fournaise Volcano erupts. This volcano is on an island in the Indian Ocean. What forces deep inside the earth cause such an awesome event? Why do volcanoes occur only in some locations? The answers to these questions begin with the ground on which we stand. It is moving. We usually don't notice it. But a fiery volcano or a shattering earthquake reminds us that the earth's surface and the material beneath it are moving. In Chapter 13, you will discover how parts of the earth move and what happens when they do.

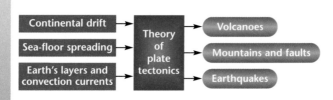

Organize Your Thoughts

Continental drift → Theory of plate tectonics → Volcanoes

Sea-floor spreading → Theory of plate tectonics → Mountains and faults

Earth's layers and convection currents → Theory of plate tectonics → Earthquakes

Goals for Learning

◆ To describe the structure of the earth
◆ To explain the theory of plate tectonics
◆ To relate volcanoes to plate tectonics
◆ To explain how mountains and faults form
◆ To relate earthquakes to plate tectonics

307

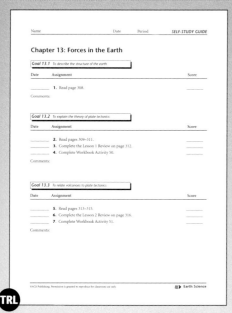

Chapter 13 Self-Study Guide

Introducing the Chapter

Have students look at the photo on page 306 and describe what is pictured and what is happening. Ask them to suggest why a volcano erupts and where the molten lava comes from. Read aloud the introductory paragraph and the Goals for Learning. Then invite students to predict what forces and movements occur inside the earth. Have students list all the events they can think of that change the surface of the earth.

Float several small, flat pieces of aluminum foil in a water-filled, clear glass baking dish. Place the dish on an overhead projector. With your finger, stir the water a little at one end of the dish. Ask students to observe and describe what happens. *(The pieces of foil move around, sometimes bumping into one another.)* Encourage discussion of ways the surface of the earth resembles this demonstration. Keep records of students' responses and refer back to them as you proceed through the chapter.

Notes and Technology Notes

Ask volunteers to read the notes that appear in the margins throughout the chapter. Then discuss them with the class.

TEACHER'S RESOURCE

The AGS Teaching Strategies in Science Transparencies may be used with this chapter. The transparencies add an interactive dimension to expand and enhance the *Earth Science* program content.

CAREER INTEREST INVENTORY

The AGS Harrington-O'Shea Career Decision-Making System-Revised (CDM) may be used with this chapter. Students can use the CDM to explore their interests and identify careers. The CDM defines career areas that are indicated by students' responses on the inventory.

Lesson at a Glance

Chapter 13 Lesson 1

Overview This lesson describes the earth's three layers and explores the theories of continental drift, sea-floor spreading, and plate tectonics.

Objectives

- To identify the earth's layers
- To explain continental drift, sea-floor spreading, and plate tectonics

Student Pages 308–312

Teacher's Resource Library **TRL**

Workbook Activity 50

Alternative Workbook Activity 50

Lab Manual 49

Resource File 29–30

Vocabulary

continental drift
convection current
core
crust
mantle
Pangaea
plate
plate tectonics
sea-floor spreading

Science Background

The earth's crust consists of a set of plates that push together, pull apart, and slide against each other. These movements are caused by convection currents in a soft layer of the mantle on which the crust and the rigid upper part of the mantle move. Most volcanic and earthquake activity occurs along boundaries between plates. Alaska has many earthquakes and more volcanic eruptions each year than any other place on the earth except Indonesia. This activity occurs because the northern Pacific plate is moving under the North American plate in this location.

 Warm-Up Activity

Have pairs of students use a hard-cooked egg to model the layers of the earth. Students should use a twisting motion to gently push a clear-plastic drinking straw into the side of the egg, through the shell,

---

 Objectives

After reading this lesson, you should be able to

- identify the earth's layers.
- explain continental drift, sea-floor spreading, and plate tectonics.

Core
Dense center of the earth made of solid and melted metals

Mantle
Layer of the earth that surrounds the core

Crust
Outer layer of the earth

The most abundant element inside the earth—including its crust, mantle, and core—is iron.

The Earth's Layers

Although we cannot directly see the interior of the earth, scientists use instruments to collect data about it. These data are used to make a model of what the inside of the earth is like.

The earth is made up of three main layers. At the center is a dense **core**. The core is solid iron and nickel, surrounded by melted iron and nickel. The core is about 3,500 kilometers thick. Outside the core is the **mantle**. The mantle is made of liquid and solid rock that moves and churns. The entire mantle is about 2,900 kilometers thick. The outermost layer of the earth is the **crust**. Compared to the other layers, the crust is very thin and cold. It is between 8 and 70 kilometers thick. The continents and ocean floor are part of the crust. The thickest part of the crust is found below large mountain ranges.

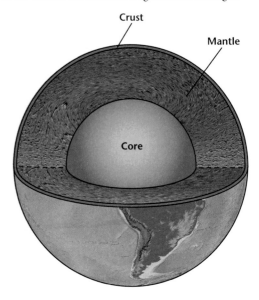

Crust

Mantle

Core

---

until it comes out the shell on the other side. Tell them to carefully pull the straw from the egg and examine the layers. Ask which part of the egg represents each layer of the earth. *(shell = crust; egg white = mantle; yolk = core)* Then ask how the three layers compare in thickness. *(Crust is thinnest; core is thickest.)*

2 Teaching the Lesson

Before beginning the lesson, have students scan the pages and list words with which they are unfamiliar. After they have finished reading, have students work in pairs to write definitions for these words.

Demonstrate the motion of a convection current by using a large beaker containing vegetable oil, a ring stand, a candle or an alcohol burner, and red food coloring. Using the stand, set up the beaker so that the heat source is directly heating only one side of the beaker. When the oil begins to heat, squeeze a few drops of food coloring into the beaker. Ask students to explain why they think the drops of food coloring follow a circular path. *(Convection currents form because, as the oil is warmed, it expands and becomes less dense than the oil on the other side of the beaker. It drifts upward, carrying the drops of food coloring with it. It cools, becomes heavier, and sinks on the opposite side of the beaker.)*

Continental Drift

Continental drift

Theory that the major landmasses of the earth move

Pangaea

Single landmass from which Alfred Wegener thought the continents separated millions of years ago

A theory, such as Wegener's theory of continental drift, is a possible explanation for many related observations.

Have you ever noticed that some continents, such as Africa and South America, look as if they might fit together? In 1912, a German scientist named Alfred Wegener proposed the theory of **continental drift** to explain why.

According to this theory, the earth's continents used to be joined as a single, large landmass called **Pangaea**. Wegener believed Pangaea started breaking up millions of years ago. The continents slowly moved to their present positions.

225 million years ago

180 million years ago

Present day

Besides the puzzle fit of the continents, Wegener had other evidence to support his theory. For example, fossils found on one continent were similar to those found on other continents. Mountain ranges and rock layers seemed to continue from one continent to another. In addition, glacial deposits were found at the equator where no glaciers could exist. Could the glacial deposits have formed when the continents were in a different place? Wegener thought so.

Sea-Floor Spreading

After World War II, new instruments allowed scientists to map the ocean floor. Here is what scientists discovered about the long, underwater mountain ranges called mid-ocean ridges:

- ◆ A rift valley splits these ridges in half.
- ◆ The amount of heat coming from a mid-ocean ridge is almost eight times greater than the heat from other parts of the ocean floor.
- ◆ Magma rises from beneath the ocean floor through cracks in the rift.
- ◆ The age of the ocean floor increases with distance from a ridge.

Forces in the Earth   Chapter 13   **309**

PRONUNCIATION GUIDE

Use this list to help students pronounce difficult words in this lesson. Refer to the pronunciation key on the Chapter Planning Guide for the sounds of these symbols.

Nazca   (näs´ kä)

Pangaea (pan jē´ ə)

LEARNING STYLES

Body/Kinesthetic

Give each student a copy of a map of Africa and one of South America. Have students mount their maps on heavy paper and cut out each continent. Then have them fit the continents together along their Atlantic coastlines. Ask students to explain how the fit of the two continents supports Wegener's theory of continental drift. (*Although they do not match up exactly, the continents fit together well enough to support the idea that they were once part of the same piece of land and formed by breaking apart.*)

---

3   Reinforce and Extend

IN THE COMMUNITY

What is the makeup of the earth's crust in your community? Have students explore U.S. Geological Survey Web sites and any community resources with information about soil and bedrock profiles or natural resources. Students can compile their information and use it to diagram a profile of the earth's crust in your area. Compare its thickness with other regions of the country and with ocean crust.

LEARNING STYLES

Logical/Mathematical

Ask students to pretend they are building a model of the earth with a radius of 1 meter. Help them calculate the radii of the model's core, mantle, and crust. Then ask students to calculate the percentage of the earth's radius represented by each part.

(*core:* $\frac{3,500}{6,470} = 0.55$, *or 55 percent;*

mantle: $\frac{2,900}{6,470} = 0.44$, *or 44 percent;*

crust: $\frac{70}{6,470} = 0.01$, *or 1 percent*)

Invite volunteers to model a wedge of the earth on the board, measuring the part of a meter needed to represent each layer of the earth. (*core = 55 centimeters; mantle = 44 centimeters; crust = 1 centimeter*)

SCIENCE JOURNAL

Ask students to imagine that they are exploring the sea floor and observing what happens at a mid-ocean ridge. Have them write a journal entry about what they see and what it means.

Sea-floor spreading
Theory that the ocean floor spreads apart as new crust is formed at mid-ocean ridges

Plate tectonics
Theory that the earth's surface is made of large sections of crust that move

Plate
Large section of the earth's crust that moves

The theory of **sea-floor spreading** explains these observations. This theory states that hot magma from the mantle rises and pours out onto the ocean floor through cracks in a rift. The magma cools, hardens, and forms new crust. This new crust piles up around the rift, forming a mid-ocean ridge. More rising magma pushes the new crust away on both sides of the ridge. This process widens the oceans and pushes the continents apart.

Plate Tectonics

The ideas of sea-floor spreading and continental drift have led to one of the most important theories in science—**plate tectonics**. This theory states that the earth's crust is made of large sections, or **plates**. As shown on the map, most plates include ocean crust and continental crust.

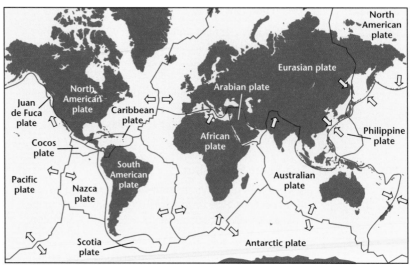

⇨ Plate movement — Plate boundary

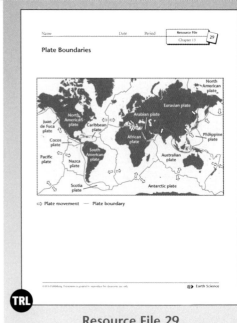

Resource File 29

? Did You Know?

Plates usually move slowly, about 4 to 10 centimeters per year. That's about as fast as your hair grows.

Plates move in three different ways: they move apart, collide, or slide past each other. How they move determines what happens where they meet.

Look at the diagram below. The South American and African plates are moving apart. Where plates move apart, a rift forms. The Nazca and South American plates are moving toward each other. Here the Nazca plate is forced under the South American plate, forming a deep trench. The Nazca plate melts as it sinks into the mantle. Some plates slide past each other. The map on page 310 shows the Pacific plate sliding northwest past the North American plate.

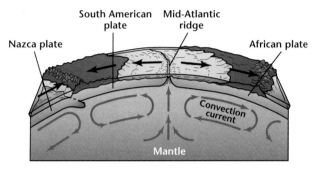

The pushing, pulling, and grinding of plates cause volcanoes and earthquakes. Magma that reaches the surface produces volcanoes where plates collide or spread apart. You will learn more about volcanoes and earthquakes later in this chapter.

Convection Currents

The last piece in the plate tectonics puzzle is what causes the plates to move. In other words, why does magma rise at mid-ocean ridges in the first place? Most scientists think the answer is **convection currents**. A convection current is the circular movement of a liquid or gas as it heats. Convection currents in the partly melted upper mantle can push the plates along as if on a conveyor belt. Look at the convection currents shown in the diagram above. Compare their movement to the movement of the plates.

Plate Tectonics

Resource File 30

Call attention to the maps on page 309 and have students comment about the rate at which the continents are moving apart. *(They should infer that the movement is very slow, since it has taken many millions of years.)* Solicit and list students' predictions on the board. Then have a volunteer read aloud the Did You Know? feature on page 311.

LEARNING STYLES

Visual/Spatial

Have students use blocks of wood to demonstrate the three different ways plates can move. Point to various plate boundaries on the world map on page 310 and have students model what is happening at each boundary.

AT HOME

Suggest that students design an activity to map the pattern of convection currents in a room as it is heated or cooled. For example, students might work with a family member to diagram a room at home, showing its heating vents and cold air returns. Then they can add arrows to show what happens to warm air as it enters, rises, cools, and sinks.

LEARNING STYLES

LEP/ESL

Students who are learning English may be confused by the use of "ordinary" words such as *plate, core,* and *crust* in a study of the earth. Use the common meaning of such words to help students understand the scientific meaning. (For example, have them tell how the earth's crust is like the crust on a loaf of bread.)

Lesson 1 Review Answers

1. The core is at the earth's center; it is dense and made of iron and nickel. The mantle surrounds the core; it is churning rock, molten in places. The crust is very thin and comparatively cold; it makes up the continents and ocean floor. **2.** The theory states that the earth's continents were once joined as a single large landmass called Pangaea. Millions of years ago, Pangaea broke up and the continents slowly moved to their present positions. **3.** They probably formed where tectonic plates pull apart, allowing magma to ooze out and harden into a ridge. As more magma comes out, this ridge is pushed apart and built up. **4.** The theory states that the earth's crust is made of large sections, or plates, that collide, move apart, or slide past each other. **5.** Hot rock in the mantle moves in a circular pattern because of convection currents. The continents are dragged in the direction of these currents, as though on conveyor belts.

Achievements in Science

Ask students to imagine they are traveling in a submersible on the ocean floor. When they arrive at a mid-ocean ridge, what observations would they make and what tests would they perform to determine what is happening at this location? Allow students to discuss their ideas. Then have volunteers read aloud the feature on page 312. Have students compare their ideas and the actual methods used by scientists to draw conclusions about sea-floor spreading. Ask students to name special challenges the depth of the ridges caused scientists. *(Humans cannot withstand the extreme pressures of the ocean bottom, so they could not leave the submersible. Special drills would have had to be designed to reach such depths.)* Discuss why the three investigations described in the feature had to be performed in this order. *(Ridges first had to be located, or mapped. This allowed scientists to visit the ridges and observe the rocks there. Finally, they could drill to extract and study rock samples along the ridge.)*

Portfolio Assessment

Sample items include:
- Vocabulary definitions from Teaching the Lesson
- Lesson 1 Review answers

Write the answers to these questions on a sheet of paper.

1. Describe the layers of the earth.

2. What is the theory of continental drift?

3. Explain how mid-ocean ridges probably formed.

4. What is the theory of plate tectonics?

5. Why do the earth's plates move?

Achievements in Science

The Theory of Sea-Floor Spreading

How did scientists discover the underwater mountain ranges known as mid-ocean ridges? They used a tool called sonar. Sonar is a device that bounces sound waves off underwater objects. The echoes of these sound waves are recorded. The time it takes for the echo to reach the sonar device tells how far away the object is. This information allowed scientists to map mid-ocean ridges.

How did scientists connect mid-ocean ridges to sea-floor spreading? They took a dive to the ocean floor in *Alvin*, a deep-sea submersible. *Alvin* can stand up to the crushing water pressure at the ocean bottom. *Alvin's* crew took pictures of rocks that looked like toothpaste squeezed from a giant tube. These strange rocks were igneous rocks. They form when liquid rock erupts from deep in the earth and quickly cools. The rocks showed evidence of many eruptions. Scientists think these eruptions from mid-ocean ridges pushed the ocean floor to the sides. This pushing is sea-floor spreading.

More evidence of sea-floor spreading came from rock samples. Scientists on a ship drilled through 6 kilometers of water. The drills took samples of the ocean floor around a ridge. The scientists determined the ages of the rock samples. They discovered that samples taken farthest from the ridge were the oldest. The youngest rocks were at the center of the ridge. This was more evidence of sea-floor spreading.

Lab Manual 49, pages 1–2

Workbook Activity 50

How Volcanoes Form

A **volcano** is a mountain that builds around a **vent**, or opening, where magma pushes up through the surface of the earth. The mountain is shaped like a cone. It is built up by rock particles, ash, and hardened lava that erupt from the volcano. Some of this erupted material is so tiny that it is carried by the wind for several kilometers before landing.

The vent at the top of a volcano may look like a funnel-shaped crater. A wider opening forms if the crater's walls collapse into the vent. Sometimes the top part of a volcano is completely blown off by a large eruption.

Most volcanoes form where two plates meet. For example, Mount St. Helens in Washington formed where the Juan de Fuca plate sinks beneath the North American plate. The sinking Juan de Fuca plate melts into magma, which then rises to the surface. Where plates collide beneath the oceans, the volcanoes may rise above sea level to form islands. The Aleutian Islands of Alaska and the islands of Japan formed this way.

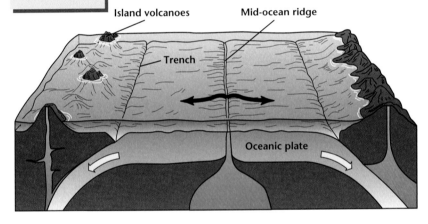

Island volcanoes   Mid-ocean ridge

Trench

Oceanic plate

Lesson at a Glance

Chapter 13 Lesson 2

Overview This lesson describes how volcanoes form along plate boundaries and compares the types of volcanoes.

Objectives

■ To explain how volcanoes form

■ To describe three types of volcanoes

Student Pages 313–316

Teacher's Resource Library

Workbook Activity 51

Alternative Workbook Activity 51

Vocabulary

cinder cone	vent
composite volcano	volcano
shield volcano	

Science Background

Although shield volcanoes do not have steep sides, they can be enormous. Hawaii's Mauna Loa, rising gently from the Pacific, is the world's largest active volcano. Measured from its base on the sea floor, it is taller than Mount Everest. Cinder cones tend to be small. They often occur in clusters or on the sides of shield and composite volcanoes. Cinder cones erode quickly because their rock particles are not held together with lava. The alternating eruptions of lava and rock give composite volcanoes a broad base with sides that grow progressively steeper toward the summit.

1 Warm-Up Activity

Display two plastic bottles of unchilled carbonated beverage. *Do not use glass bottles.* Open one bottle and have students describe what they see. (*Bubbles of gas are escaping from the liquid.*) Explain that melted rock can contain dissolved gases. The gases are under great pressure within the earth. When the pressure is released, the gases escape. Ask students to predict what will happen if you shake and open the second bottle. (*The liquid will explode out of it.*) Shake the bottle and open it over a sink. Compare this to the explosive eruptions of some volcanoes.

Pronunciation Guide

Use this list to help students pronounce difficult words in this lesson. Refer to the pronunciation key on the Chapter Planning Guide for the sounds of these symbols.

Aleutian	(ə lü′ shən)
Juan de Fuca	(hwän də fyü′ kə)
Kilauea	(kē laủ ā′ ə)
Mauna Loa	(maủ nə lō′ ə)
Paricutín	(pä rē′ kü tēn′)

2 Teaching the Lesson

As they read the lesson, have students make diagrams with labels to illustrate volcano formation and volcano types.

Ask students where volcanoes are most likely to form. (*at the boundaries of tectonic plates*) Invite students to give reasons. (*At points where plates collide or pull apart, magma can travel upward through the crust.*) Have students study the map on page 310 to review plate boundaries. Locate your area on the map and ask students how likely it is that a volcanic eruption would occur in your area. (*Help students infer that the possibility of a volcanic eruption depends on the area's geology.*)

Display a map that features the Ring of Fire around the Pacific Ocean. Have students compare this ring with the plate boundaries on page 310. Point out that more than half of the earth's active volcanoes above sea level ring the Pacific Ocean. Ask students why they think so many are concentrated in this area. (*Most active volcanoes lie along boundaries where plates are pushing together; explosive eruptions occur in these areas. Volcanoes located along boundaries where plates are separating generally have quieter lava flows.*)

TEACHER ALERT

! Rock in the mantle is under such great pressure that it is largely solid, despite its great heat. (The atoms are so tightly packed that they cannot change into the liquid state.) A decrease in pressure is usually what causes magma to form. Once formed, magma rises to the surface because it is less dense than the surrounding rock.

3 Reinforce and Extend

Did You Know?

Have volunteers look up the meanings of the words *composite*, *shield*, and *cinder*. Ask students why they think these words were chosen to name types of volcanoes. After students have offered possible explanations, have them read the Did You Know? feature on page 314.

Cinder cone

Small volcano with steep sides and explosive eruptions; made of ash and rock

 Did You Know?

The rock particles that create cinder cones are called cinders. Shield volcanoes are so named because they are shaped like a warrior's shield.

Types of Volcanoes

Volcanoes are grouped into three types. This grouping is based on how the volcano erupts, the material that comes out, and the shape of the volcano. Compare the photos to the following descriptions.

Cinder cones are small volcanoes with steep sides and narrow bases. Their eruptions are explosive, shooting ash and igneous rock high into the air. Because of this, cinder cones are built up with layers of loose rock particles. Most cinder cones are less than 500 meters high. These small volcanoes are found in western North America and in other parts of the world.

Paricutín is a large, well-known cinder cone in Mexico. It began in 1943 when hot gas and lava came out of cracks in a cornfield. It erupted ash, rock, and lava almost constantly for 9 years. It grew to 410 meters high. In 1952, this cinder cone stopped erupting. Paricutín provided a rare opportunity for geologists to watch the birth, life, and death of a volcano.

Sunset Crater Volcano in Arizona is a cinder cone.

GLOBAL CONNECTION

 Point out to students that large-scale volcanic eruptions affect the entire globe. They release huge amounts of ash and gases, which can block out sunlight and affect climates. Ask interested students to research the effects of the 1815 eruption of Mount Tamboro in Indonesia and the 1991 eruption of Mount Pinatubo in the Philippines. They should report how sunlight and temperature were affected.

ONLINE CONNECTION

 The following sites combine encyclopedic information about volcanoes with clever, appealing presentations. The first site offers virtual field trips.

http://volcano.und.nodak.edu/vw.html

www.learner.org/exhibits/volcanoes/

http://pubs.usgs.gov/gip/volc

Kilauea Volcano on the island of Hawaii is a shield volcano. It has been erupting constantly since 1983. The photo on the cover of this book shows the lava from this volcano flowing over a cliff and into the ocean.

Shield volcanoes are low and broad with wide craters. They are not very explosive. Thin basalt lava flows from their quiet eruptions. Shield volcanoes are built up by layer after layer of lava that has spread out and hardened.

Mauna Loa Volcano in Hawaii is the largest volcano in the world. This shield volcano extends down to the ocean floor.

Composite volcanoes form when gentle eruptions of lava alternate with explosive eruptions of ash and rock. The gentle eruptions add thin layers of lava to the mountain. The explosive eruptions add rocky layers. Composite volcanoes grow to be very tall.

Mount Fuji in Japan is a composite volcano.

Lesson 2 Review Answers

1. a mountain that develops where magma erupts onto the earth's surface 2. Most volcanoes form where two tectonic plates meet. 3. steep sides, narrow base, height less than 500 meters, explosive eruptions, made of ash and rock 4. low, broad, with a wide crater, shaped like a warrior's shield, quiet eruptions, made of thin layers of basalt lava 5. Gentle eruptions, which form broad, thin layers of lava, alternate with violent eruptions, which build rocky layers with steeper slopes.

Science in Your Life

Have a volunteer read aloud the first paragraph of the feature on page 316. Invite students who have experienced an earthquake or volcano to describe what it is like. If possible, have on hand pictures showing the destructive effects of these events. After students finish reading the feature, discuss why MR fluid can act as a shock absorber. *(As a semisolid, it would absorb the shock waves rather than transmit them.)* Ask students to research appropriate emergency preparations and actions to take for an earthquake.

Portfolio Assessment

Sample items include:
• Diagrams from Teaching the Lesson
• Lesson 2 Review answers

Write the answers to these questions on a sheet of paper.

1. What is a volcano?

2. How do volcanoes relate to plate tectonics?

3. What are the characteristics of a cinder cone?

4. Describe a shield volcano.

5. How do composite volcanoes form?

Science in Your Life

Living on a Tectonic Plate

Earthquakes and volcanoes usually occur where two tectonic plates come together. If you live on or near a plate boundary, you may know people who have experienced an earthquake or volcano. Perhaps you have experienced one yourself. What is the best way to prepare for these events? What should you do in such an emergency?

Many cities lie close to or on plate boundaries. Builders design structures in these cities to withstand the force of earthquakes. The worker in the photo is strengthening a freeway support in a city affected by earthquakes.

A new product may help to reduce earthquake damage to buildings. It is called magnetorheological (MR) fluid. It is a mixture of oil and metal particles. When exposed to a magnetic force, MR fluid thickens into a material like cold peanut butter. It changes back to a liquid when the magnetic force is gone.

Since earthquakes cause strong magnetic forces, scientists are testing MR fluid as a possible shock absorber for buildings. The fluid can be put in special containers controlled by a computer. Hundreds of these devices can be placed within a building's structure. When an earthquake hits, these devices can respond by cushioning and supporting the building.

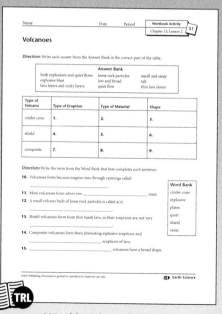

Objectives

After reading this lesson, you should be able to

◆ describe two ways that mountains form (in addition to volcanoes).

◆ identify forces that cause mountains to form.

◆ name three types of movement along faults.

Folding

Bending of rock layers that are squeezed together

You may have heard the expression "as old as the hills." In fact, mountains and hills are still being built. The process is usually so slow, however, that you don't notice it. Movements of the earth's crust cause these landforms to rise above the surrounding landscape.

Folding Plates

Mountains can form when plates collide. You have already read about how volcanic mountains form when one plate sinks beneath another. This usually happens when a dense ocean plate collides with a continental plate. The Cascade Range in northwestern United States and the Andes in Peru were built this way.

When a continental plate collides with another continental plate, the plates usually crumple like a rug. The rock layers of the plates bend without breaking, as shown in the diagram. This process is called **folding**. Folding can occur either where the two plates meet or somewhere in the middle of a plate. The Himalayas in Asia were formed where two plates met and folded.

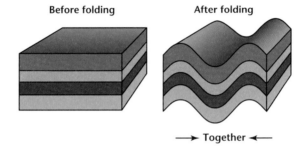

Before folding   After folding

→ Together ←

Lesson at a Glance

Chapter 13 Lesson 3

Overview In this lesson, students learn about the types of plate movements that give rise to mountains. They also learn about the geological results of different fault movements.

Objectives

■ To describe two ways that mountains form (in addition to volcanoes)

■ To identify forces that cause mountains to form

■ To name three types of movement along faults

Student Pages 317–321

Teacher's Resource Library

Workbook Activity 52

Alternative Workbook Activity 52

Lab Manual 50

Vocabulary

fault	reverse fault
folding	strike-slip fault
normal fault	

Science Background

When layers of the earth's crust are subjected to great stress, some bend and others break. Large folds can occur from bending rock. Rock layers that are squeezed together and forced upward form folded mountains. These can be identified by the deformed pattern of the layers of sedimentary rock. When rocks break and slide past each other as a result of plate movements, a fault is formed. Tectonic forces can put enough tension on the crust to form a large number of normal faults. Large blocks of rock drop down, causing blocks on the other side of the fault to tilt upward, forming fault-block mountains.

 Warm-Up Activity

Stack three or four small, flexible throw rugs on top of each other. Ask students to imagine that they are layers of rock in the earth's crust. Place the stack on a flat

Continued on page 318

Continued from page 317

surface. Have students observe what happens as you grasp opposite ends of the stack, one with each hand, and slowly bring your hands together. (*The rugs bend and form folds.*) Explain that certain forces can cause the earth's crust to fold. This is one way that mountains are formed.

2 Teaching the Lesson

Have students read the lesson to discover cause-and-effect relationships. Remind them that one cause can produce several effects, and different causes can have the same effect. When they finish reading, have students use a graphic organizer to show at least three causes and effects they learned about.

Use maps or globes with raised topographical features so that students can feel the patterns formed by mountain ranges along the boundaries of the earth's plates.

Let pairs of students build models of the three types of faults using layers of different colored clay. Then have the partners use their models to explain how each type of fault forms.

3 Reinforce and Extend

LEARNING STYLES

Body/Kinesthetic
Make a model of a fault by cutting a 12-centimeter-thick sheet of polystyrene in half with an angled cut. One edge should have an angle of 60° and the adjacent edge an angle of 120°. Ask students to use the model to demonstrate the movement at a normal fault, a reverse fault, and a strike-slip fault.

SCIENCE JOURNAL

Ask students to imagine that they are a rock layer in the earth's crust. Have them write a short story describing their experiences as they undergo folding or faulting.

Fault
Break in the earth's crust along which movement occurs

Normal fault
Break in the crust in which the overhanging block of rock has slid down

Reverse fault
Break in the crust in which the overhanging block of rock has been raised

Strike-slip fault
Break in the crust in which the blocks of rock move horizontally past each other

Faults

When pressed together, some rocks break rather than bend. A **fault** is a break in the earth's crust along which movement occurs. Some faults are visible on the earth's surface. Most faults, however, are deep underground. Rock movement along faults can cause mountains to form.

There are three types of faults shown in the diagram below. In a **normal fault**, the two sides of the fault pull apart. The overhanging rock on one side drops down. In a **reverse fault**, the two sides push together. The overhanging rock on one side is pushed up. In a **strike-slip fault**, blocks of rock slide against each other horizontally. The San Andreas fault in California is a strike-slip fault.

Blocks of rock along a fault usually move short distances at a time. When enough pressure builds up, the rocks move and the pressure is released. When the pressure builds up again, more movement occurs.

Over time, movement along faults can raise large blocks of rock, forming mountains. Rock movement along faults built the Grand Tetons of Wyoming and the Wasatch Range of Utah.

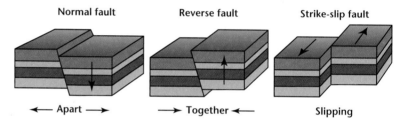

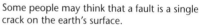

Science Myth

Some people may think that a fault is a single crack on the earth's surface.

Fact: A fault is a deep break in the earth's crust. Most faults are very long and travel far underground. Because of this, many smaller faults actually make up a large fault.

CROSS-CURRICULAR CONNECTION

Geography
Assign a different mountain range to each student or pair of students. Their task is to find out how the range was formed and gather or draw pictures of its mountains to illustrate how their profiles reveal the type of force that shaped them. Organize students' visuals into three categories for display: formation by folding, by faulting, and by volcanic activity.

Science Myth

Ask students to direct you in drawing a fault on the board. Read aloud the myth part of the feature on page 318. Invite students to explain why they think this statement is not true. Read the rest of the feature together. Have volunteers come to the board and change the illustration to make it more accurate. Interested students might research and report on the San Andreas fault system, which is very large and includes many small faults.

Lesson 3 REVIEW

Write the answers to these questions on a sheet of paper.

1. What are three ways that mountains form?

2. Define folding.

3. What is a fault?

4. Compare the direction of movement in a reverse fault and in a strike-slip fault.

5. How do normal faults differ from reverse faults?

Technology Note

Earthquakes are best known for causing destruction. But the data collected by studying earthquakes can be useful. In the next lesson, you will learn that earthquakes cause energy waves to travel through the earth. Scientists use these waves to learn about the interior of the earth. With a technique called seismic tomography, they can even create images of the earth's flowing mantle.

To understand this technique, think of turning on a lamp in a dark room. The lamp sends out light waves. These waves light up things so you can see them. Seismic tomography uses earthquake waves to "light up" the earth's interior.

The process is not an easy one. First, a computer processes wave data from thousands of recent earthquakes. Then this information is used to make a series of images. Each image represents a slice of the earth's interior. When the slices are put together, a three-dimensional picture of the earth is produced. This picture provides information about convection currents within the earth's mantle.

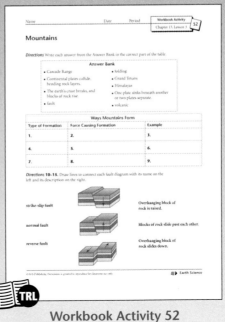

Workbook Activity 52

Lesson 3 Review Answers

1. An ocean plate may sink beneath a continental plate causing volcanic mountains to form; two plates may collide beneath an ocean, causing volcanic islands or seamounts. Two continental plates may collide and fold, or a squeezed plate may fold in the middle. Movement along a fault may raise blocks of rock, forming mountains. **2.** bending and crumpling of rock layers that are squeezed together **3.** a deep break in the earth's crust along which movement occurs **4.** In a reverse fault, two sides of a fault push together so that the overhanging rock is pushed up. In a strike-slip fault, the two sides of the fault slide against each other horizontally. **5.** A normal fault results when two blocks of rock pull apart and the overhanging rock on one side drops down. A reverse fault occurs when two blocks of rock push together and the overhanging rock on one side is raised.

Portfolio Assessment

Sample items include:
• Cause-and-effect graphic organizers from Teaching the Lesson
• Lesson 3 Review answers

Investigation 13-1

The Purpose portion of the student investigation begins with a question to draw students into the activity. Encourage students to read the investigation steps and formulate their own questions before beginning the investigation. This investigation will take approximately 30 minutes to complete. Students will use these process and thinking skills: making models, observing, recognizing cause and effect, and comparing and contrasting.

Preparation

- Gather enough telephone books or catalogs so that each pair of students has two books of approximately the same thickness.
- Space pairs so that they can move without interference during the investigation.
- Students may use Lab Manual 50 to record their data and answer the questions.

Procedure

- Have both students participate in all stages of the investigation, working cooperatively to model normal, reverse, and strike-slip faults.
- Be sure students angle the book spines, as shown in the second figure, for steps 5 through 7.
- Students should hold books firmly so that they do not sag.
- This investigation could be used as a springboard for Lesson 4. As students model the faults, ask what they think might happen if rock layers like these were to move against each other suddenly. *(an earthquake)*

INVESTIGATION

13-1

Materials
- ◆ 2 thick telephone books or catalogs

Making Models of Folding and Faults

Purpose

How could you model the formation of mountains? In this investigation, you will model the movement of rock layers where folding and faults occur.

Procedure

1. Copy the data table on your paper.

Type of Rock Movement	Sketch of Model

2. Work with a partner to model folding rock layers. Have your partner hold a telephone book as shown below. Your partner should grasp it firmly with both hands.

3. Have your partner slowly push both hands together, squeezing the book. In the data table, sketch the folds that appear and record the type of rock movement you modeled.

4. Switch places and repeat step 3 so your partner has a turn to sketch.

320 *Chapter 13 Forces in the Earth*

Lab Manual 50

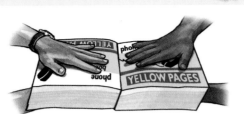

5. Use two telephone books to model rock layers along a fault. With your partner, hold the books together as shown above. Be sure to place the book spines at an angle.

6. Slowly move the books to model rock movement at a normal fault. If needed, refer to the diagram on page 318.

7. Sketch what happens to the books and record the type of movement you modeled.

8. Repeat steps 6 and 7 two more times, modeling rock movement along a reverse fault and then along a strike-slip fault.

Questions and Conclusions

1. What kind of plate motion might produce the change you saw in step 3?

2. Compare and contrast the motion of the rock layers you modeled for a normal fault and a reverse fault.

3. How did you move the books to model a strike-slip fault?

4. How do the models demonstrate mountain building?

Explore Further

Use modeling clay to create a model of a normal fault, a reverse fault, and a strike-slip fault. Use arrow labels to show the direction of movement in each model. What other ways can you model faults?

Results

In step 3, students should observe that the book pages bulge upward in the center, forming a fold. In step 6, students should move one book lower than the other, keeping the spines at an angle, to demonstrate how a normal fault occurs when opposing rock layers pull apart. In step 8, students should move one of the books higher than the other while pushing them together to demonstrate how a reverse fault occurs. They should slide the spines across each other to demonstrate a strike-slip fault.

Questions and Conclusions Answers

1. continental plates colliding and crumpling

2. In a normal fault, the two sides pull apart and rock layers on one side drop down. In a reverse fault, the two sides push together, raising rock layers on one side.

3. slid them horizontally in opposite directions along their spines

4. They imitate the way layers of rock in the earth's crust bend, break, and move as the plates they are on slide past each other or are forced together or apart.

Explore Further Answers

Students will need to cut through their layers of clay at an angle to model broken edges of rock. They can press small poster-board squares on the angled ends to make the movements of the surfaces easier to see. Students might suggest modeling faults using a thick sheet of foam cut in half at an angle or layers of cardboard glued together and then cut at an angle.

Assessment

Check students' drawings to be sure they are correct. Be sure students understand the difference in appearance and movement of normal, reverse, and strike-slip faults. Verify that students' answers indicate an understanding of lesson concepts. Include the following items from this investigation in student portfolios:

• Data table and sketches

• Answers to Questions and Conclusions and Explore Further sections

Lesson at a Glance

Chapter 13 Lesson 4

Overview This lesson explains the forces that cause earthquakes, how earthquake waves move, and how scientists use the waves to determine the origin of an earthquake.

Objectives

- To explain what causes earthquakes
- To describe earthquake waves and explain what a seismograph does
- To explain how an earthquake is located and how its strength is measured

Student Pages 322–328

Teacher's Resource Library **TRL**

Workbook Activity 53

Alternative Workbook Activity 53

Lab Manual 51–52

Vocabulary

earthquake	Richter scale
epicenter	seismograph
focus	tsunami

Science Background

Every year more than 800,000 earthquakes occur. People do not feel most of them because they register less than 2 on the Richter scale. Earthquakes are classified according to the depth of their focus. Shallow-focus earthquakes (which originate between the earth's surface and 70 kilometers below) account for most earthquakes. Intermediate-focus (70–300 kilometers in depth) and deep-focus earthquakes (300–700 kilometers in depth) usually occur along ocean trenches where one tectonic plate is being pushed under another.

 Warm-Up Activity

Find two pieces of a wood board with rough edges. Place them together to model a fault. Ask students to predict what will happen when you try to slide the surfaces past one another. *(Rough edges will catch. More energy will need to be applied. When enough force is applied, the friction caused by tangled obstructions will be overcome and the pieces will move with a jerk.)* Place

---

Objectives

After reading this lesson, you should be able to

- explain what causes earthquakes.
- describe earthquake waves and explain what a seismograph does.
- explain how an earthquake is located and how its strength is measured.

Earthquake
Shaking of the earth's crust

What does it feel like when you sit in the bleachers at a sporting event? When someone stands up, sits down, or walks nearby, you probably feel the bleachers shake. Shaking also occurs in the rocks of the earth's crust. This shaking is called an **earthquake**.

Causes of Earthquakes

An earthquake is a shaking of the earth's crust that occurs when energy is suddenly released. An erupting volcano releases energy and causes some earthquakes. But most earthquakes occur when rocks break or move suddenly along a fault. For example, two blocks of rock that are sliding past each other may get snagged on the jagged rocky sides. Friction holds the blocks together, but they are still being pushed. Energy builds up. When the pushing overcomes the friction, the blocks move suddenly and a lot of energy is released, causing an earthquake.

Like volcanoes, most earthquakes occur near plate boundaries. This is where most fault movements occur. In fact, the boundary between two plates that are sliding past each other is a large fault. Smaller faults occur near such large faults. An example of this is the San Andreas fault along the coast of California. This large fault is where the Pacific plate meets the North American plate. When these plates suddenly slip, an earthquake occurs. Many smaller faults branch off this large fault.

The entire San Andreas fault system is about 1,300 kilometers long. In some places, it cuts deeper than 16 kilometers into the earth.

---

small plastic models of trees, houses, and people on the two boards. Have students tell what they think will happen to the models when you move the boards again. *(They will be knocked over or off the boards by the sudden movement.)* Explain that in this lesson, students will learn how movements along faults cause earthquakes.

Earthquake Waves

The energy from an earthquake travels through rock in waves. There are three different types of earthquake waves. Primary waves, or P-waves, cause rock particles to vibrate back and forth. Secondary waves, or S-waves, cause rocks to vibrate up and down or side to side. Both P-waves and S-waves travel inside the earth. When P-waves or S-waves reach the earth's surface, they cause long waves, or L-waves. L-waves travel along the surface of the earth. L-waves are the most destructive of earthquake waves because they cause the ground to bend and twist.

Earthquake waves are detected by an instrument called a **seismograph**, shown below. A seismograph uses a suspended pen that does not move and a roll of paper that does move. When the earth shakes, the paper chart also shakes. This makes the pen record a jagged line instead of a straight one. A seismograph records all three kinds of earthquake waves. P-waves are recorded first. They move the fastest and are the first to arrive at the recording station. P-waves also make the shortest lines on the chart. S-waves follow the P-waves. S-waves make longer lines. The L-waves arrive last. They make the longest lines. In the diagram below, you can see how the recordings of the different waves look.

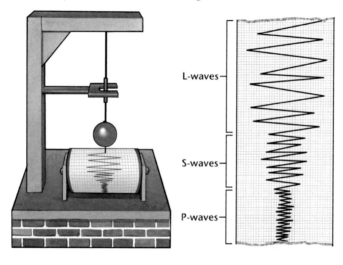

Math

Students need to understand exponential growth to appreciate the differences in severity represented by each number on the Richter scale. Display one sugar cube to represent an earthquake that registers 1 on the Richter scale. Pile 10 sugar cubes next to this to represent 2 on the Richter scale. Explain that each whole number increase on the scale represents a tenfold increase in measured amplitude of earthquake waves. Have students calculate how many sugar cubes would be needed to represent an earthquake registering at each level up to 7 on the Richter scale. *(3: 100; 4: 1,000; 5: 10,000; 6: 100,000; 7: 1,000,000)*

CAREER CONNECTION

Discuss with students how earthquake-prone areas need buildings that are adapted to withstand earthquake shock waves. Explain that building designs need to include some system of "shock absorbers" or other feature that allows the building to bend. Ask interested students to research the special training that architectural engineers need in order to design buildings in regions that have frequent earthquakes.

LEARNING STYLES

Auditory/Verbal

Pair students and refer them to the diagram for locating the epicenter of an earthquake on page 324. Have partners take turns explaining how an epicenter is located, step by step. Listeners can evaluate the explanations and tell which parts were unclear.

Focus

Point inside the earth where rock first moves, starting an earthquake

Epicenter

Point on the earth's surface directly over the focus of an earthquake

Richter scale

Scale used to measure the strength of an earthquake

Locating the Epicenter

The point inside the earth where the earthquake starts is called the **focus**. The point on the earth's surface directly above the focus is called the **epicenter**. Scientists can pinpoint the epicenter of an earthquake. To do this, they compare the arrival times of the P-waves and the S-waves.

To locate the epicenter, scientists compare seismograph readings from at least three locations. For example, suppose Station A detects waves that show an earthquake started 100 kilometers away. On a map, a circle with a 100-kilometer radius is drawn around Station A. Readings at Station B put the earthquake at 200 kilometers away. So, a 200-kilometer-radius circle is drawn around Station B. Readings at Station C show the earthquake to be 50 kilometers away. A circle with a 50-kilometer radius is drawn around Station C. The point where the three circles meet is the earthquake's epicenter.

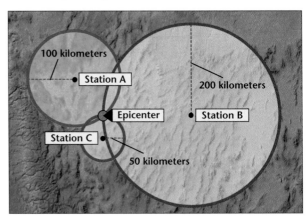

Earthquake Strength and Its Effect

The strength of an earthquake is measured on the **Richter scale**. This scale is based on seismograph wave measurements. The Richter scale assigns every earthquake a number from 1 to 9. Each number represents an earthquake that is 10 times stronger than the next lowest number. The strongest earthquake ever recorded had a measurement of 8.9 on this scale.

The effect of an earthquake on a given region depends on the strength of the earthquake and the distance from the epicenter. Earthquakes can cause great damage and loss of life. Most injuries result from the collapse of buildings, bridges, and other structures in heavily populated areas.

An earthquake damaged this Los Angeles, California, highway in 1994.

Even earthquakes on the ocean floor can cause much damage. They may trigger **tsunamis**, or large sea waves. A tsunami may reach a height of 35 meters, as tall as a 10-story building. Large tsunamis can destroy coastal towns.

Predicting Earthquakes

Scientists hope to save lives by learning to predict where and when an earthquake will occur. They watch for several signs. For example, a sudden drop in the level of well water often precedes an earthquake. Bulges in the earth's surface near a fault could indicate the buildup of stress. Near a fault, seismic activity produces an almost constant occurrence of P-waves and S-waves. A change in the speed of the P-waves may signal a coming earthquake. Scientists use these clues to predict earthquakes. If earthquakes could be accurately predicted, many lives could be saved.

Forces in the Earth   Chapter 13   **325**

Lesson 4 Review Answers

1. shaking of the earth's crust as energy is suddenly released 2. a seismograph 3. All three waves are ways that earthquake energy travels through rock. P-waves travel fastest and make rock particles vibrate back and forth. S-waves travel slower and make rocks vibrate up and down. L-waves travel slowest and move along the surface of the earth, causing it to bend and twist. 4. The Richter scale uses seismograph readings to assign an earthquake a number from 1 to 9. Each number on the scale represents a tenfold increase in earthquake strength. 5. the strength of the earthquake and the distance from its epicenter

Write the answers to these questions on a sheet of paper.

1. What is an earthquake?

2. What instrument is used to measure earthquake waves?

3. Compare and contrast the three kinds of earthquake waves.

4. Describe how the Richter scale is used to identify an earthquake's strength.

5. What two factors determine the effect of an earthquake?

Science at Work

Write the terms *seismograph, seismometer,* and *seismologist* on the board. Have a volunteer circle the part of each word that is the same. Explain that the Greek word *seismos* means "shock" or "earthquake." Discuss where students have seen the word parts *-graph, -meter,* and *-ologist* and what they might mean. *(a written or printed representation, an instrument for measuring, one who studies)* Ask students to predict the meaning of each term on the board. Then have them read the feature on page 326. After they finish reading, ask students why they think seismologists need strong math, science, and computer skills.

Portfolio Assessment

Sample items include:
• Outline from Teaching the Lesson
• Lesson 4 Review answers

Science at Work

Seismologist

Seismologists study earthquakes and the seismic waves caused by earthquakes. Their job is to detect earthquakes and earthquake-related faults.

Seismologists use many instruments to collect data. Seismographs and seismometers are instruments that receive and record seismic waves. Magnetometers detect and measure magnetic fields. Seismologists interpret data from these instruments to detect the coming of an earthquake. They also determine the location and strength of earthquakes. Much of their job involves managing data on a computer.

A bachelor's degree in geology is needed for a beginning job in seismology. Research positions require a master's or doctoral degree.

Seismologists must have strong science, math, and computer skills. Good communication skills are important for writing reports and working on a team. Seismologists need to be willing to travel to faraway survey sites. Some seismologists may perform their jobs from a ship.

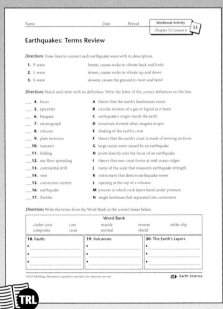

INVESTIGATION

Materials

- index card
- large drawing paper
- tape
- drawing compass
- centimeter ruler

Locating an Earthquake

Purpose

How do scientists find the epicenter of an earthquake? In this investigation, you will make a map that pinpoints the source of an earthquake.

Procedure

1. Copy the data table on your paper.

Station	Distance to Epicenter (kilometers)	Distance to Epicenter on Map (centimeters)*
1		
2		
3		

*Based on scale: ___ kilometers = ___ centimeters

2. Make a dot in the top right corner of the index card. Label the dot Station 1. Make a dot in the middle of the right edge. Label it Station 2. Make a dot in the bottom left corner. Label it Station 3.

3. Tape the index card to the middle of the drawing paper.

4. Study the report below. Record the distance information in the data table.

> National Seismographic Network
>
> To: All Member Stations
> From: A. Arliss
> Subject: Main shock at 4:42 A.M. today
>
> Based on seismograph readings, we have determined the following:
>
> | Monitoring Station | Distance to Epicenter |
> |---|---|
> | 1 | 900 kilometers |
> | 2 | 1,100 kilometers |
> | 3 | 1,150 kilometers |

Investigation 13-2

The Purpose portion of the student investigation begins with a question to draw students into the activity. Encourage students to read the investigation steps and formulate their own questions before beginning the investigation. This investigation will take approximately 30 minutes to complete. Students will use these process and thinking skills: measuring, converting, recording data, inferring, applying information to new situations, and drawing conclusions.

Preparation

- You may wish to cut equal-size sections of drawing paper (at least 45 by 45 centimeters) for each student or pair to use.
- Gather compasses and review their use with students.
- Duplicate world maps or have on hand several world atlases for the Explore Further activity.
- Students may use Lab Manual 52 to record their data and answer the questions.

Procedure

- Have students work individually or in pairs to complete the investigation. Partners should cooperate to mark the index card, record data, determine the map scale, and draw the circles for each station.
- Tell students to tape the entire edge of the index card to the paper so that the compass will not catch on loose edges.
- You may want to suggest that students establish a scale of 100 kilometers = 1 centimeter.

SAFETY ALERT

- Point out the Safety Alert in the text. Tell students to use caution with the sharp tip of the compass.

Continued on page 328

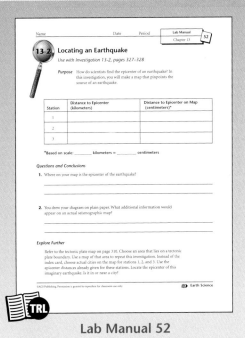

Locating an Earthquake

Use with Investigation 13-2, pages 327–328

Purpose How do scientists find the epicenter of an earthquake? In this investigation, you will make a map that pinpoints the source of an earthquake.

Station	Distance to Epicenter (kilometers)	Distance to Epicenter on Map (centimeters)*
1		
2		
3		

*Based on scale: _____ kilometers = _____ centimeters

Questions and Conclusions

1. Where on your map is the epicenter of the earthquake?

2. You drew your diagram on plain paper. What additional information would appear on an actual seismographic map?

Explore Further

Refer to the tectonic plate map on page 310. Choose an area that lies on a tectonic plate boundary. Use a map of that area to repeat this investigation. Instead of the index card, choose actual cities on the map for stations 1, 2, and 3. Use the epicenter distances already given for these stations. Locate the epicenter of this imaginary earthquake. Is it in or near a city?

Lab Manual 52

Continued from page 327

Results

Results depend on the map scale chosen. Circle radii around stations 1, 2, and 3 would be 9, 11, and 11.5 centimeters for a scale of 100 kilometers = 1 centimeter. These circles would intersect at a point about 4 centimeters above the index card and about 4.5 centimeters in from the card's upper left corner.

Questions and Conclusions Answers

1. Answers depend on the scale chosen. For a scale of 100 kilometers = 1 centimeter, the epicenter is on the drawing paper about 4 centimeters above the index card and about 4.5 centimeters in from the card's upper left corner.

2. The actual map would include boundaries, cities and towns, roads, and geographic features such as mountains, rivers, and plains.

Explore Further Answers

You may want to suggest that students choose a section of the boundary of the Pacific and North American plates off the coast of California. Whether the epicenter falls near a city depends on which cities students choose for their station locations.

Assessment

Check that students convert kilometers to centimeters and use their compasses correctly. Be sure that their scale and conversions are reasonable and that their circles reflect accurate measurement of radii. You might include the following items from this investigation in student portfolios:

* Data table

* Map

* Answers to Questions and Conclusions and Explore Further sections

5. Based on the size of your paper, determine a map scale to convert these distances from kilometers to centimeters. (Each centimeter distance will be the radius of a circle around a station on your map.) Record this scale in the data table. Record the converted distances in the third column of the table.

6. In the data table, find the epicenter's distance from Station 1 in centimeters. Use the ruler to set your compass for that distance. Place the point of the compass on Station 1. Draw a circle. **Safety Alert: Use care when drawing with a compass. The point is sharp.**

7. Repeat step 6 for the remaining stations.

Questions and Conclusions

1. Where on your map is the epicenter of the earthquake?

2. You drew your map on plain paper. What additional information would appear on an actual seismographic map?

Explore Further

Refer to the tectonic plate map on page 310. Choose an area that lies on a tectonic plate boundary. Use a map of that area to repeat this investigation. Instead of the index card, choose actual cities on the map for Stations 1, 2, and 3. Use the epicenter distances already given for these stations. Locate the epicenter of this imaginary earthquake. Is it in or near a city?

- The earth has three main layers: the core, the mantle, and the crust.

- The theory of continental drift states that the continents were once joined as a single landmass that slowly separated and moved apart over time.

- The theory of sea-floor spreading states that the ocean floor spreads as new crust is formed at mid-ocean ridges.

- The theory of plate tectonics states that the earth's crust is made of several large plates that move.

- Convection currents in the mantle push the crust, causing the plates to move.

- Volcanoes occur where magma pushes up through the earth's surface. This happens most often at plate boundaries.

- Volcanoes are grouped into three types: cinder cones, shield volcanoes, and composite volcanoes.

- Mountains can form from volcanic eruptions, from folding, and from movement at faults.

- An earthquake is a shaking of the earth's crust. Most earthquakes occur near plate boundaries.

- Earthquake energy travels through the earth as waves. A seismograph detects and records these waves.

- The epicenter of an earthquake can be located by using the arrival times of earthquake waves at different locations.

- The strength of an earthquake is measured on the Richter scale.

Science Words

cinder cone, 314	crust, 308	Pangaea, 309	shield volcano, 315
composite volcano, 315	earthquake, 322	plate, 310	strike-slip fault, 318
continental drift, 309	epicenter, 324	plate tectonics, 310	tsunami, 325
convection current, 311	fault, 318	reverse fault, 318	vent, 313
core, 308	focus, 324	Richter scale, 324	volcano, 313
	folding, 317	sea-floor spreading, 310	
	mantle, 308	seismograph, 323	
	normal fault, 318		

Chapter 13 Summary

Have volunteers read aloud each Summary item on page 329. Ask volunteers to explain the meaning of each item. Direct students' attention to the Science Words box on the bottom of page 329. Have them read and review each word and its definition.

Chapter 13 Review

Use the Chapter Review to prepare students for tests and to reteach content from the chapter.

Chapter 13 Mastery Test

The Teacher's Resource Library includes two parallel forms of the Chapter 13 Mastery Test. The difficulty level of the two forms is equivalent. You may wish to use one form as a pretest and the other form as a posttest.

Review Answers
Vocabulary Review

1. earthquake 2. folding 3. seismograph 4. sea-floor spreading 5. epicenter 6. continental drift 7. convection current 8. plate tectonics 9. mantle 10. fault

Concept Review

11. C 12. A 13. B 14. Cinder cone— small, steep sides, narrow base, explosive eruptions, made of rock and ash; shield— low, broad, wide crater, gentle eruptions, made of layers of lava; composite— wide base, steep upper slopes, tall, both explosive and gentle eruptions, made of alternating rock layers and lava layers 15. Layers of the earth fold; volcanic material builds up at eruption sites; fault movements raise large blocks of rock. 16. strength or magnitude of earthquake tremors 17. A strike-slip; B reverse; C normal

---

TEACHER ALERT

In the Chapter Review, the Vocabulary Review activity includes a sample of the chapter's vocabulary terms. The activity will help determine students' understanding of key vocabulary terms and concepts presented in the chapter. Other vocabulary terms used in the chapter are listed below:

cinder cone	reverse fault
composite volcano	Richter scale
core	shield volcano
crust	strike-slip fault
focus	tsunami
normal fault	vent
Pangaea	volcano
plate	

Word Bank
continental drift
convection current
earthquake
epicenter
fault
folding
mantle
plate tectonics
sea-floor spreading
seismograph

Vocabulary Review

Choose the word or phrase from the Word Bank that best completes each sentence. Write the answer on your paper.

1. The earth's crust shakes during a(n) _____.

2. The bending of rock layers is _____.

3. An instrument used to record earthquake waves is a(n) _____.

4. The idea that new crust forms along rifts in the ocean floor is called _____.

5. The point on the earth's surface above the focus of an earthquake is its _____.

6. The idea that the earth's landmasses move is the _____ theory.

7. The circular movement of a gas or liquid as it heats is a(n) _____.

8. The idea that the earth's crust is made of moving sections is the theory of _____.

9. The layer of the earth between the core and the crust is the _____.

10. A break in the earth's crust where the earth moves in different directions is a(n) _____.

Concept Review

Choose the word or phrase that best completes each sentence. Write the letter of the answer on your paper.

11. The earth's surface is part of the _____.
   A core
   B atmosphere
   C crust
   D mantle

Name _____ Date _____ Period _____ | Mastery Test A, Page 1 / Chapter 13

Chapter 13 Mastery Test A

Part A Read each sentence. Write the letter of the correct answer on the line.

_____ 1. Plates move because of convection currents in the ___.
   A ocean   B mantle   C epicenter   D continental drift

_____ 2. The innermost layer of the earth, its core, is ___.
   A the thickest layer
   B made of nickel and iron
   C solid
   D all the above

_____ 3. Earthquake waves that travel slowest and do the most damage are called ___.
   A L-waves   B S-waves   C P-waves   D tsunami waves

_____ 4. Volcanic mountains usually form ___.
   A in the middle of a plate
   B in cornfields
   C where two plates meet
   D where a plate folds

_____ 5. Magma pouring through a rift onto the ocean floor ___.
   A becomes an island
   B forms new ocean crust
   C signals an earthquake
   D all of the above

Part B Match each term with its description. Write the letter of the correct description on the line.

_____ 6. mantle   A small volcano with steep sides
_____ 7. continental drift   B Mount Fuji, for example
_____ 8. cinder cone   C break in the earth's crust along which movement occurs
_____ 9. fault   D low, broad volcano
_____ 10. composite volcano E theory that the earth's continents move
_____ 11. shield volcano   F place within the earth where an earthquake starts
_____ 12. focus   G instrument that measures earthquake strength
_____ 13. Richter scale   H churning liquid and solid rock beneath the crust

©AGS Publishing. Permission is granted to reproduce for classroom use only.   Earth Science

---

Name _____ Date _____ Period _____ | Mastery Test A, Page 2 / Chapter 13

Chapter 13 Mastery Test A, continued

Part C Write the terms from the Word Bank that best complete the sentences.

14. A _____ detects and records earthquake waves.
15. Plate _____ is the theory that the earth's surface is made of large sections moving over the mantle.
16. Plates collide, move apart, or _____ past each other.
17. Sea-floor spreading helps explain how continents _____ over time.
18. An earthquake occurs when rocks break or move suddenly at a _____.
19. The three main layers of the earth are the _____, mantle, and _____.
20. When continental plates collide and bend, mountains form by _____.

Word Bank
core
crust
fault
folding
move apart
seismograph
slide
tectonics

Part D Write a short answer for each question.

21. What are three ways mountains form? _____

22. What are three types of faults? _____

23. Why did Alfred Wegener believe the continents were once joined? _____

24. How do blocks of rock move at a strike-slip fault? _____

25. How do scientists determine where the epicenter of an earthquake lies? _____

©AGS Publishing. Permission is granted to reproduce for classroom use only.   Earth Science

Chapter 13 Mastery Test A

12. Continental drift, sea-floor spreading, and plate tectonics all help explain _____.
  A how the earth's surface changes
  B where convection currents come from
  C why the earth has layers
  D the age of the earth

13. Where two plates meet, they usually _____.
  A explode
  B scrape or squeeze each other
  C stop moving
  D become attached

Write the answer to each of the following questions.

14. Name the three types of volcanos and one unique feature of each.

15. Describe two of the three ways that mountains form.

16. Explain what the Richter scale measures.

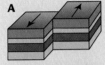

17. Look at the lettered diagrams. Name the type of fault each diagram represents.

Critical Thinking

Write the answer to each of the following questions.

18. Tell how mountains, volcanoes, and earthquakes are related to the earth's plates.

19. Review the factors that determine the effect of an earthquake. What factors might determine the effect of a tsunami?

20. A string of active volcanoes rings the Pacific Ocean basin. In fact, the circle is called the Ring of Fire. What conclusion might you draw about the earth's crust under this ring? Why?

Test-Taking Tip Decide which questions you will do first and last. Limit your time on each question accordingly.

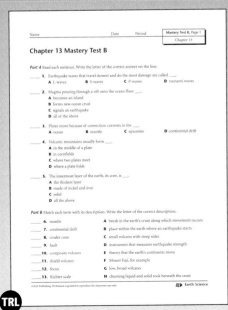

Chapter 13 Mastery Test B

---

18. Mountains form, volcanoes erupt, earthquakes occur, and new ocean crust forms where tectonic plate boundaries move and release energy. **19.** Tsunamis would be larger, more powerful, and more destructive the closer they are to the epicenter of an earthquake when they strike land. The effect of tsunamis also depends on the strength of the earthquake. **20.** The Ring of Fire marks the boundaries of tectonic plates that are actively grinding against each other or being forced one under the other. This tectonic activity may cause magma to reach the crust's surface, forming a volcano.

ALTERNATIVE ASSESSMENT

Alternative Assessment items correlate to the student Goals for Learning at the beginning of this chapter.

■ Provide each student with a diagram of the earth's layers. Have students label each layer and describe what it is like.

■ Ask students to explain the plates of the earth's crust using the map on page 310. Then have them use blocks of clay or wood to demonstrate three ways that tectonic plates can move.

■ Show students a diagram of the Ring of Fire around the Pacific Ocean. Have them compare it to the map on page 310 and explain why so many volcanoes are located in this ring.

■ Have students work together to design an activity that models how mountains and faults form at plate boundaries. Students may use clay, catalogs, or other bendable materials.

■ Using their models from the preceding assessment activity, students can model what happens at plate boundaries that causes earthquakes. Ask them to explain why this motion can cause widespread destruction.

Planning Guide

A Record of the Earth's History

		Student Text Lesson		
		Student Pages	Vocabulary	Lesson Review
Lesson 1	The Rock Record	334–339	✔	✔
Lesson 2	The Ages of Rocks and Fossils	340–346	✔	✔
Lesson 3	Eras in the Geologic Time Scale	347–352	✔	✔

Chapter Activities

Student Text
Science Center
Teacher's Resource Library
Community Connection 14: Recording
Local Fossils

Assessment Options

Student Text
Chapter 14 Review

Teacher's Resource Library
Chapter 14 Mastery Tests A and B
Chapters 1–14 Final Mastery Test

Achievements in Science	Science at Work	Science in Your Life	Investigation	Science Myth	Note	Technology Note	Did You Know	Science Integration	Science Journal	Cross-Curricular Connection	Online Connection	Teacher Alert	Applications (Home, Career, Community, Global, Environment)	Auditory/Verbal	Body/Kinesthetic	Interpersonal/Group Learning	Logical/Mathematical	Visual/Spatial	LEP/ESL	Workbook Activities	Alternative Workbook Activities	Lab Manual	Resource File	Self-Study Guide
337			338		✔			335	335	336	336	335	335, 336	336	336					54	54	53, 54, 55		✔
	344	345					341	343	343	342, 343		341	341, 342				342		341	55	55	56	31, 32	✔
		352		349	✔	✔	350, 351	349	351	349, 350		348	350			351	348			56	56			✔

Pronunciation Key

a hat	e let	ī ice	ô order	ù put	sh she	ə {	a in about
ā age	ē equal	o hot	oi oil	ü rule	th thin		e in taken
ä far	ėr term	ō open	ou out	ch child	₮H then		i in pencil
â care	i it	ȯ saw	u cup	ng long	zh measure		o in lemon
							u in circus

Alternative Workbook Activities

The Teacher's Resource Library (TRL) contains a set of lower-level worksheets called Alternative Workbook Activities. These worksheets cover the same content as the regular Workbook Activities but are written at a second-grade reading level.

Skill Track Software

Use the Skill Track Software for Earth Science for additional reinforcement of this chapter. The software program allows students using AGS textbooks to be assessed for mastery of each chapter and lesson of the textbook. Students access the software on an individual basis and are assessed with multiple-choice items.

Chapter 14: A Record of the Earth's History
pages 332–355

Lessons

1. **The Rock Record** pages 334–339

Investigation 14-1 pages 338–339

2. **The Ages of Rocks and Fossils** pages 340–346

Investigation 14-2 pages 345–346

3. **Eras in the Geologic Time Scale** pages 347–352

Chapter 14 Summary page 353

Chapter 14 Review pages 354–355

Skill Track Software for Earth Science

Teacher's Resource Library

Workbook Activities 54–56

Alternative Workbook Activities 54–56

Lab Manual 53–56

Community Connection 14

Resource File 31–32

Chapter 14 Self-Study Guide

Chapter 14 Mastery Tests A and B

Chapters 1–14 Final Mastery Test

(Answer Keys for the Teacher's Resource Library begin on page 400 of the Teacher's Edition. The Materials List for the Lab Manual activities begins on page 415.)

Science Center

Have students prepare a display of prehistoric life. The display should be divided into four sections that represent the four eras on the geologic time scale—the Precambrian, Paleozoic, Mesozoic, and Cenozoic Eras. Encourage students to create models or drawings of the plants and animals that lived during each era. Remind students to label each of their models or drawings.

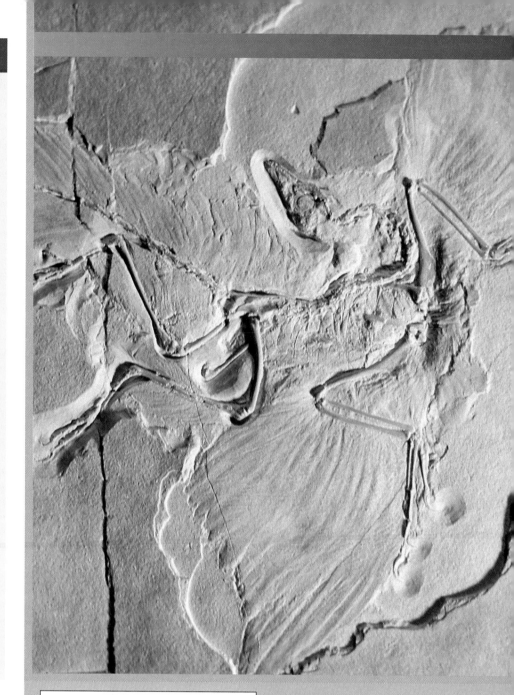

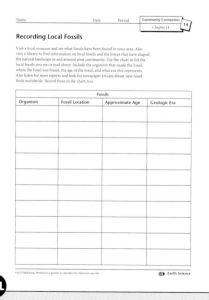

Community Connection 14

14 A Record of the Earth's History

Imagine a quiet forest. All is still. Suddenly, a blurry shape flies by close to the ground. Landing on a low branch, the shape shows itself to be a bird about the size of a crow. At least it *looks* like a bird. It has wings and feathers. But it also has a head like a lizard. Sharp teeth line its mouth, and its wings end in claws. Is this a creature from a movie? No, it is a real part of our past, preserved in the rock shown in the photo. Evidence, such as these remains, provides clues to what life on the earth was like long ago. In Chapter 14, you will learn about geologic time. You also will find out about the kinds of evidence scientists use to reconstruct the earth's history.

Organize Your Thoughts

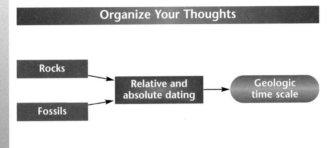

Rocks → Relative and absolute dating → Geologic time scale

Fossils → Relative and absolute dating

Goals for Learning

◆ To define geologic time

◆ To explain how fossils form

◆ To explain relative and absolute dating of rocks

◆ To outline major events in the earth's history

333

Introducing the Chapter

Direct students' attention to the photo on page 332. Ask them to identify what they see. When they recognize it as a fossil, possibly of a bird, ask how they knew what it was. Point out the chapter title and ask why fossils like the one shown might be part of the record of the earth's history. Then have a volunteer read aloud the introductory paragraph on page 333.

Brainstorm with students a list of plants and animals that lived in the distant past. Let students suggest ways the plants and animals on their list could be classified. Allow students to speculate on the age of the fossil shown in the photo. Ask them to tell how they think scientists determine the age of ancient fossils. Finally, ask students why fossils are important to scientists.

Have students read the Goals for Learning on page 333 and ask them to rewrite each goal as a question that they can answer as they read the chapter.

Notes and Technology Notes

Ask volunteers to read the notes that appear in the margins throughout the chapter. Then discuss them with the class.

TEACHER'S RESOURCE

The AGS Teaching Strategies in Science Transparencies may be used with this chapter. The transparencies add an interactive dimension to expand and enhance the *Earth Science* program content.

CAREER INTEREST INVENTORY

The AGS Harrington-O'Shea Career Decision-Making System-Revised (CDM) may be used with this chapter. Students can use the CDM to explore their interests and identify careers. The CDM defines career areas that are indicated by students' responses on the inventory.

TRL   TRL

Chapter 14 Self-Study Guide

Lesson at a Glance

Chapter 14 Lesson 1

Overview This lesson introduces the concept of geologic time and explains what fossils are. Students also learn different ways fossils can form.

Objectives

- To define geologic time
- To explain what a fossil is
- To describe three ways fossils form

Student Pages 334–339

Teacher's Resource Library TRL

Workbook Activity 54

Alternative Workbook Activity 54

Lab Manual 53–55

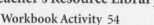

Vocabulary

cast	mold
fossil	petrification
geologic time	

Science Background

In the early 1800s, the French zoologist Georges Cuvier noticed that fossils of seashells in any one layer, or stratum, of rock differed significantly from fossils in the strata above and below. He proposed that the earth's history was divided into very long stages during which different sets of plants and animals developed. Cuvier's study of fossils is considered the beginning of the science of paleontology.

Much of what is known about the earth's past is inferred from fossils. When most living things die, they decay without leaving a trace. However, sometimes when a living thing is buried in sediment soon after death, it is fossilized. Because hard parts, such as bones and teeth, do not decay as easily as soft parts, they are more often found in the fossil record than are soft tissues. From an organism's teeth, a scientist can make inferences about its diet. Bone remains can indicate whether an organism walked on two or four legs and other aspects of an organism's basic skeletal structure. However, the fossil record indicates very little about an organism's behavior or its soft tissue.

Objectives

After reading this lesson, you should be able to

- define geologic time.
- explain what a fossil is.
- describe three ways fossils form.

Geologic time

All the time that has passed since the earth formed

Does a year seem like a long time to you? Your idea of time depends on what you compare it to. Compared to events in your life, a year probably is a long time. Compared to the history of most nations, a year is not very long at all. Scientists who study the earth describe a long time in terms of millions or billions of years. For example, the carving of the Grand Canyon took about 6 million years. Compared to that amount of time, a year is not even noticeable.

Geologic Time

Most events in earth science are compared to **geologic time**—all the time that has passed since the earth formed. Scientists estimate that the earth is about 4.6 billion years old. Compared to this amount of time, even the Grand Canyon is fairly young.

When an event, such as a hurricane, happens today, it is recorded. Newspaper reports, videotapes, and photographs record the event. No such records exist for most of the earth's events. Yet much has happened in the earth's long history. Mountains have built up, continents have moved, living things have come and gone. These events left records in the rock of the earth's crust. As you will see, scientists study rock layers to learn what happened in the past and the order in which events took place.

The Colorado River has carved the Grand Canyon over millions of years.

334   *Chapter 14   A Record of the Earth's History*

1 Warm-Up Activity

Ahead of time, press a common classroom object, such as a pencil or a drawing compass, into a piece of clay. Remove the object. Show students the clay imprint and ask them to identify what they think made the impression. Discuss with students what they can and cannot tell about the object from its imprint.

Fossils are evidence
that living things
on the earth have
changed over time.
Fossils also show
that the earth's
climates haven't
always been the
same.

Fossils

Among the most important records of the earth's history are **fossils**. Fossils, like the one shown on page 332, are the traces or remains of organisms preserved in the earth's crust. Organisms are living things and include plants and animals. Fossils are evidence that certain kinds of life existed. Other living things may have been present on the earth in the past. However, unless these living things left fossils, scientists have no evidence of their existence.

It's not easy to become a fossil. When an organism dies, its soft parts usually decay. They might also be eaten by other creatures. The parts most likely to become fossils are the hard parts, such as wood, teeth, bones, and shells. Usually, these parts must be buried quickly in some way in order to become fossils. Most organisms that become fossils are buried by sediment on the ocean floor. Burial might also occur during sandstorms, volcanic eruptions, floods, or avalanches.

Types of Fossils

Most fossils preserve the shape of the organism but not the actual body matter. For example, some fossils form when minerals replace the original parts of a buried organism. This process is called **petrification**. The photo shows petrified wood. Over thousands of years, the wood was dissolved by groundwater and replaced by the minerals in the water.

What details can you see preserved in this petrified wood?

A Record of the Earth's History   Chapter 14   **335**

Have students scan the lesson and write down the headings. Ask them to write a question that they expect will be answered under each heading. As students read the text, have them look for answers to their questions.

Ask students to tell what they know about fossils and describe fossils they have seen. If any students have ever been on a fossil hunt, have them describe their experiences and the results of their hunt.

 Reinforce and Extend

TEACHER ALERT

 Students may tend to associate fossils only with animal remains. However, fossils also include plants. Fossils of plants give clues to the earth's climate and to what animals may have eaten for food.

SCIENCE INTEGRATION

 Environment

Suggest that partners research the Petrified Forest National Park in Arizona. The petrified remains of a forest are located in what is now a desert. Partners might write a short report about how the petrified wood was formed and what scientists can tell about the past climate and environment of the region from the petrified remains.

SCIENCE JOURNAL

 Tell students to imagine they have found an important fossil. Ask them to write a story describing their discovery and telling what they think might have happened when the fossil formed.

CAREER CONNECTION

 Invite a paleontologist or a person who works with fossils at a local natural history museum to discuss his or her work. Ask the guest to bring, if possible, fossils or slides to show the class. Suggest that students prepare a list of questions ahead of time to ask the speaker.

Mold
Type of fossil that forms when the shape of a plant or an animal is left in a rock

Cast
Type of fossil that forms when minerals fill a mold; a model of an organism

Another type of fossil forms when an organism leaves an imprint behind. For example, a plant or an animal may become buried in sediment that later forms rock. Eventually, the organism decays or dissolves. The space left in the rock, called a **mold**, has the shape of the plant or animal. If minerals fill the mold, a **cast** forms. The cast becomes a model of the original plant or animal. In the photo below, find both a mold and a cast of a trilobite. This sea animal lived 500 million years ago.

Many buried trilobites created the molds and casts in this rock.

Fossils, such as this amber, offer a glimpse of life from the past.

Sometimes, the actual body matter of an organism is preserved as a fossil. For example, remains of woolly mammoths, ancient ancestors of elephants, have been found preserved in ice and frozen soil. The remains of saber-toothed tigers have been discovered trapped in petroleum deposits called tar pits. The insects in the photo on the left were trapped in tree sap. The sap hardened into a material called amber, preserving the actual body of each insect.

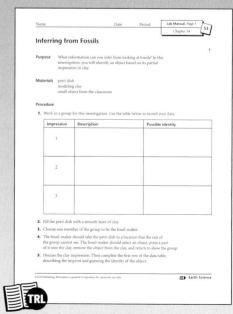

Write the answers to these questions on a sheet of paper.

1. What is geologic time?

2. What is a fossil?

3. What are three ways that fossils form?

4. Describe the process of petrification.

5. Explain how a cast forms from a buried organism.

Achievements in Science

Uncovering the History of Life

Fossils are keys to understanding the past. Paleontologists are scientists who uncover and study fossils. These scientists have learned much about the history of plant and animal life on the earth.

Fossils show what past climates were like. For example, fossils of palm and magnolia leaves have been found in Greenland. This shows that Greenland, an icy region today, had a warm, wet climate about 80 million years ago.

Fossils tell about an area's history. For example, paleontologists have found fossil shellfish in the Rocky Mountains. Since fossil shellfish are found in rocks formed under an ocean, this indicates that the Rocky Mountains were once underwater.

Fossils reveal past forms of life that are now extinct. Richard Owen was a British paleontologist who examined fossil teeth discovered in the 1820s. Other scientists thought the teeth belonged to a large lizard. Owen had a different idea. He thought the teeth belonged to a huge reptile that was unlike any known reptiles. In 1841, he proposed a name for this new group of animals—Dinosauria. The term *dinosaur* soon became part of scientific language.

How do paleontologists uncover fossils? When these scientists find part of a fossil in a rock, they dig the rock away from it. They start with large tools or even explosives. As they get closer to the fossil, they use smaller tools to carefully free the fossil. Then they use delicate tools and tiny brushes to clean the fossil.

A Record of the Earth's History   Chapter 14   **337**

Lesson 1 Review Answers

1. Geologic time is all the time that has passed since the earth formed. **2.** A fossil is the traces or remains of an organism preserved in the earth's crust. **3.** The three ways fossils form are when minerals in groundwater replace the original parts of a buried organism (petrification); when organisms leave an imprint behind in sediment that later becomes rock (and/or when material fills this imprint, creating a cast); and when the actual body of an organism is preserved in ice, frozen soil, tar, or amber. **4.** Minerals in groundwater replace the original parts of a buried organism. **5.** A plant or animal becomes buried in sediment that later becomes rock. The organism decays or dissolves. The space left in the rock has the shape of the organism. This is called a mold. Sometimes minerals fill the mold, forming a cast, which is a model of the original plant or animal.

Achievements in Science

Ask volunteers to read aloud the feature on page 337. Explain to students that Owen used the term *Dinosauria* because in Greek *deinos* means "fearfully great" and *sauros* means "lizard." Owen named many of the dinosaurs, including the anthodon, cardiodon, and echinodon.

Portfolio Assessment

Sample items include:
- Questions and answers from Teaching the Lesson
- Lesson 1 Review answers

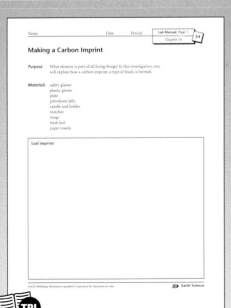

Lab Manual 54, pages 1–2

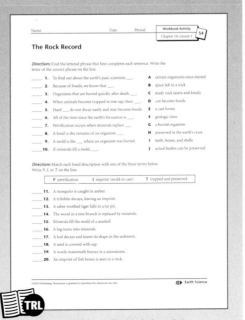

Workbook Activity 54

Investigation 14-1

The Purpose portion of the student investigation begins with a question to draw students into the activity. Encourage students to read the investigation steps and formulate their own questions before beginning the investigation. The first part of this investigation will take approximately 30 minutes to complete. After the plaster cast hardens overnight, an additional 15 minutes is required the following day. Students will use these process and thinking skills: making models, observing, comparing and contrasting, and drawing conclusions.

Preparation

- Gather enough seashells for each student or pair of students. Bivalve shells with texture, such as scallop shells, work best for this investigation.
- Small, rinsed milk cartons can be substituted for the plastic containers. They can simply be thrown away after the plaster is poured into the mold.
- Keep paper towels on hand to wipe up spills.
- Place a plastic bag in a trash can to collect any leftover plaster of paris.
- Students may use Lab Manual 55 to answer the questions.

Procedure

- Students may work alone or with a partner to do this investigation.
- Students might find it easier to make a clear impression if they coat the shell or the clay with petroleum jelly before making the impression. This will make it easier to remove the shell without damaging the impression.
- Remind students to wash their hands after using the petroleum jelly.
- Read to the class the directions on the package of plaster of paris. Be sure students follow these directions. Before students mix the plaster, remind them that they should add the plaster powder to the water, not the reverse. The plaster should have the consistency of a thick milkshake when it is ready to use.
- Be sure to wipe out reusable plastic containers and rinse them before any remnants of plaster harden.

Making a Model of a Fossil

Purpose

How does a clay impression model a fossil formation? In this investigation, you will make a model of a mold and a cast.

Procedure

1. Cover your work space with newspaper. Flatten the modeling clay into a slab that is about 2 centimeters thick.

2. Gently press a seashell into the clay to form an impression.

3. Remove the seashell and inspect the impression. If the details of the shell cannot be seen clearly, repeat step 2.

4. Use your finger to gently coat the impression with a thin layer of petroleum jelly. Wash your hands.

5. In the container, mix the plaster of paris powder and water according to directions. Make enough plaster of paris to fill the impression. **Safety Alert: Wipe up any spills immediately. Avoid getting the plaster of paris on your hands or face.**

6. Pour the plaster of paris into the clay impression and allow it to harden overnight.

7. Remove the hard plaster of paris from the clay.

8. Clean your work space and wash the equipment.

Materials

- newspaper
- modeling clay
- seashell
- petroleum jelly
- plaster of paris powder
- plastic container
- water
- spoon

Name _____ Date _____ Period _____ **Lab Manual** Chapter 14 **55**

14-1 **Making a Model of a Fossil**
Use with Investigation 14-1, pages 338–339

Purpose How does a clay impression model fossil formation? In this investigation, you will make a model of a mold and a cast.

Questions and Conclusions

1. What part of your model represents a mold?

2. What part of your model represents a cast?

3. How do the mold and cast compare?

Explore Further

Use a clean chicken or turkey bone and repeat the procedure. Then find out how a museum model is made from dinosaur fossils.

©AGS Publishing. Permission is granted to reproduce for classroom use only.   ▶ Earth Science

Questions and Conclusions

1. What part of your model represents a mold?

2. What part of your model represents a cast?

3. How do the mold and cast compare?

Explore Further

Use a clean chicken or turkey bone and repeat the procedure. Then find out how a museum model is made from dinosaur fossils.

SAFETY ALERT

◆ Caution students to wipe up any spills immediately.

◆ Caution students to keep their hands away from their faces when doing this investigation. Plaster of paris can irritate the membranes of the eyes, nose, and mouth.

- Do not let students pour leftover plaster of paris in the sink, as it can harden and clog the drain.
- You might want to make a classroom display of students' fossil casts.
- Challenge students to describe how the clay impression models the formation of a fossil.

Results

The seashell should form a distinct impression (or mold) in the clay. After the plaster of paris has hardened and is removed from the clay, students should have a model (or cast) of the original seashell.

Questions and Conclusions Answers

1. The impression in the clay represents the mold.

2. The hardened plaster of paris represents the cast.

3. The space left in the clay that has the shape of the shell is the mold. When it is filled with plaster of paris, it forms a cast, which is a same-size model of the original shell. The interior of the mold and the exterior of the cast have the same shape, size, and surface pattern.

Explore Further Answers

In general, a museum model is made by making a mold of the dinosaur bones from resin or plaster. Casts are made from the molds. Internal steel and wire armatures are used to support the cast bones.

Assessment

Compare students' fossil model with their original seashell to evaluate how carefully students worked. Check their answers to be sure they understand the difference between a mold and a cast. You might also include the following items from this investigation in student portfolios:

- Final shell casting or a photo of it
- Answers to Questions and Conclusions and Explore Further sections

Lesson at a Glance

Chapter 14 Lesson 2

Overview In this lesson, students learn about relative and absolute dating of rocks. They explore the principles of superposition, crosscutting relationships, and index fossils, as well as radioactive dating methods based on half-life.

Objectives

- To explain how a rock's relative age is determined
- To explain how a rock's absolute age is determined

Student Pages 340–346

Teacher's Resource Library **TRL**

Workbook Activity 55

Alternative Workbook Activity 55

Lab Manual 56

Resource File 31–32

Vocabulary

absolute dating
half-life
index fossil
principle of crosscutting relationships
principle of superposition
radioactive element
relative dating

Science Background

In the late 1700s, William Smith was studying sedimentary rock in England. He concluded that where rock layers, or strata, were stacked up, the layer at the top must be the one formed most recently. Smith saw that fossils can be clues to the relative ages of rocks. For example, if a certain kind of shellfish was found in a rock layer in one part of England, and a fossil exactly like it was found in a rock layer 200 kilometers away, the two layers must be the same age. He concluded that this must be so even if the layer is near the top of a stack in one location and near the bottom in the other location.

Learning about the past by studying rock strata is difficult. No single area contains a complete history in rock. In most areas, some or all of the past sedimentary strata

---

Objectives

After reading this lesson, you should be able to

- explain how a rock's relative age is determined.
- explain how a rock's absolute age is determined.

Relative dating

Method that compares two rock layers to find out which is older

Principle of superposition

In layers of sedimentary rocks, the oldest layer is on the bottom and the youngest layer is on the top if the layers have not been overturned.

To find the age of a fossil, scientists find the age of the rock in which the fossil was found. How is this done? It's not as difficult as you might think.

Principles of Relative Dating

One way to find the age of a rock is to compare it to other rocks. In this method, called **relative dating**, you place rock layers in order from oldest to youngest without using actual dates. Some basic principles can guide you when using relative dating.

If you are unpacking a box of books, you can be fairly certain that the book on the bottom was put in before the books on top. You can apply this simple idea to relative dating. Look at the layers of sedimentary rock shown in the diagram below. The oldest layer is at the bottom. The **principle of superposition** states that if sedimentary rock layers have not been overturned, the oldest rock layer is on the bottom and the youngest rock layer is on the top. Based on this principle, a fossil found in one layer of rock is older than a fossil found in a layer above it.

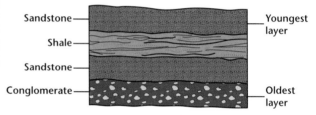

Principle of superposition

---

have been eroded away. In mountainous areas, strata have been folded, cracked, tilted, raised, lowered, or even turned upside down. Even if scientists could rely on perfectly preserved rock strata, the layers would tell them only how old one fossil or rock layer is in relation to another. Therefore, scientists make use of radioactive elements to help them estimate the actual ages of rocks and fossils.

1 Warm-Up Activity

Show students a clear glass jar filled with three or four layers of different colors of aquarium gravel. Ask them if they know which color of gravel was added to the jar first and which was added last. *(Students should say the gravel at the bottom of the jar was added first and the gravel at the top of the jar was added last.)* Explain that scientists can tell which rock layers are oldest and which are youngest by their relative positions.

Principle of crosscutting relationships

A feature, such as a rock structure or a fault, that cuts across rock layers is younger than the rock layers.

Index fossil

Fossil that can be used to establish the relative age of the rock in which the fossil occurs

Suppose you saw a nail stuck in a tree trunk. You would realize that the tree grew first and the nail was later pounded into it. A similar principle is used to determine the relative ages of some rocks. According to the **principle of crosscutting relationships**, a rock that cuts through another rock must be younger than the rock it cuts. The diagram below illustrates this principle. The rock features in the diagram are numbered from oldest (1) to youngest (6).

The igneous rock pocket (5) formed when magma forced its way up through cracks in the existing rock layers. According to the principle of crosscutting relationships, this section of igneous rock is younger than the sedimentary rock layers (1 to 4).

The diagram also shows a fault cutting through layers of rock. Using the principle of crosscutting relationships, you can see that the fault (6) occurred after the pocket of igneous rock formed. So the fault is the youngest rock feature.

How do the rock layers in the diagram also show the principle of superposition?

Some fossils, called **index fossils**, can be used to establish the relative ages of rocks that contain these fossils. Index fossils, such as the trilobites shown on page 336, are useful because they are widespread and lived for a relatively short period of time. Therefore, when scientists find an index fossil anywhere in the world, they know the relative age of the rock in which the fossil was found.

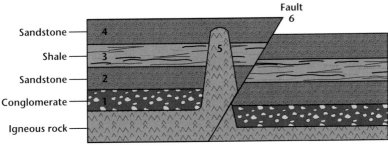

Principle of crosscutting relationships

Did You Know?

Scientists estimate that only about 1 percent of all past organisms became fossils.

---

2 Teaching the Lesson

The diagram on page 341 (Resource File 31) illustrates the principle of superposition as well as the principle of crosscutting relationships. Create an overhead transparency of this diagram. After students have read the section on relative dating, show the transparency. Have volunteers explain the two principles, noting how they differ. Then ask students to rewrite the two principles in their own words.

Finally, discuss with students the differences between relative dating and absolute dating. Ask them in what ways each dating method is useful and in what ways each method has limitations.

TEACHER ALERT

Explain that, although absolute dating methods provide an actual age for a rock or fossil, such ages are only approximations. There is a significant margin of error in this dating approach. The true age of a rock or fossil may be plus or minus several thousands or even millions of years from the approximation.

3 Reinforce and Extend

LEARNING STYLES

LEP/ESL

Provide different colors of modeling clay. Ask students to make a model of rock layers that illustrates the principles of superposition and crosscutting relationships. Have students explain, orally or in writing, how their model demonstrates these principles.

IN THE COMMUNITY

Arrange a field trip to a location where rock layers can be observed. Have students identify which layers are the oldest and the youngest. Ask students to see if there is any evidence of crosscutting features.

Did You Know?

Have a volunteer read aloud the Did You Know? feature on page 341. Ask students why they think most organisms did not become fossils. Explain that most dead organisms are not buried fast enough to be preserved. Instead, they are exposed to air, water, and other living things and either decay or are eaten. Explain that bacteria and other microorganisms break down soft tissue, so soft tissue is rarely present in the fossil record.

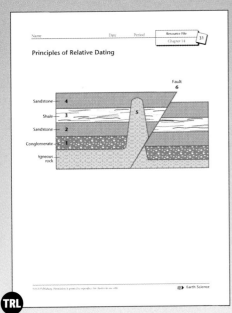

TRL

Resource File 31

Explain that, in general, archaeologists study cultural artifacts buried in the earth, while paleontologists study fossils buried in the earth. Let pairs of students work together to research two or three major archaeological or paleontological finds. Ask them to prepare a sticky note that lists the basic details of each find, such as the location of the find, the type of object found, and its age and significance. Ask each pair to share these results with the class. Then have them point to the location of each find on a large world map and post their sticky notes on the map. When all pairs have finished, review the map. Are there some areas of the world that seem to yield more information about the past than others?

CROSS-CURRICULAR CONNECTION

History

Let small groups of students research the work done by archaeologists. Tell students to find out what is done on a dig and how rock layers reveal information about the people or animals that lived in an area. Let each group present a brief report on the topic.

LEARNING STYLES

Logical/Mathematical

Give each student a long piece of uncooked spaghetti and a marker. Tell students the piece of spaghetti represents the amount of carbon-14 in an organism that has just died. Ask them to imagine that 5,730 years, or one half-life, has passed. Tell students to color half the spaghetti to represent the carbon-14 that has decayed. Explain that the uncolored spaghetti represents the remaining carbon-14. Repeat the procedure two more times. Each time ask students how much carbon-14 is left.

Absolute dating
Method that determines the actual age of a rock or fossil

Radioactive element
Element that breaks apart, or decays, to form another element

Half-life
Length of time it takes for half of the atoms of a radioactive element to decay

Absolute Dating Using Half-Life

Relative dating is useful, but **absolute dating** is more specific. Scientists use absolute dating to find the absolute age, or actual age, of a rock or fossil. Absolute dates are measured in years, just as your age is.

Scientists find the absolute age of a rock by studying certain **radioactive elements** the rock contains. Radioactive elements break apart, or decay, to form other elements. This decay happens at a constant rate. The length of time it takes for half of the atoms of a radioactive element to decay is the element's **half-life**. By comparing the amounts of different elements in a rock, scientists can determine the absolute age of the rock.

For example, the radioactive element carbon-14, a form of carbon, is used in absolute dating of some fossils. All living things contain carbon-14. When an organism dies, the carbon-14 starts to decay, forming nitrogen-14. The diagram below shows the rate of decay. The half-life of carbon-14 is 5,730 years. After 5,730 years, half of the carbon-14 is decayed. Every 5,730 years after that, half of the remaining carbon-14 decays. By measuring the amount of carbon-14 and nitrogen-14 in a sample, scientists can determine how many years ago the organism died.

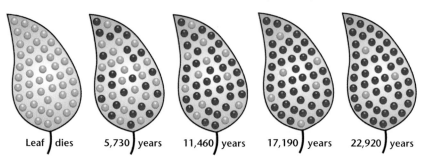

| Leaf dies | 5,730 years | 11,460 years | 17,190 years | 22,920 years |

Key:
- Carbon-14
- Nitrogen-14

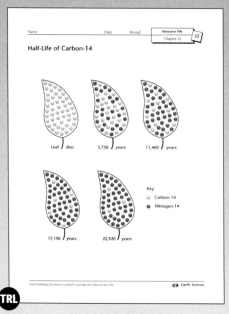

Resource File 32

After about 50,000 years, almost all carbon-14 in an organism has decayed to nitrogen-14. Therefore, carbon-14 cannot be used to date fossils older than 50,000 years. Other radioactive elements with longer half-lives are used to determine the absolute age of older fossils and rocks.

For example, uranium-238 occurs in some igneous rocks and decays to form lead-206. The half-life of uranium-238 is about 4.5 billion years. Scientists can compare the uranium-238 content of a rock to its lead-206 content. From such a comparison, they can determine the absolute age of the rock. Using this method on meteorites, scientists have determined the age of the earth to be 4.6 billion years old.

This well-preserved fossil was discovered in Wyoming. According to absolute dating methods, this ancient fish lived about 40 million years ago.

CROSS-CURRICULAR CONNECTION

Language Arts
Have students write a letter to your local or regional geological service requesting information about the geological history of your area. They might also ask for information about safe places to look for fossils in your area.

SCIENCE INTEGRATION

Physical Science
Ask students to use the Periodic Table of Elements in Appendix E to determine the chemical symbols for carbon, nitrogen, uranium, and lead. Then ask them to find out what is meant by carbon-14, nitrogen-14, uranium-238, and lead-206. (*The number that follows the element name is the mass number, which is equal to the total number of neutrons and protons in an atom. Every element has a unique, identifying number of protons, but the number of neutrons can vary. Atoms of the same element having different numbers of neutrons are called isotopes. Carbon-12 and carbon-14 are isotopes. An atom of carbon-12, the most common isotope of carbon, has 6 protons and 6 neutrons. A carbon-14 atom has 6 protons and 8 neutrons and is radioactive. It decays to nitrogen-14, a common, nonradioactive isotope of nitrogen having 7 protons and 7 neutrons. An atom of radioactive uranium-238 has 92 protons and 146 neutrons. It eventually decays to lead-206, which has 82 protons and 124 neutrons.*)

SCIENCE JOURNAL

Have students imagine they are scientists living 5 million years in the future. Ask them to describe the kinds of fossils they might find from the present time.

Lesson 2 Review Answers

1. Relative dating determines which of two rocks is older, while absolute dating determines the actual age of a rock or fossil. **2.** The principle of superposition states that the oldest layer of rock is on the bottom and the youngest layer is on the top. For example, a fossil found in a deeper layer is older than one found in a higher layer. The principle of crosscutting relationships states that a rock or feature that cuts through another rock must be younger than the rock it cuts. For example, a fault that cuts through rock layers is younger than the rock layers. **3.** Absolute age can be determined by comparing the amount of a radioactive element in a rock with the amount of its decayed element. **4.** A radioactive element's half-life is the length of time required for half of the atoms of the radioactive element to decay. **5.** Uranium-238 would be used to determine the absolute age of fossils that are more than 50,000 years old.

Science at Work

Have volunteers take turns reading aloud the paragraphs of the feature on page 344. Point out that knowing about rock layers and fossils is important to people who explore for oil and natural gas because certain rocks and fossils are clues to the presence of these resources. Also point out that there are many career opportunities in the petroleum industry, from scientists and engineers to legal and administrative positions. Suggest that students investigate some of these careers.

Portfolio Assessment

Sample items include:
- Written statements from Teaching the Lesson
- Lesson 2 Review answers

Write the answers to these questions on a sheet of paper.

1. How does relative dating differ from absolute dating?

2. Define the principles of superposition and crosscutting relationships. Give an example of each.

3. How can a rock's absolute age be determined?

4. What is a radioactive element's half-life?

5. For what kind of fossils would uranium-238 be used to determine absolute age?

▼◄▲▼◄▲▼◄▲▼◄▲▼◄▲▼◄▲▼◄▲▼◄▲▼◄▲▼◄▲▼◄▲▼◄▲▼◄▲▼◄▲▼

Science at Work

Petroleum Engineer

Petroleum engineers travel the world searching for underground deposits of oil or natural gas. Once these deposits are located, petroleum engineers decide on the best way to recover, or get at, the oil or gas. To do this, they often use computer models and other technology. Then petroleum engineers work with geologists to set up drilling equipment and manage drilling operations. An important part of this job is making sure that people and the environment are not in danger.

Petroleum engineers work for petroleum companies, exploration companies, or governments. Petroleum engineers often work where oil or gas is being recovered or processed. These places include Alaska, Texas, Louisiana, Oklahoma, California, western and northern Canada, and countries overseas. Petroleum engineers also work on oil rigs, which are large ships that drill for oil that is located under oceans.

Petroleum engineers must have at least a bachelor's degree in petroleum engineering. Strong computer and technology skills are also required for their work. These engineers need to be good problem-solvers and careful planners. Because of the likelihood of travel, a petroleum engineer should be willing to learn about other cultures and languages.

344 *Chapter 14   A Record of the Earth's History*

TRL

Workbook Activity 55

14-2 INVESTIGATION

Materials

- 2 sheets of paper
- marking pen
- 16 beans
- clock or watch
- graph paper

Making a Half-Life Model

Purpose

How does a radioactive element show age? In this investigation, you will model and graph the decay of a radioactive element.

Procedure

1. Copy the data table on a sheet of paper.

| Time | Mass (grams) | |
	Radioactive Element	New Element
0		
1 half-life		
2 half-lives		
3 half-lives		

2. Label one sheet of paper *radioactive element* and another sheet of paper *new element*.

3. Place all of the beans on the sheet marked *radioactive element*. Each bean represents 1 gram of a radioactive element in a rock sample. At time 0, before any decay has occurred, record the mass in grams of the radioactive element.

4. Assume that the half-life of the beans is 1 minute. Note your starting time on the clock as time 0.

5. Wait 1 minute. Then remove half of the beans from the *radioactive element* paper and place them on the *new element* paper. Record the mass of each element at 1 half-life.

6. Repeat step 5 two times: at 2 half-lives and at 3 half-lives.

The Purpose portion of the student investigation begins with a question to draw students into the activity. Encourage students to read the investigation steps and formulate their own questions before beginning the investigation. This investigation will take approximately 30 minutes to complete. Students will use these process and thinking skills: making models, collecting and interpreting data, interpreting graphs, and drawing conclusions.

Preparation

- Count out 16 beans for each student.

- Be sure to use nontoxic beans. One bag of dried beans from a grocery store should be enough for a class. Larger beans, such as pinto beans or navy beans, will be easier for students to manipulate.

- Students may use Lab Manual 56 to record their data and answer the questions.

Procedure

- Have students work independently or in cooperative groups. Assign one student to gather equipment. All students in a group should record results and clean up when finished.

- Before beginning the activity, review with students how to compile their data into a graph.

SAFETY ALERT

- Caution students not to put the beans in their mouth.
- Caution students to keep their beans contained. Beans spilled on the floor could create a hazardous situation.

Continued on page 346

Name   Date   Period   Lab Manual 56 / Chapter 14

14-2 Making a Half-Life Model

Use with Investigation 14-2, pages 345–346

Purpose How does a radioactive element show age? In this investigation, you will model and graph the decay of a radioactive element.

| Time | Mass (grams) | |
	Radioactive Element	New Element
0		
1 half-life		
2 half-lives		
3 half-lives		

Questions and Conclusions

1. What do the beans that did not get moved represent?

2. What do the beans that did get moved represent?

3. How much of the radioactive element was left after 2 half-lives? After 3 half-lives?

4. How much of the radioactive element would be left after 4 half-lives?

Explore Further

This investigation shows only one of many different ways to make a half-life model. Design a half-life model yourself. You might shake pennies in a box and remove the "heads" or "tails" after each shake, or half-life. You might also use beans of different colors. Graph your data as you proceed. After a couple of half-lives are graphed, extend the graph to predict how many "radioactive atoms" will remain after additional half-lives. Check your predictions.

©AGS Publishing. Permission is granted to reproduce for classroom use only.   Earth Science

Lab Manual 56

Continued from page 345

Results

After one half-life, students should have 8 beans on each sheet of paper; after two half-lives, students should have 4 beans on the radioactive element sheet and 12 beans on the new element sheet; after three half-lives, students should have 2 beans on the radioactive element sheet and 14 beans on the new element sheet.

Questions and Conclusions Answers

1. They represent the number of grams of the radioactive element left in the rock.

2. They represent the number of grams of the radioactive element that decayed to form the new element.

3. 4 grams; 2 grams

4. 1 gram

Explore Further Answers

A half-life experiment could be carried out in a number of ways. The important thing for students to remember is that, for each half-life, half of the *remaining* radioactive material decays. That is, 50 percent of the original amount of the radioactive material will decay after the first half-life, but only 25 percent of the *original* amount of the element will decay after the second half-life—not another 50 percent. If students choose to perform the heads-and-tails variation, explain that each "half-life" may or may not result in the decay of exactly half of the radioactive material. Probability dictates that over a large number of trials, the ratio of heads to tails will work out approximately evenly.

Assessment

Verify that students transfer only half of the remaining beans after each half-life. Check students' graphs to be sure that their data are accurately plotted. Check students' answers to the questions to be sure they understand the investigation. You might also include the following items from this investigation in student portfolios:

• Data table

• Graph

• Answers to Questions and Conclusions and Explore Further sections

7. Draw a graph like the one shown here. Place the time in half-lives along the bottom axis and the mass of the radioactive element in grams along the side axis. Plot your data and connect the points.

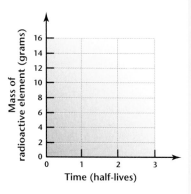

Questions and Conclusions

1. What do the beans that did not get moved represent?

2. What do the beans that did get moved represent?

3. How much of the radioactive element was left after 2 half-lives? After 3 half-lives?

4. How much of the radioactive element would be left after 4 half-lives?

Explore Further

This investigation shows only one of many different ways to make a half-life model. Design a half-life model yourself. You might shake pennies in a box and remove the "heads" or "tails" after each shake, or half-life. You might also use beans of different colors. Graph your data as you proceed. After a couple of half-lives are graphed, extend the graph to predict how many "radioactive atoms" will remain after additional half-lives. Check your predictions.

Geologic time scale

Outline of the events of the earth's history

Precambrian Era

Oldest and longest era of the earth's history; began about 4.6 billion years ago and ended about 540 million years ago

We know the earth has changed over time. But how the earth actually began is still a big question. Scientists use the evidence they have to suggest theories about the earth's origin.

Using evidence from the rock record and fossil record, scientists have developed the **geologic time scale**, shown on page 348. The geologic time scale is an outline of major events in the earth's history. Find the four major units, or eras, of geologic time. Notice how eras are divided into smaller units called periods. Some periods are divided into even smaller units called epochs. Refer to this table as you read about each era.

The Precambrian Era

The **Precambrian Era** is the oldest and longest era. It accounts for about 85 percent of all geologic time. The Precambrian Era began with the formation of the earth and ended about 540 million years ago.

Most Precambrian rocks are igneous or metamorphic. They form the foundation of the continents. These ancient rocks are exposed in some areas where the earth's crust has lifted and eroded. Precambrian rocks can be seen in the Black Hills of South Dakota, the Appalachian Mountains in the eastern United States, and the Ozark Mountains of Missouri.

Simple organisms probably first appeared at least 3.5 billion years ago, early in the Precambrian Era. These organisms may have included relatives of algae, fungi, and bacteria. The fossil record contains limited evidence of Precambrian organisms.

Warm-Up Activity

Have students use social studies books or newspapers to find examples of time lines. Ask them to discuss the purpose of time lines and tell why they are useful. Have students use the time lines they found to identify the time spans covered by the time lines.

Teaching the Lesson

Have students turn to the geologic time scale on page 348. Ask them why the history of the earth is shown on this kind of time scale rather than on a more traditional horizontal or vertical time line. Help students realize that a time line usually covers only a specific period of time, while the geologic time scale covers all of the earth's history, something that would be difficult to show on a standard time line.

Before students begin reading, have them write the names of the four eras discussed in the lesson to use as headings. Tell students that as they read, they are to select the most important facts to write under each heading.

Reinforce and Extend

TEACHER ALERT

Students may have differing views on the origin and age of the earth and on the course of geologic and human development.

LEARNING STYLES

Visual/Spatial

Suggest that students make a chart similar to the one on page 348 for their own life. They could designate eras, such as Infancy, Childhood, and Adolescence; periods, such as Elementary School and High School; and epochs, such as Grade 1 and Junior Year. Have them add years and important events to the chart.

The Geologic Time Scale						
Era	Period	Epoch	Years Before the Present (approximate)		Forms of Life	Physical Events
			Began	Ended		
Cenozoic	Quaternary	Recent	11,000		Humans dominate	West Coast uplift continues in U.S.; Great Lakes form
		Pleistocene	2,000,000	11,000	Primitive humans appear; mammoths	Ice age
	Tertiary	Pliocene	7,000,000	2,000,000	Modern horse, camel, elephant develop	North America joined to South America
		Miocene	23,000,000	7,000,000	Grasses; grazing animals thrive	North America joined to Asia; Columbia Plateau
		Oligocene	38,000,000	23,000,000	Mammals progress; elephants in Africa	Himalayas start forming; Alps continue rising
		Eocene	53,000,000	38,000,000	Ancestors of modern horse, other mammals	Coal forming in western U.S.
		Paleocene	65,000,000	53,000,000	Many new mammals appear	Uplift in western U.S. continues; Alps rising
Mesozoic	Cretaceous		145,000,000	65,000,000	Dinosaurs die out; flowering plants	Uplift of Rockies and Colorado Plateau begins
	Jurassic		208,000,000	145,000,000	First birds appear; giant dinosaurs	Rise of Sierra Nevadas and Coast Ranges
	Triassic		245,000,000	208,000,000	First dinosaurs and mammals appear	Palisades of Hudson River form
Paleozoic	Permian		280,000,000	245,000,000	Trilobites die out	Ice age in South America; deserts in western U.S.
	Pennsylvanian		310,000,000	280,000,000	First reptiles, giant insects; ferns, conifers	Coal-forming swamps in North America and Europe
	Mississippian		345,000,000	310,000,000	Early insects	Limestone formation
	Devonian		395,000,000	345,000,000	First amphibians appear	Mountain building in New England
	Silurian		435,000,000	395,000,000	First land animals (spiders, scorpions)	Deserts in eastern U.S.
	Ordovician		500,000,000	435,000,000	First vertebrates (fish)	Half of North America submerged
	Cambrian		540,000,000	500,000,000	Trilobites, snails; seaweed	Extensive deposition of sediment in inland seas
Precambrian			4,600,000,000	540,000,000	First jellyfish, bacteria, algae	Great volcanic activity, lava flows, metamorphism of rocks; evolution of crust, mantle, core

The Paleozoic Era

The **Paleozoic Era** began about 540 million years ago and ended about 245 million years ago. It was a time of great development of life in the oceans. At times, oceans covered large portions of the continents. Paleozoic rocks contain fossils of trilobites, sponges, and shellfish. The first land plants and animals also developed during this era. In the geologic time scale on page 348, note the progression of life from amphibians to insects to reptiles. Many ancient insects were huge. Some dragonflies had the wingspan of eagles!

During the Paleozoic Era, the earth's crust underwent many changes. For example, the Appalachian Mountains formed during this time as the crust buckled over millions of years. Much of the coal, oil, and natural gas we use today for energy formed from the organisms that lived in large swamps and shallow seas during this era. Many rock layers built up over the dead organic matter. Heat and pressure slowly turned the organic matter into coal, oil, and natural gas.

Compare the trilobite model above with the fossils shown on page 336.

Mesozoic Era

Era characterized by dinosaurs; began about 245 million years ago and ended about 65 million years ago

 Did You Know?

Scientists have considered many theories to explain why the dinosaurs died out. One theory suggests that dinosaurs became extinct after a huge asteroid or comet hit the earth. The dust from the impact may have blocked out the sun for months. Plants would have died, as would have the plant-eating dinosaurs. Then dinosaurs that ate the plant-eaters would have died. A gigantic crater discovered in 1990 in the Gulf of Mexico supports this theory.

The Mesozoic Era

The **Mesozoic Era** began about 245 million years ago and ended 65 million years ago. Life on land flourished during this time. Trees similar to our palm and pine trees were common. Small mammals and birds first appeared. But this era is often called the Age of Reptiles because they were the major form of life on land. The most dominant of the reptiles were the dinosaurs.

In many ways, the kinds of dinosaurs were like the kinds of animals today. Some ate meat and some ate plants. Some were larger than an elephant, while others were as small as a chicken. Some were fierce and others were gentle. Some traveled in herds and some were loners. Even their color probably varied, though we cannot tell this from the fossil record.

The end of the Mesozoic Era is marked by the end of the dinosaurs. Why the dinosaurs died out, or became extinct, during this time is still a mystery.

This is a fossil model of the largest Tyrannosaurus rex *skeleton ever discovered. It is displayed at The Field Museum in Chicago.*

The Cenozoic Era

We are living in the **Cenozoic Era**. It began about 65 million years ago. During this era, the Alps and the Himalayas formed as the earth's plates continued to collide. Late in the era, several ice ages occurred. An ice age is a period of time when glaciers cover large portions of the land. About 2 million years ago, glaciers carved out huge basins and formed the Great Lakes.

Although dinosaurs became extinct at the close of the Mesozoic Era, mammals survived and flourished. The Cenozoic Era is known as the Age of Mammals. In this era, mammals, including humans, became the dominant form of life. The variety of mammals grew. The population, or total number, of each kind of mammal grew as well. At the same time, the kinds and numbers of birds, reptiles, fish, insects, and plants also increased.

Scientists estimate that about 30 million kinds of animals and plants live on the earth today. This is a small percent of all the kinds of organisms that have ever existed. Scientists also believe that about 100 kinds of organisms become extinct each day. Two factors that threaten the survival of plants and animals are pollution and the destruction of the natural environment. Many people are working to save animals and plants from extinction.

As time continues, living things and the earth that supports them will continue to change.

Did You Know?

If you compared the earth's entire history to a one-year calendar, the Precambrian Era would be the first $10\frac{1}{2}$ months. Dinosaurs would appear around December 12 and become extinct by December 27. The first humans would show up during the last few hours of New Year's Eve.

Technology Note

Scientists use fossils to find the ages of rocks. Scientists also use fossils to find deposits of oil. Some fossils, called conodonts, were formed in a variety of colors. The colors are related to how hot the rock was when the fossil formed. This is important because oil forms underground only at certain temperatures. The colors of the conodonts, then, help scientists locate rock layers that might contain oil.

Ask a volunteer to read aloud the Did You Know? feature on page 351. Provide one-year calendars and ask students to work in groups to mark the calendar with the details given in the feature. Ask each group to write three conclusions based on their work with the calendar.

SCIENCE JOURNAL

Point out that the earth has gone through many changes and continues to change. Ask students to write a description of some of the changes they think the earth will go through next.

LEARNING STYLES

Interpersonal/ Group Learning

Have students work in small groups. Have each group make a list of threatened and endangered species and then choose three animals and explain why they are threatened or endangered. Let each group propose at least one way to protect each of the animals.

Lesson 3 Review Answers

1. The geologic time scale is an outline of the events of the earth's history. **2.** The Precambrian Era is the oldest and longest era. There was much volcanic activity. Simple life forms developed. **3.** Possible answers: Paleozoic—fish, amphibians, reptiles; Mesozoic—dinosaurs, mammals, birds; Cenozoic—more mammals, humans **4.** Paleozoic—about 540 million to 245 million years ago; Mesozoic—about 245 million to 65 million years ago; Cenozoic—about 65 million years ago to the present **5.** Possible answers: Precambrian—great volcanic activity; Paleozoic—half of North America submerged; Mesozoic—rise of Sierra Nevadas and Coast Ranges—Cenozoic: North America joined to South America

Science in Your Life

Ask volunteers to take turns reading aloud the feature on page 352. Ask why fossil fuels are called fossil fuels and why they are a nonrenewable resource. Point out that, in addition to the limited supply of fossil fuels, there are other reasons to cut down on the use of these fuels. Discuss with students some of these reasons, including environmental issues, such as pollution, global warming, and nonbiodegradable plastics in landfills, and political issues, such as dependence on other countries to supply the fuels. For a more indepth look at energy resources, ask students to read Appendix B. Then invite a volunteer to moderate a class discussion of the pros and cons of various energy choices.

Portfolio Assessment

Sample items include:
- List of facts from Teaching the Lesson
- Lesson 3 Review answers

Write the answers to these questions on a sheet of paper.

1. What is the geologic time scale?

2. Describe the Precambrian Era.

3. Name two forms of life that first appeared during each of the Paleozoic, Mesozoic, and Cenozoic Eras.

4. What time periods were spanned by the Paleozoic, Mesozoic, and Cenozoic Eras?

5. For each era of geologic time, name a major change that occurred in the earth's crust during that era.

Science in Your Life

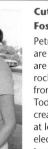

Cutting Down on Fossil Fuels

Petroleum, coal, and natural gas are fossil fuels. Deposits of fossil fuels are found in layers of underground rock. They formed there long ago from decayed plants and animals. Today fossil fuels are burned to create energy. They currently supply at least 60 percent of the world's electrical needs. They also are used to make cosmetics, paints, dry-cleaning chemicals, asphalt, and many other products.

Fossil fuels are nonrenewable. This means there is a limited supply of fossil fuels. They won't last forever, and we are using them up quickly. Because of this, scientists are improving ways to use renewable sources of energy. Renewable energy includes wind, hydroelectric, solar, geothermal, and nuclear energy. You can read about these forms of energy in Appendix B.

Make a list of ways you use gasoline, electricity, motor oil, coal, and natural gas. Then list other products you use that are made from fossil fuels. What can you do to reduce your use of fossil fuels?

Name _____ Date _____ Period _____   **Workbook Activity**
Chapter 14, Lesson 3   **56**

Eras in the Geologic Time Scale: Terms Review

Directions Match each term with its description. Write the letter of the correct description on the line.

_____ **1.** principle of superposition

_____ **2.** Paleozoic Era

_____ **3.** geologic time scale

_____ **4.** fossil

_____ **5.** radioactive element

_____ **6.** index fossil

_____ **7.** principle of crosscutting relationships

_____ **8.** petrification

_____ **9.** half-life

_____ **10.** Mesozoic Era

A era marked by trilobites and other sea life

B youngest feature cuts across other rock layers

C fossil that provides clues to the age of a rock

D element that decays to form another element

E outline of the earth's history

F dinosaur era

G oldest rock layer is on the bottom

H minerals replace a buried organism

I preserved remains of an organism

J length of time for half of an element's atoms to decay

Directions **11–18.** In each box below, write the numbers 1 to 4 on the lines to show the correct order in geologic history.

_____ Paleozoic Era
_____ Cenozoic Era
_____ Precambrian Era
_____ Mesozoic Era

_____ Swamps form; coal begins to develop.
_____ The earth's crust and mantle form.
_____ The Rocky Mountains form.
_____ The Great Lakes form after the last ice age.

Directions Contrast each pair of terms. Explain how the terms in each pair are different.

19. absolute dating—relative dating _____

20. cast—mold _____

©AGS Publishing. Permission is granted to reproduce for classroom use only.   **Earth Science**

Workbook Activity 56

■ Geologic time is all the time that has passed since the earth formed—about 4. 6 billion years.

■ Rocks contain clues about events that happened in the earth's past.

■ Fossils are evidence that certain organisms existed.

■ Fossils form when plant or animal remains become replaced with minerals, leave an imprint, or become preserved.

■ Relative dating is a method used to find the relative age of a rock layer by comparing it to other layers.

■ The principle of superposition states that the youngest layer in sedimentary rock is the top layer.

■ The principle of crosscutting relationships states that a rock feature that cuts through other rock layers is younger than those layers.

■ Absolute dating is a method used to determine the actual age of a rock layer.

■ Absolute dating relies on the decay of radioactive elements in a rock or fossil. How fast a radioactive element decays depends on its half-life.

■ The events in the earth's history occurred over geologic time and are outlined on the geologic time scale.

■ Earth's history is divided into four eras: Precambrian, Paleozoic, Mesozoic, and Cenozoic. Each era is unique in terms of the living things that developed and the changes that took place in the earth's crust.

Science Words

absolute dating, 342	geologic time scale, 347	Paleozoic Era, 349	principle of superposition, 340
cast, 336	half-life, 342	petrification, 335	radioactive element, 342
Cenozoic Era, 351	index fossil, 341	Precambrian Era, 347	relative dating, 340
fossil, 335	Mesozoic Era, 350	principle of crosscutting relationships, 341	
geologic time, 334	mold, 336		

Chapter 14 Summary

Have volunteers read aloud each Summary item on page 353. Ask volunteers to explain the meaning of each item. Direct students' attention to the Science Words box on the bottom of page 353. Have them read and review each word and its definition.

Chapter 14 Review

Use the Chapter Review to prepare students for tests and to reteach content from the chapter.

Chapter 14 Mastery Test

The Teacher's Resource Library includes two parallel forms of the Chapter 14 Mastery Test. The difficulty level of the two forms is equivalent. You may wish to use one form as a pretest and the other form as a posttest.

Chapters 1–14 Final Mastery Test TRL

The Teacher's Resource Library includes the Final Mastery Test. This test is pictured on pages 398–399 of this Teacher's Edition. The Final Mastery Test assesses the major learning objectives of this text, with emphasis on Chapters 7–14.

Review Answers
Vocabulary Review

1. superposition 2. relative dating 3. fossil 4. mold 5. absolute dating 6. index fossil 7. petrification 8. cast 9. geologic time 10. half-life

Concept Review

11. B 12. D 13. A 14. B 15. A 16. D 17. B 18. A

Chapter 14 R E V I E W

Vocabulary Review

Word Bank

absolute dating
cast
fossil
geologic time
half-life
index fossil
mold
petrification
superposition
relative dating

Choose the word or phrase from the Word Bank that best matches each definition. Write the answer on your paper.

1. principle stating that a rock layer is younger than the layer below it and older than the layer above it

2. method used to determine how old a rock layer is by comparing it to another rock layer

3. trace or remains of an organism preserved in the earth's crust

4. impression left in a rock by an organism

5. method that determines the actual age of a rock or fossil

6. fossil that provides clues to the age of the rock in which the fossil occurs

7. process by which original plant or animal parts are replaced with minerals

8. model of an organism

9. total amount of time since the earth was formed

10. length of time it takes for half of the atoms of a radioactive element to decay

Concept Review

Choose the word or phrase that best completes each sentence. Write the letter of the answer on your paper.

11. The geologic time scale divides the history of the earth into four _____.
   A epochs   B eras   C periods   D events

12. Scientists study _____ to learn about the history of life on the earth.
   A mammals   C radioactive elements
   B reptiles   D fossils

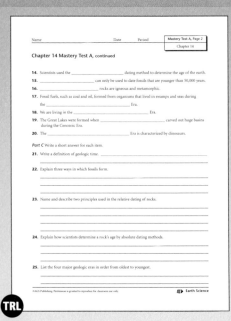

Chapter 14 Mastery Test A

13. To find the absolute age of a rock, scientists use _____.
   A radioactive uranium   **C** the principle of superposition
   B relative dating   **D** crosscutting relationships

14. To find the relative age of a rock, scientists use _____.
   A carbon-14   **C** absolute dating
   B index fossils   **D** half-lives

15. During the _____ Era, dinosaurs and other reptiles were the major forms of life on the earth.
   A Mesozoic   **C** Precambrian
   B Paleozoic   **D** Cenozoic

16. A radioactive element decays to form _____.
   A an index fossil   **C** carbon-14
   B petrified wood   **D** another element

17. According to the principle of crosscutting relationships, a rock feature that cuts across other rock layers is _____ than the rock layers.
   A older   **B** younger   **C** harder   **D** sharper

18. During the Cenozoic Era, the Great Lakes basins were carved out by _____.
   A glaciers   **B** rivers   **C** wind   **D** mudslides

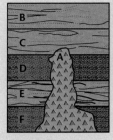

Critical Thinking

Write the answer to each of the following questions.

19. In the diagram, which lettered rocks are younger than rock D? Explain your answer in terms of two scientific principles.

20. An organism dies and becomes a fossil. Later scientists discover the fossil and find it contains 100 units of carbon-14 and 300 units of nitrogen-14. How many half-lives have occurred? How many years ago did the organism die?

Test-Taking Tip Before you begin a test, look it over quickly. Try to set aside enough time to complete each section.

Review Answers
Critical Thinking

19. rocks A, B, and C; according to the principle of superposition, rocks B and C are younger because they are above rock D; according to the principle of crosscutting relationships, rock A is younger because it cuts through rock D.
20. 2 half-lives; 11,460 years ago

ALTERNATIVE ASSESSMENT

Alternative Assessment items correlate to the student Goals for Learning at the beginning of this chapter.

- Give each student an index card and ask students to write in their own words a definition of *geologic time*. Also ask them to list three events that have happened in the earth's history.

- Ask students to create a three-column chart and use each column to explain one way a fossil forms. Encourage them to draw pictures to go with their explanations.

- Have students create a Venn diagram to show how relative dating and absolute dating of rocks are alike and different.

- Write the names of the four eras in geologic time as headings on the board. Call out the names of plants, animals, and physical events from the geologic time scale on page 348. Have volunteers write the life form or event under the correct heading on the board.

Chapter 14 Mastery Test B

Appendix A: Metric and Customary Measurement

Metric Measures

Length
1,000 meters (m) = 1 kilometer (km)
100 centimeters (cm) = 1 m
10 decimeters (dm) = 1 m
1,000 millimeters (mm) = 1 m
10 cm = 1 decimeter (dm)
10 mm = 1 cm

Area
100 square millimeters (mm^2) = 1 square
   centimeter (cm^2)
10,000 cm^2 = 1 square meter (m^2)
10,000 m^2 = 1 hectare (ha)

Volume
1,000 cubic meters (m^3) = 1 cubic
   centimeter (cm^3)
1,000 cubic centimeters (cm^3) = 1 liter (L)
1 cubic centimeter (cm^3) = 1 milliliter (mL)
100 cm^3 = 1 cubic decimeter (dm^3)
1,000,000 cm^3 = 1 cubic meter (m^3)

Capacity
1,000 milliliters (mL) = 1 liter (L)
1,000 L = 1 kiloliter (kL)

Mass
100 grams (g) = 1 centigram (cg)
1,000 kilograms (kg) = 1 metric ton (t)
1,000 grams (g) = 1 kg
1,000 milligrams (mg) = 1 g

Temperature Degrees Celsius (°C)
0°C = freezing point of water
37°C = normal body temperature
100°C = boiling point of water

Time
60 seconds (sec) = 1 minute (min)
60 min = 1 hour (hr)
24 hr = 1 day

Customary Measures

Length
12 inches (in.) = 1 foot (ft)
3 ft = 1 yard (yd)
36 in. = 1 yd
5,280 ft = 1 mile (mi)
1,760 yd = 1 mi
6,076 feet = 1 nautical mile

Area
144 square inches (sq in.) = 1 square foot
   (sq ft)
9 sq ft = 1 square yard (sq yd)
43,560 sq ft = 1 acre (A)

Volume
1,728 cubic inches (cu in.) = 1 cubic foot
   (cu ft)
27 cu ft = 1 cubic yard (cu yard)

Capacity
8 fluid ounces (fl oz) = 1 cup (c)
2 c = 1 pint (pt)
2 pt = 1 quart (qt)
4 qt = 1 gallon (gal)

Weight
16 ounces (oz) = 1 pound (lb)
2,000 lb = 1 ton (T)

Temperature Degrees Fahrenheit (°F)
32°F = freezing point of water
98.6°F = normal body temperature
212°F = boiling point of water

To change	To	Multiply by	To change	To	Multiply by
centimeters	inches	0.3937	meters	feet	3.2808
centimeters	feet	0.03281	meters	miles	0.0006214
cubic feet	cubic meters	0.0283	meters	yards	1.0936
cubic meters	cubic feet	35.3145	metric tons	tons (long)	0.9842
cubic meters	cubic yards	1.3079	metric tons	tons (short)	1.1023
cubic yards	cubic meters	0.7646	miles	kilometers	1.6093
feet	meters	0.3048	miles	feet	5,280
feet	miles (nautical)	0.0001645	miles (statute)	miles (nautical)	0.8684
feet	miles (statute)	0.0001894	miles/hour	feet/minute	88
feet/second	miles/hour	0.6818	millimeters	inches	0.0394
gallons (U.S.)	liters	3.7853	ounces avdp	grams	28.3495
grams	ounces avdp	0.0353	ounces	pounds	0.0625
grams	pounds	0.002205	pecks	liters	8.8096
hours	days	0.04167	pints (dry)	liters	0.5506
inches	millimeters	25.4000	pints (liquid)	liters	0.4732
inches	centimeters	2.5400	pounds advp	kilograms	0.4536
kilograms	pounds avdp	2.2046	pounds	ounces	16
kilometers	miles	0.6214	quarts (dry)	liters	1.1012
liters	gallons (U.S.)	0.2642	quarts (liquid)	liters	0.9463
liters	pecks	0.1135	square feet	square meters	0.0929
liters	pints (dry)	1.8162	square meters	square feet	10.7639
liters	pints (liquid)	2.1134	square meters	square yards	1.1960
liters	quarts (dry)	0.9081	square yards	square meters	0.8361
liters	quarts (liquid)	1.0567	yards	meters	0.9144

Appendix B: Alternative Energy Sources

Fossil Fuels

We fly through the air in planes. We roll down highways in cars. On the coldest days, our homes are warm. Our stores are full of products to satisfy our needs and wants.

The power that runs our lives comes from fossil fuels. A fossil is the remains of ancient life. Fossil fuels formed from the remains of dead matter—animals and plants. Over millions of years, forests of plants died, fell, and became buried in the earth. Over time, the layers of ancient, dead matter changed. The carbon in the animals and plants turned into a material we now use as fuel. Fossil fuels include coal, oil, natural gas, and gasoline.

Fossil fuels power our lives and our society. In the United States, electricity comes mainly from power plants that burn coal. Industries use electricity to run machines. In our homes, we use electricity to power lightbulbs, TVs, and everything else electric. Heat and hot water for many homes come from natural gas or oil, or from fuels that come from oil. Of course, cars and trucks run on gasoline, which is also made from oil.

Powering our society with fossil fuels has made our lives more comfortable. Yet our need for fossil fuels has caused problems. Fossil fuels are a nonrenewable source of energy. That means that there is a limited supply of these fuels. At some point, fossil fuels will become scarce. Their cost will increase. And one day the supply of fossil fuels will run out. We need to find ways now to depend less and less on fossil fuels.

Fossil fuels cause pollution. The pollution comes from burning them. It is like the exhaust from a car. The pollution enters the air and causes disease. It harms the environment. One serious effect of burning fossil fuels is global warming. Carbon dioxide comes from the burning of fossil fuels. When a large amount of this gas enters the air, it warms the earth's climate. Scientists believe that warming of the climate will cause serious problems.

Renewable Energy

Many people believe that we should use renewable fuels as sources of energy. Renewable fuels never run out. They last forever.

What kinds of fuels last forever? The energy from the sun. The energy in the wind. The energy in oceans and rivers. We can use these forms of energy to power our lives. Then we will never run out of fuel. We will cut down on pollution and climate warming. Using renewable energy is not a dream for the future. It is happening right now—right here—today.

Energy from the Sun

As long as the sun keeps shining, the earth will get energy from sunlight. Energy from the sun is called solar energy. It is the energy in light. When you lie in the sun, your skin becomes hot. The heat comes from the energy in sunlight. Sunlight is a form of renewable energy we can use forever.

We use solar energy to make electricity. The electricity can power homes and businesses. Turning solar energy into electricity is called photovoltaics, or PV for short. Here's how PV works.

Flat solar panels are put near a building or on its roof. The panels face the direction that gets the most sunlight. The panels contain many PV cells. The cells are made from silicon—a material that absorbs light. When sunlight strikes the cells, some of the light energy is absorbed. The energy knocks some electrons loose in the silicon. The electrons begin to flow. The electron flow is controlled. An electric current is produced. Pieces of metal at the top and bottom of each cell make a path for electrons. The path leads the electric current away from the solar panel. The electric current flows through wires to a battery. The battery stores the electrical energy. The electrical wiring in a building is connected to the battery. All the electricity used in the building comes from the battery.

Today, PV use is 500 times greater than it was 20 years ago. And PV use is growing about 20 percent per year. Yet solar energy systems are still not perfect. PV cells do not absorb all the sunlight that strikes them, so some energy is lost. Solar energy systems also are not cheap. Still, every year, PV systems are improved. The cost of PV electricity has decreased. The amount of sunlight PV cells absorb has increased.

On a sunny day, every square meter of the earth receives 1,000 watts of energy from sunlight. Someday, when PV systems are able to use all this energy, our energy problems may be solved.

Energy from the Wind

Sunlight warms different parts of the earth differently. The North Pole gets little sunlight, so it is cold. Areas near the equator get lots of sunlight, so they are warm. The uneven warming of the earth by the sun creates the wind. As the earth turns, the wind moves, or blows. The blowing wind can be used to make electricity. This is wind energy. Because the earth's winds will blow forever, the wind is a renewable source of energy.

Wind energy is not new. Hundreds of years ago, windmills created energy. The wind turned the large fins on a windmill. As the fins spun around, they turned huge stones inside the mill. The stones ground grain into flour.

Modern windmills are tall, metal towers with spinning blades, called wind turbines. Each wind turbine has three main parts. It has blades that are turned by blowing wind. The turning blades are attached to a shaft that runs the length of the tower. The turning blades spin the shaft. The spinning shaft is connected to a generator. A generator changes the energy from movement into electrical energy. It feeds the electricity into wires, which carry it to homes and factories.

Wind turbines are placed in areas where strong winds blow. A single house may have one small wind turbine near it to produce its electricity. The electricity produced by the wind turbine is stored in batteries. Many wind turbines may be linked together to produce electricity for an entire town. In these systems, the electricity moves from the generator to the electric company's wires. The wires carry the electricity to homes and businesses.

Studies show that in the United States, 34 of the 50 states have good wind conditions. These states could use wind to meet up to 20 percent of their electric power needs. Canada's wind conditions could produce up to 20 percent of its energy from wind too. Alberta already produces a lot of energy from wind, and the amount is expected to increase.

Energy from Inside the Earth

Deep inside the earth, the rocks are burning hot. Beneath them it is even hotter. There, rocks melt into liquid. The earth's inner heat rises to the surface in some places. Today, people have developed ways to use this heat

to create energy. Because the inside of the earth will always be very hot, this energy is renewable. It is called geothermal energy (*geo* means earth; *thermal* means heat).

Geothermal energy is used where hot water or steam from deep inside the earth moves near the surface. These areas are called "hot spots." At hot spots, we can use geothermal energy directly. Pumps raise the hot water, and pipes carry it to buildings. The water is used to heat the space in the buildings or to heat water.

Geothermal energy may also be used indirectly to make electricity. A power plant is built near a hot spot. Wells are drilled deep into the hot spot. The wells carry hot water or steam into the power plant. There, it is used to boil more water. The boiling water makes steam. The steam turns the blades of a turbine. This energy is carried to a generator, which turns it into electricity. The electricity moves through the electric company's wires to homes and factories.

Everywhere on the earth, several miles beneath the surface, there is hot material. Scientists are improving ways of tapping the earth's inner heat. Someday, this renewable, pollution-free source of energy may be available everywhere.

Energy from Trash

We can use the leftover products that come from plants to make electricity. For example, we can use the stalks from corn or wheat to make fuel. Many leftover products from crops and lumber can fuel power plants. Because this fuel comes from living plants, it is called bioenergy (*bio* means life or living). The plant waste itself is called biomass.

People have used bioenergy for thousands of years. Burning wood in a fireplace is a form of bioenergy. That's because wood comes from trees. Bioenergy is renewable, because people will always grow crops. There will always be crop waste we can burn as fuel.

Some power plants burn biomass to heat water. The steam from the boiling water turns turbines. The turbines create electricity. In other power plants, biomass is changed into a gas. The gas is used as fuel to boil water, which turns the turbine.

Biomass can also be made into a fuel for cars and trucks. Scientists use a special process to turn biomass into fuels, such as ethanol. Car makers are designing cars that can run on these fuels. Cars that use these fuels produce far less pollution than cars that run on gas.

Bioenergy can help solve our garbage problem. Many cities are having trouble finding places to dump all their trash. There would be fewer garbage dumps if we burned more trash to make electricity.

Bioenergy is a renewable energy. But it is not a perfect solution to our energy problems. Burning biomass creates air pollution.

Energy from the Ocean

Have you ever been knocked over by a small wave while wading in the ocean? If so, you know how much power ocean water has. The motion of ocean waves can be a source of energy. So can the rise and fall of ocean tides. There are several systems that use the energy in ocean waves and tides. All of them are very new and still being developed.

In one system, ocean waves enter a funnel. The water flows into a reservoir, an area behind a dam where water is stored. When the dam opens, water flows out of the reservoir. This powers a turbine, which creates electricity. Another system uses the waves' motion to operate water pumps, which run an electric generator. There is also a system that uses the rise and fall of ocean waves. The waves compress air in a container. During high tide, large amounts of ocean water enter the container. The air in the container is under great pressure. When the high-pressure air in the container is released, it drives a turbine. This creates electricity.

Energy can also come from the rise and fall of ocean tides. A dam is built across a tidal basin. This is an area where land surrounds the sea on three sides. At high tide, ocean water is allowed to flow through the dam. The water flow turns turbines, which generate electricity. There is one serious problem with tidal energy. It damages the environment of the tidal basin and can harm animals that live there.

The oceans also contain a great deal of thermal (heat) energy. The sun heats the surface of the oceans more than it heats deep ocean water. In one day, ocean surfaces absorb solar energy equal to 250 billion barrels of oil! Deep ocean water, which gets no sunlight, is much colder than the surface.

Scientists are developing ways to use this temperature difference to create energy. The systems they are currently designing are complicated and expensive.

Energy from Rivers and Dams

Dams built across rivers also produce electricity. When the dam is open, the flowing water turns turbines, which make electricity. This is called hydroelectric power (*hydro* means water). The United States gets 7 percent of its electricity from hydroelectric power. Canada gets up to 60 percent of its electricity from hydroelectric plants built across its many rivers.

Hydroelectric power is a nonpolluting and renewable form of energy—in a way. There will always be fresh water. However, more and more people are taking water from rivers for different uses. These uses include drinking, watering crops, and supplying industry. Some rivers are becoming smaller and weaker because of the water taken from them. Also, in many places dams built across rivers hurt the environment. The land behind the dam is "drowned." Once the dam is built, fish may not be able swim up or down the river. In northwestern states, salmon have completely disappeared from many rivers that have dams.

Energy from Hydrogen Fuel

Hydrogen is a gas that is abundant everywhere on the earth. It's in the air. It is a part of water. Because there is so much hydrogen, it is a renewable energy source. And hydrogen can produce energy without any pollution.

The most likely source of hydrogen fuel is water. Water is made up of hydrogen and oxygen. A special process separates these elements in water. The process produces oxygen gas and hydrogen gas. The hydrogen gas is changed into a liquid or solid. This hydrogen fuel is used to produce energy in a fuel cell.

Look at the diagram on page 363. Hydrogen fuel (H_2) is fed into one part of the fuel cell. It is then stripped of its electrons. The free electrons create an electric current (e). The electric current powers a lightbulb or whatever is connected to the fuel cell.

Meanwhile, oxygen (O_2) from the air enters another part of the fuel cell. The stripped hydrogen (H+) bonds with the oxygen, forming water (H_2O). So a car powered by a fuel cell has pure water leaving its tailpipe. There is no exhaust to pollute the air.

When a regular battery's power is used up,

the battery dies. A fuel cell never runs down as long as it gets hydrogen fuel.

A single fuel cell produces little electricity. To make more electricity, fuel cells come in "stacks" of many fuel cells packaged together. Stacked fuel cells are used to power cars and buses. Soon, they may provide electric power to homes and factories.

Hydrogen Fuel Cell

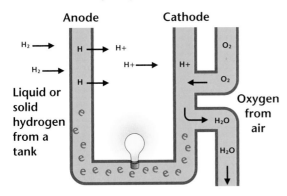

Hydrogen fuel shows great promise, but it still has problems. First, hydrogen fuel is difficult to store and distribute. Today's gas stations would have to be changed into hydrogen-fuel stations. Homes and factories would need safe ways to store solid hydrogen.

Second, producing hydrogen fuel by separating water is expensive. It is cheaper to make hydrogen fuel from oil. But that would create pollution and use nonrenewable resources. Scientists continue to look for solutions to these problems.

Energy from Atoms

Our sun gets its energy—its heat and light—from fusion. Fusion is the joining together of parts of atoms. Fusion produces enormous amounts of energy. But conditions like those on the sun are needed for fusion to occur. Fusion requires incredibly high temperatures.

In the next few decades, scientists may find ways to fuse atoms at lower temperatures. When this happens, we may be able to use fusion for energy. Fusion is a renewable form of energy because it uses hydrogen atoms. It also produces no pollution. And it produces no dangerous radiation. Using fusion to produce power is a long way off. But if the technology can be developed, fusion could provide us with renewable, clean energy.

Today's nuclear power plants produce energy by splitting atoms. This creates no air pollution. But nuclear energy has other problems. Nuclear energy is fueled by a substance we get from mines called uranium. There is only a limited amount of uranium in the earth. So it is not renewable. And uranium produces dangerous radiation, which can harm or kill living things if it escapes the power plant. Used uranium must be thrown out, even though it is radioactive and dangerous. In 1999, the United States produced nearly 41 tons of radioactive waste from nuclear power plants. However, less uranium is being mined. No new nuclear power plants have been built. The amount of energy produced from nuclear power is expected to fall. People are turning toward less harmful, renewable energy sources: the sun, wind, underground heat, biomass, water, and hydrogen fuel.

Fuel That U.S. Electric Utilities Used to Generate Electricity in 2000

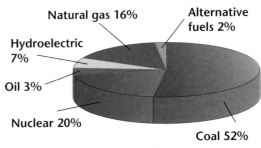

Source: U.S. Dept. of Energy Hydropower Program

Appendix C: The Solar System

The planets in our solar system are very different from each other. Some are huge balls of gas, and others are small, rocky worlds. Some are frozen, and others are burning hot. Some have violent storms raging in their atmosphere, and others have almost no atmosphere. The table below lists many facts about each planet. As you study these facts, look for similarities, differences, and patterns.

Features	Mercury	Venus	Earth	Mars	Jupiter	Saturn	Uranus	Neptune	Pluto
Unique Characteristics	fastest moving planet; closest planet to sun	hottest planet; brightest planet in Earth's night sky	only planet that has liquid water and supports life	reddish color; only planet explored by exploration robots	fastest rotation; largest planet; Great Red Spot	biggest ring system; great storms	rotates on its side; blue-green color	storms; blue-green color; Great Dark Spot	coldest and smallest planet; longest revolution time
Diameter (kilometers)	4,879	12,014	12,756	6,794	142,984	120,536	51,118	49,528	2,390
Relative Mass (Earth = 1)	0.055	0.82	1	0.11	318	95	15	17	0.002
Average Distance from Sun (millions of kilometers)	58	108	150	228	779	1,434	2,873	4,496	5,870
Rotation (Earth time)	59 days	243 days*	1 day	24 hours and 38 minutes	10 hours	11 hours	17 hours*	16 hours	6 days*
Revolution (Earth time)	88 days	224 days	365 days	687 days	12 years	29 years	84 years	164 years	248 years
Surface Temperature (°C)	−183 to 427	460	−89 to 58	−82 to 0	−150	−170	−200	−210	−220
Atmospheric Composition	very thin: sodium and helium gas	thick: carbon dioxide gas	thick: nitrogen and oxygen gas	thin: carbon dioxide gas	thick: hydrogen and helium gas	thick: hydrogen and helium gas	thick: hydrogen, helium, and methane gas	thick: hydrogen, helium, and methane gas	thin: methane gas
Surface Composition	rocky	rocky	rocky	rocky	gaseous	gaseous	gaseous	gaseous	rocky
Number of Moons	0	0	1	2	60	31	22	11	1
Ring System	no	no	no	no	yes	yes	yes	yes	no

*planet rotates from east to west, the opposite direction of Earth's rotation

Source: NASA

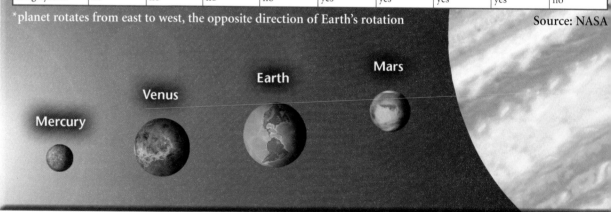

Pluto

Neptune

Uranus

Saturn

Jupiter

Appendix D: Space Exploration

Our knowledge of outer space has grown tremendously since the space age began in the 1950s. Orbiters, landers, probes, satellites, and space stations—as well as crews and scientists—continue to uncover new information about the solar system and beyond. The following timeline displays some of the important missions of space exploration. Each entry lists the name of the spacecraft, the country sponsoring it, and the mission's significance.

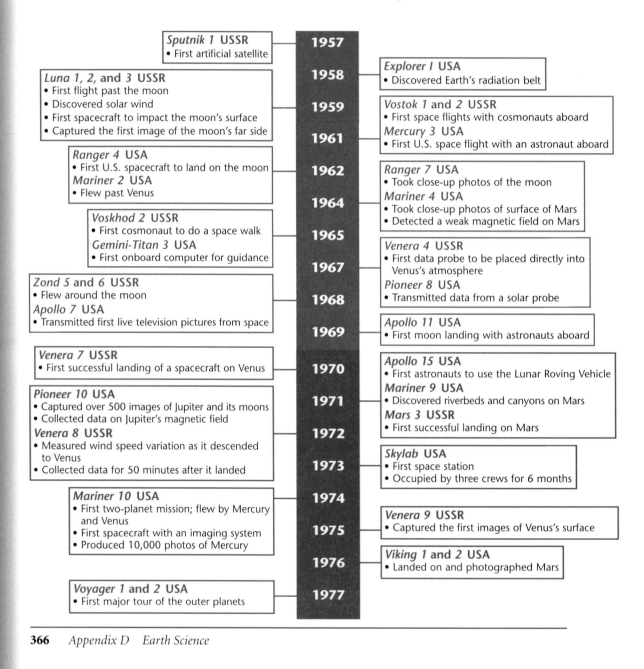

Sputnik 1 USSR
• First artificial satellite

1957

Explorer I USA
• Discovered Earth's radiation belt

1958

Luna 1, 2, and 3 USSR
• First flight past the moon
• Discovered solar wind
• First spacecraft to impact the moon's surface
• Captured the first image of the moon's far side

1959

Vostok 1 and 2 USSR
• First space flights with cosmonauts aboard
Mercury 3 USA
• First U.S. space flight with an astronaut aboard

1961

Ranger 4 USA
• First U.S. spacecraft to land on the moon
Mariner 2 USA
• Flew past Venus

1962

Ranger 7 USA
• Took close-up photos of the moon
Mariner 4 USA
• Took close-up photos of surface of Mars
• Detected a weak magnetic field on Mars

1964

Voskhod 2 USSR
• First cosmonaut to do a space walk
Gemini-Titan 3 USA
• First onboard computer for guidance

1965

Venera 4 USSR
• First data probe to be placed directly into Venus's atmosphere
Pioneer 8 USA
• Transmitted data from a solar probe

1967

Zond 5 and 6 USSR
• Flew around the moon
Apollo 7 USA
• Transmitted first live television pictures from space

1968

Apollo 11 USA
• First moon landing with astronauts aboard

1969

Venera 7 USSR
• First successful landing of a spacecraft on Venus

1970

Apollo 15 USA
• First astronauts to use the Lunar Roving Vehicle
Mariner 9 USA
• Discovered riverbeds and canyons on Mars
Mars 3 USSR
• First successful landing on Mars

1971

Pioneer 10 USA
• Captured over 500 images of Jupiter and its moons
• Collected data on Jupiter's magnetic field
Venera 8 USSR
• Measured wind speed variation as it descended to Venus
• Collected data for 50 minutes after it landed

1972

Skylab USA
• First space station
• Occupied by three crews for 6 months

1973

Mariner 10 USA
• First two-planet mission; flew by Mercury and Venus
• First spacecraft with an imaging system
• Produced 10,000 photos of Mercury

1974

Venera 9 USSR
• Captured the first images of Venus's surface

1975

Viking 1 and 2 USA
• Landed on and photographed Mars

1976

Voyager 1 and 2 USA
• First major tour of the outer planets

1977

STS-1 Columbia USA
• First winged, reusable space shuttle to be launched

Venera 13 USSR
• First color views of Venus's surface

Venera 15 and 16 USSR
• Produced maps of Venus

Soyuz T-14 USSR
• First relief mission to replace cosmonauts on *Soyuz-T13*

Ginga Japan
• Studied sources of gamma rays and X-rays in the Milky Way galaxy

STS-31 Discovery USA, Europe
• Deployed the Hubble Space Telescope

Soyuz TM-1 USSR
• First commercial passenger to make a space shuttle flight

Galileo USA
• Flew past Venus

STS-61 Endeavor USA
• Repaired the Hubble Space Telescope

Galileo USA
• Began orbiting Jupiter

Mars Pathfinder USA
• Returned data about Mars, including thousands of images
• Landed on Mars and released an exploration robot to explore its surface

Cassini Europe
• Began a 7-year flight to Saturn

IMAGE USA
• First weather satellite to monitor space storms

Muses-C Japan
• Collected sample from an asteroid

Deep Impact USA
• Will attempt to excavate the interior of a comet

Europa USA
• Will attempt to orbit Jupiter's moon Europa

BepiColumbo Europe
• Will attempt to orbit Mercury

1980
1981
1982
1983
1984
1985
1986
1987
1988
1989
1990
1991
1992
1993
1994
1995
1996
1997
1998
1999
2000
2001
2002
2003
2004
2005
2006 and beyond

Voyager 1 USA
• Flew past Titan, one of Saturn's moons

Solar Maximum Mission USA
• Monitored the sun, especially solar flares

Suisei Japan
• Flew past and studied comet Halley

Mir USSR
• First space station to conduct research and deploy other spacecraft

Voyager 2 USA
• Flew past Uranus

Voyager 2 USA
• Flew past Neptune

Magellan USA
• Began mapping the surface of Venus

Ulysses Europe and USA
• Orbited Jupiter on its way to the sun

Clementine USA
• Generated the first lunar topographic map

NEAR USA
• Orbited and studied asteroids near Earth

International Space Station
• First orbiting research facility

Stardust USA
• Collected sample from a comet

Mars 2001 Odyssey USA
• Mapping surface minerals, looking for water, and studying potential radiation hazards to future missions

Mars Express Europe
• Will attempt to study Mars's surface and atmosphere in great detail

Venus Express Europe
• Will attempt to study Venus's atmosphere in great detail

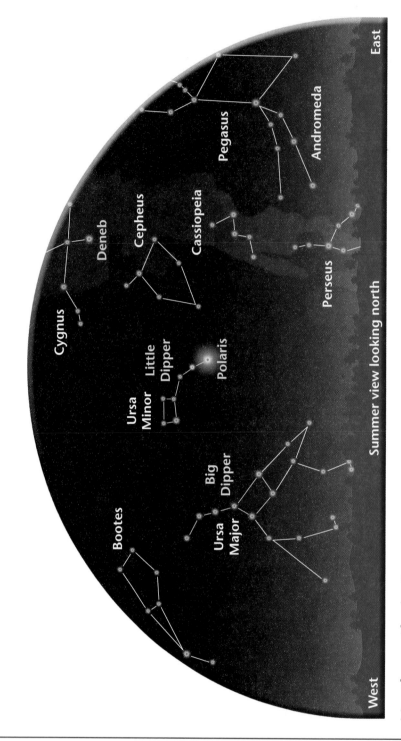

East

Andromeda

Pegasus

Deneb

Cepheus

Cassiopeia

Cygnus

Perseus

Little
Dipper

Polaris

Ursa
Minor

Bootes

Big
Dipper

Ursa
Major

West

Summer view looking north

Northern Sky in Summer

If you look in the northern sky in August, you may see the stars in these constellations. The Big Dipper is low and toward the west. Cygnus, also called the Northern Cross, is almost directly overhead. The Little Dipper is upside-down. Polaris is the last star in the Little Dipper's handle.

Compare the Little Dipper here to its winter position shown on page 370. Can you see how the Little Dipper appears to rotate around Polaris during the year? The other stars in the Northern Hemisphere appear to rotate around Polaris, too.

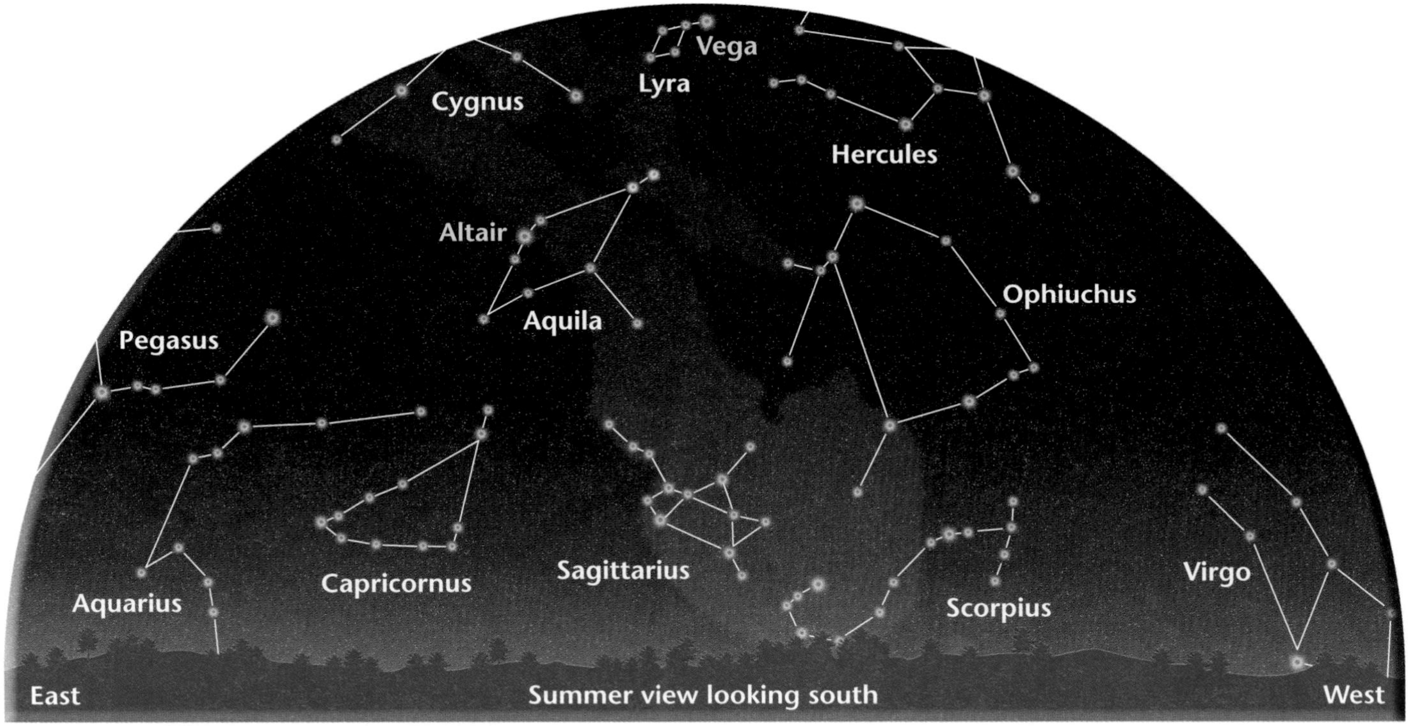

Southern Sky in Summer

If you look in the southern sky in August, you may see the stars in the constellations shown here. Find the constellation Aquila, the Eagle. Altair is the brightest star in this constellation. High in the sky, almost straight up, is the constellation Lyra, the Lyre. Lyra contains a bright star named Vega. Three stars—Altair, Vega, and Deneb (in the high northern sky)—form the Summer Triangle. The faint band of starlight stretching across the sky from south to north is the Milky Way.

Summer view looking south

East

West

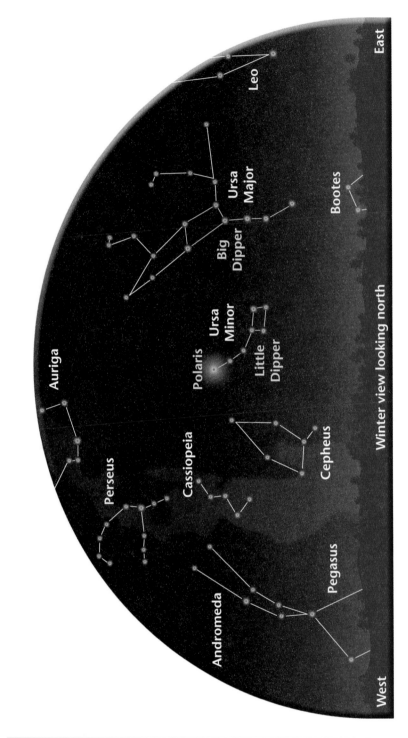

Winter view looking north

Northern Sky in Winter

If you look in the northern sky in February, you may see the stars in the constellations shown here. Toward the east, the Big Dipper appears to stand on its handle. Which two stars in the Big Dipper always line up to point to Polaris? The Little Dipper appears to hang from Polaris, also called the North Star. Compare this view to the summer sky on page 368. Polaris remains in the same position in the northern sky all year long. Because of this, it is a good reference star, telling which way is north.

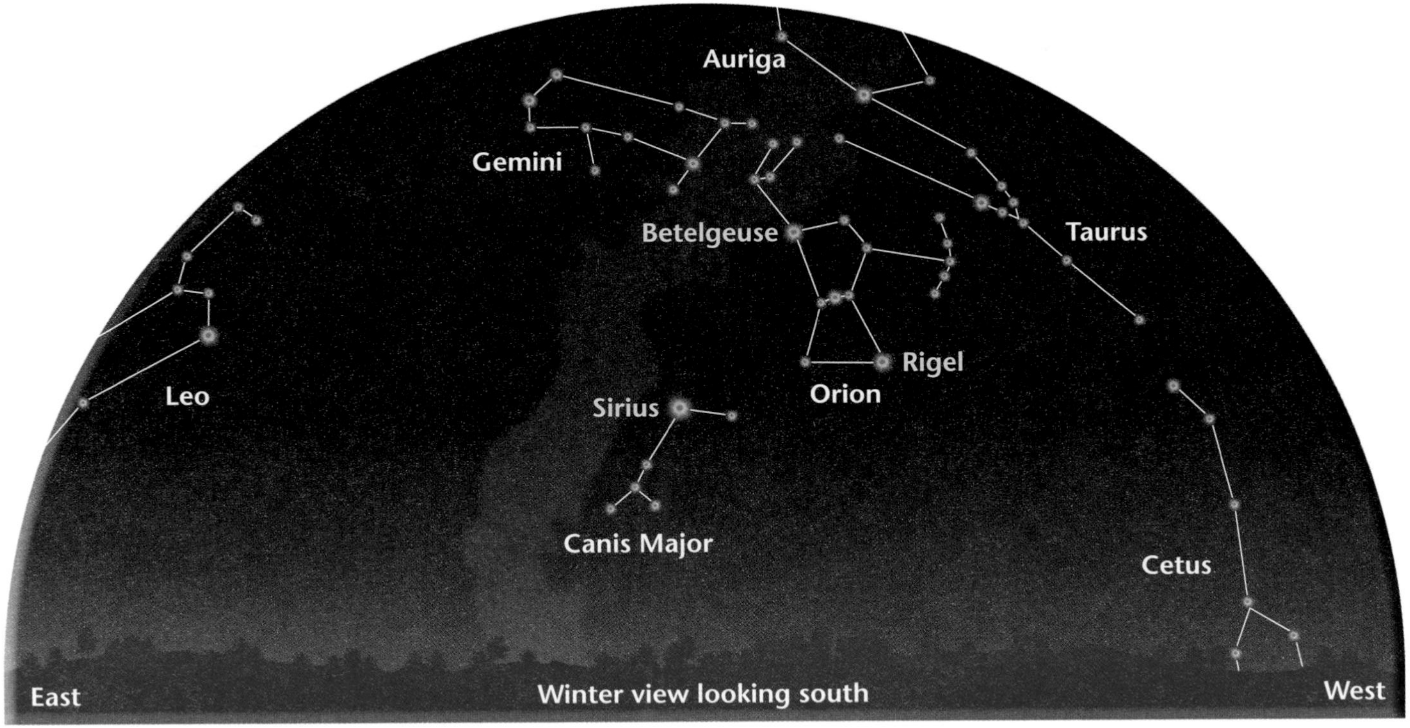

Southern Sky in Winter

If you look in the southern sky in February, you may see the stars in the constellations shown here. Find Orion in the center. Can you see why the ancient stargazers named this constellation the Hunter? Orion contains two supergiants: Betelgeuse and Rigel.

Three other bright stars make up Orion's belt. Canis Major, also called the Great Dog, contains the star Sirius, which is the brightest star in the sky. Leo, toward the east, looks like a backward question mark.

Winter view looking south

East

West

Leo

Gemini

Canis Major

Sirius

Betelgeuse

Auriga

Orion

Rigel

Taurus

Cetus

Appendix F: The Periodic Table of Elements

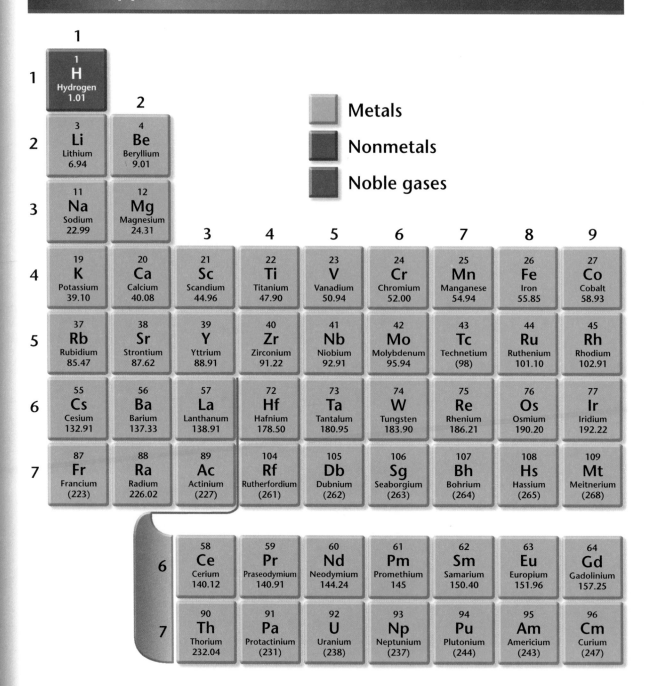

Metals

Nonmetals

Noble gases

	1	2	3	4	5	6	7	8	9
1	1 **H** Hydrogen 1.01								
2	3 **Li** Lithium 6.94	4 **Be** Beryllium 9.01							
3	11 **Na** Sodium 22.99	12 **Mg** Magnesium 24.31							
4	19 **K** Potassium 39.10	20 **Ca** Calcium 40.08	21 **Sc** Scandium 44.96	22 **Ti** Titanium 47.90	23 **V** Vanadium 50.94	24 **Cr** Chromium 52.00	25 **Mn** Manganese 54.94	26 **Fe** Iron 55.85	27 **Co** Cobalt 58.93
5	37 **Rb** Rubidium 85.47	38 **Sr** Strontium 87.62	39 **Y** Yttrium 88.91	40 **Zr** Zirconium 91.22	41 **Nb** Niobium 92.91	42 **Mo** Molybdenum 95.94	43 **Tc** Technetium (98)	44 **Ru** Ruthenium 101.10	45 **Rh** Rhodium 102.91
6	55 **Cs** Cesium 132.91	56 **Ba** Barium 137.33	57 **La** Lanthanum 138.91	72 **Hf** Hafnium 178.50	73 **Ta** Tantalum 180.95	74 **W** Tungsten 183.90	75 **Re** Rhenium 186.21	76 **Os** Osmium 190.20	77 **Ir** Iridium 192.22
7	87 **Fr** Francium (223)	88 **Ra** Radium 226.02	89 **Ac** Actinium (227)	104 **Rf** Rutherfordium (261)	105 **Db** Dubnium (262)	106 **Sg** Seaborgium (263)	107 **Bh** Bohrium (264)	108 **Hs** Hassium (265)	109 **Mt** Meitnerium (268)

6	58 **Ce** Cerium 140.12	59 **Pr** Praseodymium 140.91	60 **Nd** Neodymium 144.24	61 **Pm** Promethium 145	62 **Sm** Samarium 150.40	63 **Eu** Europium 151.96	64 **Gd** Gadolinium 157.25
7	90 **Th** Thorium 232.04	91 **Pa** Protactinium (231)	92 **U** Uranium (238)	93 **Np** Neptunium (237)	94 **Pu** Plutonium (244)	95 **Am** Americium (243)	96 **Cm** Curium (247)

Atomic number
Element symbol
Element name
Average atomic mass

18

| 2 | He | Helium | 4.00 |

13

| 5 | B | Boron | 10.81 |

14

| 6 | C | Carbon | 12.01 |

15

| 7 | N | Nitrogen | 14.01 |

16

| 8 | O | Oxygen | 16.00 |

17

| 9 | F | Fluorine | 19.00 |

| 10 | Ne | Neon | 20.18 |

13	Al	Aluminum	26.98
14	Si	Silicon	28.09
15	P	Phosphorus	30.97
16	S	Sulfur	32.07
17	Cl	Chlorine	35.45
18	Ar	Argon	39.95

10   **11**   **12**

28	Ni	Nickel	58.70
29	Cu	Copper	63.55
30	Zn	Zinc	65.39
31	Ga	Gallium	69.72
32	Ge	Germanium	72.59
33	As	Arsenic	74.92
34	Se	Selenium	78.96
35	Br	Bromine	79.90
36	Kr	Krypton	83.80

46	Pd	Palladium	106.42
47	Ag	Silver	107.90
48	Cd	Cadmium	112.41
49	In	Indium	114.82
50	Sn	Tin	118.69
51	Sb	Antimony	121.75
52	Te	Tellurium	127.60
53	I	Iodine	126.90
54	Xe	Xenon	131.30

78	Pt	Platinum	195.09
79	Au	Gold	196.97
80	Hg	Mercury	200.59
81	Tl	Thallium	204.40
82	Pb	Lead	207.20
83	Bi	Bismuth	208.98
84	Po	Polonium	209
85	At	Astatine	(210)
86	Rn	Radon	(222)

110	Uun	Ununnilium	(269)
111	Uuu	Unununium	(272)
112	Uub	Ununbium	(277)
114	Uuq	Ununquadium	(289)
116	Uuh	Ununhexium	(289)

65	Tb	Terbium	158.93
66	Dy	Dysprosium	162.50
67	Ho	Holmium	164.93
68	Er	Erbium	167.26
69	Tm	Thulium	168.93
70	Yb	Ytterbium	173.04
71	Lu	Lutetium	174.97

97	Bk	Berkelium	(247)
98	Cf	Californium	(249)
99	Es	Einsteinium	(254)
100	Fm	Fermium	(257)
101	Md	Mendelevium	(258)
102	No	Nobelium	(259)
103	Lr	Lawrencium	(260)

Note: *The atomic masses listed in the table reflect current measurements.*
The atomic masses listed in parentheses are those of the element's most stable or most common isotope.

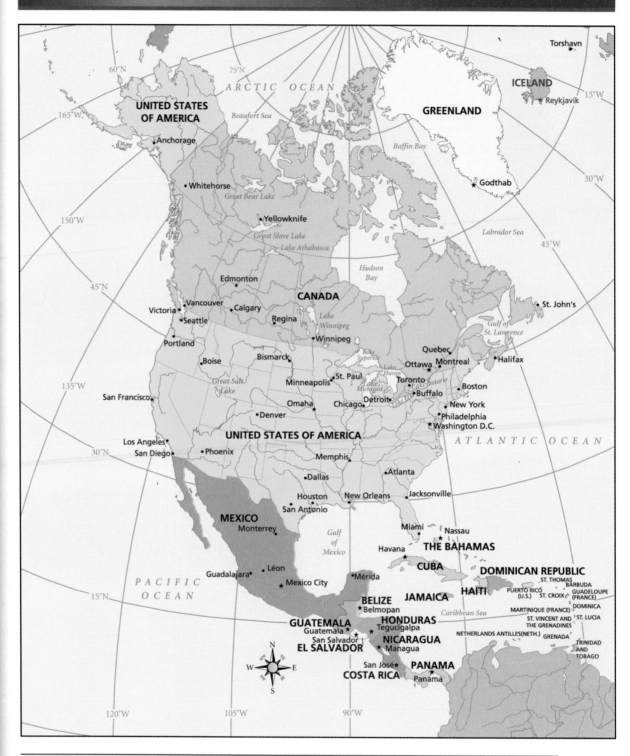

Glossary

A

Absolute dating (ab´sə lüt dā´ting) Method that determines the actual age of a rock or fossil (p. 342)

Absolute magnitude (ab´sə lüt mag´nə tüd) How bright a star actually is (p. 109)

Air mass (âr´ mas´) Large section of the atmosphere with the same temperature and humidity throughout (p. 239)

Air pressure (âr´ presh´ər) Force of air against a unit of area (p. 231)

Alluvial fan (ə lü´vē əl fan´) Fan-shaped area of land deposited where a mountain stream moves onto flat land (p. 289)

Altitude (al´tə tüd´) Height above the earth's surface (p. 212)

Anemometer (an´ə mom´ə tər) Instrument used to measure wind speed (p. 233)

Apparent magnitude (ə par´ənt mag´nə tüd) How bright a star looks (p. 109)

Asteroid (as´tə roid) Rocky object, smaller than a planet, that orbits a star (p. 100)

Asteroid belt (as´tə roid belt´) Region between Mars and Jupiter where most asteroids orbit the sun (p. 100)

Astronomer (ə stron´ə mər) Scientist who studies outer space and objects in it (p. 4)

Astronomy (ə stron´ə mē) Study of outer space and objects in it (p. 2)

Atmosphere (at´mə sfir) Envelope of gas surrounding an object in space (p. 82)

Atom (at´əm) Smallest particle of an element that has the characteristics of that element (p. 138)

Axis (ak´sis) Imaginary line through the earth that connects the North and South Poles (p. 29)

B

Barometer (bə rom´ə tər) Instrument used to measure air pressure (p. 231)

Benthos (ben´thos) Organisms that live on the ocean floor (p. 271)

Black hole (blak´ hōl´) Region in space with tremendous gravity, caused by the collapse of a huge star (p. 119)

C

Cast (kast) Type of fossil that forms when minerals fill a mold; a model of an organism (p. 336)

Cenozoic Era (sen´ə zō´ik ir´ə) Era described as the Age of Mammals; began about 65 million years ago and continues today (p. 351)

Chemical property (kem´ə kəl prop´ər tē) Characteristic that describes how a substance changes into a different substance (p. 133)

Chemical rock (kem´ə kəl rok´) Sedimentary rock that forms from chemicals dissolved in water (p. 187)

Chemical weathering (kem´ə kəl weᴛʜ´ər ing) Breaking apart of rocks caused by a change in their chemical makeup (p. 281)

Cinder cone (sin´dər kōn´) Small volcano with steep sides and explosive eruptions; made of ash and rock (p. 314)

Cirque (sərk) Bowl-like basin in a mountain that is carved out by an alpine glacier (p. 295)

Cirrus cloud (sir´əs kloud´) High, wispy cloud made of ice crystals (p. 213)

a	hat	e	let	ī	ice	ô	order	ù	put	sh	she	ə	a in about
ā	age	ē	equal	o	hot	oi	oil	ü	rule	th	thin		e in taken
ä	far	ėr	term	ō	open	ou	out	ch	child	ᴛʜ	then		i in pencil
â	care	i	it	ò	saw	u	cup	ng	long	zh	measure		o in lemon
													u in circus

Clastic rock (klas´tik rok´) Sedimentary rock made mainly from fragments of other rocks (p. 186)

Cleavage (klē´vij) Ability to split along flat surfaces (p. 165)

Climate (klī´mit) Average weather of a region over a long period of time (p. 247)

Cold front (kōld´ frunt´) Boundary ahead of a cold air mass that is pushing out and wedging under a warm air mass (p. 239)

Comet (kom´it) Ball of ice, rock, frozen gases, and dust that orbits the sun (p. 101)

Compass rose (kum´pəs rōz´) Part of a map that shows the major compass directions (p. 9)

Composite volcano (kəm poz´it vol kā´nō) Tall volcano; formed from quiet lava flows that alternate with eruptions of rock and ash (p. 315)

Compound (kom´pound) Substance formed when the atoms of two or more elements join chemically (p. 141)

Condense (kən dens´) Change from a gas to a liquid (p. 211)

Conglomerate (kən glom´ ər it) Clastic rock made of rounded pebbles cemented together (p. 186)

Constellation (kon´stə lā´shən) Pattern of stars seen from Earth (p. 121)

Continent (kon´tə nənt) One of the seven major land areas of the earth (p. 27)

Continental drift (kon´tə nən´təl drift´) Theory that the major landmasses of the earth move (p. 309)

Continental shelf (kon´tə nən´təl shelf´) Part of a continent that extends from a shoreline out into an ocean (p. 270)

Continental slope (kon´tə nən´təl slōp´) Steep slope between the continental shelf and the deep ocean floor (p. 270)

Contour interval (kon´tûr in´tər vəl) Vertical distance between contour lines on a topographic map (p. 16)

Contour line (kon´tûr līn´) Line on a map that connects points of equal elevation (p. 15)

Convection current (kən vek´shən kėr´ənt) Circular motion of a gas or liquid as it heats (p. 311)

Core (kôr) Dense center of the earth made of solid and melted metals (p. 308)

Crater (krā´tər) Circular low area surrounded by a rim, usually caused by an object hitting the ground (p. 70)

Crust (krust) Outer layer of the earth (p. 308)

Crystal (kris´tl) Basic shape that a mineral tends to take (p. 164)

Cumulus cloud (kyü´myə ləs kloud´) Puffy, white cloud occurring at medium altitudes (p. 213)

Current (kėr´ənt) Large stream of water flowing in oceans, in rivers, and in some large lakes (p. 269)

D

Degree (di grē´) Unit for measuring angles in a circle or sphere (p. 42)

Delta (del´tə) Fan-shaped area of land formed when sediment is deposited where a river empties into a lake or an ocean (p. 289)

Deposition (dep´ə zish´ən) Dropping of eroded sediment (p. 289)

Divide (də vīd´) Ridge that separates drainage basins (p. 261)

Drainage basin (drā´nij bā´sn) Land area that is drained by a river and its tributaries (p. 261)

E

Earthquake (ėrth´kwāk´) Shaking of the earth's crust (p. 322)

Earth science (ėrth´ sī´əns) Study of the earth's land, water, air, and outer space (p. 2)

Element (el´ə mənt) Substance that cannot be changed or separated into other kinds of substances (p. 137)

Epicenter (ep´ə sen´tər) Point on the earth's surface directly over the focus of an earthquake (p. 324)

Equator (i kwā´tər) Line of 0° latitude halfway between the poles (p. 42)

Erosion (i rō´zhən) Wearing away and moving of weathered rock and soil (p. 286)

Evaporate (i vap´ə rāt´) Change from a liquid to a gas (p. 211)

Extrusive rock (ek strü´siv rok´) Igneous rock that forms from cooled lava on the earth's surface (p. 183)

F

Fault (fȯlt) Break in the earth's crust along which movement occurs (p. 318)

Floodplain (flud´plān´) Low, flat area that a river covers when it overflows its banks (p. 288)

Focus (fō´kəs) Point inside the earth where rock first moves, starting an earthquake (p. 324)

Fog (fog) Stratus cloud that forms near the ground (p. 212)

Folding (fōld´ing) Bending of rock layers that are squeezed together (p. 317)

Foliated rock (fō´lē ā´təd rok´) Metamorphic rock in which minerals have been rearranged into visible bands (p. 192)

Fossil (fos´əl) Trace or remains of an organism preserved in the earth's crust (p. 335)

Fracture (frak´chər) Tendency to break with jagged edges (p. 165)

Front (frunt) Moving boundary line between two air masses (p. 239)

Full moon (fül´ mün´) Phase of the moon when the earth is between the sun and the moon (p. 66)

Fusion (fyü´zhən) Process by which particles combine to form a new particle (p. 108)

G

Galaxy (gal´ək sē) Group of billions of stars (p. 122)

Geologic time (jē´ə loj´ik tīm´) All the time that has passed since the earth formed (p. 334)

Geologic time scale (jē´ə loj´ik tīm skāl´) Outline of the events of the earth's history (p. 347)

Geologist (jē ol´ə jist) Scientist who studies the solid parts of the earth and how they change (p. 3)

Geology (jē ol´ə jē) Study of the solid parts of the earth (p. 2)

Geyser (gī´zər) Place where hot groundwater and steam blast into the air (p. 260)

Glacier (glā´shər) Thick mass of ice that covers a large area (p. 294)

Gravity (grav´ə tē) Force of attraction between any two objects (p. 56)

Greenhouse effect (grēn´hous´ ə fekt´) Warming of the atmosphere because of trapped heat energy from the sun (p. 88)

Grid (grid) Set of horizontal and vertical lines on a map (p. 38)

Groundwater (ground´ wȯ´tər) Water that sinks into the ground (p. 257)

H

Hachure (ha shúr´) Short line that points toward the center of a depression on a topographic map (p. 16)

Half-life (haf´ līf´) Length of time it takes for half of the atoms of a radioactive element to decay (p. 342)

Hardness (härd´nəs) Ability of a mineral to resist being scratched (p. 159)

Hemisphere (hem´ə sfir) Half of the earth (p. 49)

a	hat	e	let	ī	ice	ȯ	order	ù	put	sh	she	ə {	a	in about
ā	age	ē	equal	o	hot	oi	oil	ü	rule	th	thin		e	in taken
ä	far	ėr	term	ō	open	ou	out	ch	child	₮H	then		i	in pencil
â	care	i	it	ȯ	saw	u	cup	ng	long	zh	measure		o	in lemon
													u	in circus

High (hī) Cold area of high air pressure (p. 240)

Horn (hôrn) Jagged, pyramid-shaped peak formed by the intersection of three or more cirques (p. 295)

Humidity (hyü mid´ə tē) Amount of water vapor in the air (p. 232)

Hurricane (hėr´ə kän´) Severe tropical storm with high winds that revolve around an eye (p. 245)

I

Igneous rock (ig´nē əs rok´) Rock formed from melted minerals that have cooled and hardened (p. 178)

Index fossil (in´deks fos´əl) Fossil that can be used to establish the relative age of the rock in which the fossil occurs (p. 341)

International date line (in´tər nash´ə nəl dāt´ līn´) Imaginary line that defines the start of a day (p. 33)

Intrusive rock (in trü´siv rok´) Igneous rock that forms underground from cooled magma (p. 181)

Ionosphere (ī on´ə sfir) Layer of the atmosphere containing ions, or electrically charged particles (p. 209)

Isobar (ī´sə bär) Line on a weather map connecting areas of equal air pressure (p. 240)

L

Latitude (lat´ə tüd) Angle that describes the distance north or south of the equator (p. 42)

Lava (lä´və) Magma that comes out onto the earth's surface (p. 183)

Legend (lej´ənd) List of map symbols and their meanings (p. 8)

Light-year (līt´ yir´) Distance that light travels in one year (p. 114)

Longitude (lon´jə tüd) Angle that describes the distance east or west of the prime meridian (p. 46)

Low (lō) Warm area of low air pressure (p. 240)

Lunar eclipse (lü´nər i klips´) Passing of the moon through the earth's shadow (p. 67)

Luster (lus´tər) How a mineral reflects light (p. 158)

M

Magma (mag´mə) Hot, liquid rock inside the earth (p. 181)

Magnitude (mag´nə tüd) Brightness of a star (p. 109)

Mantle (man´tl) Layer of the earth that surrounds the core (p. 308)

Map (map) Drawing that shows part of the earth's surface as seen from above (p. 7)

Maria (mär´ē ə) Low, flat plains on the moon's surface that appear as dark areas (p. 70)

Mass (mas) Amount of material that an object contains (p. 56)

Matter (mat´ər) Anything that has mass and takes up space (p. 132)

Meander (mē an´dər) Looping curve in a river (p. 288)

Mechanical weathering (mə kan´ə kəl weŦH´ər ing) Breaking apart of rocks without changing their mineral composition (p. 280)

Meridian (mə rid´ē ən) Line of longitude (p. 46)

Mesosphere (mes´ə sfir) Third layer of the atmosphere; the coldest layer (p. 209)

Mesozoic Era (mes´ə zō´ik ir´ə) Era characterized by dinosaurs; began about 245 million years ago and ended about 65 million years ago (p. 350)

Metamorphic rock (met´ə môr´fik rok´) Rock that has been changed by intense heat, pressure, and chemical reactions (p. 179)

Meteor (mē´tē ər) Brief streak of light seen when an asteroid enters the earth's atmosphere and burns up (p. 100)

Meteorite (mēʹtē ə rītʹ) Piece of rock that hits the surface of a planet or moon after traveling through space (p. 70, 101)

Meteorologist (mēʹtē ə rolʹə jist) Scientist who studies the air and weather (p. 4)

Meteorology (mēʹtē ə rolʹə jē) Study of the earth's air and weather (p. 2)

Metric system (metʹrik sisʹtəm) System of measurement used by scientists (p. 3)

Mid-ocean ridge (midʹ ōʹshən rijʹ) Mountain chain on the ocean floor (p. 270)

Milky Way galaxy (milʹkē wāʹ galʹək sē) Group of stars to which our solar system belongs (p. 123)

Mineral (minʹər əl) Element or compound found in the earth (p. 154)

Mixture (miksʹchər) Two or more elements or compounds mixed together, but not joined chemically (p. 144)

Mold (mōld) Type of fossil that forms when the shape of a plant or an animal is left in a rock (p. 336)

Moon (mün) Natural satellite that orbits a planet (p. 78)

Moraine (mə rānʹ) Ridge of sediment deposited by a glacier (p. 296)

Mouth (mouth) Place where a river flows into a larger body of water (p. 289)

N

Nebula (nebʹyə lə) Cloud of gas and dust in space (p. 117)

Nekton (nekʹton) Free-swimming ocean animals (p. 271)

Neutron star (nüʹtron stärʹ) Very small, very dense star that remains after a supernova (p. 119)

New moon (nüʹ münʹ) Phase of the moon when the moon is between the sun and the earth (p. 66)

Nonfoliated rock (non fōʹlē āʹtəd rokʹ) Metamorphic rock that does not show bands (p. 192)

Normal fault (nôrʹməl fȯltʹ) Break in the crust in which the overhanging block of rock has slid down (p. 318)

North Pole (nôrthʹ pōlʹ) Point farthest north on the earth (p. 29)

Nova (nōʹvə) Brilliant explosion of a collapsed red giant (p. 118)

Nucleus (nüʹklē əs) Atom's center, which is made of protons and neutrons (p. 138)

O

Oceanographer (ōʹshə nogʹrə fər) Scientist who studies the oceans (p. 4)

Oceanography (ōʹshə nogʹrə fē) Study of the earth's oceans (p. 2)

Orbit (ôrʹbit) Curved path that an object follows as it revolves around another object (p. 56)

Organic rock (ôr ganʹik rokʹ) Sedimentary rock that forms from the remains of living things (p. 188)

Oxbow lake (oksʹbōʹ lākʹ) C-shaped body of water formed when a meander is cut off from the rest of the river (p. 288)

Oxidation (oksʹsə dāʹshən) Process in which minerals combine with oxygen to form new substances (p. 281)

P

Paleozoic Era (pāʹlē ə zōʹik irʹə) Era marked by great development in sea life; began about 540 million years ago and ended about 245 million years ago (p. 349)

Pangaea (pan jēʹə) Single landmass from which Alfred Wegener thought the continents separated millions of years ago (p. 309)

a	hat	e	let	ī	ice	ô	order	u̇	put	sh	she	ə	a in about
ā	age	ē	equal	o	hot	oi	oil	ü	rule	th	thin		e in taken
ä	far	ėr	term	ō	open	ou	out	ch	child	ᴛʜ	then		i in pencil
â	care	i	it	ȯ	saw	u	cup	ng	long	zh	measure		o in lemon
													u in circus

Parallel (par´ə lel) Line of latitude (p. 42)

Petrification (pet´rə fə kā´shən) Replacement of the original parts of a buried organism with minerals (p. 335)

Phases of the moon (fāz´əz ov ᴛʜə mün´) Changes in the moon's appearance as it orbits the earth (p. 66)

Physical property (fiz´ə kəl prop´ər tē) Characteristic of a substance or an object that can be observed without changing the substance into a different substance (p. 133)

Planet (plan´it) Large object in space that orbits a star such as the sun (p. 78)

Plankton (plangk´tən) Tiny organisms that live at or near the ocean surface (p. 271)

Plate (plāt) Large section of the earth's crust that moves (p. 310)

Plate tectonics (plāt´ tek ton´iks) Theory that the earth's surface is made of large sections of crust that move (p. 335)

Polar easterly (pō´lər ē´stər lē) Wind near a pole; blows from the east (p. 223)

Porous (pôr´əs) Containing many spaces through which air and water can move (p. 259)

Precambrian Era (prē´kam´brē ən ir´ə) Oldest and longest era of the earth's history; began about 4.6 billion years ago and ended about 540 million years ago (p. 347)

Precipitation (pri sip´ə tā´shən) Moisture that falls to the earth from the atmosphere (p. 216)

Prevailing westerly (pri vā´ling wes´tər lē) Wind generally between 30°N and 60°N latitudes (or 30°S and 60°S); blows from the west (p. 223)

Prime meridian (prīm´ mə rid´ē ən) Line of 0° longitude (p. 46)

Principle of crosscutting relationships (prin´sə pəl ov kròs´kut´ing ri lā´shən ships) A feature, such as a rock structure or a fault, that cuts across rock layers is younger than the rock layers (p. 341)

Principle of superposition (prin´sə pəl ov sü´pər pə zish´ən) In layers of sedimentary rocks, the oldest layer is on the bottom and the youngest layer is on the top if the layers have not been overturned (p. 340)

Property (prop´ər tē) Characteristic that describes matter (p. 133)

Psychrometer (sī krom´ə tər) Instrument used to measure relative humidity (p. 232)

R

Radioactive element (rā´dē ō ak´tiv el´ə mənt) Element that breaks apart, or decays, to form another element (p. 342)

Rain gauge (rān´gāj´) Instrument used to measure the amount of rainfall (p. 234)

Red giant (red´ jī´ənt) Star that has expanded after using up its hydrogen (p. 118)

Relative dating (rel´ə tiv dāt´ing) Method that compares two rock layers to find out which is older (p. 340)

Relative humidity (rel´ə tiv hyü mid´ə tē) Amount of water vapor in the air compared to the maximum amount of water vapor the air can hold (p. 232)

Reservoir (rez´ər vwär) Artificial lake created by placing a dam across a river (p. 263)

Reverse fault (ri vėrs´ fòlt´) Break in the crust in which the overhanging block of rock has been raised (p. 318)

Revolution (rev´ ə lü´shən) Movement of one object in its orbit around another object in space (p. 60)

Richter scale (rik´tər skāl´) Scale used to measure the strength of an earthquake (p. 324)

Rock (rok) Natural, solid material made of one or more minerals (p. 178)

Rock cycle (rok´ sī´kəl) Series of natural changes that cause one type of rock to become another type of rock (p. 194)

Rotation (rō tā´shən) Spinning of the earth or other object in space (p. 29)

Runoff (run´ôf´) Water that runs over the earth's surface and flows into streams (p. 257)

S

Salinity (sə lin´ə tē) Saltiness of water (p. 267)

Scale (skāl) Part of a map that shows the relationship between map distance and actual distance (p. 10)

Sea-floor spreading (sē´flôr´ spred´ing) Theory that the ocean floor spreads apart as new crust is formed at mid-ocean ridges (p. 310)

Seamount (sē´mount) Underwater mountain that is usually a volcano (p. 270)

Sediment (sed´ə mənt) Solid material, such as sand, soil, pebbles, and organic matter, that is carried in air, water, or ice and settles out (p. 185)

Sedimentary rock (sed´ə mən´tər ē rok´) Rock formed from pieces of other rock and organic matter that have been pressed and cemented together (p. 179)

Seismograph (sīz´mə graf) Instrument that detects and records earthquake waves (p. 323)

Shield volcano (shēld´ vol kā´nō) Low, broad volcano with a wide crater; formed from thin layers of lava (p. 315)

Sinkhole (singk´hōl´) Funnel-shaped depression that results when the roof of a cave collapses (p. 260)

Soil (soil) Mixture of tiny pieces of weathered rock and the remains of plants and animals (p. 282)

Solar eclipse (sō´lər i´klips) Passing of the moon between the earth and the sun (p. 67)

Solar system (sō´lər sis´təm) A star, such as the sun, and all of the objects that revolve around it in space (p. 79)

South Pole (south´ pōl´) Point farthest south on the earth (p. 29)

Specific gravity (spi sif´ik grav´ə tē) Mineral's weight compared to the weight of water (p. 165)

Spring (spring) Place where groundwater flows naturally out of the ground (p. 260)

Standard time zone (stan´dərd tīm´ zōn´) Area that has the same clock time (p. 32)

Star (stär) Glowing ball of hot gas that makes its own energy and light (p. 78)

States of matter (stāts´ ov mat´ər) Basic forms in which matter exists, including solid, liquid, and gas (p. 132)

Stratosphere (strat´ə sfir) Second layer of the atmosphere; includes the ozone layer (p. 209)

Stratus cloud (strā´təs kloud´) Low, flat cloud that forms in layers (p. 212)

Streak (strēk) Color of the mark a mineral makes on a white tile (p. 158)

Strike-slip fault (strīk´slip´ fôlt´) Break in the crust in which the blocks of rock move horizontally past each other (p. 318)

Submersible (səb mėr´sə bəl) Small underwater research vessel (p. 4)

Subsoil (sub´soil´) Layer of soil directly below the topsoil (p. 282)

Sunspot (sun´spot´) Dark area on the sun's surface that gives off less energy than the rest of the sun (p. 82)

a	hat	e	let	ī	ice	ô	order	u̇	put	sh	she	ə	a in about
ā	age	ē	equal	o	hot	oi	oil	ü	rule	th	thin		e in taken
ä	far	ėr	term	ō	open	ou	out	ch	child	ᴛʜ	then		i in pencil
â	care	i	it	ȯ	saw	u	cup	ng	long	zh	measure		o in lemon
													u in circus

Supergiant (sü´pər jī´ənt) One of the largest stars, formed when a star expands after using up its hydrogen; larger than a red giant (p. 118)

Supernova (sü´pər nō´və) Brilliant explosion of a collapsed supergiant (p. 119)

T

Telescope (tel´ə skōp) Instrument that collects light, making faint objects easier to see and enlarging distant objects (p. 70)

Texture (teks´chər) Size of crystals in an igneous rock (p. 182)

Thermocline (thėr´mō klīn) Ocean layer between about 300 and 1,000 meters below the surface, where the temperature drops sharply (p. 268)

Thermosphere (thėr´mə sfir) Outermost layer of the atmosphere; includes most of the ionosphere (p. 209)

Tides (tīdz) Regular rising and falling of the earth's major bodies of water (p. 68)

Topographic map (top´ə graf´ik map´) Map that shows the shape and elevation of the land surface (p. 15)

Topsoil (top´soil´) Top layer of soil, rich with oxygen and decayed organic matter (p. 282)

Tornado (tôr nā´dō) Powerful wind storm with a whirling, funnel-shaped cloud and extremely low pressure (p. 245)

Trade wind (trād´ wind´) Strong, reliable wind just north or south of the equator; blows from the east (p. 223)

Trench (trench) Deep valley on the ocean floor (p. 270)

Tributary (trib´yə ter´ē) River that joins another river of equal or greater size (p. 261)

Troposphere (trop´ə sfir) Bottom layer of the atmosphere, extending from ground level up to about 16 kilometers above the earth (p. 208)

Tsunami (sü nä´mē) Large sea wave caused by vibrations of the earth (p. 325)

U

Unit (yü´nit) Known amount used for measuring (p. 3)

Universe (yü´nə vėrs´) Everything that exists (p. 123)

V

Vent (vent) Round opening through which magma reaches the surface of the earth (p. 313)

Volcano (vol kā´nō) Mountain that develops where magma pushes up through the earth's surface (p. 313)

W

Warm front (wôrm´ frunt´) Boundary ahead of a warm air mass that is pushing out and riding over a cold air mass (p. 239)

Water cycle (wȯ´tər sī´kəl) Movement of water between the atmosphere and the earth's surface (p. 256)

Water table (wȯ´tər tā´bəl) Top of the groundwater layer (p. 259)

Water vapor (wȯ´tər vā´pər) Water in the form of a gas (p. 211)

Wave (wāv) Up-and-down motion of water caused by energy moving through the water (p. 268)

Weather (weŦH´ər) State of the atmosphere at a given time and place (p. 230)

Weathering (weŦH´ər ing) Breaking down of rocks on the earth's surface (p. 280)

White dwarf (wīt´ dwôrf´) Small, white, hot, dense star that remains after a nova (p. 118)

Wind belt (wind´ belt´) Pattern of wind movement around the earth (p. 222)

Wind cell (wind´ sel´) Continuous cycle of rising warm air and falling cold air (p. 221)

Wind vane (wind´ vān´) Instrument used to find wind direction (p. 233)

Index

A

Absolute dating, 342–343
Absolute magnitude, 109
Achievements in Science
    Almanacs, 57
    Artificial Glaciers, 299
    Balloon Pilots, 210
    Black Holes, 120
    Celebrating Earth Day, 6
    Cloud Seeding, 218
    Creating New Elements, 140
    Doppler Radar, 241
    Field Guides for Rocks and
        Minerals, 184
    Global Positioning
        Systems, 39
    Protecting the
        Environment, 272
    The Rock Cycle Theory, 196
    The Struggle to Accept the
        Solar System, 91
    The Theory of Sea-Floor
        Spreading, 312
    A Trip Around the World,
        30
    Uncovering the History of
        Life, 337
    Working with Metals, 156
Africa, 27
Agricola, Georgius, 184
Air, 145
Air masses, 239
Air pressure, 231–232
    measuring, 236–237
Air temperature, 230
Air-traffic controller, 45
Aldrin, Buzz, 71
Aleutian Islands, 313

Alluvial fan, 289
Almanacs, 57
Alpine glaciers, 294, 295–296
Alternative energy sources,
    358–363
Altitude, 212
Aluminum, 154, 171
    recycling, 172
Alvin (submersible),
    4, 312
Amber, 336
Americium, 140
Andes, 317
Anemometer, 233
Aneroid barometer, 231
Angle of light, 63–64
Antarctica, 27, 294
Antarctic Ocean, 28
Apatite, 160
Apollo missions, 65, 71
Appalachian Mountains, 347,
    349
Apparent magnitude, 109
Arctic Ocean, 28
Armstrong, Neil, 71
Army Signal Service, 238
Artificial glaciers, 299
Artificial satellites, 69
Asia, 27
Asteroid belt, 100
Asteroids, 100–101
Astronauts, 71, 80
Astronomers, 4, 97, 111, 115,
    119
Astronomical distance
    see Stars, distances of
Astronomy, 2
Atlantic Ocean, 28, 268
Atlantic time zone, 34

Atmosphere, 82
    defined, 204
    gases in, 204–206
    layers of, 208–209
Atmospheric scientist, 235
Atoms, 138
Australia, 27
Axis, 29, 31

B

Bacteria, 206
Balloon pilots, 210
Banneker, Benjamin, 57
Barometer, 231–232, 239
Bar scale, 10
Basalt, 183, 198
Bauxite, 171, 172
Bays, 268
Beaches, 290
Benthos, 271
Berkelium, 140
Big Dipper, 115, 121
Biodegradable materials, 134
Biosphere, 3, 188, 205–206,
    249, 271, 335–337,
    347–351, 361
Black Hills, 347
Black holes, 119, 120
Bopp, Thomas, 101
Break pattern of minerals,
    165
Bronze, 156
Building products, minerals
    used in, 171

C

Calcite, 154, 160, 188
    making, 190–191
Calcium, 160

Calcium carbonate, 187
California Current, 269
Californium, 140
Carbon-14, 342–343
Carbon dioxide, 88, 89, 145,
   205
Carbon dioxide cycle
   see Oxygen-carbon
      dioxide cycle
Carbonic acid, 281
Careers
   see Science at Work
Carson, Rachel, 272
Cartographer, 12, 47
Cascade Range, 317
Cassini (spacecraft), 94
Cast, 336
Castle Geyser, 260
Caves, 260, 281, 283
Celsius scale, 230
Cenozoic Era, 351
Centimeter, 11
Central Standard Time (CST),
   35
Central time zone, 34
Cernan, Eugene, 71
Chalk, 188
Channeling machines, 193
Charon, 96
Chemical change
   see Chemical properties
Chemical engineer, 146
Chemical properties, 133
Chemical rocks, 187
Chemical weathering, 281,
   284–285
Chlorine, 141
Chromosphere, 82
Cinder cones, 314
Cinders, 314
Cirques, 295
Cirrus clouds, 213
Clastic rocks, 186–187
Cleavage, 165

Climates, 247
   factors that affect, 248
Climate zones, 247–248, 250
Clouds, 211–213, 229, 255
   formation of, 211
   observing, 215
   seeding, 218
   types of, 212–213
Coal, 188, 189, 198
Cold front, 239
Colorado River, 263
Color of minerals, 157, 164
   observing, 162–163
Color of stars, 110
Comets, 101
Compass directions, 9
Compass roses, 9, 11
Composite volcanoes, 315
Compounds, 141–142, 145,
   154, 204
   formulas for, 143–144
Computers, 4
Concave mirror, 72
Condensation, 211
Conglomerate, 186, 198
Conodonts, 351
Constellations, 121, 368–371
Continental climate, 248
Continental drift, 309
Continental glaciers, 294,
   297–298
Continental shelf, 270
Continental slope, 270
Continents, 27
Contour interval, 16
Contour lines, 15–17
Convection currents, 311
Convex lens, 72
Copernicus, Nicolaus, 91
Copper, 153, 155, 156, 170
Core, 308
Corundum, 160
Crater, 70
Crust, 308

Crystals, 164
Cumulus clouds, 213, 217
Curium, 140
Currents
   convection, 311
   ocean, 269
Cuyahoga River, 272
Cycles
   see Nitrogen cycle
   see Oxygen-carbon dioxide
      cycle
   see Rock cycle
   see Water cycle

D

Day, 29, 31
Dead Sea, 257
Degrees, 42, 43, 230
Delta, 289
Density
   see Specific gravity of
      minerals
Deposition, 289
Depression, 16
Deserts, 300
   steppes and, 249
Diamond, 138, 154, 159, 160,
   171
Did You Know?
   Alvin (submersible), 4
   ancient maps, 9
   Army Signal Service, 238
   atmosphere composition,
      204
   atmosphere layers, 209
   comets, 101
   crystals, 164
   Dead Sea, 257
   diamond and graphite, 138
   dinosaur extinction, 350
   fossils, 186, 341
   geologic time scale, 351
   greenhouse effect, 89
   hydrogen, 143

Did You Know? (continued)
  items left on the moon, 71
  Large and Small
      Magellanic Clouds, 122
  lead, 139
  malachite, 171
  Mimas, 94
  minerals in food, 160
  Minnesota lakes, 262
  mirrors, 158
  moonquakes, 323
  moon's far side, 65
  Mount Waialeale, 234
  Niagara Falls, 287
  ocean water, 267
  plasma, 132
  plate movement, 311
  Pluto, 96
  pumice, 183
  Sahara desert, 300
  space technology, 5
  standard time zones, 32
  starlight, 114
  sunlight traveling to Earth,
      81
  volcano types, 314
  water on Mars, 90
Dinosaurs, 337, 350
Divides, 261
Dolomite, 154
Doppler radar, 241
Drainage basin, 261

E

Earth, 88–89
  atmosphere of, 203–217
  earth-moon system, 55–68
  surface temperature of, 88
  gravitational pull of, 56
  layers of, 308
  revolution of, 60
  rotation of, 29, 31,
      36–37, 60
  shape of, 26

Earth (continued)
  surface features of, 27–28
  unique features of, 88–89
  water in, 255–274
Earth chemistry, 131–149
Earth Day, 6
Earthquakes, 310, 319,
      322–325
  causes of, 322
  locating, 327–328
  predicting, 325
  strength and effect of,
      324–325
Earthquake waves, 323
Earth science, 2
  importance of, 5
  tools used in, 3–4
Eastern Hemisphere, 49
Eastern time zone, 34
Eclipses, 67
Einsteinium, 140
Electrons, 138
Elements, 137–139, 204
  creating new, 140
Elevations, 16
Elliptical galaxy, 122
El Niños, 5
Energy
  alternative sources, 358–363
  nuclear, 143
  renewable and
  nonrenewable sources, 352,
      358–363
  solar, 83
Environment, degradation of,
      134, 189, 207, 214, 272,
      291–293, 301, 352, 358
Environment, protecting, 6,
      214, 235, 272, 302
Environmental Protection
      Agency (EPA), 272
Environmental science
      technician, 214
Epicenter, 324

Equator, 42
Equivalence scale, 11
Erosion, 195
  comparing, 292–293
  glaciers as cause of, 294–298
  people as cause of, 291
  river, 286
  role of gravity in, 301
  water as cause of, 286–290
Europa, 93
Europe, 27
Evaporation, 211
  exploring, 265–266
Extrusive rocks, 183

F

Fahrenheit scale, 230
Faults, 318
  models of, 320–321
Federal Emergency
      Management Agency,
      250
Feldspar, 154, 160, 182, 281
Fermium, 140
Field guides for rocks and
      minerals, 184
Finger Lakes, 298
Fission, 143
Floating, measuring the effect
      of salt water on, 273–274
Floodplain, 288
Floodplain manager, 302
Fluorite, 160
Fog, 212
Folding, 317
  models of, 320–321
Folding plates, 317
Foliated rocks, 192
Forces, 56, 68, 80, 100,
      118–119, 120, 194–195,
      231, 240, 279–301,
      307–325
Formulas for compounds, 143
Fossett, Steve, 30

Fossil fuels, cutting down on, 352
Fossils, 186, 335, 337
    ages of, 340–343
    index, 341
    model of, 338–339
    types of, 335–336
Fracture, 165
Franklin, Benjamin, 57
Front, 239
Full moon, 66
Fusion, 108, 118

G

Galaxies, 122–123
Galilei, Galileo, 91
Galileo (spacecraft), 92
Ganymede, 93
Garnet, 171
Gases, 81–82, 88–89, 92, 94, 95, 100, 101, 108, 117, 131, 132, 145, 183, 192, 204–211, 257, 362–363
    in atmosphere, 204–206
Geographic information system, 12
Geologic time, 334
    eras in, 347–351
Geologic time scale, 347–348
Geologists, 3, 155, 178
Geology, 2
Geosynchronous operational environmental satellites (GOES), 246
Geysers, 260
Glaciers, 294
    alpine, 294
    artificial, 299
    continental, 294, 297–298
    erosion caused by, 294–298
Global ocean, 28
Global positioning system (GPS), 17, 30, 39, 69

Global winds, 222–223
Gneiss, 192, 198
Gold, 137, 154, 155, 157, 159, 170, 171
    properties of, 161
Grand Canyon, 334
Grand Tetons, 318
Granite, 182
Graphite, 138, 154, 170
Gravity, 56, 80, 118
    effect of, 56
    glaciers and, 295
    role of, in erosion, 301
    tides and, 68
Great Bear, 121
Great Lakes, 262, 298, 351
Great Red Spot, 92
Greenhouse effect, 88, 89
Greenland, 294
Greenwich, England, 46
Greenwich meridian, 46
Grid, 38
Groundwater, 257, 259
Gulf of Alaska, 268
Gulf of Mexico, 261
Gulfs, 268
Gulf Stream, 269
Gypsum, 154, 160, 187

H

Hachures, 16
Hailstones, 217, 234
Hale, Alan, 101
Hale-Bopp, 101
Half-life, 342–343
    model of, 345–346
Halite, 154
Hardness of minerals, 159–160
    observing, 162–163
Hawking, Stephen, 120
Heat, 82, 88, 108, 117, 143, 161, 179, 192, 194–195, 211, 221, 256, 269, 309, 311, 359–363

Heat lightning, 244
Helium, 81
Hemispheres, 49
High, 240
Himalayas, 317
Horn, 295
Hubble Space Telescope, 116, 119
Humid continental climate, 249
Humidity, 232
Humid subtropical climate, 249
Hurricanes, 229, 245, 334
Hutton, James, 196
Hydroelectric dam, 263
Hydroelectric power plant operator, 264
Hydroelectric power plants, 263
Hydrogen, 81, 143
Hydrologic cycle
    see Water cycle
Hydrosphere
    see Atmosphere
    see Water cycle
    see Water on the earth

I

Ice cap climate, 249
Ice crystals, 216
Igneous rocks, 178, 181–183, 194, 347
Impurities, 157
Index fossils, 341
Indian Ocean, 28
Inner planets, 86–90
International date line, 33
International Space Station (ISS), 62
Intrusive rocks, 181–182
Investigations
    Comparing Erosion, 292–293

Investigations (continued)
Describing Location on a Round Surface, 40–41
Exploring Evaporation, 265–266
Exploring Light Angle, 63–64
Finding Specific Gravity, 168–169
Identifying Rocks, 197–198
Locating an Earthquake, 327–328
Making Calcite, 190–191
Making a Constellation Model, 125–126
Making a Half-Life Model, 345–346
Making a Map, 13–14
Making a Model of a Fossil, 338–339
Making a Model of an Orbit, 58–59
Making a Model of Rain, 219–220
Making Models of Folding and Faults, 320–321
Measuring Air Pressure, 236–237
Measuring the Effect of Salt Water on Floating, 273–274
Measuring Physical Properties of Objects, 135–136
Modeling Distances in the Solar System, 98–99
Modeling the Earth's Rotation, 36–37
Observing Brightness, 112–113
Observing Chemical Weathering, 284–285
Observing Clouds, 215
Observing Color, Streak, and Hardness, 162–163
Observing Sunspots, 84–85
Reading a Topographic Map, 19–20
Separating a Mixture, 147–148
Using a Weather Map, 242–243
Io, 93
Ionosphere, 209
Iron, 139, 155, 156, 160
Irregular galaxy, 122
Isobars, 240

J

Jeweler, 167
Juan de Fuca plate, 313
Jupiter, 92–93

K

Kilauea Volcano, 315

L

Lake Erie, 272
Lake Havasu, 263
Lakes, 262
Lake Superior, 262
Lake Winnipeg, 298
Landforms
see Alluvial fan
see Beaches
see Caves
see Deltas
see Faults
see Floodplains
see Lakes
see Meanders
see Mountains
see Oxbow lakes
see Rivers
see River valley
see Sand dunes
see Sea stack
see Volcanoes
Landslides, 301

Large and Small Magellanic Clouds, 122
Latitude, 42–44
locating points by, 48
Lava, 183, 194
Lead, 139, 170
Light, angle of, 63–64
Lightning, 132
heat, 244
Light pollution, 124
Light-years, 114–115
Lignite, 189
Limestone, 188, 192, 198
Liquids, 131, 132, 192
Lithosphere
see Crust
see Earth, layers of
see Mantle
Little Ghost Nebula, 117
Longitude, 46
locating points by, 48
Low, 240
Lunar eclipse, 67
Luster of minerals, 158, 159, 164
L-waves, 323

M

Magellan (spacecraft), 88
Magma, 181, 183, 192, 194, 309, 310, 311
Magnetorheological (MR) fluid, 316
Magnitude, 109–110
Mantle, 308
Map legends, 8
Mapmaker, 47
Map projection, 47
Maps, 7
grid system on, 38
making, 13–14
topographic, 15–17
Map scales, 10–11

Marble, 192, 193, 198
Maria, 70
Marine climate, 248
Mariner 10 (spacecraft), 86
Marine west coast climate, 249
Mars, 89–90
Mass, 56
Matter, 131, 132
    properties of, 133
    states of, 132
Matterhorn, 295
Meanders, 288
Measurement, 3
    see also Investigations
Mechanical weathering, 280
Mediterranean climate, 249
Mediterranean Sea, 268
Melroy, Pamela Ann, 62
Mendelevium, 140
Mercator projection, 47
Mercury, 80, 86
Mercury barometer, 231
Meridians, 46
Mesosphere, 209
Mesozoic Era, 350, 351
Metallic luster, 158
Metals, working with, 156
Metamorphic rocks, 179, 192, 195, 347
Meteor, 100
Meteor Crater, 101
Meteorite, 70, 101
Meteorologists, 4, 5, 69, 241, 246
Meteorology, 2
Metric system, 3
Metric units, 3
Metric and customary measurement, 356–357
Mica, 154, 182
Mid-ocean ridges, 270, 309
Milky Way galaxy, 107, 123
Mimas, 94

Minerals, 153–172, 170, 179
    common uses of, 170–171
    defined, 154
    features of, 154
    field guides for, 184
    locating and mining, 155
    properties of, 157–160, 164–166
Mining, 155
Mississippi River, 288
Missouri River, 288
Mixtures, 144–145
    separating, 147–148
Model, 7
Mohs' scale of hardness, 159–160
Mold, 336
Mono Lake, 187
Moon, 78–79
    Apollo missions to, 71
    movement of, 65–68
    phases of, 66
    revolution of, 65
    rotation of, 65
    surface of, 70
Moraines, 296, 297
Mountains, 317–318
Mountain time zone, 34
Mount St. Helens, 313
Mount Waialeale, 234
Mouth, 289

N

National Aeronautics and Space Administration (NASA), 116
National Radio Astronomy Observatory, 111
National Weather Service (NWS), 238, 246
Natural resoures, 83, 154–155, 172, 178, 214, 258–259, 262–263, 358–363

Natural satellite, 69
Nazca plate, 310
Nebula, 117
Nekton, 271
Nelson, Gaylord, 6
Neptune, 95–96
Neutron star, 119
Neutrons, 138
New moon, 66
Newton, Isaac, 91
Niagara Falls, 287
Night, 29, 31
Nitrogen, 139, 145, 204, 206
Nitrogen cycle, 206
Nobelium, 140
Nonfoliated rocks, 192
Normal fault, 318
Norphel, Chewang, 299
North America, 27
    map of, 376
North American plate, 322
North Atlantic Drift, 269
Northern Hemisphere, 49, 60, 61
North Pole, 29, 43
North Star, 121
North wind, 233
Notes
    alpine glaciers, 296
    atoms, 139
    climate types, 248
    degrees, 43
    diamonds, 170
    Earth's origin, 347
    Earth's surface temperature, 88
    fossils, 335
    glacier formation, 294
    granite, 182
    Hale-Bopp comet, 101
    ice shelves, 297
    iron, 308
    Kilauea Volcano, 315
    landslides, 301

Notes (continued)
  map symbols, 11
  matter, 142
  meanders, 288
  mine shafts, 155
  photosynthesis, 205
  saltwater bodies, 268
  solar system motion, 79
  star color, 110
  system definition, 3
  theory definition, 309
  tide factors, 68
  topographic maps, 16
  water cycle, 216, 257
  world ocean, 28
Nova, 118
Nuclear energy, 143
Nuclear reactions, 82, 108,
  117, 143, 363
Nucleus, 138

O

Obsidian, 183, 198
Ocean currents, 269
Ocean floor, 270
  age of, 309
Ocean life, 271
Oceanographers, 4
Oceanography, 2
Ocean waves, 268
Odyssey (orbiter), 90
Ohio River, 288
Orbit, 56
  model of, 58–59
Organic rocks, 188
Orthographic projection, 47
Outer planets, 92–96
Owen, Richard, 337
Oxbow lake, 288
Oxidation, 281
Oxygen-carbon dioxide cycle,
  205
Oxygen, 139, 145, 154, 204
Ozark Mountains, 347

Ozone, 207
Ozone holes, 207

P

Pacific Ocean, 28, 261, 268
Pacific time zone, 34
Paleontologists, 337
Paleozoic Era, 349
Pangaea, 309
Parallels, 42
Paricutín, 314
Park, mapping, 18
Parker Dam, 263
Periodic Table of Elements,
  139, 140, 372–373
Petrification, 335
Petroleum engineer, 344
Phases of moon, 66
Phosphorus, 160
Photogrammetry, 48
Photosynthesis, 205
Photovoltaic (PV) cell, 102
Physical change
  see Physical properties
Physical properties, 133
  measuring, 135–136
Piton de la Fournaise, 307
Plains, 270
Planets, 78–79
  inner, 86–90
  outer, 92–96
Plankton, 271
Plasma, 132
Plastic, 134
Plates, 310
Plate tectonics, 310–311
Pluto, 96
Plutonium, 140
Polar climates, 248, 249
Polar easterlies, 223
Pollution
  laws on, 214
  light, 124
Poor Richard's Almanack, 57

Porous, 259
Precambrian Era, 347, 351
Precious metals, 171
Precipitation, 216–217,
  234, 256–257, 259
Prevailing westerlies, 223
Prime meridian, 46
Principle of crosscutting
  relationships, 341
Principle of superposition, 340
Properties, 133
  of gold, 161
Protons, 138
Proxima Centauri, 114
Psychrometer, 232
Pulitzer, Joseph, 57
Pumice, 183, 198
P-waves, 323, 325
Pyrite, 157, 158, 159

Q

Quartz, 137, 154, 157, 160,
  170, 171, 182, 187
Quick test, 160

R

Radioactive elements, 342
Rain, 216
  model of, 219–220
Rainbows, 203
Raindrops, 217
Rain gauge, 234
Ratio, 11
Recycling, 134, 172
Red giant, 118
Reflecting telescopes, 72
Refracting telescopes, 72
Relative dating, 340–341
Relative humidity, 232
Reservoirs, 263
Reverse fault, 318
Revolution, 60
Rhyolite, 198
Richter scale, 324

River deposits, 289
River erosion, 286
Rivers, 261–262
River valley, life of, 287–288
Robinson projection, 47
Rock cycle, 194–195
    theory of, 196
Rock record, 334–336
Rocks, 177–198
    ages of, 340
    chemical, 187
    clastic, 186–187
    defined, 178
    elements in, 139
    extrusive, 183
    field guides for, 184
    foliated, 192
    identifying, 197–198
    igneous, 178, 181–183, 347
    intrusive, 181–182
    metamorphic, 179, 192,
        195, 347
    nonfoliated, 192
    organic, 188
    sedimentary, 177, 179,
        185–188, 189, 195
    types of, 178–179
Rock salt, 187
Rotation, 29, 60
Runoff, 257, 259
Rust, 133

S

Salinity, 267
Salt, physical properties of, 133
Salt water, 257, 267
    measuring its effect on
        floating, 273–274
San Andreas fault, 318, 322
Sand dunes, 300
Sandstone, 187, 192, 198

Satellites, 78–79
    artificial, 69
    natural, 69
Saturn, 94
Savannah, 249
Schist, 192, 198
Schmitt, Harrison, 71
Science at Work
    Air-Traffic Controller, 45
    Astronomer, 97
    Atmospheric Scientist, 235
    Cartographer, 12
    Chemical Engineer, 146
    Environmental Science
        Technician, 214
    Floodplain Manager, 302
    Hydroelectric Power Plant
        Operator, 264
    Jeweler, 167
    Petroleum Engineer, 344
    Seismologist, 326
    Space Shuttle and
        International Space
        Station Crews, 62
    Stonemason, 180
    Telescope Technician, 111
Science in Your Life
    Cutting Down on Fossil
        Fuels, 352
    Erosion Caused by People,
        291
    The Good and Bad of Coal,
        189
    Lasting Plastic, 134
    Light Pollution, 124
    Living on a Tectonic Plate,
        316
    Mapping a Park, 18
    Natural and Artificial
        Satellites, 69

Ozone: Protector and
        Pollutant, 207
    Recycling Aluminum, 172
    A Solar House, 83
    Time Zones, 35
    Your Climate Zone, 250
    Your Water Budget, 258
Science Myths
    air vs. oxygen, 145
    deserts, 300
    dinosaurs and people, 349
    distance between the earth
        and the sun, 61
    facing north, 9
    heat lightning, 244
    light-year, 114
    mineral characteristics, 160
    ocean floor, 271
    raindrops, 217
    rocks vs. minerals, 179
    gravity in space, 80
Science, nature of, xviii–xix
Scientific method, xviii–xix
    see also Investigations
Seaborg, Glenn, 140
Seaborgium, 140
Sea-floor spreading, 309–310,
        312
Seamount, 270
Seas, 268
Seasons, 60–61
Sea stack, 290
Sediment, 185
Sedimentary rocks, 177, 179,
        185–188, 189, 195
Seismic tomography, 319
Seismograph, 323
Seismologist, 326
Shale, 186, 198
Shield volcanoes, 315
Shooting stars, 100
Silent Spring, 272

Silicon, 154
Silver, 155, 171
Sinkhole, 260
Sirius, 110, 114
Slate, 192, 198
Sleet, 216
Snow, 216
Society
    see Technology and society
Sodium, 141
Sodium chloride, 141, 267
Soil, 282
Solar and Heliospheric
    Observatory (SOHO),
    82
Solar cell, 102
Solar eclipse, 67
Solar flares, 77
Solar house, 83
Solar system, 77–101, 364–365
    asteroids in, 100–101
    comets in, 101
    distances in, 98–99
    inner planets in, 86–90
    objects in, 79–80
    outer planets in, 92–96
    sun in, 81–82
Solar wind, 101
Solids, 131, 132, 154
South America, 27
Southern Hemisphere, 49, 61
Southern Ocean, 28
South Pole, 29, 43
Space, growing minerals in,
    164
Space exploration, 366–367
Space shuttle, 62
Specific gravity of minerals,
    165–166, 168–169
Spiral galaxies, 123
Spirit of Freedom (hot air
    balloon), 30
Spring, 260

Standard time zones, 32–34, 35
Stars, 78–79, 108–110, 132
    birth of, 117
    brightness of, 108–110
    color of, 110
    death of, 118–119
    distances of, 114–115
    observing brightness of,
        112–113
Steel, 156
Stellar equilibrium
    see Stars, birth of
    see Stars, death of
Steppes, deserts and, 249
Stonemason, 180
Storms, 244–245
Stratosphere, 209
Stratus clouds, 212
Streak of minerals, 158–159
    observing, 162–163
Streak plate, 158
Strike-slip fault, 318
Subarctic climate, 249
Submersible, 4
Subsoil, 282
Sugar, physical properties of,
    133
Sulfur, 154, 157
Sun, 81–82
Sunspots, 82
    observing, 84–85
Supergiant, 118
Supernova, 119
S-waves, 323, 325

T
Table salt, 141
Talc, 160
Tar pits, 336
Technology and society, 3–5,
    17, 30, 39, 48, 65, 69, 71,
    72, 83, 102, 116, 134,
    140, 143, 155, 156, 161,

Technology and society
    (continued)
    170–171, 172, 188–189,
    193, 207, 218, 224, 238,
    241, 246, 263, 272, 283,
    291, 299, 312, 316, 319,
    324–325, 342–343, 352,
    358–363, 366–367
Technology Notes
    cave mapping, 283
    coal, 188
    conodonts, 351
    global positioning system
        (GPS), 17
    gold, 161
    Hubble Space Telescope,
        116
    hydroelectric power plants,
        263
    map projections, 47
    marble, 193
    nuclear fission, 143
    photogrammetry, 48
    photovoltaic (PV) cell, 102
    telescopes, 72
    weather balloons, 5
    weather satellites, 246
    wind power 224
Tectonic plate, living on, 316
Telescopes, 70, 72, 108
Telescope technician, 111
Temperature, 230
Temperate climates, 248, 249
Texture of rocks, 182
Theories, xix, 91, 196,
        309–312, 347, 350
Thermocline, 268
Thermometers, 230
Thermosphere, 209
Thunderheads, 244
Thunderstorms, 244
Tides, 68
Titan, 94

Topaz, 160, 171
Topographic maps, 15–17
    reading, 19–20
    using, 16–17
Topsoil, 282
Tornadoes, 245
Tourmaline, 171
Trade winds, 223
Trench, 270
Tributaries, 261
Trilobites, 336, 349
Tropical climates, 248, 249
Tropical desert, 249
Tropical rain forest, 249
Tropic of Cancer, 42
Tropic of Capricorn, 42
Troposphere, 208, 209, 244
Tsunamis, 325
Tundra climate, 249

U

Universe, 123
Uranus, 95
Ursa Major, 121

V

Vent, 313
Venus, 87–88
Volcanoes, 155, 194, 307
    formation of, 313
    types of, 314–315

Voyager (spacecraft), 92, 95
Warm front, 239
Wasatch Range, 318
Water, 131
    as cause of erosion,
        286–290
    on the earth, 255–274
    properties of ocean,
        267–268
    salt, 257, 267
    sources of fresh, 259–263
Water budget, 258
Water cycle, 216, 256–257
Water table, 259, 260
Water vapor, 211, 232
Wave deposits, 290
Wave erosion, 290
Waves
    earthquake, 323
    ocean, 268
Weather, 230
    collecting data on, 238
    conditions and
        measurements, 230–234
    patterns and predictions,
        238–240
Weather balloons, 5, 238
Weathering, 195, 280
    chemical, 281, 284–285
    mechanical, 280

Weather maps, 240, 242–243
Weather satellites, 238, 246
Weather stations, 238
Wegener, Alfred, 309
Western Hemisphere, 49
White Cliffs of Dover, 188
White dwarf, 118
Wind belts, 222
Wind cells, 221
Wind erosion and deposits,
    300
Wind farms, 224
Windmills, 224
Wind patterns, 221–223
Wind speed and direction, 233
Wind turbine, 224
Wind vane, 233
*The World Almanac and Book
    of Facts*, 57
World map, 374–375
World ocean, 28

Y

Yellowstone River, 287

Z

Zinc, 160

Photo Credits

Cover background—Courtesy of U.S. Geological Survey; cover inset—© Antony Edwards/Image Bank/Getty Images; pp. iii, xx—© James Randklev/Corbis; p. x—© Francois Gohier/Photo Researchers, Inc.; p. 4 (left)—© Norbert Wu Photography; p. 4 (right)—Courtesy of NASA Jet Propulsion Laboratory; p. 5—© Brecelj Bojan/Corbis/Sygma; p. 7—© Air Photographics, Inc.; p. 12—© Gibson Stock Photography; p. 18—© Bruce Iverson Photomicrography; p. 24—Courtesy of KidSat, NASA Jet Propulsion Laboratory; p. 35—© Bonnie Kamin/Index Stock Imagery; p. 45—© David Lawrence/Corbis; p. 54—Courtesy of NASA Goddard Space Flight Center; pp. 56, 61, 67, 78, 79, 81, 88, 96, 100, 104, 118, 256 (image of sun)—Courtesy of Solar and Heliospheric Observatory (European Space Agency, NASA); pp. 56, 66, 67, 68, 74 (image of moon)—Courtesy of NASA; p. 62—Courtesy of NASA; p. 68 (left)—© Peter Gregg/Color-Pic Inc.; p. 68 (right)—© Peter Gregg/Color-Pic Inc.; p. 71—Courtesy of NASA, Apollo 17; p. 76—© The Stocktrek Corp/Brand X Pictures/Alamy.com; p. 79, 86, 100, 104, 364—Courtesy of NASA, Mariner 10, U.S. Geological Survey Astrogeology Team; p. 78, 79, 87, 88, 100, 104, 364—Courtesy of Magellan Project, NASA Jet Propulsion Laboratory; p. 79, 89, 100, 104, 364—Courtesy of NASA, Hubble Heritage Team (STScI/AURA); p. 90—Courtesy of NASA Jet Propulsion Laboratory; p. 79, 92, 100, 104, 364—Courtesy of NASA, Hubble Heritage Team (STScI/AURA); p. 93—Courtesy of NASA Jet Propulsion Laboratory; p. 79, 94, 100, 365—Courtesy of NASA, Hubble Heritage Team (STScI/AURA); p. 79, 95 (top), 104, 365—Courtesy of NASA, U.S. Naval Observatory; p. 79, 95 (bottom), 96, 104, 365—Courtesy of NASA Jet Propulsion Laboratory; p. 97—© Addison A. Geary/Stock Boston; p. 101 (top)—© Francois Gohier/Photo Researchers, Inc.; p. 101 (bottom)—© Dennis di Cicco/Corbis; p. 106—Courtesy of NASA, European Southern Observatory; p. 111—Courtesy of National Radio Astronomy Observatory, Associated Universities, Inc., National Science Foundation; p.115—Courtesy of Sébastien Giguère (www.astrosurf.com/sg); p. 117—Courtesy of NASA, Hubble Heritage Team (STScI/AURA); p. 119 (left)—Courtesy of NASA, Chandra X-ray Observatory Center, MPE; p. 119 (right)—Courtesy of NASA, STScI; pp. 122, 123—Courtesy of National Optical Astronomy Observatory, Association of Universities for Research in Astronomy, National Science Foundation; p. 124—Courtesy of NASA, National Oceanic and Atmospheric Administration, DMP; p. 130—© Michael T. Sedam/Corbis; p. 134—© Bill Banaszewski/Visuals Unlimited; p. 137—© Tom McHugh/Photo Researchers, Inc.; p. 141 (left)—© Photo Reseachers, Inc.; p. 141 (center)—© Yoav Levy/Phototake; pp. 141 (right), 164 (left)—© A.J. Copley/Visuals Unlimited; p. 144—© John Sohlden/Visuals Unlimited; p. 146—© Bob Daemmrich/The Image Works, Inc.; p. 154—© Stan Osolinski/Dembinsky Photo Associates; p. 155 (left)—© Mark A. Schneider/Photo Reseachers, Inc.; p. 155 (right)—© Lester V. Bergman/Corbis; p. 157—© Ken Lucas/Visuals Unlimited; p. 158 (left)—© Alan Curtis/Leslie Garland Picture Library/Alamy.com; p. 158 (right)—© Mark A. Schneider/Dembinsky Photo Associates; p. 164 (right)—© Doug Sokell/Visuals

Unlimited; p. 167—© Reporters Press Agency/eStock Photo; p. 172—© David Young-Wolff/Stone/Getty Images; p. 175 (top)—© Ken Lucas/Visuals Unlimited; p. 175 (bottom)—© José Manuel Sanchis Calvete/Corbis; p. 176—© Manfred Gottschalk/Animals Animals; p. 178—© Hubert Stadler/Corbis; p. 179 (top)—© W. Cody/Corbis; p. 179 (bottom)—© David Muench/Corbis; p. 180—© Annie Griffiths Belt/Corbis; p. 182—© Doug Sookell/Visuals Unlimited; p. 183—© Mark A. Schneider/Photo Researchers, Inc.; p. 186 (left)—© John D. Cunningham/Visuals Unlimited; p. 186 (right)—© Jonathan Blair/Corbis; p. 187—© John Gerlach/Visuals Unlimited; p. 192 (top)—© Ann Swengel/Visuals Unlimited; p. 192 (bottom)—© Greg Pease/Stone/Getty Images; p. 202—© Royalty Free/Corbis; p. 207—Courtesy of NASA; p. 212—© Visuals Unlimited; p. 213 (top)—© David Matherly/Visuals Unlimited; p. 213 (bottom)—© Royalty Free/Corbis; p. 214—© Jerry Mason/Science Photo Library/Photo Researchers, Inc.; p. 216—© A.J. Copley/Visuals Unlimited; p. 228—© NASA/Science Photo Library/Photo Researchers, Inc.; p. 231—© Leonard Lessin/Photo Researchers, Inc.; p. 233—© E.R. Degginger/Color-Pic Inc.; p. 234—© Runk/Schoenberger/Grant Heilman Photography; p. 235—© Shepard Sherbell/Corbis/SABA; p. 238—Courtesy of the National Oceanic and Atmospheric Administration; p. 245—© Royalty Free/Corbis; p. 249 (top)—© Kurt Scholz/SuperStock; p. 249 (center)—© Dominique Braud/Dembinsky Photo Associates; p. 249 (bottom)—© Kjell B. Sandved/Visuals Unlimited; p. 254—© Doug Wilson/Corbis; p. 260 (left)—Courtesy of U.S. Geological

Survey; p. 260 (right)—© AP/Wide World Photos; p. 263—© Lester Sloan/Woodfin Camp & Associates; p. 264—© Lester Lefkowitz/Corbis; p. 278—© Visuals Unlimited; p. 280—© Royalty Free/Corbis; p. 281 (left)—© John Prior Images/Alamy.com; p. 281 (right)—© John Lemker/Earth Scenes/Animals Animals; p. 282—© Adam Woolfitt/Corbis; p. 286—© Royalty Free/Corbis; p. 288—Courtesy of NASA Jet Propulsion Laboratory; p. 290—© Randy Wells/Stone/Getty Images; p. 291—© John Sohlden/Visuals Unlimited; p. 294—© Gerald & Buff Corsi/Visuals Unlimited; p. 295 (top)—© Visuals Unlimited; p. 295 (bottom)—© Donald Johnston/Stone/Getty Images; p. 296—© Lawrence Dodge; p. 301—Courtesy of Terry Taylor, Colorado State Patrol; p. 302—© Patti McConville/Image Bank/Getty Images; p. 306—© Sylvain Grandadam/Image Bank/Getty Images; p. 314—© Tom Bean/Corbis; p. 315 (top)—Courtesy of U.S. Geological Survey; p. 315 (bottom)—© Stone/Getty Images; p. 316—© Dana White/PhotoEdit; p. 322—Courtesy of U.S. Geological Survey; p. 325—© Robert Yager/Stone/Getty Images; p. 326—© PhotoEdit; p. 332—© Francois Gohier/Photo Researchers, Inc.; p. 334—© Danny Lehman/Corbis; p. 335—© Phil Degginger/Stone/Getty Images; p. 336 (top)—© A.J. Copley/PhotoDisc; p. 336 (bottom)—© Howard Grey/Stone/Getty Images; p. 343—© Kaj R. Svensson/ Photo Researchers, Inc.; p. 344—© Keith Wood/Stone/Getty Images; p. 349—© A.J. Copley/Visuals Unlimited; p. 350—© Phil Martin/PhotoEdit; p. 352—© Michael Newman/PhotoEdit; pp. 358, 360, 361—© Royalty Free/Corbis

Midterm Mastery Test

Midterm Mastery Test

Part A Read each sentence. Write the letter of the correct answer on the line.

_____ **1.** You would check the map ___ to find out what a color on the map means.
   A legend **B** scale **C** compass rose **D** contour line

_____ **2.** When it is winter in the Northern Hemisphere, it is ___ in the Southern Hemisphere.
   A fall **B** winter **C** spring **D** summer

_____ **3.** The layer of the sun's atmosphere that gives off light is the ____.
   A chromosphere **B** nucleus **C** photosphere **D** corona

_____ **4.** You can locate any place on Earth if you know its ___.
   A time zone **C** hemisphere
   B latitude and longitude **D** distance from the international date line

_____ **5.** The hottest stars are ___.
   A blue-white **B** yellow **C** white **D** red

_____ **6.** A chemical property of iron is its ___.
   A mass **B** color **C** appearance **D** ability to rust

_____ **7.** You can use ___ to tell gold from pyrite.
   A color **B** luster **C** streak **D** break pattern

_____ **8.** About 70 percent of the earth's surface is covered with ___.
   A land **B** oceans **C** continents **D** standard time zones

_____ **9.** ___ are the source of light for all objects in space.
   A planets **B** stars **C** moons **D** comets

_____ **10.** The principal force pulling an object into orbit around another object is ____.
   A gravity **B** tides **C** revolution **D** rotation

Midterm Mastery Test Page 1

Midterm Mastery Test, continued

Part B Match each term with its definition. Write the letter of the correct definition on the line.

_____ **11.** scale
_____ **12.** Mercury
_____ **13.** lunar eclipse
_____ **14.** supergiant
_____ **15.** astronomy
_____ **16.** prime meridian
_____ **17.** nebula
_____ **18.** Jupiter
_____ **19.** meteorology
_____ **20.** fracture
_____ **21.** solar eclipse
_____ **22.** supernova
_____ **23.** mineral
_____ **24.** cleavage
_____ **25.** black hole
_____ **26.** equator
_____ **27.** nucleus

A study of outer space
B line of 0° longitude
C largest planet in the solar system
D study of the earth's air
E tendency to break with jagged edges
F region of great gravity and no light
G shadow of the earth on the moon when the earth passes between the sun and the moon
H shows relationship between map distance and actual distance
I ability to split along flat surfaces
J cloud of dust and gas in space
K atom's center, made of protons and neutrons
L line of 0° latitude
M one of the largest stars
N the planet that is closest to the sun
O element or compound found in the earth
P shadow of the moon on the earth when the moon passes between the sun and the earth
Q exploding star

Midterm Mastery Test Page 2

Midterm Mastery Test, continued

Part C Write the term from the Word Bank that best completes each sentence.

Word Bank				
axis	crater	inner	luster	outer
compass rose	crystal	latitude	matter	temperature
compound	hardness	liquid	orbit	topographic

28. _____ is anything that has weight and takes up space.

29. The shape of a(n) _____ is an ellipse.

30. If you want to know the directions on a map, you look at the _____.

31. _____ is a measure of how well a mineral resists being scratched.

32. Mercury, Venus, Earth, and Mars are the _____ planets.

33. Matter usually exists on the earth as a solid, _____, or gas.

34. The imaginary line that runs through the North and South Poles is the _____.

35. When an object hits the moon's surface, it can cause a(n) _____ to form.

36. Usually heat or electricity is needed to separate elements in a(n) _____.

37. _____ lines are imaginary lines that run east and west around the earth.

38. _____ is the way a mineral picks up or reflects light.

39. Jupiter, Saturn, Uranus, Neptune, and Pluto are the _____ planets.

40. _____ maps show the shape and elevation of the land surface.

41. The basic shape that minerals tend to take is a(n) _____.

42. The color of a star depends on its _____.

Midterm Mastery Test Page 3

Midterm Mastery Test, continued

Part D Write the answer to each question.

43. What is a map?
_____

44. How are comets, asteroids, and meteorites different?
_____
_____
_____

45. How does the earth's rotation cause day and night?
_____
_____

46. Name and describe the three shapes of galaxies.
_____
_____

47. What are three common physical properties of matter?
_____

48. How does the earth's revolution cause the seasons?
_____
_____
_____

49. What are seven basic physical properties of minerals?
_____
_____

50. Why do mixtures not have chemical formulas?
_____
_____

Midterm Mastery Test Page 4

Final Mastery Test

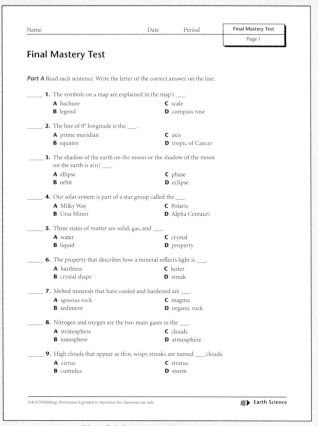

Final Mastery Test

Part A Read each sentence. Write the letter of the correct answer on the line.

_____ **1.** The symbols on a map are explained in the map's ___.
A hachure   C scale
B legend   D compass rose

_____ **2.** The line of 0° longitude is the ___.
A prime meridian   C axis
B equator   D tropic of Cancer

_____ **3.** The shadow of the earth on the moon or the shadow of the moon on the earth is a(n) ___.
A ellipse   C phase
B orbit   D eclipse

_____ **4.** Our solar system is part of a star group called the ___.
A Milky Way   C Polaris
B Ursa Minor   D Alpha Centauri

_____ **5.** Three states of matter are solid, gas, and ___.
A water   C crystal
B liquid   D property

_____ **6.** The property that describes how a mineral reflects light is ___.
A hardness   C luster
B crystal shape   D streak

_____ **7.** Melted minerals that have cooled and hardened are ___.
A igneous rock   C magma
B sediment   D organic rock

_____ **8.** Nitrogen and oxygen are the two main gases in the ___.
A stratosphere   C clouds
B ionosphere   D atmosphere

_____ **9.** High clouds that appear as thin, wispy streaks are named ___ clouds.
A cirrus   C stratus
B cumulus   D storm

Earth Science

Final Mastery Test Page 1

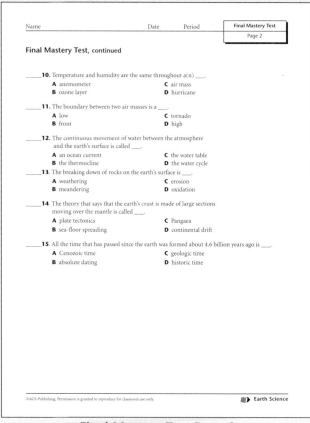

Final Mastery Test, continued

_____ **10.** Temperature and humidity are the same throughout a(n) ___.
A anemometer   C air mass
B ozone layer   D hurricane

_____ **11.** The boundary between two air masses is a ___.
A low   C tornado
B front   D high

_____ **12.** The continuous movement of water between the atmosphere and the earth's surface is called ___.
A an ocean current   C the water table
B the thermocline   D the water cycle

_____ **13.** The breaking down of rocks on the earth's surface is ___.
A weathering   C erosion
B meandering   D oxidation

_____ **14.** The theory that says that the earth's crust is made of large sections moving over the mantle is called ___.
A plate tectonics   C Pangaea
B sea-floor spreading   D continental drift

_____ **15.** All the time that has passed since the earth was formed about 4.6 billion years ago is ___.
A Cenozoic time   C geologic time
B absolute dating   D historic time

Earth Science

Final Mastery Test Page 2

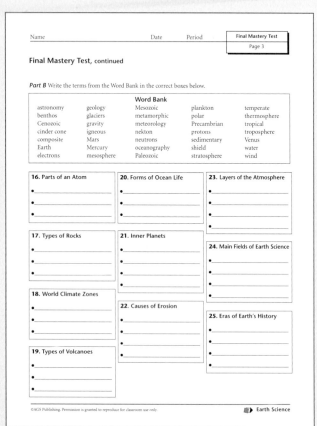

Final Mastery Test, continued

Part B Write the terms from the Word Bank in the correct boxes below.

Word Bank

astronomy	geology	Mesozoic	plankton	temperate
benthos	glaciers	metamorphic	polar	thermosphere
Cenozoic	gravity	meteorology	Precambrian	tropical
cinder cone	igneous	nekton	protons	troposphere
composite	Mars	neutrons	sedimentary	Venus
Earth	Mercury	oceanography	shield	water
electrons	mesosphere	Paleozoic	stratosphere	wind

16. Parts of an Atom
- _____
- _____
- _____

17. Types of Rocks
- _____
- _____
- _____

18. World Climate Zones
- _____
- _____
- _____

19. Types of Volcanoes
- _____
- _____
- _____

20. Forms of Ocean Life
- _____
- _____
- _____

21. Inner Planets
- _____
- _____
- _____
- _____

22. Causes of Erosion
- _____
- _____
- _____

23. Layers of the Atmosphere
- _____
- _____
- _____

24. Main Fields of Earth Science
- _____
- _____
- _____
- _____

25. Eras of Earth's History
- _____
- _____
- _____
- _____

Earth Science

Final Mastery Test Page 3

Final Mastery Test, continued

Part C Match each term with its description. Write the letter of the correct description on the line.

_____ **26.** telescope   A measure of density
_____ **27.** moon   B made of only one kind of atom
_____ **28.** hardness   C often seen in fair weather
_____ **29.** equator   D curve in a river
_____ **30.** element   E measures relative humidity
_____ **31.** geology   F makes distant objects easier to see
_____ **32.** specific gravity   G measures air pressure
_____ **33.** petrification   H 0° latitude
_____ **34.** sedimentary rock   I orbits a planet
_____ **35.** stratus cloud   J resistance to scratching
_____ **36.** psychrometer   K water that sinks into the ground
_____ **37.** groundwater   L often brings rain
_____ **38.** cumulus cloud   M pressed and cemented together
_____ **39.** barometer   N measure of distance in space
_____ **40.** fault   O study of the earth's land
_____ **41.** meander   P changed by heat, pressure, or chemical reactions
_____ **42.** light-year   Q water that flows over the earth's surface
_____ **43.** earthquake   R how some fossils form
_____ **44.** runoff   S break in the earth's crust along which movement occurs
_____ **45.** metamorphic rock   T shaking of the earth's crust

Earth Science

Final Mastery Test Page 4

Final Mastery Test

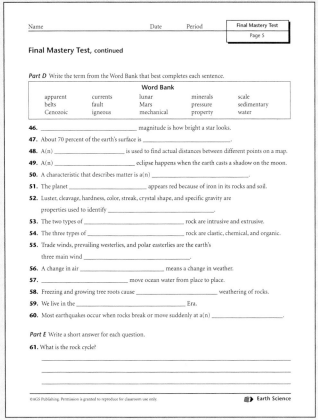

Final Mastery Test Page 5

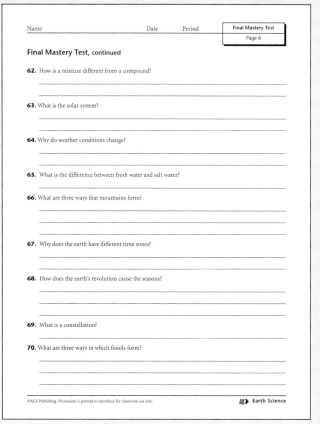

Final Mastery Test Page 6

The lists below show how items from the Midterm and Final correlate to the chapters in the student edition.

Midterm Mastery Test

Chapter 1: 1, 11, 15, 19, 30, 40, 43

Chapter 2: 4, 8, 16, 26, 34, 37, 45

Chapter 3: 2, 10, 13, 21, 29, 35, 48

Chapter 4: 3, 9, 12, 18, 32, 39, 44

Chapter 5: 5, 14, 17, 22, 25, 42, 46

Chapter 6: 6, 27, 28, 33, 36, 47, 50

Chapter 7: 7, 20, 23, 24, 31, 38, 41, 49

Final Mastery Test

Chapter 1: 1, 24, 31, 48

Chapter 2: 2, 29, 47, 67

Chapter 3: 3, 26, 49, 68

Chapter 4: 21, 27, 51, 63

Chapter 5: 4, 42, 46, 69

Chapter 6: 5, 16, 30, 50, 62

Chapter 7: 6, 28, 32, 52

Chapter 8: 7, 17, 34, 45, 53, 54, 61

Chapter 9: 8, 9, 23, 35, 38, 55

Chapter 10: 10, 11, 18, 36, 39, 56, 64

Chapter 11: 12, 20, 37, 44, 57, 65

Chapter 12: 13, 22, 41, 58

Chapter 13: 14, 19, 40, 43, 60, 66

Chapter 14: 15, 25, 33, 59, 70

Workbook Activities

Workbook Activity 1—Earth Science
1. geology **2.** oceanography **3.** meteorology **4.** astronomy
5. environment **6.** metric system **7.** lens **8.** exploration robot
9. submersible **10.** computer **11.** earth science **12.** geologist
13. weather **14.** balloons **15.** El Niño

Workbook Activity 2—Understanding Maps
1. F **2.** C **3.** B **4.** A **5.** D **6.** E **7.** G **8.** Both represent a place or object.
9. A compass rose indicates directions; a scale relates distance on a
map to distance on the earth. **10.** A symbol is an object that stands
for something else. A legend is a list of symbols and their meanings.

Workbook Activity 3—Topographic Maps: Terms Review
1. D **2.** E **3.** B **4.** A **5.** C **6.** contour interval **7.** hachure **8.** compass
rose **9.** scale **10.** map **11.** legend **12.** metric system **13.** contour lines
14. unit **15.** submersible

Workbook Activity 4—The Earth's Features
1–11. Students should label continents and oceans correctly as
shown on page 27. **12.** Australia **13.** Pacific **14.** 67 kilometers **15.** 16.2
percent **16.** Pacific **17.** All the major areas of water connect with
each other. **18.** Both spin around, but the earth does not stop
spinning due to friction like the top. **19.** The earth is curved; you
would not be able to see around the curve. **20.** Students should draw
a circular graph that shows that oceans make up 70 percent of the
earth's surface and land 30 percent.

Workbook Activity 5—The Earth's Rotation and Time
1. 7:00 A.M. **2.** 1:00 P.M. **3.** 6:00 P.M. **4.** 11:00 P.M. **5.** 5:00 P.M.
6. 9:00 A.M. **7.** 8:00 P.M. **8.** 6:00 A.M. **9.** 2 hours **10.** forward

Workbook Activity 6—A Grid System on a Map
1. A6 **2.** A1 **3.** A3 **4.** E4 **5.** B6 **6.** C3 **7.** C6 **8.** D1, E1 **9.** Parker School
10. B3 **11.** B6, C5, C4, D4, D3 **12.** E1 **13.** C5, B6 **14.** B3, possibly A3,
C3, D3, E3, E4 **15.** the house on Barn Street

Workbook Activity 7—Latitude
1. C **2.** E **3.** B **4.** F **5.** D **6.** A **7.** G **8.** 38°N **9.** 37°N **10.** 34°N **11.** 33°N
12. 42°N **13.** parallels; They are all parallel to one another, or
equidistant at each point. **14.** 0° **15.** 90°N

Workbook Activity 8—Longitude
1. 80°W **2.** 107°W **3.** 90°W **4.** 71°W **5.** 100°W **6.** 102°W **7.** 90°W
8. 83°W **9.** 115°W **10.** 76°W **11.** Amarillo, Texas **12.** Pierre, South
Dakota **13.** St. Louis, Missouri **14.** Green Bay, Wisconsin
15. Columbus, Ohio

Workbook Activity 9—A Grid System on a Globe: Terms Review
Across: 1. hemisphere **3.** prime **4.** meridian **6.** latitude
7. international **11.** standard **12.** degree **13.** equator **14.** rotation
Down: 2. parallel **3.** pole **5.** continent **8.** axis **9.** longitude **10.** grid

Workbook Activity 10—The Effect of Gravity
1. Gravity holds the earth in orbit around the sun. **2.** Gravity holds
the moon in orbit around the earth. **3.** larger **4.** larger **5.** smaller
6. pull **7.** mass **8.** distance **9.** orbit **10.** sun

Workbook Activity 11—The Earth's Movement in Space
1. revolution **2.** year **3.** rotation **4.** day **5.** tilted **6.** axis **7.** summer
8. directly **9.** winter **10.** angle **11.** indirect **12.** winter **13.** direct
14. summer **15.** in between **16.** spring **17.** in between **18.** fall **19.** in
between **20.** spring

Workbook Activity 12—The Moon's Movement in Space
1. Both involve movements of bodies in space. **2.** Revolution is the
orbiting of an object around another; rotation is the spinning of an
object on its axis. **3.** Both the earth and moon revolve and rotate.
4. The earth is a planet and the moon is a satellite of the earth. The
earth rotates much quicker than the moon and revolves around the
sun much slower than the moon revolves around the earth. **5.** Both
involve the blocking of sunlight. **6.** A lunar eclipse causes the moon
to pass through the earth's shadow, while a solar eclipse means the
moon casts a shadow on the earth. **7.** Both are phases of the moon.
8. A new moon appears dark from the earth, while a full moon
appears fully lit. **9.** Both indicate the changing level of ocean water
caused by the gravitational pull of the moon. **10.** High tide is the
bulge of water pulled by the moon, while low tide is the lower level
between the bulges. **11.** B **12.** A **13.** D **14.** E **15.** C

Workbook Activity 13—The Moon's Surface: Terms Review
Across: 2. crater **5.** mass **7.** tide **8.** ellipse **11.** my **12.** solar **13.** eclipse
Down: 1. gravity **3.** telescope **4.** revolution **5.** meteorite **6.** full
9. lunar **10.** phases **11.** maria

Workbook Activity 14—The Solar System
1. Both are objects in space. **2.** A star makes its own light, while a
planet reflects the light of a star. **3.** Both are objects in space. Both are
part of the solar system. Both travel in orbits. **4.** A planet is a large
object that orbits the sun, while a moon is a smaller object that orbits
a planet. **5.** Both are objects in space. **6.** A moon reflects the light of a
star. It orbits a planet. A star makes its own light. It does not travel in
an orbit. **7.** Both are objects in space. Both are part of the solar
system. **8.** A planet reflects the light of a star and travels in an orbit
around a star. The sun is a star. It makes its own light. It does not
orbit. Planets orbit around it. **9.** star **10.** helium **11.** nuclear reactions
12. three **13.** chromosphere **14.** cooler **15.** mass

Workbook Activity 15—The Inner Planets
1. Mercury **2.** Venus **3.** Earth **4.** Mars **5.** 243 Earth days **6.** 24 hours,
38 minutes **7.** east to west **8.** west to east **9.** −183°C to 427°C **10.** 15°C
11. thick clouds that trap heat **12.** dense, protective atmosphere
13. craters, flat areas **14.** none **15.** 2

Workbook Activity 16—The Outer Planets
1. Jupiter **2.** Saturn **3.** Uranus **4.** Neptune **5.** Pluto **6.** Pluto
7. Neptune **8.** Jupiter **9.** Uranus **10.** Saturn **11.** Pluto **12.** Uranus
13. Jupiter **14.** Neptune **15.** Saturn

Workbook Activity 17—Other Objects in the Solar System: Terms Review
1. I **2.** Q **3.** H **4.** C **5.** T **6.** R **7.** B **8.** O **9.** J **10.** D **11.** S **12.** K **13.** N
14. A **15.** E **16.** P **17.** F **18.** G **19.** L **20.** M

Workbook Activity 18—Stars
1. Apparent magnitude is how bright a star looks. **2.** sun **3.** brighter
4. −26.7 **5.** Sirius **6.** 10,000°C **7.** cooler **8.** lower **9.** fusion **10.** Four
hydrogen particles in a star can fuse. They form one helium particle
plus energy. The energy makes the star hot and makes it shine.

Workbook Activity 19—Distances to Stars
1. 300,000 kilometers per second **2.** distance **3.** 9.5 trillion
kilometers **4.** 104.5 trillion kilometers **5.** 300 light-years **6.** 14 years
ago **7.** 8 minutes and 20 seconds ago **8.** The star will appear to have
shifted in relation to more distant stars. Measuring these relative
distances enables astronomers to calculate each star's distance.
9. Astronomers compare the absolute and apparent magnitudes of
the stars. They know that if two stars have the same absolute
magnitude, the dimmer star is farther away. **10.** Alpha Centauri
11. Sirius **12.** Vega **13.** Pollux **14.** Capella **15.** Aldebaran

Workbook Activity 20—The Life of a Star

1. supergiant 2. supernova 3. neutron star 4. black hole 5. red giant
6. nova 7. white dwarf 8. dead star 9. billions 10. nebula 11. collapse
12. expand 13. hydrogen 14. Betelgeuse 15. supergiant

Workbook Activity 21—Groups of Stars: Terms Review

Across: 2. fusion 4. universe 7. Milky Way 8. neutron star
10. supernova **Down:** 1. constellations 3. galaxy 5. nebula
6. supergiant 9. nova 11. light-years 12. the sun 13. Polaris
14. elliptical 15. black hole

Workbook Activity 22—Matter

1. mass 2. state 3. property 4. physical 5. chemical 6. liquid 7. solid
8. gas 9. liquid 10. gas 11–13. Possible answers: solid, light-colored,
smooth 14. burns to form ash and gases 15. Physical properties can
be observed without changing the substance. Chemical properties
are observed as a substance is changed.

Workbook Activity 23—The Smallest Parts of Matter

1. E 2. D 3. B 4. A 5. C 6. oxygen 7. aluminum 8. calcium 9. Na
10. hydrogen

Workbook Activity 24—Compounds and Mixtures: Terms Review

1. Both are substances that make up matter. 2. A compound is made of
two or more kinds of atoms combined chemically. An element is made
of only one kind of atom. 3. Both are made of two or more substances
combined. 4. A compound consists of atoms joined chemically in a
specific ratio; separating these atoms requires chemical energy. A
mixture is a physical combination of elements and/or compounds that
can be separated physically. 5. sodium and chlorine 6. one
7. compounds 8. F 9. D 10. H 11. A 12. B 13. G 14. E 15. C

Workbook Activity 25—Minerals

Across: 1. shafts 2. melt 3. rocks 7. river 8. alive 11. atomic 12. living
13. quartz **Down:** 1. strip mining 3. rare 4. surface 5. chemical
6. Antarctica 9. earth 10. gold

Workbook Activity 26—Properties Used to Identify Minerals

1. D 2. B 3. C 4. F 5. A 6. E 7. gold 8. diamond 9. talc
10. hardness 11. luster 12. soft 13. yellow 14. white 15. penny

Workbook Activity 27—Other Physical Properties of Minerals

1. crystals 2. atoms 3. cubes 4. salt
5. quartz 6. microscope 7. space
8. break 9. cleavage 10. fracture
11. density 12. specific gravity
13. water 14. twice 15. jeweler

Workbook Activity 28—Common Uses of Minerals: Terms Review

1. C 2. F 3. A 4. D 5. G 6. B 7. E 8. H 9. bauxite 10. iron 11. quartz
12. gypsum 13. corundum 14. talc 15. copper

Workbook Activity 29—Rocks and Rock Types

1. geologists 2. minerals 3. sedimentary 4. metamorphic 5. igneous
6. cemented 7. pressure 8. melted 9. sandstone 10. gneiss 11. basalt
12. about 3,000 13. about 20 14. some sedimentary rocks and some
igneous rocks 15. some igneous rocks and all metamorphic rocks

Workbook Activity 30—Igneous Rocks

1. about 1,400°C 2. magma 3. texture 4. hot, melted rock
5. extrusive 6. under the ground 7. on the surface 8. large 9. small
or none 10. granite 11. obsidian 12. buildings 13. sharp tools

14. They cooled slowly, so large crystals formed. 15. It cooled very
quickly and formed no crystals.

Workbook Activity 31—Sedimentary Rocks

Across: 1. conglomerate 4. electricity 5. organic 7. chalk
9. sediment 11. coal 12. cemented 13. water **Down:** 1. chemical
2. limestone 3. beach 6. clastic 8. river 9. shale 10. ocean

Workbook Activity 32—Metamorphic Rocks

1. deep inside 2–3. heat, pressure 4–5. foliated, nonfoliated 6. bands
7. sheets of rock 8. one 9. mineral crystals 10. visible bands 11. no
bands 12. slate 13. marble 14. tiles 15. columns

Workbook Activity 33—The Rock Cycle: Terms Review

1. N 2. G 3. L 4. B 5. I 6. K 7. M 8. C 9. A 10. D 11. E 12. H 13. F
14. 0 15. J 16. compacting and cementing 17. heat and pressure
18. melting 19. cooling and hardening 20. weathering and erosion

Workbook Activity 34—Gases in the Atmosphere

1–10. The Oxygen-Carbon Dioxide Cycle: 3, 1, 6, 4, 2, 5; The
Nitrogen Cycle: 3, 5, 1, 4, 6, 2 11. the layer of gases that surrounds
the earth 12. 21 percent 13. 78 percent 14. Plants take in nitrogen-
containing compounds from the soil (through their roots) and
carbon dioxide from the air (through their leaves). 15. Animals take
in nitrogen when they eat plants or plant-eating animals; they take
in oxygen when they breathe in air.

Workbook Activity 35—Layers of the Atmosphere

1. thermosphere 2. mesosphere 3. stratosphere 4. troposphere
5–8. Possible answers: Thermosphere—highest layer starting at 80
kilometers above the earth; thinnest air; temperature can increase to
2,000°C because nitrogen and oxygen absorb the sun's energy; most
of the ionosphere is found in this layer. Mesosphere—coldest layer;
temperature decreases with altitude; located from about 50 to 80
kilometers above the earth. Stratosphere—clear and dry, from about
16 to 50 kilometers above the earth; the ozone layer is in the lower
half; temperature increases with height; airplanes usually fly here.
Troposphere—from the earth's surface to 16 kilometers above the
earth; air particles are packed most tightly; smallest layer, but
contains 75 percent of the air particles in the atmosphere; clouds
and weather activity occur here. 9. Air particles are packed more
tightly in this layer because of the weight of the layers of air above it.
10. Air gets colder and thinner (containing less oxygen) as you go
higher in the troposphere. 11. The ozone layer is in the lower half of
the stratosphere and is important because it absorbs harmful
radiation from the sun. 12. thermosphere 13. troposphere 14. Most
ions are found between 60 and 300 kilometers above the earth, in a
section of the atmosphere called the ionosphere. The sun's energy
strips electrons from nitrogen and oxygen atoms, making them
electrically charged particles called ions. 15. The sun's energy does
not cause interference at night.

Workbook Activity 36—Clouds

1. cloud 2. altitude 3. mountain
4. fog 5. three 6. shape 7. cumulus
8. cirrus 9. evaporate 10. condense
11. vapor 12. fair 13. stratus
14. water 15. ice crystals

Workbook Activity 37—Precipitation

1. C 2. D 3. A 4. B 5. F 6. H 7. E 8. G 9. moisture that falls to the
earth from the atmosphere 10. near the equator 11. middle and
high latitudes 12. Rain freezes when it hits an object because the

temperature near the ground is between 3°C and 0°C. **13.** Both are solid forms of precipitation. **14.** Snow is formed when ice crystals combine in clouds and fall through air that is below freezing. Sleet is formed when raindrops fall through a layer of cold air and freeze into ice particles. **15.** the temperature of the air below the clouds

Workbook Activity 38—Wind Patterns: Terms Review
Across: 1. precipitation **5.** vapor **6.** trade **8.** meso **9.** stratosphere **12.** fog **13.** cirrus **15.** easterly **16.** stratus **17.** westerly **18.** belt
Down: 2. ionosphere **3.** troposphere **4.** cell **6.** thermosphere **7.** evaporate **10.** atmosphere **11.** cumulus **13.** condense **14.** altitude

Workbook Activity 39—Weather Conditions and Measurements
1. thermometer **2.** barometer **3.** psychrometer **4.** anemometer **5.** wind vane **6.** rain gauge **7.** the state of the atmosphere at a given time and place **8.** Both measure air temperature in degrees. A Fahrenheit thermometer uses the Fahrenheit scale (water freezes at 32° and boils at 212°). A Celsius thermometer uses the Celsius scale (water freezes at 0° and boils at 100°). **9.** Air pushes on a short metal can inside the barometer. A pointer connected to the can shows the amount of air pressure on a dial on the front. **10.** Humidity is the amount of water vapor in air; relative humidity is the amount of water vapor in air compared to the air's capacity to hold water vapor. **11.** The wind is blowing from west to east; it is a west wind. **12.** Measure rainfall with the scale on a rain gauge; measure snow depth with a meterstick; measure hail by its diameter as well as its depth on the ground. **13.** west wind **14.** Drier weather may be on the way. **15.** 0°C

Workbook Activity 40—Weather Patterns and Predictions
1. D **2.** F **3.** E **4.** G **5.** C **6.** A **7.** B **8.** warm front **9.** The air pressure falls with a steady precipitation. Then skies clear, it becomes warmer, and the air pressure rises. **10.** cold front **11.** Storm clouds form fast and heavy rain falls for a brief time. Then it becomes clear and cooler. **12.** high **13.** The weather is fair and cool, with high air pressure and winds blowing outward in a clockwise rotation. **14.** low **15.** The weather is cloudy and warm, often with precipitation, and with low air pressure and air flowing inward in a counterclockwise rotation.

Workbook Activity 41—Storms
1. tornado **2.** thunderheads **3.** thunderstorm **4.** lightning **5.** thunder **6.** prairies **7.** hurricane **8.** before **9.** low **10.** rain **11.** friction **12.** moisture **13.** eye **14.** storms **15.** equator

Workbook Activity 42—World Climates: Terms Review
1. polar **2.** temperate **3.** tropical **4–6.** angle of sunlight, altitude, proximity to a large body of water **7.** B **8.** E **9.** F **10.** I **11.** D **12.** G **13.** K **14.** J **15.** A **16.** H **17.** C **18.** wind speed **19.** relative humidity **20.** air pressure

Workbook Activity 43—The Water Cycle
1. Water changes into a gas and rises into the atmosphere. **2.** Water vapor turns into a liquid. **3.** Moisture falls to the earth from the atmosphere. **4.** Water runs over the earth's surface and flows into streams and rivers. **5.** Water sinks into the ground. **6.** The sun evaporates surface water. **7.** It will evaporate or become runoff. **8.** You could plant grass and other plants to soak up the water. **9.** an ocean **10.** No. The salt water would kill the crops.

Workbook Activity 44—Sources of Fresh Water
1. H **2.** F **3.** E **4.** G **5.** D **6.** A **7.** I **8.** C **9.** B **10.** the top layer of groundwater **11.** The roof of a cave collapses. **12.** rivers, lakes, reservoirs **13.** 3 percent **14.** Lakes lose water through evaporation, outflowing streams or rivers, and moving groundwater. Lakes are fed by precipitation, runoff, springs, and incoming streams or rivers. **15.** to store water, control flooding, and produce electricity

Workbook Activity 45—Oceans: Terms Review
1. groundwater **2.** runoff **3.** water cycle **4.** tributary **5.** sinkhole **6.** water table **7.** porous **8.** drainage basin **9.** reservoir **10.** divide **11.** salinity **12.** trench **13.** mid-ocean ridge **14.** thermocline **15.** continental shelf **16.** continental slope **17.** seamount **18.** nekton, benthos **19.** currents **20.** geysers

Workbook Activity 46—Weathering
1. topsoil **2.** subsoil **3.** weathered rock **4.** solid rock **5.** rich in oxygen and decayed organic matter **6.** contains minerals washed down from topsoil; may have a yellowish or reddish color; plant roots grow into this layer **7.** chunks of partially weathered rock **8.** layer of solid rock that top layers rest on **9.** C **10.** A **11.** D **12.** B **13.** air, water, and living things **14.** Plants grow in cracks of rock and their roots eventually split the rock. Water freezes in the cracks of rock and expands, pushing the rock apart. **15.** Oxidation of iron in rock causes rust to form. Water changes and washes away some minerals in rock, causing the rock to fall apart.

Workbook Activity 47—Erosion Caused by Water
1. Both change rocks and soil. **2.** Weathering breaks down rocks; erosion moves and wears away rocks and soil that are already weathered. **3.** Both are the land on either side of a river, carved by the running water. **4.** A valley's shape varies according to its age; it may be wide and shallow or narrow and steep. A canyon is a narrow, steep valley. **5.** Both are results of river erosion. **6.** A meander is a bend in a river caused by the erosion of some of its banks more than others. An oxbow lake is a body of water formed from a meander that is cut off. **7.** Both are fan-shaped areas of land formed by moving water. **8.** A delta forms where a river meets a lake or an ocean. An alluvial fan forms at the base of a mountain where a river meets level land. **9.** Both are ways that waves change the shoreline of a lake or ocean. **10.** Wave erosion chips away at a rocky shore, forming cliffs, towers, and other shapes. Wave deposition brings sediment from nearby rocks to different parts of the shoreline. **11.** Both are stages in the life of a river. **12.** A young river is narrow and fast and carves a V-shaped valley; it has many falls and rapids. A mature river is wider, slower, has meanders, and has a wide, U-shaped valley. **13.** Water running downhill is a powerful force that erodes river banks and riverbeds by wearing away, moving, and depositing rock and other sediment. **14.** Sediment is moved by river water, eroding the riverbed and banks. Eventually the sediment is dropped during the process of deposition, often changing the shape of the shoreline. **15.** Over time a river valley becomes wide and flat with more meanders and a larger floodplain.

Workbook Activity 48—Erosion Caused by Glaciers
1. H **2.** E **3.** C **4.** G **5.** A **6.** D **7.** F **8.** B **9.** gravity **10.** Rocks and loose sediment freeze to the bottom and sides of a glacier, acting as grinding and cutting tools as the glacier moves. **11.** A typical V-shaped valley would be gouged out by an alpine glacier moving down the mountain, leaving a U-shaped valley. **12.** Continental glaciers carved wide, deep basins. As the glaciers melted, they filled these basins, creating the Great Lakes. **13.** Moraines, or ridges of sediment deposits, around a lake are evidence of a glacier that melted long ago to form both the moraines and the lake. **14.** Antarctica and Greenland **15.** Year-round cold temperatures and heavy snowfall are needed for glaciers to form.

Workbook Activity 49—Erosion Caused by Wind and Gravity: Terms Review
Across: 1. deposition **3.** moraine **5.** weathering **9.** cirque **10.** alpine

12. mechanical 15. mouth 16. soil 17. subsoil 18. floodplain
Down: 1. delta **2.** oxbow **4.** oxidation **6.** erosion **7.** glacier
8. chemical **11.** alluvial **12.** meander **13.** horn **14.** topsoil

Workbook Activity 50—Movement of the Earth's Crust
1–3. 8 to 70 kilometers thick; outer layer; continents and ocean floor
4–6. 2,900 kilometers thick; middle layer; churning, hot rock
7–9. 3,500 kilometers thick; innermost layer; iron and nickel
10. Pangaea **11.** plates, move apart, collide **12.** convection **13.** Once the earth's continents were joined as a single landmass. The continents have since broken apart and slowly moved to their present positions. **14.** A big rift in the middle of an ocean allows magma to escape, continually forming new ocean floor and pushing continents apart. The hardened magma forms long, underwater mountain ranges called mid-ocean ridges. **15.** The earth's crust is broken into large sections, or plates, which move because of convection currents in the mantle underneath them.

Workbook Activity 51—Volcanoes
1. explosive blasts **2.** loose rock particles **3.** small and steep **4.** quiet flows **5.** thin lava layers **6.** low and broad **7.** both explosions and quiet flows **8.** lava layers and rocky layers **9.** tall **10.** vents **11.** plates **12.** cinder cone **13.** explosive **14.** quiet **15.** shield

Workbook Activity 52—Mountains
The order for answers 1–9 will vary. Possible answer set: **1.** fault
2. The earth's crust breaks, and blocks of rock rise. **3.** Grand Tetons **4.** folding **5.** Continental plates collide, bending rock layers. **6.** Himalayas **7.** volcanic **8.** One plate sinks beneath another or two plates separate. **9.** Cascade Range **10–11.** strike-slip fault—bottom diagram—Blocks of rock slide past each other. **12–13.** normal fault—top diagram—Overhanging block of rock slides down. **14–15.** reverse fault—middle diagram—Overhanging block of rock is raised.

Workbook Activity 53—Earthquakes: Terms Review
1. P-wave—fastest, causes rocks to vibrate back and forth **2.** L-wave—slowest, causes the ground to twist and bend **3.** S-wave—slower, causes rocks to vibrate up and down **4.** C **5.** H **6.** N **7.** K **8.** D **9.** F **10.** G **11.** M **12.** I **13.** A **14.** L **15.** B **16.** E **17.** J **18.** normal, reverse, strike-slip **19.** cinder cone, shield, composite **20.** core, mantle, crust

Workbook Activity 54—The Rock Record
1. C **2.** A **3.** D **4.** J **5.** I **6.** F **7.** G **8.** H **9.** B **10.** E **11.** T **12.** I **13.** T **14.** P **15.** I **16.** P **17.** I **18.** T **19.** T **20.** I

Workbook Activity 55—The Ages of Rocks and Fossils
1. Both are used to understand the ages of rocks and fossils. **2.** Relative dating compares rock layers to find out which is older. Absolute dating determines the actual age of a rock or fossil by measuring the amount of radioactive decay. **3.** Index fossils, such as trilobite fossils, are used to determine the relative age of the rock in which they are found. **4.** The principle of superposition states that if sedimentary rock layers have not been overturned, the oldest rock layer is on the bottom and the youngest rock layer is on the top. **5.** According to the principle of crosscutting relationships, a rock or fault that cuts through another rock must be younger than the rock it cut. **6.** Scientists measure the amount of radioactive decay that has occurred in a rock or fossil and then calculate its age based on the radioactive element's half-life. **7.** A **8.** A **9.** A **10.** A **11.** R **12.** R **13.** A **14.** R **15.** R

Workbook Activity 56—Eras in the Geologic Time Scale: Terms Review
1. G **2.** A **3.** E **4.** I **5.** D **6.** C **7.** B **8.** H **9.** J **10.** F **11.** 2 **12.** 4 **13.** 1 **14.** 3 **15.** 2 **16.** 1 **17.** 3 **18.** 4 **19.** Relative dating compares two rock layers to determine which is older. Absolute dating measures the decay of a radioactive element in a rock to determine its actual age. **20.** A mold is an imprint left in a rock by an organism. A cast forms when minerals fill a mold, leaving behind a model of the original organism.

Alternative Workbook Activities

Alternative Workbook Activity 1—Earth Science
1. metric unit **2.** meteorology **3.** geologist **4.** environment **5.** geology **6.** exploration vehicle **7.** oceanography **8.** earth science **9.** weather **10.** astronomy

Alternative Workbook Activity 2—Understanding Maps
1. A **2.** D **3.** E **4.** C **5.** B **6.** Both are units that measure length. **7.** Both are scales showing the relationship between distance on a map and distance on the earth. **8.** Both are used to represent a place or an object. A map is one kind of model. **9.** Both are fields of earth science. **10.** Both show information that helps people read a map.

Alternative Workbook Activity 3—Topographic Maps: Terms Review
1. D **2.** C **3.** E **4.** B **5.** A **6.** scale **7.** contour interval **8.** map **9.** geologist **10.** contour line **11.** hachure **12.** unit **13.** submersible **14.** topographic map **15.** legend

Alternative Workbook Activity 4—The Earth's Features
1–11. Students should label continents and oceans correctly as shown on page 27. **12.** Asia **13.** Arctic **14.** The earth is curved; you would not be able to see around the curve. **15.** Students should draw a circular graph that shows that oceans make up 70 percent of the earth's surface and land 30 percent.

Alternative Workbook Activity 5—The Earth's Rotation and Time
1. 7:00 P.M. **2.** 1:00 P.M. **3.** 6:00 P.M. **4.** 11:00 P.M. **5.** 1:00 A.M. **6.** 1:00 A.M. **7.** 8:00 P.M. **8.** 2 hours **9.** forward **10.** sleeping

Alternative Workbook Activity 6—A Grid System on a Map
1. A7 **2.** B3 **3.** B7 **4.** A1 **5.** C3 **6.** B6 **7.** C6 **8.** City High School **9.** D1, E1 **10.** the house on Barn Street

Alternative Workbook Activity 7—Latitude
1. C **2.** E **3.** B **4.** F **5.** D **6.** A **7.** G **8.** parallels; They are all parallel to one another, or equidistant at each point. **9.** 0° **15.** 90°S

Alternative Workbook Activity 8—Longitude
1. 115°W **2.** 107°W **3.** 80°W **4.** 90°W **5.** 71°W **6.** 100°W **7.** 102°W **8.** 76°W **9.** 90°W **10.** 83°W

Alternative Workbook Activity 9—A Grid System on a Globe: Terms Review
Across: 1. North Pole **4.** latitude **8.** international **10.** degree **Down: 2.** rotation **3.** longitude **5.** equator **6.** axis **7.** South Pole **9.** grid

Alternative Workbook Activity 10—The Effect of Gravity
1. earth, sun **2.** moon, earth **3.** larger **4.** larger **5.** smaller **6.** gravity **7.** mass **8.** closer **9.** orbit **10.** sun

Alternative Workbook Activity 11—The Earth's Movement in Space
1. revolution **2.** year **3.** spins **4.** day **5.** seasons **6.** directly **7.** warmer **8.** angle **9.** summer **10.** indirect **11.** winter **12.** in between **13.** fall **14.** in between **15.** spring

Alternative Workbook Activity 12—The Moon's Movement in Space
1. Both spin on an axis, and both revolve around a larger body. **2.** The earth rotates every 24 hours and revolves in 365 days, while the moon takes 29 days to rotate and to revolve. **3.** Both eclipses are caused by objects in space lining up and blocking sunlight. **4.** A lunar eclipse is when the earth throws a shadow over the moon, and a solar eclipse is when the moon casts a shadow on the earth. **5.** Both are phases of the moon. **6.** A new moon occurs when the moon appears dark from the earth, while a full moon appears fully lit. **7.** C **8.** A **9.** D **10.** B

Alternative Workbook Activity 13—The Moon's Surface: Terms Review
Across: **3.** crater **5.** maria **7.** telescope **8.** revolution **11.** phases
Down: **1.** gravity **2.** orbit **4.** tides **5.** meteorite **6.** solar **9.** lunar **10.** new

Alternative Workbook Activity 14—The Solar System
1. Both are objects in space. **2.** A moon reflects the light of a star. It orbits a planet. A star makes its own light. It does not travel in an orbit. **3.** Both are objects in space. **4.** A star makes its own light, while a planet reflects the light of a star. **5.** Both are objects in space. Both are part of the solar system. Both travel in orbits. **6.** A planet is a large object that orbits the sun, while a moon is a smaller object that orbits a planet. **7.** three **8.** helium **9.** cooler **10.** corona

Alternative Workbook Activity 15—The Inner Planets
1. Mercury **2.** Venus **3.** Earth **4.** Mars **5.** Venus **6.** Mercury **7.** Earth **8.** Mercury **9.** Venus **10.** Mars

Alternative Workbook Activity 16—The Outer Planets
1. Jupiter **2.** Saturn **3.** Uranus **4.** Neptune **5.** Pluto **6.** Saturn **7.** Pluto **8.** Jupiter **9.** Uranus **10.** Neptune

Alternative Workbook Activity 17—Other Objects in the Solar System: Terms Review
1. E **2.** M **3.** C **4.** I **5.** A **6.** O **7.** B **8.** F **9.** J **10.** G **11.** H **12.** N **13.** D **14.** K **15.** L

Alternative Workbook Activity 18—Stars
1. Apparent magnitude is how bright a star looks. **2.** sun **3.** Deneb **4.** −1.4 **5.** Aldebaran **6.** 10,000°C **7.** 5,500°C **8.** Deneb **9.** fusion **10.** Four hydrogen particles in a star can fuse. They form one helium particle plus energy. The energy makes the star hot and makes it shine.

Alternative Workbook Activity 19—Distances to Stars
1. 300,000 kilometers per second **2.** distance **3.** 9.5 trillion kilometers **4.** 646 trillion kilometers **5.** 8 years ago **6.** Alpha Centauri **7.** Sirius **8.** Vega **9.** Pollux **10.** Capella

Alternative Workbook Activity 20—The Life of a Star
1. supernova **2.** neutron star **3.** black hole **4.** red giant **5.** white dwarf **6.** dead star **7.** billions **8.** supergiant **9.** X rays **10.** gravity

Alternative Workbook Activity 21—Groups of Stars: Terms Review
Across: **3.** universe **5.** Milky Way **6.** neutron star Down: **1.** constellations **2.** galaxy **4.** nebula **7.** nova **8.** the sun **9.** spiral **10.** color

Alternative Workbook Activity 22—Matter
1. matter **2.** states **3.** characteristic **4.** physical **5.** chemical **6.** solid **7.** liquid **8.** gas **9.** chemical **10.** physical

Alternative Workbook Activity 23—The Smallest Parts of Matter
1. A **2.** D **3.** B **4.** C **5.** silicon **6.** aluminum **7.** Fe **8.** calcium **9.** Na **10.** K

Alternative Workbook Activity 24—Compounds and Mixtures: Terms Review
1. Both are substances that make up matter. **2.** A compound is made of two or more kinds of atoms combined chemically. An element is made of only one kind of atom. **3.** Both are made of two or more substances combined. **4.** A compound consists of atoms joined chemically in a specific ratio; separating these atoms requires chemical energy. A mixture is a physical combination of elements and/or compounds that can be separated physically. **5.** two **6.** sodium and chlorine **7.** H **8.** F **9.** B **10.** A **11.** D **12.** I **13.** G **14.** E **15.** C

Alternative Workbook Activity 25—Minerals
Across: **1.** shafts **3.** earth **7.** atomic **8.** living **9.** rare Down: **1.** strip mining **2.** surface **4.** chemical **5.** Antarctica **6.** rocks

Alternative Workbook Activity 26—Properties Used to Identify Minerals
1. B **2.** D **3.** E **4.** C **5.** A **6.** luster **7.** soft **8.** yellow **9.** white **10.** penny

Alternative Workbook Activity 27—Other Physical Properties of Minerals

1. crystals **2.** salt **3.** quartz **4.** space **5.** break **6.** cleavage **7.** fracture **8.** specific gravity **9.** twice **10.** jeweler

Alternative Workbook Activity 28—Common Uses of Minerals: Terms Review
1. G **2.** C **3.** H **4.** F **5.** B **6.** D **7.** E **8.** A **9.** iron **10.** gypsum

Alternative Workbook Activity 29—Rocks and Rock Types
1. geologists **2.** minerals **3.** sedimentary **4.** metamorphic **5.** igneous **6.** sandstone **7.** basalt **8.** about 20 **9.** some sedimentary rocks and some igneous rocks **10.** All metamorphic rocks form underground, where intense heat, pressure, and chemical reactions twist and squeeze the rock.

Alternative Workbook Activity 30—Igneous Rocks
1. about 1,400°C **2.** magma **3.** mineral crystals **4.** hot, melted **5.** extrusive **6.** on the surface **7.** large **8.** obsidian **9.** They cooled slowly. When hot, melted rock cools slowly, it forms large crystals. **10.** It cooled too quickly for crystals to form.

Alternative Workbook Activity 31—Sedimentary Rocks
Across: **1.** conglomerate **3.** electricity **4.** organic **6.** sediment **7.** coal **8.** cemented Down: **1.** chemical **2.** limestone **5.** clastic **6.** shale

Alternative Workbook Activity 32—Metamorphic Rocks
1. inside **2.** heat, pressure **3.** foliated, nonfoliated **4.** bands **5.** sheets **6.** harder **7.** visible bands **8.** no bands **9.** marble **10.** tiles

Alternative Workbook Activity 33—The Rock Cycle: Terms Review
1. E **2.** F **3.** I **4.** B **5.** H **6.** D **7.** G **8.** C **9.** A **10.** J **11.** A **12.** C **13.** D **14.** B **15.** E

Alternative Workbook Activity 34—Gases in the Atmosphere
1–3. 1, 4, 2, 3 **4–7.** 1, 3, 2, 5, 4 **8.** the layer of gases that surrounds the earth **9.** 21 percent oxygen, 78 percent nitrogen **10.** The atmosphere contains nitrogen and oxygen, which are needed by all living things. (From Chapter 4, the atmosphere also provides a protective layer that moderates the earth's surface temperature.)

Alternative Workbook Activity 35—Layers of the Atmosphere
1. thermosphere **2.** mesosphere **3.** stratosphere **4.** troposphere **5–8.** Possible answers: Thermosphere—highest layer starting at 80 kilometers above the earth; thinnest air; temperature can increase to 2,000°C because nitrogen and oxygen absorb the sun's energy; most of the ionosphere is found in this layer. Mesosphere—coldest layer; temperature decreases with altitude; located from about 50 to 80 kilometers above the earth. Stratosphere—clear and dry, from about 16 to 50 kilometers above the earth; ozone layer is in the lower half; temperature increases with height; airplanes usually fly here. Troposphere—from the earth's surface to 16 kilometers above the earth; air particles are packed most tightly; smallest layer, but contains 75 percent of air particles in the atmosphere; clouds and weather activity occur here. **9.** mesosphere; thermosphere **10.** troposphere

Alternative Workbook Activity 36—Clouds

```
R R O A V W A T E R V A P O R
C L V E O L D R R M S S E T J
S U A L T I T U D E U T A H E
E T M F C N H R A R U D E R C
S O R U E F B D Z T K O N E O
C N X A D A I T K O N V A U D
O W O V T U C R P A I H A P Z
N F H U L U S T B A P R P E X
D R E F B G S U T X O N O R Z
E P L O G S I N B A S O R F L
N C K G T V U P O L M U A G O
S R I A N O D E N F W S T H S
E J T Q M H E R S T V K E N I
```

1. cloud 2. altitude 3. mountain
4. fog 5. cumulus 6. cirrus
7. evaporate 8. condense
9. water vapor 10. stratus

Alternative Workbook Activity 37—Precipitation

1. C 2. F 3. D 4. H 5. A 6. E 7. B 8. G 9. moisture that falls to the earth from the atmosphere 10. the temperature of the air below the clouds

Alternative Workbook Activity 38—Wind Patterns: Terms Review

Across: 1. precipitation **6.** meso **7.** stratosphere **10.** fog **11.** vapor **13.** westerly **14.** stratus **15.** belt **Down: 2.** ionosphere **3.** troposphere **4.** cell **5.** thermosphere **8.** atmosphere **9.** cumulus **12.** altitude

Alternative Workbook Activity 39—Weather Conditions and Measurements

1. thermometer 2. barometer 3. psychrometer 4. anemometer 5. wind vane 6. rain gauge 7. the state of the atmosphere at a given time and place 8. No. 38°C is very hot so you don't need a coat. 9. Weather with some kind of precipitation may be coming. 10. Humidity is the amount of water vapor in air; relative humidity is the amount of water vapor in air compared to the air's capacity to hold water vapor.

Alternative Workbook Activity 40—Weather Patterns and Predictions

1. D 2. C 3. E 4. A 5. F 6. B 7. The air pressure falls with a steady precipitation. Then skies clear, it becomes warmer, and the air pressure rises. 8. Storm clouds form fast and heavy rain falls for a brief time. Then it becomes clear and cooler. 9. The weather is fair and cool, with high air pressure and winds blowing outward in a clockwise rotation. 10. The weather is cloudy and warm, often with precipitation, and with low air pressure and air flowing inward in a counterclockwise rotation.

Alternative Workbook Activity 41—Storms

```
T H U N D E R S T O R M
H H C G B T U A O L W G
U I U S P R A I R I E S
N P E N Y I P G N G T I
D W A D S U R A H U P E
E A S G N E B H D T H R
R H C W U R Y O N S I C
H U R R I C A N E I C T
E T B P T A Y W S N B H
A Y I E N H O E N G S P
D G E C R L S I P R A E
S P R A P B E H W T U G
```

1. tornadoes 2. thunderheads
3. thunderstorm 4. hurricane
5. lightning 6. prairies 7. eye 8. low
9. rain 10. thunder

Alternative Workbook Activity 42—World Climates: Terms Review

1–3. thunderstorm, tornado, hurricane 4–6. polar, temperate, tropical 7. B 8. E 9. F 10. C 11. A 12. D 13. rain gauge—amount of rainfall 14. barometer—air pressure 15. wind vane—wind direction

Alternative Workbook Activity 43—The Water Cycle

1. Water changes into a gas and rises into the atmosphere. 2. Water vapor turns into a liquid. 3. Moisture falls to the earth from the atmosphere. 4. Water runs over the earth's surface and flows into streams. 5. Water sinks into the ground. 6. The sun evaporates surface water. 7. No. The salt water would kill the grass. 8. You could plant grass and other plants to soak up the water. 9. an ocean 10. It will evaporate or become runoff.

Alternative Workbook Activity 44—Sources of Fresh Water

1. C 2. E 3. D 4. B 5. F 6. A 7. Precipitation or runoff soaks into the ground, eventually collecting above an underground solid rock layer.

8. A geyser is a type of spring. Instead of flowing out of the ground, the water shoots into the air because it has been heated by hot rock or magma. Sometimes steam shoots into the air as well. 9. 3 percent 10. A lake forms naturally. A reservoir is an artificial lake.

Alternative Workbook Activity 45—Oceans: Terms Review

1. groundwater 2. runoff 3. water cycle 4. tributary 5. sinkhole 6. porous 7. reservoir 8. divide 9. spring 10. trench 11. thermocline 12. continental slope 13. seamount 14. nekton 15. currents

Alternative Workbook Activity 46—Weathering

1. topsoil 2. subsoil 3. weathered rock 4. solid rock 5. C 6. A 7. D 8. B 9. air, water, and living things 10. Students' answers should contain one of these two examples of mechanical weathering: Plants grow in the cracks of rock and their roots eventually split the rock. Water freezes in the cracks of rock and expands, pushing the rock apart. Students' answers should contain one of these two examples of chemical weathering: Oxidation of iron in rock causes rust to form. Water changes and washes away some minerals in rock, causing the rock to fall apart.

Alternative Workbook Activity 47—Erosion Caused by Water

1. Both change rocks and soil. 2. Weathering breaks down rocks. Erosion moves and wears away rocks and soil that are already weathered. 3. Both are stages in the life of a river. 4. A young river is narrow and fast and carves a V-shaped valley; it has many falls and rapids. A mature river is wider, slower, has meanders, and has a wide, U-shaped valley. 5. Both are fan-shaped areas of land formed by moving water. 6. A delta forms where a river meets a lake or an ocean. An alluvial fan forms at the base of a mountain where a river meets level land. 7. A meander is a looping curve in a river. 8. An oxbow lake forms when a meander is cut off from the rest of the river. This can happen when a river overflows its banks and flows in a straighter path. 9. Over time a river valley becomes broad and flat with more meanders and a larger floodplain. 10. Waves can erode the land, leaving cliffs, towers, and other rocky shapes. Waves can also deposit sediment on shore to create sandy beaches.

Alternative Workbook Activity 48—Erosion Caused by Glaciers

1. E 2. F 3. B 4. C 5. A 6. D 7. gravity 8. Rocks and loose sediment freeze to the bottom and sides of a glacier, acting as grinding and cutting tools as the glacier moves. 9. Continental glaciers carved wide, deep basins. As the glaciers melted, they filled these basins, creating the Great Lakes. 10. Antarctica and Greenland

Alternative Workbook Activity 49—Erosion Caused by Wind and Gravity: Term Review

Across: 1. deposition **3.** moraine **5.** weathering **10.** cirque **12.** mechanical **13.** mouth **14.** continental **Down: 1.** delta **2.** oxbow **4.** oxidation **6.** erosion **7.** glacier **8.** chemical **9.** gravity **11.** alluvial

Alternative Workbook Activity 50—Movement of the Earth's Crust

1–2. 8 to 70 kilometers thick; continents and ocean floor 3–4. 2,900 kilometers thick; churning, hot rock 5–6. 3,500 kilometers thick; iron and nickel 7. Pangaea 8. move apart, collide, slide past each other 9. convection currents 10. Sea-floor spreading explains how the ocean floors are growing at mid-ocean ridges. These ridges occur where two tectonic plates meet. Sea-floor spreading results in landmasses moving farther apart, or continental drift. Continental drift explains how tectonic plates move and shift because of convection currents in the mantle underneath them. Both sea-floor spreading and continental drift occur because the earth's crust is divided into tectonic plates.

Alternative Workbook Activity 51—Volcanoes

1. loose rock particles **2.** small and steep **3.** quiet flows **4.** thin lava layers **5.** both explosions and quiet flows **6.** tall **7.** vents **8.** plates **9.** thin basalt lava **10.** mountain

Alternative Workbook Activity 52—Mountains

The order for answers 1–6 will vary. Possible answer set: **1.** fault **2.** The earth's crust breaks, and blocks of rock rise. **3.** Grand Tetons **4.** folding **5.** Continental plates collide, bending rock layers. **6.** Himalayas **7.** normal fault **8.** reverse fault **9.** strike-slip fault **10.** In a normal fault, the two sides move apart, and the overhanging rock on one side drops down. In a reverse fault, the two sides move together, and the overhanging rock on one side is pushed up.

Alternative Workbook Activity 53—Earthquakes: Terms Review

1. E **2.** I **3.** L **4.** A **5.** J **6.** G **7.** F **8.** D **9.** H **10.** C **11.** K **12.** B **13.** normal, reverse, strike-slip **14.** cinder cone, shield, composite **15.** crust, mantle, core

Alternative Workbook Activity 54—The Rock Record

1. I **2.** J **3.** D **4.** E **5.** B **6.** F **7.** G **8.** H **9.** A **10.** C **11.** I **12.** T **13.** I **14.** P **15.** T

Alternative Workbook Activity 55—The Ages of Rocks and Fossils

1. Both are used in the relative dating of rocks and fossils. **2.** The principle of superposition compares rock layers that have not been overturned to determine which is older. The principle of crosscutting relationships compares rock layers with features that have cut through the layers. **3.** Possible answer: trilobite **4.** principle of superposition **5.** When carbon-14 decays, it becomes nitrogen-14. **6.** absolute dating **7.** relative dating **8.** absolute dating **9.** relative dating **10.** relative dating

Alternative Workbook Activity 56—Eras in the Geologic Time Scale: Terms Review

1. F **2.** C **3.** E **4.** D **5.** B **6.** A **7.** G **8.** H **9.** I **10.** J **11.** 2 **12.** 4 **13.** 1 **14.** 3 **15.** 1 **16.** 3 **17.** 2 **18.** 4 **19.** Relative dating compares rock layers to determine which is older. Absolute dating measures the decay of radioactive elements in a rock to determine its actual age. **20.** A mold is an imprint left in rock by an organism. A cast forms when minerals fill a mold, leaving behind a model of the original organism.

Lab Manual

Lab Manual 1—Using Map Scales

1. Answers depend on chosen cities. **2.** Answers depend on chosen cities. **Explore Further** Check students' art and scale.

Lab Manual 2—Making a Map (Investigation 1-1)

1. Answers will vary. Students might indicate that they chose symbols that were simple in design. **2.** Answers will vary, but might include using a scale of 2 centimeters = 1 meter instead of 1 centimeter = 1 meter. This will result in a map of the same area being twice as large (for example, a map that measures 10 centimeters wide would become 20 centimeters wide). Some students may misread this question as asking them to change the scale so a same-size map shows twice as much area. **3.** The accuracy of map scales and distances will vary. **4.** Answers will vary, depending on the scale and symbols used. **Explore Further** Maps should show a reasonable use of scale. Sites selected will vary. Legend symbols will differ.

Lab Manual 3—Making a Topographic Map

1. Contour lines are farthest apart where the width of the rock changes the most between levels. **2.** The rock slope is steepest where the contour lines are closest together (and the width of the rock

changes little between levels). **3.** Answers should match students' data. **Explore Further** No. Cork floats, so unless it was weighted down with something, you could not cover it with water.

Lab Manual 4—Reading a Topographic Map (Investigation 1-2)

1. 5 meters **2.** slightly more than 5 kilometers **3.** southwest **4.** the south side **5.** No. Pine Hill is higher than Point A and Spruce Hill, so it blocks the view. **6.** woods **7.** Twin Hill **8.** 60 meters **Explore Further** Students may work in pairs to complete this activity. Students should obtain a printout of the map they plan to use. Encourage students to share their findings with the class while displaying the USGS map they used.

Lab Manual 5—Finding True North

1. west to east **2.** approximately noon; answers depend on location **3.** The actual angle varies by 40° across the United States. The compass needle is pulled to the east of true north by 15 to 20° on the West Coast and pulled 15 to 20° west in the northeastern United States. The angle is closest to zero in Mississippi, Illinois, Wisconsin, and eastern Tennessee and Kentucky. **Explore Further** The earth's magnetic north pole does not coincide entirely with true north. The farther north you are, the greater the difference between true north and magnetic north.

Lab Manual 6—Modeling the Earth's Rotation (Investigation 2-1)

1. step 4 **2.** step 6 **3.** Answers will vary, but should reflect that a given point turns slowly eastward as the earth rotates. Because of this rotation, an area facing the sun slowly moves out of the sunlight and eventually experiences nighttime. **Explore Further** Answers should include that the position of the home changes, not in relation to other points on the earth, but in relation to the sun. As the earth rotates, their home passes through day, dusk, night, dawn, and back to its original position in a 24-hour period.

Lab Manual 7—Describing Location on a Round Surface (Investigation 2-2)

1. Most students will find it difficult to describe the location of the X because of the balloon's uniformity and lack of edges or other reference points. **2.** Both are rounded. **3.** Most methods will be only partly successful. Adding other points of reference and/or a grid system would improve the location descriptions. **Explore Further** The land areas near the poles seem smaller on the globe. Some maps make the areas around the poles appear larger because the map is a stretched-out picture of the globe: if the areas around the equator are accurate, those at the poles will not be accurate. It is impossible to picture accurately all the features of a sphere on a flat map, unless the map is split into many connected sections.

Lab Manual 8—Using Latitude and Longitude

City	Latitude	Longitude
Osaka	35°N	135°E
Flers	48°N	1°W
Portland	46°N	123°W
Harare	18°S	31°E
Budapest	47°N	19°E
Madras	13°N	80°E
Wellington	41°S	175°E
Jacksonville	30°N	82°W
Brisbane	27°S	153°E
Marrakech	32°N	8°W

1. They have western longitudes. 2. Northern. There is much more land in the Northern hemisphere than in the Southern hemisphere. **Explore Further** Answers will vary.

Lab Manual 9—Making a Model of an Orbit (Investigation 3-1)

1. Answers will vary, but may include an oval, an egglike shape, or a "stretched" circle. 2. The second ellipse is longer but not as wide. It is more elliptical. 3. The ellipse would be more circular and less elongated than the others. **Explore Further** Data tables should show ellipse width decreasing and length increasing as distance between pins increases. Length should equal width when the distance between the pins is zero (a circle is drawn when only one pin is used).

Lab Manual 10—Exploring Light Angle (Investigation 3-2)

1. Spot 1 2. Spot 1. The flashlight shined more directly on the paper, creating brighter, more intense light. **Explore Further** The thermometer should register a slightly higher temperature when the flashlight is directly above it. Relate this result to the position of the sun during summer.

Lab Manual 11—Modeling the Orbit of the Moon

1. the sun 2. the way the light falls on the model; it represents the phases of the moon. **Explore Further** Drawings and diagrams will depend on the phase of the moon. For example, if the moon is in the third quarter, the three objects will form a right angle ABC where the moon is at A, the earth is at B, and the sun is at C.

Lab Manual 12—Measuring Crater Size

1. Crater depth will likely increase as height increases. 2. Crater diameter will likely increase as height increases. 3. Answers will vary. Students may notice "rays" of cornstarch thrown out from craters. 4. Crater characteristics, such as depth and diameter, are related to the forces that formed them. **Explore Further** Students may predict that increasing the mass of a falling object will increase the diameter of the crater if the drop height stays the same. They may predict that the crater will resemble the object's shape.

Lab Manual 13—Observing Sunspots (Investigation 4-1)

1. If a sunspot is visible, it is likely to be seen on consecutive days. The position and shape of the sunspot suggest that it is the same one as previously viewed. 2. Students may observe that sunspots move, change shape, and grow, shrink, or vanish over the course of days. Sunspots will seem to move west to east. With an inverted image, they will seem to move east to west. **Explore Further** Patterns over a longer period of time may include the changing of shape and location of sunspots and the disappearance and/or appearance of other sunspots.

Lab Manual 14—Modeling the Greenhouse Effect

1. The temperatures in both jars went up. 2. Sunlight heated the air inside the jars. 3. The temperature in the closed jar increased more over time because more heat was retained in the closed container than in the open container. In the open container, some heat was allowed to escape; in the closed container, the heat was trapped inside. 4. When the sun heats a planet, some heat energy is absorbed by the planet, its atmosphere traps some of the heat, and some heat escapes back into space. With the open jar model, much of the heat was allowed to escape. In the greenhouse effect, an abundance of certain gases in the atmosphere traps heat energy from the sun; less heat escapes back into space. This warms the atmosphere and also causes the planet to get warmer. This is what was modeled by the closed jar. **Explore Further** The results were the same as in the earlier investigation. Although the temperatures were cooler, the temperature in the closed jar was higher than that in the open jar. Students can conclude that air trapped in a closed container will be warmer than air in a container where heat is allowed to escape.

Lab Manual 15—Comparing the Size and Density of Planets

1. Jupiter; Mercury 2. Mercury and Earth; Saturn 3. Jupiter, Saturn, Uranus, Neptune, possibly Pluto; Mercury, Venus, Earth, Mars **Explore Further** Students will probably conclude that a bar graph or chart is best for organizing this information for comparison. They should remember to convert Earth years to Earth days so that all nine year lengths can be accurately represented and compared. A possible generalization is that the farther the planet is from the sun, the longer the length of its year. This is logical, given that the farther the planet is from the sun, the larger its orbit is.

Lab Manual 16—Modeling Distances in the Solar System (Investigation 4-2)

1. 1 centimeter = 5,000,000 kilometers 2. Mercury, Venus, Earth, Mars 3. Uranus and Neptune **Explore Further** Students' models should show an understanding and use of a realistic scale based on the information about the diameters of the planets in Appendix C.

Lab Manual 17—Observing Brightness (Investigation 5-1)

1. when they were the same distance away 2. First, flashlight B looked brighter. Then flashlight A looked brighter. In each case, the flashlight that was nearer was brighter. 3. apparent magnitude 4. They make light; their apparent brightness depends on observation distance. **Explore Further** Students should find that the flashlight with the additional tissue layers will shine more dimly. It will, therefore, need to be closer for the lights to appear equally bright. Students' systems will vary, but should indicate that more tissue layers require shorter observation distances in order to achieve equal apparent brightness.

Lab Manual 18—Observing Distant Objects

1. when it was closest to the observer 2. when it was farthest from the observer 3. Yes. As Earth moves in its orbit, nearby stars seem to move in relation to the stars behind them. 4. The stars that are closest to Earth would seem to move the most. **Explore Further** Astronomers measure distance to stars relative to other objects nearby and to the changes in their own position on Earth.

Lab Manual 19—Modeling a Supergiant

1. The balloon expanded. 2. When the air in the bottle heated up, its molecules moved farther apart and into the balloon, expanding it. 3. expansion 4. As a star uses up its hydrogen, it collapses, causing helium particles to fuse and give off heat energy. This energy heats the gases in a star and causes them to expand. The entire star expands into space, forming a red giant or supergiant. **Explore Further** When the air in the bottle and balloon cooled, the balloon collapsed. Gravity and cooling air caused this collapse and eventually cause similar effects in a star (a red giant or supergiant collapsing).

Lab Manual 20—Making a Constellation Model (Investigation 5-2)

1. Both are patterns of lights; people recognize the patterns. 2. Answers may include that the model is much smaller; stars are themselves a light source, while the model uses a flashlight; the stars in the model are arranged in a flat plane, while real stars in a constellation are varying distances from Earth; the model stars are all the same color. 3. Model larger or brighter stars by using bigger pinholes; show additional stars; use appropriate colors for different stars. **Explore Further** The location of the constellation and the season when it is most visible will vary. You might select a few student constellations that should be visible at this time of year and ask students to locate them at night.

Lab Manual 21—Measuring Physical Properties of Objects (Investigation 6-1)

1. Answers will vary. Sample answer: Yes, finding precise words to describe objects can be difficult. Some objects seem to have more specific properties than others. **2.** Examples should match actual data in the table. For example, two metal objects might both be described as "silver-colored" and "attracted to a magnet." **3.** Properties will vary. Sample answer: Feel, because each object had a unique texture. **Explore Further** First, remove objects from sight and see if students can identify objects only by the properties listed. Students may find that more descriptive clues are needed to identify some objects. For example, a solid might also be described as plastic, very lightweight, and shiny.

Lab Manual 22—Making a Model of an Atom

1. the nucleus of the atom **2.** by adding one or two white paper balls to the small balloon **3.** with two red paper balls in the outer balloon, and two black paper balls and two white paper balls in the inner balloon **Explore Further** Students might suggest some way to make the white paper balls and black paper balls stick together, such as gluing them, before placing them inside the small balloon.

Lab Manual 23—Testing Solutions

1. Students should find that salt, sugar, coffee, and detergent will dissolve quickly, with slight differences in speed. **2.** Salt, sugar, coffee, and detergent will dissolve completely. **3.** Answers will vary depending on individual results. **4.** flour (and possibly detergent, depending on water temperature and type of detergent) **5.** sand **Explore Further** Students can infer from cooking or making hot drinks that heated water can dissolve substances more readily. They could test this by repeating the investigation, adding a second set of solutions made with hot water.

Lab Manual 24—Separating a Mixture (Investigation 6-2)

1. The salt seemed to disappear. It dissolved. The sand got darker but did not dissolve. **2.** sand **3.** Most of the salt went through the filter. On the second day, all or most of the water was gone, but dried salt stayed on the bottom and sides of the beaker. **Explore Further** Mixture A: Separate by adding water and swabbing the sawdust from the surface with the cotton square. Mixture B: Separate iron filings with a magnet. Mixture C: Separate by sifting the sand through a wire screen.

Lab Manual 25—Testing the Hardness of Minerals

Students' data depend on actual mineral samples. **Explore Further** With the added samples, students will be able to establish the hardness of minerals up to 8 on Mohs' scale.

Lab Manual 26—Observing Color, Streak, and Hardness (Investigation 7-1)

1. Answers will vary, but color is probably the most obvious property to observe. **2.** Answers will vary. Students will probably find hardness to be the most difficult property to determine. **3.** Mineral colors were the same as their streaks for all samples except hematite, pyrite, and mica. **Explore Further** Students can identify the mineral sample by attempting to scratch it with their fingernail, the penny, the spoon, and the other known minerals. Answers will depend on the samples provided.

Lab Manual 27—Exploring the Arrangement of Atoms in Crystals

1. Students should find that a hexagonal pattern allowed the most washers to be placed in a single layer. **2.** Denser metallic crystals are more likely to have a hexagonal crystal pattern. **Explore Further** Students will find a variety of structures to choose from when constructing their models.

Lab Manual 28—Finding Specific Gravity (Investigation 7-2)

1. The specific gravity of each sample is higher than the specific gravity of water. **2.** Answers will depend on the minerals used. **3.** Answers will depend on the minerals used. **Explore Further** Answers will depend on the minerals used.

Lab Manual 29—Comparing Rates of Crystallization

1. temperature and time **2.** The crystals in the dish that was heated are smaller. **3.** Possible answer: For salt water, smaller crystals form in a shorter time when the solution is heated. **Explore Further** Students should note that, as in the original investigation, the crystals in the dish that was heated are smaller than those in the dish that was not heated. They should also conclude that the new investigation confirms that smaller crystals form in a shorter time when the solution is heated.

Lab Manual 30—Observing Igneous Rock Color and Texture

1. The rocks in each group are similar in the amount of time they took to form. The rocks with small crystals or no crystals likely formed more quickly than the rocks with large crystals. **2.** The samples listed in the first row probably took longer to form than the samples listed in the rows below. **3.** No. The rocks in the groups arranged by color are not grouped the same when arranged by texture. **4.** No. Rock color does not seem to be related to crystal size, so color is probably not related to the speed of crystallization. **Explore Further** Students should find that the light-colored rocks are rich in silicon, aluminum, sodium, and potassium. Dark rocks are rich in iron, magnesium, and calcium. They should conclude that the color of a rock is determined by the minerals it contains.

Lab Manual 31—Making Calcite (Investigation 8-1)

1. Tiny white crystals (calcite) were observed on the filter. **2.** The carbonate came from the washing soda; the calcium came from the calcium chloride. **3.** chemical rock **4.** The reaction was concentrated in a small area, and sedimentation of the crystals occurred quickly. **Explore Further** Students' models should illustrate the process by which these types of rock are formed. However, students should recognize that factors such as time, pressure, temperature, and method of accumulation have been altered to make the model. Possible ideas include layering pebbles with a mixture of glue and water and letting them harden to model clastic (conglomerate) rock, doing the same with bits of shell to model organic rock, and allowing salt water to evaporate to model chemical rock.

Lab Manual 32—Identifying Rocks (Investigation 8-2)

1. Answers will vary depending on the samples chosen. Rocks with distinctive textures, such as sandstone, pumice, and conglomerate, are generally easier to identify than fine-grained samples. **2.** Rocks with similar textures and similar mineral compositions may be difficult to identify. **Explore Further** Remind students to number their samples to keep them straight. Students' conclusions will vary. They might conclude that sedimentary rocks generally contain layers as well as organic matter such as fossils. Igneous rocks have a crystalline structure, although some may have crystals too small to see. Some metamorphic rocks have bands of minerals.

Lab Manual 33—Surveying Air Quality

1–2. Answers will vary. Particles might include dust, insects, lint, and bits of plants. **3–4.** The two samples will vary in kinds of particles collected and amount of particles collected. The indoor sample may have fewer particles than the outdoor sample, causing students to conclude that indoor air is cleaner. **5.** Theories should include both indoor and outdoor sources of particles. Students might also explain how air movement carries particles from one place to another. **Explore Further** Students should infer that on a very hot day with high levels of ozone or other pollution, or on a day with rain or other precipitation, or a windy day, different and/or dirtier samples would be taken.

Lab Manual 34—Comparing Evaporation Rates

1. fresh water out of direct sunlight or wind, salt water out of direct sunlight or wind, fresh water in wind, fresh water in direct sunlight **2.** The water under the fan will most likely evaporate first, followed by the water near the heat source. **3.** The salt water will likely take the longest to evaporate. **4.** Answers may vary, but will most likely match the following: Moving air increases the rate of evaporation the most. A heat source such as direct sunlight also increases evaporation rate. Salt in water slows evaporation rate. **Explore Further** Students might suggest an experiment that varies the water temperature or the humidity of the air above the water.

Lab Manual 35—Observing Clouds (Investigation 9-1)

1. Answers should match student data. Cloud identifications should be fairly consistent across the class. **2.** Answers will vary, depending on what types of clouds were observed and whether they varied from day to day. In general, cumulus clouds are related to fair weather, stratus clouds are related to rainy weather, and cirrus clouds are related to fair weather followed by rain or snow. **Explore Further** Answer will vary. Students might notice a correlation between cloud type and time of day. You might point out that the sun warms the earth in varying degrees over the course of a day.

Lab Manual 36—Making a Model of Rain (Investigation 9-2)

1. Depending on the equipment, a droplet will usually run after the first or second spray. **2.** Small droplets combined to form larger ones. Even larger droplets formed, causing several small streams to run down the slope. **3.** Tiny water droplets joined to form larger droplets, until they became heavy enough to fall. This models the way water droplets combine in clouds until they are heavy enough to fall to the earth as rain. **Explore Further** The mist usually freezes right away on the freezer surface. Therefore, drops do not form or form very slowly.

Lab Manual 37—Making a Hair Hygrometer

1. Answers should reflect the past week's weather reports. **2.** The hair stretched as humidity increased and shrank as humidity decreased. **3.** Answers will vary, but should match students' data. **Explore Further** Drawings and descriptions will vary. Two possible answers: Based on previous measurements correlating hair length and relative humidity, create a relative humidity scale instead of a millimeter scale. Tape this in the correct position alongside the pin tip so it accurately reflects the current relative humidity. Another possible answer is to use several hairs of equal length. Instead of a pin, attach a lightweight dowel rod to the end of the hairs. The hairs should attach at the left end of the rod and should hold the rod horizontal to the floor. Tie a pen or fine-point marker to the right end of the rod. Create a paper drum by taping drawing paper onto a cardboard cylinder. Mark the paper into seven equal sections to represent the days of the week. Set the hygrometer so that the marker just touches the paper drum. Turn the drum to a new section of the paper each day. The pen will create a line showing whether humidity increased or decreased each day. The line is like a graph because it records a change in one variable over time.

Lab Manual 38—Measuring Air Pressure (Investigation 10-1)

1. Air pressure increased. **2.** Air pressure decreased. **3.** Answers will vary according to local weather. However, student data should be consistent across the class. **4.** Answers will vary according to local weather. Predictions should reflect the understanding that rising air pressure suggests drier weather is coming, decreasing pressure suggests wetter weather is coming, and no change in pressure indicates a stable, or unchanging, pattern in current weather. **Explore Further** Encourage students to compare their prediction with those from both a newspaper and a televised weather report. They can then compare all of the predictions with the weather that actually occurs.

Lab Manual 39—Measuring Air and Surface Temperatures

1. Both were warmed by the sunlight. The soil in sunlight became warmer than the water because it absorbed more heat energy. **2.** a land surface on a sunny day **3.** The air above the ice became colder. The air above the hot water became warmer. **4.** An air mass reflects the surface temperature. **5.** The air mass above the land would become warmer, rising up and over the air mass above the water. **Explore Further** Students might heat a beaker of water on one side and add a drop of food coloring to observe the current. They might also use food coloring to color ice cubes and place them at one end of an aquarium or other large container of room-temperature water. As the ice melts, the colored water will sink, flow across the bottom, and begin to rise. Students should conclude that warm air rises and cool air sinks. Therefore, warmed air over land will rise and cooler air from above an ocean or lake will move inland. A cool breeze moves from the body of water toward land during the day. Students should conclude that a sea breeze is usually relatively cool.

Lab Manual 40—Using a Weather Map (Investigation 10-2)

1. Los Angeles, Omaha, Winnipeg, Dallas, and New York **2.** cold front; a short period of heavy showers followed by clear, cool weather **3.** The temperature will rise because a warm front will be coming through. **4.** Answers will vary. Possible answers include symbols for wind speed, wind direction, air pressure, and temperature. Added symbols provide more weather information that can help in planning outdoor activities, making clothing and travel decisions, and preparing for adverse weather. **Explore Further** Answers will vary depending on predictions and the local weather. Verify that students' answers reflect an understanding of weather symbols and concepts and an ability to read a weather map. Students might note that weather predictions can give a good idea of upcoming weather, but may not always be accurate. New fronts will most probably come from the west.

Lab Manual 41—Making Fresh Water from Salt Water

1. It evaporated. This water vapor went into the tube, cooled, and condensed back into water. This water dripped into flask 2. **2.** The salt stayed in flask 1. **3.** No. Salt cannot evaporate. **4.** Ocean water evaporates, as in flask 1, and then condenses somewhere else, as in flask 2. The water that condensed in flask 2 models fresh-water precipitation, and the salty residue left in flask 1 models the salt that remains in the ocean. **Explore Further** Answers will vary, but should include a way to collect and transport ocean water, an energy source or heating method, and a way to collect fresh water and transport it where it is needed.

Lab Manual 42—Exploring Evaporation (Investigation 11-1)

1. The drop in the covered dish took the longest time to evaporate. **2.** The drop under the lamp took the shortest time to evaporate. **3.** Students should conclude that heat and air circulation speed evaporation. **4.** Students should predict that water evaporates more quickly on a hot, sunny day than on a cool, cloudy day. **Explore Further** Students might suggest using an electric or a manual fan to create air circulation over a petri dish. They could vary the amount of wind modeled by changing the speed of the fan or its distance from the dish.

Lab Manual 43—Modeling How Ocean Water Gets Salty

1. Answers will vary. Possible answer: The water in dish 2 was cloudy. **2.** Some solid residue should have been left in dish 2. **3.** from the rocks **4.** The salt in ocean water comes from rocks on the ocean floor. **Explore Further** Answers will vary. Students may suggest that salt and minerals could dissolve in rivers and streams and wash into the ocean. They could design an investigation in which they show how moving water can carry salt from one place to another.

Lab Manual 44—Measuring the Effect of Salt Water on Floating (Investigation 11-2)

1. salt water 2. Answers will vary. Possible response: Objects float higher in salt water than they do in fresh water. This is because salt water is more dense than fresh water. **Explore Further** Answers will vary. Students may suggest using a series of soft-drink bottles, each with a different amount of salt in it. They may suggest a numbered scale on the float meter to make the comparison easier.

Lab Manual 45—Observing Chemical Weathering (Investigation 12-1)

1. The chips became pitted and the edges became more rounded. 2. The vinegar dissolved some of the limestone. **Explore Further** If the limestone chips are left in vinegar for longer periods of time, the reaction will continue. After a few weeks in vinegar, limestone chips would be very smooth and extremely pitted. Students should predict that the mass would decrease after soaking. They should find that granite and sandstone are most resistant to this kind of chemical weathering. Marble, because it is predominantly calcite, will react slightly with the vinegar.

Lab Manual 46—Observing the Effect of Vegetation on Soil Erosion

1. a heavy rain (and accompanying runoff) 2. The mound without grass should have changed the most. Some of the mound may have eroded away. 3. The runoff in the tray without grass should have had more dirt in it. 4. a hill without plants on it **Explore Further** Good advice would be to plant grass or other vegetation on hillsides. However, the steepness of the slope, the kind of soil, the amount of rocks, and the heaviness of the rainfall would also affect erosion.

Lab Manual 47—Comparing Erosion (Investigation 12-2)

1. The hillside with the grass held more of the water than the bare hillside, so less of the water ran all the way down the hill. The water also flowed more slowly down the grassy hillside. 2. More erosion occurred on the bare hillside than on the grassy hillside. 3. The water at the bottom of the hillside without grass was darker because it contained more soil. 4. Students might suggest planting vegetation on slopes or even on flat land to prevent erosion by water. **Explore Further** Ideas will vary, but students might suggest testing the effects of dense ground cover compared to spotty vegetation, or grass compared to other plant species. Before students attempt to carry out the new experiment, have them write a hypothesis and a detailed procedure. Once you have checked their procedures, allow students to test their hypotheses.

Lab Manual 48—Analyzing Sand

1. Answers will vary and should match students' data. Sand grains will differ in color, grain texture and size, type and variety, and dry density. 2. Answers should be based on actual data. Sample answers: Sample 1 is from a sandbox and may have come from a rock quarry near a river. The grains are mostly rounded, so they might have been carried a long distance by a river. Sample 2 is from an ocean beach. The grains are rounded pieces of shells and pieces of local rocks. The sand may have formed from ocean waves washing against the shore. 3. Answers depend on students' samples and should reflect their dry density data. **Explore Further** Students should find that the density of dry sand varies according to grain size and shape.

Lab Manual 49—Modeling Sea-Floor Spreading

1. new ocean crust 2. magma being forced up through a mid-ocean ridge 3. The Xs moved farther apart. 4. Sea-floor spreading causes continents to move farther apart. 5. The paper farthest from the slit represents the oldest rock. The paper closest to the slit represents the newest rock. **Explore Further** This represents two plates of the earth's crust colliding. Two plates that collide might fold to form mountains, or one plate might sink below the other and melt, possibly causing volcanoes to form.

Lab Manual 50—Making Models of Folding and Faults (Investigation 13-1)

1. continental plates colliding and crumpling 2. In a normal fault, the two sides pull apart and rock layers on one side drop down. In a reverse fault, the two sides push together, raising rock layers on one side. 3. slid them horizontally in opposite directions along their spines 4. They imitate the way layers of rock in the earth's crust bend, break, and move as the plates they are on slide past each other or are forced together or apart. **Explore Further** Students will need to cut through their layers of clay at an angle to model broken edges of rock. They can press small poster-board squares on the angled ends to make the movements of the surfaces easier to see. Students might suggest modeling faults using a thick sheet of foam cut in half at an angle or layers of cardboard glued together and then cut at an angle.

Lab Manual 51—Modeling Earthquake Waves

1. P-waves 2. S-waves 3. L-waves 4. L-waves **Explore Further** Students should observe that the push-pull "waves" of step 3 move fastest (P-waves), and the up-and-down "waves" in step 5 move slowest (L-waves). Students should conclude that the rolling waves on the surface are larger motions that could cause greater damage and destruction.

Lab Manual 52—Locating an Earthquake (Investigation 13-2)

1. Answers depend on the scale chosen. For a scale of 100 kilometers = 1 centimeter, the epicenter is on the drawing paper about 4 centimeters above the index card and about 4.5 centimeters in from the card's upper left corner. 2. The actual map would include boundaries, cities and towns, roads, and geographic features such as mountains, rivers, and plains. **Explore Further** You may want to suggest that students choose a section of the boundary of the Pacific and North American plates off the coast of California. Whether the epicenter falls near a city depends on which cities students choose for their station locations.

Lab Manual 53—Inferring from Fossils

1. Answers will depend on actual data. 2. Answers will depend on actual data. 3. Impressions do not directly tell you, for example, the color, age, chemical makeup, or movements of an object or living thing. Characteristics like these may be guessed by studying similar examples of the object or living thing, by studying the material in which the impression formed, or by finding out more about the environment where the impression formed. **Explore Further** Casts would provide a three-dimensional model from the impressions. This model might provide a better picture of the whole object or living thing and how its parts are related.

Lab Manual 54—Making a Carbon Imprint

1. a blackish imprint of the leaf, possibly a partial imprint 2. Students may see all or part of the leaf outline and possibly some details of the leaf's structure. 3. from the candle soot **Explore Further** Living things are made of carbon and other elements. When organisms die, radioactive carbon may be left behind after other elements decay. Carbon has a longer half-life than some other elements found in living things.

Lab Manual 55—Making a Model of a Fossil (Investigation 14-1)

1. The impression in the clay represents the mold. 2. The hardened plaster of paris represents the cast. 3. The space left in the clay that has the shape of the shell is the mold. When it is filled with plaster of paris, it forms a cast, which is a same-size model of the original shell. The interior of the mold and the exterior of the cast have the same shape, size, and surface pattern. **Explore Further** In general, a museum model is made by making molds of the dinosaur bones from resin or plaster. Casts are made from the molds. Internal steel and wire armatures are used to support the cast bones.

Lab Manual 56—Making a Half-Life Model (Investigation 14-2)

1. They represent the number of grams of the radioactive element left in the rock. **2.** They represent the number of grams of the radioactive element that decayed to form the new element. **3.** 4 grams; 2 grams **4.** 1 gram **Explore Further** A half-life experiment could be carried out in a number of ways. The important thing for students to remember is that, for each half-life, half of the *remaining* radioactive material decays. That is, 50 percent of the original amount of the radioactive material will decay after the first half-life, but only 25 percent of the original amount of the element will decay after the second half-life—not another 50 percent. If students choose to perform the heads-and-tails variation, explain that each "half-life" may or may not result in the decay of exactly half of the radioactive material. Probability dictates that over a large number of trials, the ratio of heads to tails will work out approximately evenly.

Community Connection

Completed activities will vary for each student. Community Connection activities are real-life activities that students complete outside the classroom. These activities give students practical learning and practice of the concepts taught in *Earth Science*. Check completed activities to see that students have followed directions, completed each step, filled in all charts and blanks, provided reasonable answers to questions, written legibly, and used appropriate science terms and proper grammar.

Self-Study Guides

Self-Study Guides outline suggested sections from the text and workbook. These assignment guides provide flexibility for individualized instruction or independent study.

Mastery Tests

Chapter 1 Mastery Test A
Part A 1. B **2.** D **3.** A **4.** B **5.** C
Part B 6. F **7.** A **8.** J **9.** E **10.** I **11.** B **12.** D **13.** G **14.** C **15.** H
Part C 16. A map is a drawing that shows part of the earth's surface from above. **17.** Answers will vary, but should show that the student understands at least one use of maps.
Part D 18. Newton **19.** Marshall **20.** Princeton **21.** Ralston **22.** east or northeast **23.** about 48 kilometers **24.** about 168 kilometers **25.** about 56 kilometers

Chapter 1 Mastery Test B
Part A 1. D **2.** I **3.** H **4.** E **5.** G **6.** A **7.** J **8.** F **9.** B **10.** C
Part B 11. C **12.** A **13.** B **14.** D **15.** B
Part C 16. Marshall **17.** Newton **18.** Ralston **19.** east or northeast **20.** about 56 kilometers **21.** about 168 kilometers **22.** Princeton **23.** about 48 kilometers
Part D 24. Answers will vary, but should show that the student understands at least one use of maps. **25.** A map is a drawing that shows part of the earth's surface from above.

Chapter 2 Mastery Test A
Part A 1. D **2.** B **3.** C **4.** B **5.** D
Part B 6. Zug Mt. **7.** A6 **8.** Higgins, Fayette **9.** C6 **10.** Etonville
Part C 11. 66°N **12.** A Nome **B** C. Lisburne **C** Kodiak Island **13.** A 58°N, 159°W **B** 63°N, 165°W **C** 56°N, 134°W
Part D 14. The earth takes 24 hours to rotate once on its axis. The sun shines on only one side at a time, so one side of the earth has day while the other has night. As the earth rotates, the areas of daylight and nighttime keep changing. **15.** Because of the earth's

rotation, all 24 hours of the day are occurring at any given time. The time zones reflect these time differences.

Chapter 2 Mastery Test B
Part A 1. A6 **2.** Etonville **3.** Zug Mt. **4.** Higgins, Fayette **5.** C6
Part B 6. B **7.** D **8.** D **9.** C **10.** B
Part C 11. A C. Lisburne **B** Kodiak Island **C** Nome **12.** A 56°N, 134°W **B** 58°N, 159°W **C** 63°N, 165°W **13.** 66°N
Part D 14. Because of the earth's rotation, all 24 hours of the day are occurring at any given time. The time zones reflect these time differences. **15.** The earth takes 24 hours to rotate once on its axis. The sun shines on only one side at a time, so one side of the earth has day while the other has night. As the earth rotates, the areas of daylight and nighttime keep changing.

Chapter 3 Mastery Test A
Part A 1. D **2.** C **3.** A **4.** C **5.** A
Part B 6. I **7.** F **8.** A **9.** C **10.** H **11.** E **12.** J **13.** G **14.** B **15.** D
Part C 16. new moon, first quarter, full moon, third quarter **17.** The gravitational pull of the moon causes tides, which are the regular rising and falling of the earth's major bodies of water. **18.** The tilt of the earth's axis causes sunlight to fall more directly on different parts of the earth throughout its orbit. This tilt and the earth's revolution cause the seasons. **19.** Marias, the areas that appear dark on the moon, are low, flat plains where melted rock flowed onto the surface and hardened billions of years ago. Mountains and highlands are areas that appear light. Craters are circular areas with rims that form mountains. **20.** An eclipse is either the shadow of the moon on the earth or the shadow of the earth on the moon. An eclipse happens when the sun, moon, and earth line up.

Chapter 3 Mastery Test B
Part A 1. D **2.** A **3.** B **4.** C **5.** D
Part B 6. E **7.** J **8.** G **9.** C **10.** A **11.** D **12.** H **13.** B **14.** I **15.** F
Part C 16. The tilt of the earth's axis causes sunlight to fall more directly on different parts of the earth throughout its orbit. This tilt and the earth's revolution cause the seasons. **17.** new moon, first quarter, full moon, third quarter **18.** An eclipse is either the shadow of the moon on the earth or the shadow of the earth on the moon. An eclipse happens when the sun, moon, and earth line up. **19.** The gravitational pull of the moon causes tides, which are the regular rising and falling of the earth's major bodies of water. **20.** Marias, the areas that appear dark on the moon, are low, flat plains where melted rock flowed onto the surface and hardened billions of years ago. Mountains and highlands are areas that appear light. Craters are circular areas with rims that form mountains.

Chapter 4 Mastery Test A
Part A 1. Jupiter, OP **2.** Venus, IP **3.** Neptune, OP **4.** Uranus, OP **5.** Earth, IP **6.** Mercury, IP **7.** Pluto, OP **8.** Saturn, OP **9.** Mars, IP
Part B 10. Comets are made of ice, rock, frozen gases, and dust. They follow large orbits around the sun on a different plane from the planets. Meteors are the brief streaks of light seen when asteroids enter Earth's atmosphere. Asteroids are rocky objects, smaller than planets, that have their own orbits around the sun or another star. **11.** The solar system includes the sun, all nine planets, their moons, and all other objects that revolve around the sun. Gravity between the objects in the solar system is what holds it together.
Part C 12. B **13.** C **14.** A **15.** D

Chapter 4 Mastery Test B
Part A 1. Uranus, OP **2.** Neptune, OP **3.** Earth, IP **4.** Mars, IP **5.** Mercury, IP **6.** Venus, IP **7.** Saturn, OP **8.** Pluto, OP **9.** Jupiter, OP
Part B 10. The solar system includes the sun, all nine planets, their moons, and all other objects that revolve around the sun. Gravity between the objects in the solar system is what holds it together. **11.** Comets are made of ice, rock, frozen gases, and dust. They

follow large orbits around the sun on a different plane from the planets. Meteors are the brief streaks of light seen when asteroids enter Earth's atmosphere. Asteroids are rocky objects, smaller than planets, that have their own orbits around the sun or another star.
Part C 12. C **13.** D **14.** A **15.** B

Chapter 5 Mastery Test A
Part A 1–8. 8, 7, 1, 3,6, 5, 4, 2
Part B 9. E **10.** H **11.** D **12.** I **13.** B **14.** C **15.** F **16.** J **17.** A **18.** G
Part C 19. A galaxy is a group of billions of stars. The shapes are elliptical, or oval; spiral, a pinwheel; and irregular, no regular shape. **20.** A constellation is a group of stars seen from Earth that form a pattern people have identified and named.
Part D 21. C **22.** B **23.** C **24.** D **25.** D

Chapter 5 Mastery Test B
Part A 1–8. 5, 6, 3, 4, 8, 1, 7, 2
Part B 9. F **10.** C **11.** B **12.** I **13.** A **14.** H **15.** J **16.** D **17.** G **18.** E
Part C 19. A constellation is a group of stars seen from Earth that form a pattern people have identified and named. **20.** A galaxy is a group of billions of stars. The shapes are elliptical, or oval; spiral, a pinwheel; and irregular, no regular shape.
Part D 21. D **22.** C **23.** D **24.** B **25.** C

Chapter 6 Mastery Test A
Part A 1. D **2.** A **3.** B **4.** C
Part B 5. matter **6.** solid **7.** chemical **8.** physical **9.** nucleus **10.** compound **11.** mixture **12.** hydrogen **13.** gaseous **14.** liquid
Part C 15. proton (neutron is also acceptable) **16.** neutron (proton is also acceptable) **17.** nucleus **18.** electron
Part D 19. Possible answers: color, size, weight, taste, shape, feel, smell, state **20.** 109 elements **21.** 92 elements **22.** Sodium is an element. Sodium chloride is a compound containing sodium and chlorine. **23.** Possible answers: oxygen, silicon, aluminum, iron, calcium, sodium, potassium, magnesium, titanium, hydrogen **24.** The letters are the symbols of the elements that make up the compound. The numbers tell how many atoms of each element join to form the compound. Fe_2O_3 is made of two iron atoms and three oxygen atoms chemically joined. **25.** The elements and compounds in a mixture do not join chemically and have no specific ratio, so no chemical formula is needed.

Chapter 6 Mastery Test B
Part A 1. B **2.** D **3.** C **4.** A
Part B 5. physical **6.** compound **7.** chemical **8.** matter **9.** nucleus **10.** solid **11.** liquid **12.** gaseous **13.** hydrogen **14.** mixture
Part C 15. proton (neutron is also acceptable) **16.** neutron (proton is also acceptable) **17.** nucleus **18.** electron
Part D 19. Sodium is an element. Sodium chloride is a compound containing sodium and chlorine. **20.** The letters are the symbols of the elements that make up the compound. The numbers tell how many atoms of each element join to form the compound. Fe_2O_3 is made of two iron atoms and three oxygen atoms chemically joined. **21.** Possible answers: oxygen, silicon, aluminum, iron, calcium, sodium, potassium, magnesium, titanium, hydrogen **22.** Possible answers: color, size, weight, taste, shape, feel, smell, state **23.** The elements and compounds in a mixture do not join chemically and have no specific ratio, so no chemical formula is needed. **24.** 109 elements **25.** 92 elements

Chapter 7 Mastery Test A
Part A 1. A **2.** B **3.** C **4.** C **5.** A
Part B 6. color **7.** streak **8.** hardness **9.** crystal **10.** luster **11.** Mohs' **12.** cleavage **13.** specific gravity **14.** fracture
Part C 15. A mineral is an element or a compound that occurs naturally as a solid, has a definite chemical makeup, is neither living nor made of living things, and has definite atomic patterns.

16. Possible answers: aluminum, quartz, feldspar, mica, calcite, dolomite, halite, gypsum **17.** Seven properties for identifying minerals are color, luster, streak, hardness, crystal shape (form or structure is also acceptable), break pattern (cleavage or fracture is also acceptable), and specific gravity. **18.** Quartz can scratch calcite. **19.** Copper is 8.9 times heavier than the weight of the same volume of water.
20. Possible answers: Diamonds are used in drill tips. Gold conducts electricity in computer circuits and communications equipment. Copper conducts electricity in power cords. Graphite is used as pencil lead and to lubricate locks. Talc is used in body powder. Quartz is used in clocks and to make windows, bottles, and drinking glasses. Bauxite is used to make aluminum cans, pots, and pans. Talc, iron, bauxite, gypsum, corundum, and quartz are all used to make construction materials such as paint, plaster, nails, sandpaper, and ladders.

Chapter 7 Mastery Test B
Part A 1. A **2.** B **3.** A **4.** C **5.** C
Part B 6. luster **7.** fracture **8.** specific gravity **9.** color **10.** hardness **11.** crystal **12.** Mohs' **13.** streak **14.** cleavage
Part C 15. Possible answers: Diamonds are used in drill tips. Gold conducts electricity in computer circuits and communications equipment. Copper conducts electricity in power cords. Graphite is used as pencil lead and to lubricate locks. Talc is used in body powder. Quartz is used in clocks and to make windows, bottles, and drinking glasses. Bauxite is used to make aluminum cans, pots, and pans. Talc, iron, bauxite, gypsum, corundum, and quartz are all used to make construction materials such as paint, plaster, nails, sandpaper, and ladders. **16.** Copper is 8.9 times heavier than the weight of the same volume of water. **17.** Quartz can scratch calcite. **18.** Seven properties for identifying minerals are color, luster, streak, hardness, crystal shape (form or structure is also acceptable), break pattern (cleavage or fracture is also acceptable), and specific gravity. **19.** Possible answers: aluminum, quartz, feldspar, mica, calcite, dolomite, halite, gypsum **20.** A mineral is an element or a compound that occurs naturally as a solid, has a definite chemical makeup, is neither living nor made of living things, and has definite atomic patterns.

Chapter 8 Mastery Test A
Part A 1. C **2.** B **3.** A **4.** D **5.** B
Part B 6. F **7.** A **8.** J **9.** H **10.** I **11.** B **12.** C **13.** D **14.** E **15.** G
Part C 16. intrusive **17.** magma **18.** extrusive **19.** rock cycle **20.** organic **21.** clastic **22.** nonfoliated
Part D 23. a naturally occurring solid mixture of minerals **24.** Both are begun far below the earth's surface where heat and pressure cause changes. Metamorphic rocks do not melt, but igneous rocks form from melted rock called magma. **25.** the changes that the earth's rocks go through because of forces above and below the earth's surface

Chapter 8 Mastery Test B
Part A 1. B **2.** A **3.** B **4.** C **5.** D
Part B 6. G **7.** E **8.** I **9.** C **10.** J **11.** D **12.** H **13.** A **14.** B **15.** F
Part C 16. nonfoliated **17.** rock cycle **18.** magma **19.** organic **20.** extrusive **21.** clastic **22.** intrusive
Part D 23. the changes that the earth's rocks go through because of forces above and below the earth's surface **24.** a naturally occurring solid mixture of minerals **25.** Both are begun far below the earth's surface where heat and pressure cause changes. Metamorphic rocks do not melt, but igneous rocks form from melted rock called magma.

Chapter 9 Mastery Test A
Part A 1. H **2.** F **3.** J **4.** E **5.** I **6.** C **7.** A **8.** G **9.** B **10.** D
Part B 11. B **12.** C **13.** D **14.** A **15.** D
Part C 16. The earth's atmosphere is the layer of gases that surrounds the earth. **17.** Animals breathe in air, use the oxygen to create energy, and release carbon dioxide. Plants take in carbon dioxide, which they use to create energy, and release oxygen. Animal

waste creates nitrogen in the ground. Bacteria break it down and release it into the air. Animals take in nitrogen when they feed on plants or plant-eating animals. **18.** Stratus—low, flat; less than 2,000 meters above the earth. Cumulus—puffy; 2,000 to 7,000 meters. Cirrus—thin, wispy streaks; 7,000 to 13,000 meters. **19.** Clouds are made of water droplets or ice crystals that collide to form larger drops or crystals. When the drops or crystals are large enough, they fall. If the air beneath the cloud is above freezing, they fall as rain. If the air is below freezing, they fall as snow. If rain freezes in cold air on the way down, it falls as sleet. **20.** Polar easterlies: winds in belts near the North and South Poles that move from east to west and bring cold, stormy weather. Prevailing westerlies: winds occurring between 30°N and 60°N latitudes and between 30°S and 60°S latitudes that blow from west to east. Trade winds: strong, reliable tropical winds that blow from the northeast in the Northern Hemisphere and from the southeast in the Southern Hemisphere.

Chapter 9 Mastery Test B
Part A 1. G **2.** C **3.** J **4.** E **5.** B **6.** A **7.** D **8.** F **9.** I **10.** H
Part B 11. C **12.** D **13.** B **14.** D **15.** A
Part C 16. Polar easterlies: winds in belts near the North and South Poles that move from east to west and bring cold, stormy weather. Prevailing westerlies: winds occurring between 30°N and 60°N latitudes and between 30°S and 60°S latitudes that blow from west to east. Trade winds: strong, reliable tropical winds that blow from the northeast in the Northern Hemisphere and from the southeast in the Southern Hemisphere. **17.** Stratus—low, flat; less than 2,000 meters above the earth. Cumulus—puffy; 2,000 to 7,000 meters. Cirrus—thin, wispy streaks; 7,000 to 13,000 meters. **18.** The earth's atmosphere is the layer of gases that surrounds the earth.
19. Animals breathe in air, use oxygen to create energy, and release carbon dioxide. Plants take in carbon dioxide, which they use to create energy, and release oxygen. Animal waste creates nitrogen in the ground. Bacteria break it down and release it into the air. Animals take in nitrogen when they feed on plants or plant-eating animals. **20.** Clouds are made of water droplets or ice crystals that collide to form larger drops or crystals. When the drops or crystals are large enough, they fall. If the air beneath the cloud is above freezing, they fall as rain. If the air is below freezing, they fall as snow. If rain freezes in cold air on the way down, it falls as sleet.

Chapter 10 Mastery Test A
Part A 1. C **2.** B **3.** C **4.** D **5.** A **6.** C
Part B 7. I **8.** D **9.** E **10.** C **11.** B **12.** G **13.** A **14.** F **15.** H
Part C 16. air pressure **17.** humidity **18.** wind speed **19.** temperature **20.** lightning
Part D 21. three **22.** rainy **23.** stormy **24.** Raleigh **25.** two

Chapter 10 Mastery Test B
Part A 1. B **2.** D **3.** C **4.** C **5.** A **6.** C
Part B 7. D **8.** G **9.** A **10.** F **11.** I **12.** H **13.** B **14.** E **15.** C
Part C 16. wind speed **17.** air pressure **18.** lightning **19.** humidity **20.** temperature
Part D 21. three **22.** stormy **23.** Raleigh **24.** two **25.** rainy

Chapter 11 Mastery Test A
Part A 1. water cycle **2.** currents **3.** groundwater **4.** geyser **5.** drainage basin **6.** reservoir **7.** continental shelf
Part B 8. I **9.** G **10.** A **11.** J **12.** D **13.** H **14.** C **15.** E **16.** B **17.** F
Part C 18. B **19.** D **20.** D **21.** C **22.** A
Part D 23. Salt water is too salty to drink or to use in farming or industry. Fresh water does not contain salt and can be easily treated for use in drinking, watering plants, and operating machinery. **24.** Features include continental shelves, continental slopes, mid-ocean ridges, trenches, seamounts, islands, and plains. **25.** Salt comes from rocks in the ocean floor and from incoming river water.

Chapter 11 Mastery Test B
Part A 1. reservoir **2.** continental shelf **3.** currents **4.** groundwater **5.** water cycle **6.** geyser **7.** drainage basin
Part B 8. H **9.** E **10.** J **11.** G **12.** C **13.** B **14.** D **15.** I **16.** A **17.** F
Part C 18. A **19.** D **20.** D **21.** B **22.** C
Part D 23. Salt comes from rocks in the ocean floor and from incoming river water. **24.** Salt water is too salty to drink or to use in farming or industry. Fresh water does not contain salt and can be easily treated for use in drinking, watering plants, and operating machinery. **25.** Features include continental shelves, continental slopes, mid-ocean ridges, trenches, seamounts, islands, and plains.

Chapter 12 Mastery Test A
Part A 1. G **2.** C **3.** F **4.** D **5.** B **6.** E **7.** A
Part B 8. C **9.** D **10.** C **11.** A **12.** C
Part C 13. weathering **14.** plants and animals **15.** mechanical **16.** erosion **17.** sediment
Part D 18. Gravity plays a part in all erosion by causing rivers and glaciers to flow downward. It also moves rock and soil that have been loosened by heavy rain or by freezing and thawing. **19.** Wind blows sand from one place to another. When the sand hits an obstacle, a small sand pile begins to form behind the obstacle. Sand continues to accumulate there, forming a dune. **20.** chemical weathering; possible answers: the oxidation of iron in rocks to form rust, water changing feldspar in rocks to clay and washing it away, and rain and groundwater combining with carbon dioxide to form carbonic acid that dissolves the calcite in limestone

Chapter 12 Mastery Test B
Part A 1. G **2.** B **3.** C **4.** F **5.** D **6.** A **7.** E
Part B 8. D **9.** C **10.** A **11.** C **12.** C
Part C 13. plants and animals **14.** mechanical **15.** sediment **16.** weathering **17.** erosion
Part D 18. Wind blows sand from one place to another. When the sand hits an obstacle, a small sand pile begins to form behind the obstacle. Sand continues to accumulate there, forming a dune. **19.** chemical weathering; possible answers: oxidation of iron in rocks to form rust, water changing feldspar in rocks to clay and washing it away, and rain and groundwater combining with carbon dioxide to form carbonic acid that dissolves the calcite in limestone **20.** Gravity plays a part in all erosion by causing rivers and glaciers to flow downward. It also moves rock and soil that have been loosened by heavy rain or by freezing and thawing.

Chapter 13 Mastery Test A
Part A 1. B **2.** D **3.** A **4.** C **5.** B
Part B 6. H **7.** E **8.** A **9.** C **10.** B **11.** D **12.** F **13.** G
Part C 14. seismograph **15.** tectonics **16.** slide **17.** move apart **18.** fault **19.** core, crust **20.** folding
Part D 21. by folding, volcanic eruptions, and movements along faults **22.** normal, reverse, strike-slip **23.** Wegener believed that the continents were once joined because their shapes seem to fit together and because adjacent continents have similar fossils, glacial deposits, and other geographical features. **24.** Blocks of rock slide against each other horizontally. **25.** Scientists calculate how far away from three different locations the earthquake began. Then they draw circles with those radii around those locations. The circles intersect at the epicenter.

Chapter 13 Mastery Test B
Part A 1. A **2.** B **3.** B **4.** C **5.** D
Part B 6. H **7.** E **8.** C **9.** A **10.** F **11.** G **12.** B **13.** D
Part C 14. slide **15.** seismograph **16.** core, crust **17.** move apart **18.** folding **19.** tectonics **20.** fault
Part D 21. Wegener believed that the continents were once joined because their shapes seem to fit together and because adjacent

continents have similar fossils, glacial deposits, and other geographical features. **22.** Scientists calculate how far away from three different locations the earthquake began. Then they draw circles with those radii around those locations. The circles intersect at the epicenter. **23.** by folding, volcanic eruptions, and movements along faults **24.** normal, reverse, strike-slip **25.** Blocks of rock slide against each other horizontally.

Chapter 14 Mastery Test A
Part A 1. B **2.** A **3.** B **4.** C **5.** D **6.** B **7.** C **8.** A **9.** D **10.** A
Part B 11. petrification **12.** mold **13.** cast **14.** absolute **15.** carbon-14 **16.** Precambrian **17.** Paleozoic **18.** Cenozoic **19.** glaciers **20.** Mesozoic
Part C 21. Geologic time is all the time that has passed since the earth formed. **22.** Three ways fossils form are when minerals replace the original parts of a buried organism (petrification); when organisms leave an imprint (mold) behind in sediment and/or when that imprint later becomes filled with rock (cast); and when the actual body of the organism is preserved in ice, frozen soil, tar, or amber. **23.** The principle of superposition states that if sedimentary rock layers have not been overturned, the oldest rock layer is on the bottom. The principle of crosscutting relationships states that a rock or fault that cuts across rock layers is younger than the rock layers. **24.** Scientists use the decay, or half-life, of radioactive elements to calculate the absolute ages of rocks and fossils. **25.** Precambrian, Paleozoic, Mesozoic, Cenozoic

Chapter 14 Mastery Test B
Part A 1. C **2.** A **3.** B **4.** B **5.** A **6.** B **7.** D **8.** A **9.** C **10.** D
Part B 11. carbon-14 **12.** absolute **13.** Cenozoic **14.** mold **15.** petrification **16.** Mesozoic **17.** glaciers **18.** cast **19.** Paleozoic **20.** Precambrian
Part C 21. The principle of superposition states that if sedimentary rock layers have not been overturned, the oldest rock layer is on the bottom. The principle of crosscutting relationships states that a rock or fault that cuts across rock layers is younger than the rock layers. **22.** Precambrian, Paleozoic, Mesozoic, Cenozoic **23.** Three ways fossils form are when minerals replace the original parts of a buried organism (petrification); when organisms leave an imprint behind in sediment (mold) and/or when that imprint later becomes filled with rock (cast); and when the actual body of the organism is preserved in ice, frozen soil, tar, or amber. **24.** Geologic time is all the time that has passed since the earth formed. **25.** Scientists use the decay, or half-life, of radioactive elements to calculate the absolute ages of rocks and fossils.

Chapters 1–7 Midterm Mastery Test
Part A 1. A **2.** D **3.** C **4.** B **5.** A **6.** D **7.** C **8.** B **9.** B **10.** A
Part B 11. H **12.** N **13.** G **14.** M **15.** A **16.** B **17.** J **18.** C **19.** D **20.** E **21.** P **22.** Q **23.** O **24.** I **25.** F **26.** L **27.** K
Part C 28. matter **29.** orbit **30.** compass rose **31.** hardness **32.** inner **33.** liquid **34.** axis **35.** crater **36.** compound **37.** latitude **38.** luster **39.** outer **40.** topographic **41.** crystal **42.** temperature
Part D 43. A map is a drawing that shows part of the earth's surface from above. **44.** Comets are made of ice, rock, frozen gases, and dust. They follow large orbits around the sun on a different plane from the planets. Asteroids are rocky objects, smaller than planets, that have their own orbits around the sun. Meteorites are asteroids that hit the surface of a planet or moon. **45.** As the earth rotates on its axis, the sun can shine on only one side of the earth at a time. So the side of the earth where the sun is shining has daytime, while the opposite side has nighttime. **46.** The shapes are elliptical, an oval; spiral, a pinwheel; and irregular, no regular shape. **47.** Possible

answers: color, size, weight, taste, shape, feel, smell, state **48.** As the earth revolves around the sun, the tilt of the earth's axis causes sunlight to fall more directly on different parts of the earth throughout its orbit. This tilt and the earth's revolution cause the seasons. **49.** color, luster, streak, hardness, crystal shape, break pattern, and specific gravity **50.** The atoms in the elements or compounds in a mixture do not join chemically and have no particular ratio, so no chemical formula is needed.

Chapters 1–14 Final Mastery Test
Part A 1. B **2.** A **3.** D **4.** A **5.** B **6.** C **7.** A **8.** D **9.** A **10.** C **11.** B **12.** D **13.** A **14.** A **15.** C
Part B 16. Parts of an Atom—protons, electrons, neutrons **17.** Types of Rocks—igneous, metamorphic, sedimentary **18.** World Climate Zones—polar, temperate, tropical **19.** Types of Volcanoes—cinder cone, shield, composite **20.** Forms of Ocean Life—nekton, benthos, plankton **21.** Inner Planets—Mercury, Venus, Earth, Mars **22.** Causes of Erosion—water, glaciers, wind, gravity **23.** Layers of the Atmosphere—troposphere, stratosphere, mesosphere, thermosphere **24.** Main Fields of Earth Science—geology, meteorology, astronomy, oceanography **25.** Eras of Earth's History—Precambrian, Paleozoic, Mesozoic, Cenozoic
Part C 26. F **27.** I **28.** J **29.** H **30.** B **31.** O **32.** A **33.** R **34.** M **35.** L **36.** E **37.** K **38.** C **39.** G **40.** S **41.** D **42.** N **43.** T **44.** Q **45.** P
Part D 46. apparent **47.** water **48.** scale **49.** lunar **50.** property **51.** Mars **52.** minerals **53.** igneous **54.** sedimentary **55.** belts **56.** pressure **57.** currents **58.** mechanical **59.** Cenozoic **60.** fault
Part E 61. The rock cycle is a series of natural changes that cause one type of rock to become another type of rock. **62.** The parts of a compound are joined chemically and are not easily separated. Their atoms combine in a fixed ratio, represented by a chemical formula. The parts of a mixture are not joined chemically and are easily separated. They may vary in kind and amount. **63.** The solar system is the sun, all nine planets and their moons, and all other objects that revolve around the sun. **64.** Weather conditions change because conditions in the atmosphere change. **65.** Salt water contains dissolved salt and cannot be used for drinking, farming, or industry. Fresh water contains no salt and can be used for drinking, farming, and industry. **66.** The three ways mountains form are by volcanic eruptions, by folding plates, and by movements along faults. **67.** Because the earth keeps rotating, the places that have daylight keep changing. Since the time of day keeps changing everywhere on the earth, 24 standard time zones are needed for each hour of the day. **68.** As the earth revolves around the sun, the tilt of the earth's axis causes sunlight to fall more directly on different parts of the earth throughout its orbit. This tilt and the earth's revolution cause the seasons. **69.** A constellation is a group of stars that form a pattern in the sky. **70.** A fossil forms when an organism's buried remains become replaced with minerals (petrified), leave a mold or cast in rock, or become preserved in ice, frozen soil, tar, or amber.

Materials List for Earth Science Lab Manual

Note: This is a list of the materials needed for the lab activities in the *Earth Science* Lab Manual. The lab activities that are also investigations in the Student Text are identified in this list by investigation number. Students are expected to have paper and a pencil for every lab activity; these materials are not listed. The quantities listed here are enough for one student. For most lab activities, students may work either individually or in pairs or groups.

Chapter 1

Lab Manual 1: Using Map Scales
centimeter ruler

Lab Manual 2: Making a Map
Investigation 1-1
meterstick

Lab Manual 3: Making a Topographic Map
masking tape, centimeter ruler, marking pen, clear plastic container, rock, plastic wrap, scissors, tracing paper

Lab Manual 4: Reading a Topographic Map
Investigation 1-2
none

Chapter 2

Lab Manual 5: Finding True North
cardboard, thumbtack, rod 10–15 centimeters long, protractor, masking tape, chalk, magnetic compass

Lab Manual 6: Modeling the Earth's Rotation
Investigation 2-1
globe, masking tape, flashlight

Lab Manual 7: Describing Location on a Round Surface
Investigation 2-2
2 round balloons, marker

Lab Manual 8: Using Latitude and Longitude
none

Chapter 3

Lab Manual 9: Making a Model of an Orbit
Investigation 3-1
sheet of paper, piece of corrugated cardboard, safety glasses, 2 pushpins, centimeter ruler, scissors, string

Lab Manual 10: Exploring Light Angle
Investigation 3-2
2 sheets of graph paper, flashlight, centimeter ruler

Lab Manual 11: Modeling the Orbit of the Moon
large polystyrene ball, rod about 20 centimeters long, masking tape, marking pen

Lab Manual 12: Measuring Crater Size
ring stand, clamp, ring clamp, meterstick, baking pan, cornstarch, centimeter ruler, glass marble, balance or scale, safety glasses

Chapter 4

Lab Manual 13: Observing Sunspots
Investigation 4-1
telescope or binoculars, clipboard

Lab Manual 14: Modeling the Greenhouse Effect
tape, 2 thermometers, lightweight cardboard, 2 glass jars of the same size, plastic wrap, rubber band, clock or watch, graph paper

Lab Manual 15: Comparing the Size and Density of Planets
large drawing paper, meterstick, marking pen, scissors, tape, 9 identical balloons, sand, scale or balance, funnel, string

Lab Manual 16: Modeling Distances in the Solar System
Investigation 4-2
12-meter length of adding machine paper, meterstick, tape

Chapter 5

Lab Manual 17: Observing Brightness
Investigation 5-1
masking tape, marker, 2 identical flashlights, 2 sheets of tissue paper, meterstick

Lab Manual 18: Observing Distant Objects
notebook paper, transparent tape, marker, meterstick, masking tape, small object such as a pen or a quarter

Lab Manual 19: Modeling a Supergiant
empty 2-liter soft-drink bottle and cap, balloon, large baking dish, hot water

Lab Manual 20: Making a Constellation Model
Investigation 5-2
star guide showing constellations, tissue paper, black construction paper, pin, flashlight, blackboard and chalk

Chapter 6

Lab Manual 21: Measuring Physical Properties of Objects
Investigation 6-1
assortment of objects, centimeter ruler, balance

Lab Manual 22: Making a Model of an Atom
scissors, centimeter ruler, black paper, white paper, red paper, clear balloon 5 centimeters in diameter when inflated, clear balloon 10 centimeters in diameter when inflated

Lab Manual 23: Testing Solutions
drinking glass, measuring cup, water, stirring spoon, measuring tablespoon, flour, salt, sugar, instant coffee, powdered detergent, sand, clock or stopwatch

Lab Manual 24: Separating a Mixture
Investigation 6-2
clean sheet of paper, 2 teaspoons of sand, 2 teaspoons of salt, spoon, 2 beakers, 10 tablespoons of water, filter paper, funnel

Chapter 7

Lab Manual 25: Testing the Hardness of Minerals
2 mineral samples labeled 1 and 2, copper penny, steel nail

Lab Manual 26: Observing Color, Streak, and Hardness
Investigation 7-1
labeled samples of minerals, streak plate, copper penny, steel spoon

Lab Manual 27: Exploring the Arrangement of Atoms in Crystals
small shoe box lid, metric ruler, 50 identical large round metal washers

Lab Manual 28: Finding Specific Gravity
Investigation 7-2
spring scale, string, 3 mineral samples in envelopes marked A, B, and C, beaker of water

Chapter 8

Lab Manual 29: Comparing Rates of Crystallization
marker, water, 2 glass beakers, salt, scale or balance, weighing paper, stirring stick or spoon, hot plate, clock or watch

Lab Manual 30: Observing Igneous Rock Color and Texture
hand lens, labeled samples of basalt, diorite, gabbro, granite, obsidian, pumice, rhyolite, and scoria

Lab Manual 31: Making Calcite
Investigation 8-1
safety glasses, apron, 2 test tubes in a stand, teaspoon, washing soda, plastic stirrers, calcium chloride, 2 beakers, filter paper, funnel

Lab Manual 32: Identifying Rocks
Investigation 8-2
numbered rock samples, hand lens

Chapter 9

Lab Manual 33: Surveying Air Quality
white cardboard, centimeter ruler, scissors, petroleum jelly, tape, string, magnifying glass

Lab Manual 34: Comparing Evaporation Rates
4 identical shallow dishes, 100-milliliter graduated cylinder, water, sticky notes, tablespoon, salt, stirring stick or spoon, electric fan, lamp with 100-watt bulb (optional)

Lab Manual 35: Observing Clouds
Investigation 9-1
none

Lab Manual 36: Making a Model of Rain
Investigation 9-2
newspaper, books, plastic binder (or other flat, plastic surface), spray mister containing water, magnifying glass, paper towels

Materials List for Earth Science Lab Manual

Chapter 10

Lab Manual 37: Making a Hair Hygrometer
small bowl, water, liquid dish detergent, stirring stick or spoon, centimeter ruler, human hair 20 centimeters long, paper towels, straight pin, shoe box, tape, paper, scissors

Lab Manual 38: Measuring Air Pressure
Investigation 10-1
large round balloon, scissors, glass baby-food jar, rubber band, drinking straw, glue, marking pen, index card, centimeter ruler, masking tape

Lab Manual 39: Measuring Air and Surface Temperatures
2 bowls of equal size, potting soil, centimeter ruler, room-temperature water, hot water, ice, 2 thermometers, 2 plastic cups, scissors or knife, 2 wire hangers, watch or clock

Lab Manual 40: Using a Weather Map
Investigation 10-2
copy of Resource File 23 (or copy of a map similar to the one shown on page 243 but without weather symbols)

Chapter 11

Lab Manual 41: Making Fresh Water from Salt Water
2 flasks, water, graduated cylinder, salt, plastic spoon, one-hole stopper, plastic tube 1 meter long, hot plate, ring stand

Lab Manual 42: Exploring Evaporation
Investigation 11-1
3 plastic petri dishes, plastic eye dropper, small container of water, petri dish cover, lamp with at least a 60-watt bulb, clock or stopwatch, paper towels

Lab Manual 43: Modeling How Ocean Water Gets Salty
2 clear plastic cups, marker, graduated cylinder, water, rocks, plastic wrap, 2 plastic spoons, 2 petri dishes

Lab Manual 44: Measuring the Effect of Salt Water on Floating
Investigation 11-2
2 small clear plastic soft-drink bottles, tablespoon, table salt, fine-tip waterproof marker, masking tape, drinking straw, centimeter ruler, modeling clay

Chapter 12

Lab Manual 45: Observing Chemical Weathering
Investigation 12-1
hand lens, safety glasses, 5 limestone chips or pieces of chalk, clear plastic 12-ounce cup, 1 cup of vinegar, strainer, water, paper towels

Lab Manual 46: Observing the Effect of Vegetation on Soil Erosion
2 trays, potting soil, fast-growing grass seeds, water, sprinkling can, graduated cylinder

Lab Manual 47: Comparing Erosion
Investigation 12-2
newspaper, 2 paint trays, soil, grass seeds, sprinkling can, water

Lab Manual 48: Analyzing Sand
handful of sand collected ahead of time by student, 2 white paper plates, magnifying glass, graduated cylinder, scale or balance

Chapter 13

Lab Manual 49: Modeling Sea-Floor Spreading
piece of poster board at least 30 centimeters by 40 centimeters, stapler or wide masking tape, strip of white paper 5 centimeters by 35 centimeters, scissors

Lab Manual 50: Making Models of Folding and Faults
Investigation 13-1
2 thick telephone books or catalogs

Lab Manual 51: Modeling Earthquake Waves
plastic spring toy

Lab Manual 52: Locating an Earthquake
Investigation 13-2
index card, large drawing paper, tape, drawing compass, centimeter ruler

Chapter 14

Lab Manual 53: Inferring from Fossils
petri dish, modeling clay, small object from the classroom

Lab Manual 54: Making a Carbon Imprint
safety glasses, plastic gloves, plate, petroleum jelly, candle and holder, matches, tongs, fresh leaf, paper towels

Lab Manual 55: Making a Model of a Fossil
Investigation 14-1
newspaper, modeling clay, seashell, petroleum jelly, plaster of paris powder, plastic container, water, spoon

Lab Manual 56: Making a Half-Life Model
Investigation 14-2
2 sheets of paper, marking pen, 16 beans, clock or watch, graph paper

Some Suppliers of Science Education Materials

Carolina Biological Supply Company
700 York Road
Burlington, NC 27215
800-334-5551
Fax: 800-222-7112
www.carolina.com

Fisher Science Education
4500 Turnberry Drive
Hanover Park, PA 60133
800-955-1177
Fax: 800-955-0740
www.fisheredu.com

NASCO
901 Janesville Avenue
Fort Atkinson, WI 53538
800-558-9595
Fax: 920-563-8296
www.enasco.com

Sargent-Welch
P.O. Box 5229
Buffalo Grove, IL 60089-5229
800-727-4368
Fax: 800-676-2540
www.Sargentwelch.com

**National Science
Teachers Association (NSTA)**
1840 Wilson Blvd.
Arlington, VA 22201
703-243-7100
nsta.org
suppliers.nsta.org for supplier list